eat
out in
pubs

The 2009 edition of our guide contains details of over 550 pubs. As ever, the crucial factor for selection in the guide is the quality of the food served, and though the style of cooking and the menus may vary from one pub to the next, our independent inspectors ensure that each and every pub listed reaches the required standards.

Cooking in British pubs continues to reach new heights, and there is an enormous amount of choice now available to diners. Some pubs proudly take the organic route with the support of small local suppliers, while others focus more on regional specialities and long-established local recipes. Some serve creative, contemporary cooking with more of an international flavour, but equally, there are plenty offering traditional British favourites too.

If you're having trouble choosing where to go, the descriptive texts give an insight into the individual character of each pub, highlighting what we found to be most memorable and charming, and the accompanying pictures reveal a little bit more of their personality.

Some of these pubs serve their food by the fireplace in the bar; others may have a more formal dining room, but whatever their style, they all have one thing in common: carefully prepared, flavoursome food made from fresh, quality ingredients.

Readers of the Michelin guide Eating out in Pubs write thousands of letters and emails to us every year, praising or criticising current entries or recommending new entries. Please keep these coming and help us make the next edition even better.

contents

Contents

SCOTLAND
NORTHERN IRELAND
IRELAND
REPUBLIC OF IRELAND
ISLE OF MAN
NORTH EAST
YORKSHIRE & THE HUMBER
NORTH WEST
EAST
ENGLAND
WALES
WEST MIDLANDS
SOUTH
SOUTH WEST
ISLE OF WIGHT
CHANNEL ISLANDS

ENGLAND

COUNTRY OR REGION & COUNTY NAMES

ONE OF OUR FAVOURITE SELECTIONS

TOWN/VILLAGE NAME

NAME, ADDRESS, TELEPHONE, E-MAIL AND WEBSITE OF THE ESTABLISHMENT

1

ENTRY NUMBER

Each pub or inn has its own entry number.

This number appears on the regional map at the start of each section to show the location of the establishment.

COLOURED PAGE BORDER

- Introduction
- East Midlands
- East of England
- London
- North East
- North West
- South East
- South West
- West Midlands
- Yorkshire & The Humber
- Scotland
- Wales
- Northern Ireland
- Republic of Ireland

England • East of England • Cambridgeshi

Hemingford Grey

The Cock

9

47 High St,
Hemingford Grey PE28 9BJ
Tel.: (01480)463609 – Fax: (01480)461747
e-mail: cock@cambscuisine.com Website: www.cambscuisine.com

VISA

Elgoods Black Dog, Wolf Golden Jackal, Buntingford IPA and a regularly changing guest ale

The Cock cocks a snook at most other Huntingdon hostelries and is the place to come if you are after a relaxing meal in a country pub. Centrally located, this busy 17C pub serves local ales and has kept the feel of the village local, with a split-level bar specifically for drinkers on one side, and a spacious, L-shaped dining room on the other. Rustic in feel, it has polished wood floors and an open fire, and is brightened by oil paintings – available to take home with you for the right price. The menus provide plenty of choice, from a 2 course lunch menu to a full à la carte and daily-changing fish specials. Dishes range from Jerusalem artichoke and truffle risotto to sirloin steak, but the best choice would have to come from the sausage board; a kind of mix and match between differently flavoured homemade sausages and a similarly diverse choice of mashed potato and sauces.

Food serving times

Monday-Saturday:
12pm-2.30pm,
6.30pm-9.30pm

Sunday: 12pm-3pm,
6.30pm-8.30pm

Prices

Meals: £ 15 (3 course lunch) and a la carte £ 21/25

Typical Dishes

Potted ham hock

Roast saddle of lamb

Blood orange tartlet

5mi Southeast of Huntingdon by A1198 off A14. Parking.

56

HOW TO FIND A PUB

There are 3 ways to search for a pub in this guide:
- use the regional maps that precede each section of the guide
- use the alphabetical list of pubs at the end of the guide or
- use the alphabetical list of place names also at the end of the guide

PUBS WITH BEDROOMS

For easy reference, those pubs that offer accommodation are highlighted. in blue This theme is continued on the regional maps that precede each section of the guide.

Horningsea

England • East of England • Cambridgeshire

10 **Crown and Punchbowl**

High St, Horningsea CB25 9JG
Tel.: (01223)860643 – Fax: (01223)441814
e-mail: info@the crownandpunchbowl.co.uk
Website: www.thecrownandpunchbowl.co.uk

VISA

Hobsons Choice

You won't find locals passing the time of day with a pint at the bar in the Crown and Punchbowl. Not because the locals don't patronize the place, but because there is no bar here - which makes it a weird kind of pub, if you think about it. What it does have is plenty of snug pubby charm, with rustic walls, wooden floors, open fires - and beamed ceilings low enough to present a danger to anyone over 5ft 5". Located next to a pretty church and graveyard, the pub is actually a blend of two buildings; one dating from the 17C, the other from the 19C, and inside, there are two main dining areas as well as a small private dining room for parties. Food is local, seasonal and appealing, with choices like steak and chips and confit duck leg on the à la carte, supplemented by fish specials and mix and match homemade sausage and mash, which are chalked up on blackboards. Five modern, spacious and relaxing bedrooms complete the picture.

Food serving times
Monday-Saturday:
12pm-2.30pm, 6.30pm-9pm
Sunday: 12pm-2.30pm
Prices
Meals: a la carte £ 15/40
5 rooms: £ 75/95

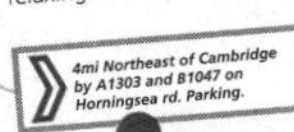

57

SYMBOLS

- Meals served in the garden or on the terrace
- A particularly interesting wine list
- No dogs allowed
- VISA Visa accepted
- AE American Express accepted
- Diners Club accepted
- MasterCard accepted

REAL ALES SERVED

A listing to indicate the number and variety of regular and guest cask beers usually served.

OPENING HOURS FOOD SERVING TIMES PRICES ROOMS

Approximate range of prices for a three-course meal, plus information on booking and annual closures.

Some inns offering accommodation may close in mid-afternoon and only allow guests to check in during evening hours. If in doubt, phone ahead.

Room prices range from the lowest-priced single to the most expensive double or twin.

The cup and saucer symbol and price relate to breakfast; if no symbol is shown, assume it is included in the price of the room.

Prices are given in £ sterling, except for the Republic of Ireland where €uro are quoted.

HOW TO GET THERE

Directions and driving distances from nearby towns, and indication of parking facilities and any other information that might help you get your bearings.

THE BLACKBOARD

An example of a typical starter, main course and dessert, chosen by the chef.

Whilst there's no guarantee that these dishes will be available, they should provide you with an idea of the style of the cuisine.

The Pub of the year

The Punch Bowl Inn

Crosthwaite, LA8 8HR

Tel: (01539) 568 237 – Fax: (01539) 568 875
e-mail: *info@the-punchbowl.co.uk* – **website** : *www.the-punchbowl.co.uk*

see page 214 for more details

Good food is a given but what else does a pub need in order to win the accolade "Pub of the Year"? The answer is – something special. Many pubs in our guide offer impressive wine lists, striking interiors, warm welcomes or enchanting locations but only one can take the title; so what's this year's recipe for success?

- *Take one attractive stone pub and place in a delightfully rural setting.*
- *Mix in characterful interior features and smart homely furnishings.*
- *Add a large spoonful of community spirit and a splash of home-brewed beer.*
- *Throw in some excellent local produce and great classical cooking.*
- *Top off with a generous handful of luxury accommodation. Et voilà.*

The Location

Set amongst the hills of the picturesque Lyth Valley in the pretty village of Crosthwaite, this attractive 17C stone inn is immersed in local life. The owners work closely with the Parish Church next door and even share their parking, while in the ultimate act of community spirit they have taken on the role of village Post Office. Don't be surprised to find the people next to you buying stamps or taxing their cars as you collect your room key from reception.

The Pub

There are several charming areas: a pleasant decked terrace; three delightful bar rooms with open fires and squashy sofas; a dining room with leather chairs and polished tables; and a snug sitting room ideal for afternoon tea. The mood is relaxed and comfortable. Four local ales are on offer – including their home-brewed "Tag Lag" – and there's an extensive selection of wines by the glass. In addition, every dish at dinner has a recommended wine to accompany it.

The Food

Cooking is classical, seasonal and relies on local produce. The extensive menu ranges from open sandwiches through to full three course meals at lunchtime, while in the evening it becomes a more substantial, gutsy affair. The baked cheese soufflé is something of a speciality and, coming complete with its own menu, the strictly regional cheese selection is an experience in itself. If it's fine dining without pretension that you're after, this is definitely it.

The Bedrooms

Classical music greets you and delicious homemade cookies wait beside flat screen TVs in the stylish, luxurious rooms; while Arran Aromatics toiletries and huge fluffy towels sit between roll-topped baths and shower units in the spacious, underfloor heated bathrooms. "Noble" features twin tubs, "Danson" boasts glorious views and they all enjoy a full turn down service. Breakfast is a truly hearty occasion and afternoon tea is included in the price of the room.

All the pubs in this guide have been selected for the quality of their cooking. However, we feel that several of them deserve additional consideration as they boast at least one extra quality which makes them particularly special.

It may be the delightful setting, the charm and character of the pub, the general atmosphere, the pleasant service, the overall value for money or the exceptional cooking.

To distinguish these pubs, we point them out with our "Inspectors' favourites" Bibendum stamp.

We are sure you will enjoy these pubs as much as we have.

SOUTH EAST

SOUTH WEST

WEST MIDLANDS

YORKSHIRE AND THE HUMBER

SCOTLAND

WALES

NORTHERN IRELAND

REPUBLIC OF IRELAND

Beer in the U.K. and Ireland

It's easy to think of beer as just bitter or lager. But that doesn't tell half the story. Between the two there's a whole range of styles and tastes, including pale ales, beers flavoured with spices, fruits and herbs, and wheat beers. It's all down to the skill of the brewer who'll juggle art, craft and a modicum of science to create the perfect pint.

Grist and wort may sound like medieval hangover cures, but they're actually crucial to the brewing process. Malted barley is crushed into grist, a coarse powder which is mashed with hot water in a large vessel called a mash tun. Depending on what sort of recipe's required, the brewer will add different cereals at this stage, such as darker malt for stout. The malt's natural sugars dissolve and the result is wort: a sweet brown liquid, which is boiled with hops in large coppers. Then comes the most important process of all: fermentation, when the hopped wort is cooled and run into fermentation vessels. The final addition is yeast, which converts the natural sugars into alcohol, carbon dioxide and a host of subtle flavours.

Finally, a beer has to be conditioned before it leaves the brewery, and in the case of cask conditioned real ales, the beer goes directly into the cask, barrel or bottle. The yeast is still active in there, fermenting the beer for a second time, often in a pub cellar. All the time there's a delicate process going on as the beer is vulnerable to attack from micro-biological organisms. But as long as the publican cares about his beer, you should get a tasty, full-flavoured pint.

Beer's as natural a product as you can get. This is what's in your pint:

Barley
It's the main ingredient in beer and rich in starch. Malted before brewing to begin the release of sugars.

Hops
Contain resins and essential oils, and used at varying times to give beer its distinctive flavour. Early on they add bitterness, later on they provide a spicy or citrus zest.

Yeast
Converts the sugars from the barley into alcohol and carbon dioxide during fermentation. It produces compounds that affect the flavour of the beer.

Water
Burton and Tadcaster have excellent local water, and that's why they became great ale brewing centres. Meanwhile, the water of London and Dublin is just right for the production of stouts and porters.

Real quality

The modern taste for real ale took off over thirty years ago when it looked like the lager industry was in the process of killing off traditional "warm ale". There are several styles, but the most popular in England and Wales is bitter, which boasts a seemingly inexhaustible variety of appearance, scent and flavour. You can have your bitter gold or copper of colour, hoppy or malty of aroma, dry or sweet of flavour (sweet flavoured bitter? This is where the term "bitter" is at its loosest). Sometimes it has a creamy head; sometimes no head at all. Typically, go to a Yorkshire pub for the former, a London pub for the latter.

Mild developed its popularity in Wales and the north west of England in Victorian times. Often dark, it's a weaker alternative to bitter, with a sweetish taste based on its hop characteristics.
In Scotland, the near equivalent of bitter is heavy, and the most popular draught ales are known as 80 shilling (export) or 70 shilling (special). And, yes, they have a heavy quality to them, though 60 shilling ale – or Light – is akin to English mild.
Full-bodied and rich, stouts (and their rarer porter relatives) are almost a meal in themselves. They're famously black in colour with hints of chocolate and caramel, but it's the highly roasted yeast flavour that leaves the strong after taste.

A vision of England sweeps across a range of historic buildings, monuments and rolling landscapes. This image, taking in wild natural borders extending from the rugged splendour of Cornwall's cliffs to pounding Northumbrian shores, seeks parity with a newer picture of Albion: redefined cities and towns whose industrial past is being reshaped by a shiny, steel-and-glass, interactive reality. The country's geographical bones and bumps are a reassuring constant: the windswept moors of the south west and the craggy peaks of the Pennines, the summery orchards of the Kentish Weald, the "flat earth" constancy of East Anglian skies and the mirrored calm of Cumbria's lakes. The pubs of England have made good use of the land's natural bounty over the past decade; streamlined establishments have stripped out the soggy carpets and soggier menus and replaced them with crisp décor and fresh, inventive cooking. England's multi-ethnic culture has borne fruit in the kitchens of your local…

An area that combines the grace of a bygone age with the speed of the 21C. To the east (Chatsworth House, Haddon Hall and Burghley House) is where Pride and Prejudice came to life, while Silverstone to the south hosts the Grand Prix. Market towns are dotted all around: Spalding's cultivation of tulips rivals that of Holland, Oakham boasts its stunning Castle and Great Hall, and the legendary "Boston Stump" oversees the bustle of a 450 year-old market. The brooding beauty of the Peak District makes it the second most visited National Park in the world. Izaac Walton popularised the river Dove's trout-filled waters in "The Compleat Angler" and its surrounding hills are a rambler's dream, as are the wildlife habitats of the National Forest and the wind-swept acres of the pancake-flat fens. Above it all looms Lincoln Cathedral's ancient spire, while in the pubs, local ale – typically brewed in Bakewell, Dovedale or Rutland – slips down a treat alongside the ubiquitous Melton Mowbray pie.

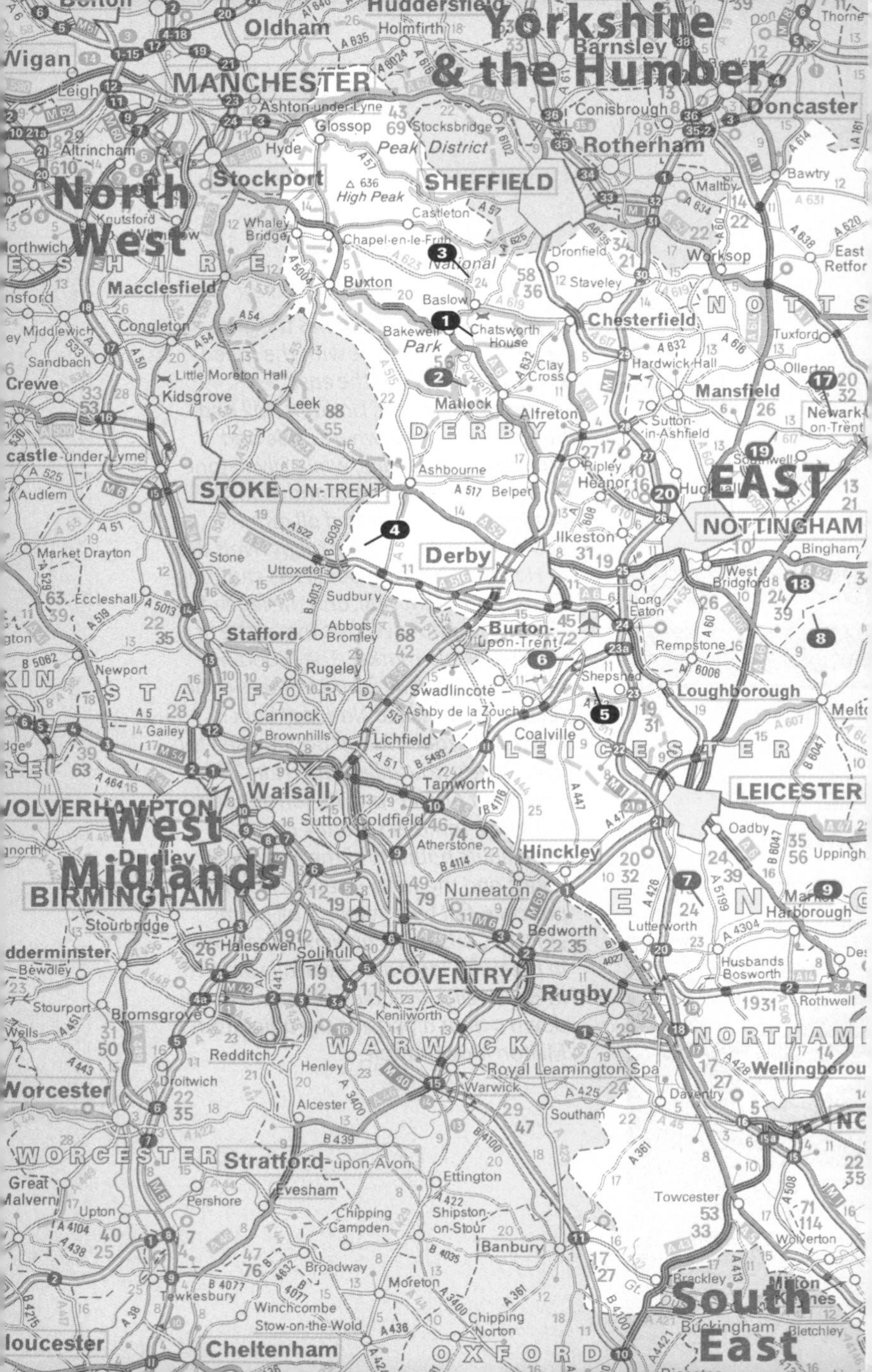

Yorkshire & the Humber
North West
West Midlands
EAST
South East
Huddersfield
Oldham
Holmfirth
Barnsley
Thorne
Wigan
Leigh
MANCHESTER
Ashton-under-Lyne
Glossop
Stocksbridge
Peak District
Conisbrough
Doncaster
Rotherham
Altrincham
Hyde
Stockport
High Peak
SHEFFIELD
Bawtry
Maltby
Knutsford
Wilmslow
Whaley Bridge
Castleton
Chapel-en-le-Frith
National
Dronfield
Worksop
East Retford
Northwich
Macclesfield
Buxton
Baslow
Staveley
Chesterfield
NOTTS
Middlewich
Congleton
Bakewell
Park
Chatsworth House
Tuxford
Sandbach
Little Moreton Hall
Clay Cross
Hardwick Hall
Ollerton
Crewe
Kidsgrove
Leek
Matlock
Derwent
Alfreton
Mansfield
Newark-on-Trent
DERBY
Sutton-in-Ashfield
Southwell
Newcastle-under-Lyme
Audlem
Ashbourne
Ripley
Heanor
Belper
Hucknall
STOKE-ON-TRENT
NOTTINGHAM
Ilkeston
Derby
Bingham
Market Drayton
Stone
Uttoxeter
West Bridgford
Eccleshall
Sudbury
Long Eaton
Stafford
Abbots Bromley
Burton-upon-Trent
Rempstone
Newport
Rugeley
Shepshed
Loughborough
STAFFORD
Swadlincote
Ashby de la Zouch
Gailey
Cannock
Coalville
Brownhills
Lichfield
LEICESTER
Tamworth
Walsall
WOLVERHAMPTON
Sutton Coldfield
Oadby
Atherstone
Uppingham
Dudley
Hinckley
BIRMINGHAM
Nuneaton
Market Harborough
Stourbridge
Bedworth
Lutterworth
Kidderminster
Halesowen
Solihull
Husbands Bosworth
Bewdley
COVENTRY
Rugby
Rothwell
Stourport
Bromsgrove
Kenilworth
Redditch
WARWICK
NORTHAMPTON
Royal Leamington Spa
Wellingborough
Henley
Warwick
Droitwich
Daventry
Worcester
Alcester
Southam
WORCESTER
Stratford-upon-Avon
Great Malvern
Evesham
Ettington
Pershore
Upton
Chipping Campden
Shipston-on-Stour
Towcester
Banbury
Wolverton
Broadway
Brackley
Milton Keynes
Tewkesbury
Moreton
Winchcombe
Stow-on-the-Wold
Chipping Norton
Buckingham
Bletchley
Gloucester
Cheltenham
OXFORD

Crowle
Scunthorpe
Immingham
Kilnsea
N.E.
LINCS
Grimsby
Spurn Head
Cleethorpes
Brigg
Humberside
Caistor
Epworth
R. Trent
Rotterdam
Zeebrugge
Gainsborough
Market Rasen
Louth
Mablethorpe
Sutton-on-Sea
Wragby
Alford
Lincoln
Horncastle
Partney
Woodhall Spa
Spilsby
Skegness
Witham
LINCOLN
MIDLANDS
Sleaford
Boston
Grantham
Hunstanton
Wells-next-the-Sea
The Wash
Donington
Sutterton
Sandringham House
Fakenham
Holbeach
Long Sutton
Mowbray
Bourne
Spalding
King's Lynn
RUTLAND
NORF
Oakham
Stamford
Welland
Crowland
Wisbech
East Dereham
Nene
Great Ouse
Eye
Outwell
Stradsett
Swaffham
Guyhirn
Peterborough
Downham Market
Watton
Corby
Whittlesey
March
Mundford
Weldon
Oundle
Chatteris
Ramsey
Littleport
Brandon
Kettering
Thrapston
CAMBRIDGE
Thetford
Ely
East of England
Huntingdon
Earith
Soham
Higham Ferrers
St. Ives
Rushden
Godmanchester
Ixworth
NORTHAMPTON
St. Neots
BEDFORD
Newmarket
Bury St. Ed
Eltisley
Stowmarket
Sandy
Potton
Cambridge
Bedford
Newport Pagnell
Biggleswade
Haverhill
Lavenham
Cam
SUFF
Ampthill
Shefford
Saffron Walden
Clare
IPSW
Woburn
Royston
Sudbury
Abbey
Letchworth
Leighton Buzzard
Hitchin
Baldock
Finchingfield
Buntingford
Stour
Luton
Stansted
Halstead

The Devonshire Arms

1 The Devonshire Arms

Devonshire Square,
Beeley DE4 2NR

Tel.: (01629)733259 – Fax: (01629)733259
e-mail: enquiries@devonshirebeeley.co.uk **Website:** www.devonshirebeeley.co.uk

VISA MC AE

Chatsworth Gold, Black Sheep, Thornbridge Jaipur, Brampton Brewery Golden Bud

Part of the famous Chatsworth estate, this historic stone inn has two distinct parts to it: one side is decidedly rural in character, typified by its low ceilings, oak beams and inglenook fireplace, while, by contrast, light streams in through the floor to ceiling windows in the brightly furnished, modern extension. Upstairs, stylish contemporary bedrooms complete the picture. Far from typical pub rooms, they have been styled by the Duchess of Devonshire and are named after the nearby Dales. Food is also far from typical, and although classics like bangers and mash and prawn cocktail are on the menu, other dishes offered might include confit duck terrine, warm salad of wood pigeon or lobster, with most of the fresh, seasonal ingredients coming from local sources and from the estate itself. Wine lovers are also well-catered for with an impressive wine list containing over 300 bins, housed in a glass-fronted cave.

Food serving times

Monday -Sunday:
12pm-3pm, 6pm-9.30pm

Prices

Meals: a la carte £ 30/45

8 rooms: £ 145/165

Typical Dishes
Chicken liver pate
Neck of lamb
Apple Crumble

5mi South East of Bakewell by A6 and B6012. Parking.

2 The Druid Inn

Main St,
Birchover DE4 2BL
Tel.: (01629)650302
Website: www.thedruidinn.co.uk

 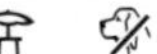 

 **Druid Ale and frequently changing guest beers**

Many local legends relate to Druid activity in the Birchover area, not least the nearby Nine Ladies stone circle, where Druids would gather to celebrate the summer solstice. You're unlikely to bump into anyone dressed in white robes and chanting Celtic poetry at this pub, however, as it's considerably more famed for its food than for any spiritual inclinations. Worship instead at the table of the Thompson brothers, who work together in the kitchen to produce tasty, wholesome food, including dishes for two to share, a selection of pies and popular sandwiches on homemade bread; favourites such as shepherd's pie or sausage and mash, as well as more restaurant-style dishes, maybe baked monkfish tail, tomato, chorizo and butterbean stew. Wash down your food with a pint of local Druid Ale – you can sit in the more rustic bar area or head down the few steps to the airy, modern dining room with its open plan kitchen.

Food serving times

Monday-Thursday:
12pm-2.30pm, 6pm-9pm

Friday-Saturday:
12pm-2.30pm, 6pm-9.30pm

Sunday: 12pm-3pm

Closed 25 December

Prices

Meals: £ 17 (weekdays only) and a la carte £ 25/35

Typical Dishes

Bakewell black pudding
Venison Wellington
Miniature desserts

7.5 mi Northwest from Matlock by A6 and 5.5 mi from Bakewell. Parking.

England • East Midlands • Derbyshire

3 The Chequers Inn

Froggatt Edge,
Hope Valley S32 3ZJ

Tel.: (01433)630231 – Fax: (01433)631072
e-mail: info@chequers-froggatt.com **Website:** www.chequers-froggatt.com

   VISA AE

 **Greene King IPA, Charles Wells Bombardier, Black Sheep**

On the eastern edge of the Peak District National park, in the heart of the Derbyshire countryside, this traditional 16C country inn is ideally set for nourishment and refreshment before or after a hike, and even has a direct path from its pretty woodland garden right up to the glorious views at Froggatt Edge. Beware when leaving by the front door, however, as the main road is right outside. Inside, clocks and farm implements decorate the walls, there's a large room with a bar, and a quieter, cosier room on the other side of the hall. Menus are chalked up on blackboards, and you place your order at the bar – satisfying favourites such as sausage and mash and pot roasted lamb shank will recharge your batteries, and – named after the nearby market town - Bakewell pudding and custard makes a fitting dessert. Weary walkers staying the night will find bedrooms comfortable – go for one at the back to avoid noise from passing traffic.

Food serving times

Monday-Friday:
12pm-2pm, 6pm-9.30pm

Saturday: 12pm-9.30pm

Sunday: 12pm-9pm

Closed 25 December

Prices

Meals: a la carte £ 21/28

5 rooms: £ 70/95

Typical Dishes

Belly pork

Calves Liver

Orange & passion fruit tart

Situated on the edge of the village. Parking.

4 The Crown Inn

Riggs Lane, Marston Montgomery DE6 2FF
Tel.: (01889)590541 – Fax: (01889)591576
e-mail: info@thecrowninn-derbyshire.co.uk
Website: www.thecrowninn-derbyshire.co.uk

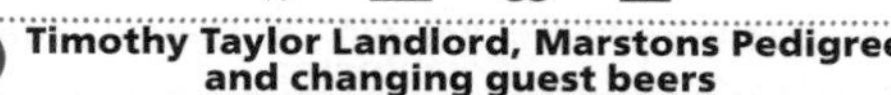

Timothy Taylor Landlord, Marstons Pedigree and changing guest beers

Not far from the thrill-seeking, bustling masses at Alton Towers, life flows at a rather more sedate pace in the peaceful hamlet of Marston Montgomery; and nowhere more so than in this traditional creeper-clad pub. Outside there's a small patio and garden ideal for the summer months, while inside the cosy low-beamed bar is furnished with comfy leather sofas and stocked with real ales ready to be pumped. Lunchtime sees a wide-ranging weekly à la carte and a good value set menu, alongside a selection of sandwiches made using speciality breads. Dinner takes on a more substantial feel, displaying everything from classic British favourites to more modern, ambitious dishes with a twist, supported by daily specials which often feature some good fish choices. Produce is carefully sourced from within the region, ensuring that the miles from field to fork are minimal. Bedrooms are simply decorated and furnished; free wi-fi is also available.

Food serving times

Monday-Saturday:
12pm-2.30pm, 7pm-9.30pm

Sunday:
12pm-2.30pm, 6pm-7.30pm
(bar snacks only)

Closed 25 December,
1 January

Prices

Meals: £ 18 and a la carte £ 24/34

7 rooms: £ 60/80

Typical Dishes

Baked crottin of goats cheese
Pavé of beef
Dark chocolate tart

7.5mi Southeast of Ashbourne by A515. Parking.

5 The Queen's Head

2 Long St,
Belton LE12 9TP

Tel.: (01530)222359 – Fax: (01530)224860
e-mail: enquiries@thequeenshead.org **Website:** www.thequeenshead.org

 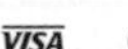 

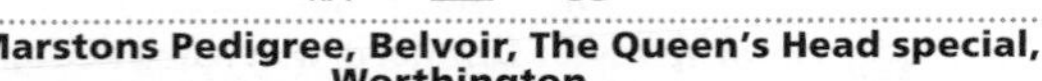

Marstons Pedigree, Belvoir, The Queen's Head special, Worthington

A pub of two halves: turn right for the cool lounge and bar, all calming creams, comfy chocolate leather furniture, sleek lines and pale wood, or turn left to dine more formally in the stylishly stark, two-roomed restaurant. There are various seasonally-evolving menus from which to choose, with dishes all proudly made from local produce: lunch might mean a sandwich, steak or fish and chips, whilst more elaborate evening offerings could include roast squab pigeon, with potato and foie gras terrine; pan-fried halibut or roast pheasant. The daily-changing set menu is a well-priced alternative and also proving popular are the "bring your own wine" evenings held on the first Wednesday of every month. For larger parties there's a separate function room, for al fresco dining there's a covered deck and for sleeping it all off there are bright, individually furnished contemporary bedrooms, which come in varying shapes and sizes.

Food serving times

Monday-Thursday:
12.30pm-2.30pm,
7pm-9.30pm

Friday-Saturday:
12.30pm-2.30pm, 7pm-10pm

Sunday: 12pm-4pm

Closed 25 December,
1 January

Prices

Meals: £ 17 (3 course lunch and dinner) and a la carte £ 22/28

6 rooms: £ 65/110

Typical Dishes

Warm crab tart
Sea bream
Chocolate terrine

6mi West of Loughborough by A6 on the B5234. On the Diseworth/ Breedon rd. Parking.

6 The Three Horseshoes Inn

Main St,
Breedon-on-the-Hill DE73 8AN
Tel.: (01332)695129
e-mail: ian@thehorseshoes.com **Website:** www.thehorseshoes.com

Marstons Pedigree

The Three Horseshoes has undergone a restoration job which displays admirable attention to detail and of which the owners are justifiably proud. Logs burn in the fireplace, candles cast a welcoming glow and various artefacts, signs and pictures tell their individual stories. While the cooking may have international touches, this is fundamentally simple, honest food, with no unnecessary garnishes; just bold flavours from locally sourced, seasonal produce. Choose from dishes such as beef, mushroom and red wine casserole or pheasant with Savoy cabbage and whisky; homemade desserts come from the classic school of puddingry and might include treacle oat tart or bread and butter pudding. The drinks on offer are as well thought out as the venue and the menu – but mind you don't start getting rowdy after too much malt of the month; it hasn't held prisoners since 1885, but you never know when the village lock up might be brought back into use.

Food serving times

Monday-Saturday:
12pm-2pm, 6pm-9.15pm

Sunday: 12pm-2pm

Closed 25 and
31 December, 1 January

Prices

Meals: a la carte £ 25/32

Typical Dishes

Brie and tomato tart
Rib eye steak
Chocolate whisky trifle

4mi Southwest of Castle Donington by Breedon rd off A453. Parking.

Bruntingthorpe

7 Joiners Arms

Church Walk,
Bruntingthorpe LE17 5QH
Tel.: (0116)2478258
e-mail: stephenjoiners@btconnect.com **Website:** www.thejoinersarms.co.uk

 **IPA, Heineken, Amstel, Guinness**

You might well drive past this charming 18C inn at first, unaware of its sign swinging slowly and silently in the breeze, shyly announcing its status as a public house. It's actually less pub and more dining destination these days; its bar occupying a small corner and its tables neatly laid up for candlelit dinners. The style here is smart and orderly, with exposed beams overhead and watercolours by a local artist brightening the walls. A tight trio operate in the kitchen, creating appealing homemade dishes using locally sourced ingredients. A core of well-chosen, hearty classics is supplemented by more up-to-date flavours, plus a daily-changing blackboard menu, so there's something to please everyone. The set three course lunch menu represents good value; as it's still early, you might want to try one of the wines available by the glass rather than drain a whole bottle. This place is popular but not huge, so booking is advisable.

Food serving times

Tuesday-Saturday:
12pm-1.45pm,
6.30pm-9.30pm

Sunday: 12pm-1.45pm

Closed 25-26 December

Booking essential

Prices

Meals: £ 14 (set price lunch) and a la carte £ 24/29

Typical Dishes
Duck fat toast
Rump of Lamb
Blueberry soufflé

Between Leicester and Husbands Bosworth off A5199.

8 Red Lion Inn

2 Red Lion St,
Stathern LE14 4HS
Tel.: (01949)860868 – Fax: (01949)861579
e-mail: info@theredlioninn.co.uk **Website:** www.theredlioninn.co.uk

Inspectors' favourites

Brewsters Hop Head, Grainstore Olive Oil, Batemans XB, Fuller's London Pride, Greene King IPA

The Red Lion Inn lies at the heart of the village of Stathern and the emphasis here is firmly on food; ingredients are locally sourced, the menus change everyday according to what produce is fresh in - and a map provided on their reverse shows exactly where and from whom the ingredients for your dishes have come. Lunch might see ox tongue terrine or eggs Benedict on offer, while dinner might include pigeon breast or smoked haddock. A good value set menu is available at lunch but booking is essential whenever you wish to eat. Saturdays in the summer months mean barbeques and Pimms on the terrace; in winter, a fireside seat has to be best. Taken a liking your chair? Chances are it's for sale, as are many of the pieces of furniture and pictures on the walls - ask a member of staff – prices are negotiable. Home made preserves are also for sale too, plus a cookbook from its sister pub, the Olive Branch at Clipsham.

Food serving times

Tuesday-Saturday:
12pm-2pm, 7pm-9.30pm

Sunday: 12pm-3pm

Closed 1 January

Booking essential

Prices

Meals: £ 16 (3 course lunch) and a la carte £ 26/33

Typical Dishes

Thai style pigeon
Lincolnshire sausages
Rhubarb and ginger crumble

8mi North of Melton Mowbray by A607. Parking.

Thorpe Langton

9 The Bakers Arms

Main St,
Thorpe Langton LE16 7TS
Tel.: (01858)545201 – Fax: (01858)545924
Website: www.thebakersarms.co.uk

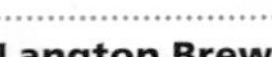 **Langton Brewery Baker's Dozen**

The Langtons are well signposted off the A6, so you should have no trouble tracking down this popular thatched inn – situated on the village's quiet main street. Inside, it's traditional décor all the way, with floral and chintz in abundance; and several comfy, softly lit seating areas and a snug help to create a warm and cosy atmosphere. The oft-changing blackboard menus offer classic dishes such as steak, kidney and ale pie, breast of duck and sausage and mash. Fish also have pride of place on the menu – and more so on Thursdays, for fish night - while all mains come with fresh vegetables and what has become the pub's trademark: dauphinoise potatoes. Cooked using fresh, carefully-sourced and seasonal ingredients, flavours are natural and clearly defined. Jan from a few doors up provides the puds, of which the dessert plate for two is a favourite. Service sometimes takes a while to warm up, but is efficient nonetheless.

Food serving times

Tuesday-Friday:
6.30pm-9.30pm

Saturday:
12pm-2pm, 6.30pm-9.30pm

Sunday: 12pm-2pm

Closed Monday,
Tuesday-Friday lunch,
Sunday dinner

Booking essential

Prices

Meals: a la carte £ 22/33

Typical Dishes

Goats' cheese tartlet
Pork fillet
Tarte Tatin

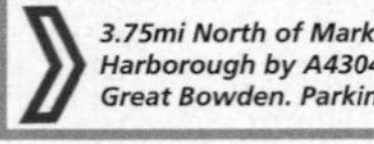

3.75mi North of Market Harborough by A4304 via Great Bowden. Parking.

10 The Blue Bell Inn

1 Main Rd,
Belchford LN9 6LQ
Tel.: (01507)533602

 **Black Sheep and weekly changing local ale**

This whitewashed pub is situated in a tiny village between Louth and Horncastle in the heart of the Lincolnshire Wolds and is a popular destination for walkers following the Viking Way, a footpath stretching from the Humber Bridge to Rutland. You can't miss the big blue bell which hangs outside the pub, however, when you delve deeper into it, nobody really knows why it is there, since the pub was originally named after the bluebell flower. It is very much a traditional pub, carpeted throughout, with wooden beams, a typical black wood bar and a friendly, old-fashioned feel. There are old-style armchairs in the cosy bar and linen-clad tables in the similarly styled dining room. It is run by a young couple – Darren and Shona – she manages, whilst he cooks. Dishes are listed on numerous small blackboards on the wall above the fire in the bar and include sandwiches and old pub favourites, alongside more ambitious creations.

Food serving times

Tuesday-Saturday:
11.30am-2pm, 6.30pm-9pm

Sunday: 12pm-2pm

Closed 2nd and 3rd weeks in January

Prices

Meals: a la carte £ 18/30

Typical Dishes

Seared king scallops

Gressingham duck breast & confit leg

Chocolate truffle torte

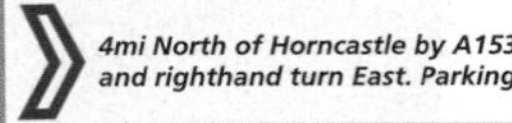

4mi North of Horncastle by A153 and righthand turn East. Parking.

11 The Gregory

The Drift,
Harlaxton NG32 1AD
Tel.: (01476)577076
Website: www.thegregory.co.uk

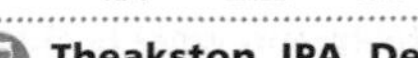
Theakston, IPA, Deuchars

This pub has been part of the local community since the 19C, when workers from the Gregory family's Estate – which covered most of Harlaxton – made it their favourite haunt. Later it was relocated by the Squire to its present spot, where it took responsibility for the delivery of coal from the canal boats at the nearby wharf; it's believed that the weighbridge still lies under the current property. Don't be put off by the busy road running past the front door, as following an extensive refurbishment, it's definitely worth taking a look inside. The menu has had a facelift and now displays a selection of classic pub favourites, albeit in a more modern style. Lunchtime sees sandwiches, salads and maybe cottage pie or beer battered haddock, while dinner might feature local Lincolnshire sausage or regional rump of lamb; for supporters of the old menu there's still the odd ambitious dish, such as fillet of Grey Mullet or pea and mint risotto.

Food serving times

Tuesday-Saturday:
12pm-2pm, 7pm-9pm

Sunday: 12pm-2pm

Closed 25-26 December

Prices

Meals: a la carte £ 18/25

Typical Dishes

Ham hock terrine
Roast cod
Baked egg custard & rhubarb

South West : 2m by A607 from Grantham

12 Wig & Mitre

30-32 Steep Hill,
Lincoln LN2 1LU
Tel.: (01522)535190 – Fax: (01522)532402
e-mail: email@wigandmitre.com **Website:** www.wigandmitre.com

   AE 

 **Batemans XB, Black Sheep Special**

This pub stands between the castle, which is still used as a court - hence the wig - and the cathedral - hence the bishop's mitre. Open all year round and serving food all day, the owners also run the adjacent wine shop and each dish on the à la carte has a wine recommendation, with even Krug champagne being sold by the glass. Part 14C, part 16C and part 20C extension, the Wig and Mitre is certainly a unique building. Downstairs, there's a small cosy bar with scrubbed tables at the front and lounge style seating at the rear, while upstairs there's another small bar, two smaller period dining rooms, plus a light and airy beamed restaurant with pictures of old judges on the walls. The same menus are served upstairs and down and might include smoked salmon and scrambled eggs for breakfast, sandwiches and other light meals at lunch, with perhaps a caviar starter, followed by steak or duck breast in the evening.

Food serving times
Monday-Sunday:
8am-11.50pm

Prices
Meals: £ 14 (3 course lunch)/20 and a la carte £ 21/38

Typical Dishes
Cheese soufflé
Aberdeen Angus fillet steak
Prune crème brûlée

Close to the Cathedral. Parking in Castle car park in Castle Square.

Surfleet Seas End

13 The Ship Inn

154 Reservoir Rd,
Surfleet Seas End PE11 4DH
Tel.: (01775)680547 – Fax: (01775)680541
e-mail: info@shipinnsurfleet.com **Website:** www.shipinnsurfleet.com

 **Tom Woods Best Bitter, Cottage Brewery, Fen Ales, Slaters**

The area of Lincolnshire east of the A1 is hardly known as a gastronomic haven, making The Ship Inn something of a culinary lighthouse. The chef works closely with local producers to source quality ingredients and serves up good old fashioned pub food, so expect the likes of sausage and mash or leek and potato pie, with homemade, old school desserts such as apple and blackberry crumble. From outside, this big square block looks little like a pub, but inside it's spacious, with lots of room in the bar for the locals, and plenty of space for diners too. The full-length windows in the first floor restaurant afford excellent views of the jetty and the fens beyond and the upstairs terrace is a welcoming sight when the temperature begins to climb. Take full advantage of your trip by joining the Pie Club, membership of which grants discounts on pie meals as well as the gift of a pie on your birthday. Bedrooms are large and plainly furnished.

Food serving times

Tuesday-Thursday:
12pm-2pm, 6.30pm-9pm

Friday-Saturday:
12pm-2pm, 7pm-9pm

Sunday: 12pm-2pm

Closed 1 January

Bar lunch

Prices

Meals: £ 9 and a la carte £ 15/25

4 rooms: £ 60/75

Typical Dishes

Home-cured salmon
Roast wild mallard
Bakewell tart

4mi North of Spalding by A16. Parking.

14 The Chequers

Main Street,
Woolsthorpe-by-Belvoir NG32 1LU
Tel.: (01476)870701
e-mail: justinnabar@yahoo.co.uk **Website:** www.chequersinn.net

Brewsters and guest beers from micro breweries

The Chequers still has the feel of a village pub: locals sit supping real ale on their stools at the bar and the fixtures for matches on the adjacent cricket pitch hang by the front door, while framed menus from famous restaurants and cruise liners, and the framed Mouton Rothschild labels are a clue to the owners' passion for good food and drink. Made with locally sourced ingredients wherever possible, cooking is simple yet modern, and menus might include classics such as sausage and mash or Stilton pork pie, or for the more adventurous, dishes like clam, squid and salmon risotto or roast rabbit leg. Close to the famous castle in the Vale of Belvoir, this part-17C pub has several areas in which to dine; sit at one of the long tables in the bar or try the more intimate dining room - the cosiest seat in the house is the leather banquette next to the wood burning stove. Four bedrooms are situated next door in the converted stable block.

Food serving times

Monday-Saturday:
12pm-2.30pm, 6pm-9.30pm

Sunday:
12pm-4pm, 6pm-8.30pm

Closed 25-26 December dinner, 1 January dinner

Prices

Meals: £ 15/17
and a la carte £ 21/31

4 rooms: £ 49/59

Typical Dishes
Smoked salmon
Pot roast chicken
Caramel pannacotta

7.5mi West of Grantham by A607. Parking.

The Collyweston Slater

15 The Collyweston Slater

87-89 Main Road,
Collyweston PE9 3PQ

Tel.: (01780)444288 – Fax: (01780)444270
e-mail: info@collywestonslater.co.uk **Website:** www.collywestonslater.co.uk

Everards Original, Slaters Ale, Everards Tiger , Pedigree

This stone-built pub successfully combines modern décor and contemporary furnishings with rural charm and a relaxed atmosphere. Featuring high-backed leather chairs and chunky pine tables, the restaurant feels light and fresh, while the bar area with its tub chairs and welcoming wood burner is more cosy. There's always a way to build up your appetite, be it at one of the monthly quiz or jazz nights, or from playing giant Jenga or Connect 4 in the garden and listening to the gentle "chink" of petanque balls ringing through the air. Although European in its base, the cooking makes good use of local ingredients, focusing on careful preparation and the use of bold flavours rather than unnecessary showiness. The monthly-changing main menu is concise and is supported heavily by daily specials: dishes might include rainbow trout with warm potato salad or sautéed tiger prawns with chorizo. Bedrooms are comfortable, stylish and well-priced.

Food serving times

Monday-Saturday:
12pm-2pm, 6pm-9pm

Sunday: 12pm-2.30pm

Closed 25 December

Prices

Meals: £ 15 (3 course lunch) and a la carte £ 20/28

5 rooms: £ 60/85

Typical Dishes
Ginger spiced scallops
Corn fed chicken
Citrus pannacotta

3mi Southwest of Stamford by A43. Parking.

16 The Falcon Inn

Fotheringhay,
Oundle PE8 5HZ

Tel.: (01832)226254 – Fax: (01832)226046
e-mail: info@thefalcon-inn.co.uk **Website:** www.thefalcon-inn.co.uk

IPA, Fools Nook, Barnwell Bitter and frequently changing guest beers

As you enter the village of Fotheringhay and catch a glimpse of its magnificent floodlit church, you might well be surprised at its size, until you know that this village was once an important centre – and that the now razed castle was both the birthplace of Richard III and the deathplace of Mary, Queen of Scots. Antique pictures celebrating these links hang on the walls at The Falcon Inn, and the 15C bell clappers on show further emphasise its historical credentials. You enter the stone inn through the bottle-green front door, into the bar with its open log fires; the conservatory at the rear, with its views of the church, is a popular place in which to dine. There's a freshness and light touch to the cooking here; flavours are kept clean and the kitchen uses ingredients when they're at their seasonal best. Locals tend to drink in the tiny tap bar at the back, and the adjacent cottage room is popular for private parties.

Food serving times

Monday-Saturday:
12.15pm-2.15pm,
6.15pm-9.15pm

Sunday:
12pm-3pm, 6.15pm-8.30pm

Prices

Meals: a la carte £ 22/35

Typical Dishes

Chicken & courgette terrine

Rump of lamb

Caramelised lemon tart

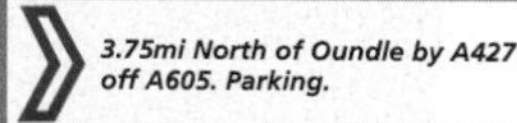

3.75mi North of Oundle by A427 off A605. Parking.

17 Caunton Beck

Main St,
Caunton NG23 6AB

Tel.: (01636)636793 – Fax: (01636)636828
e-mail: email@cauntonbeck.com **Website:** www.wigandmitre.com

 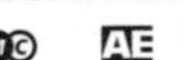 

 **Batemans Valiant, Marstons Pedigree**

Ducks breed on the banks of the Beck, which runs behind this pretty brick pub, and if you approach from the north, you'll make a splash through a ford on you way into the village. There's been a pub at this site for over 300 years, at one point in a state of semi-ruin, but these days, it's modern, welcoming, well-run, and popular with the locals, who enjoy sampling the cask ales. Like its sister pub, the Wig and Mitre, it opens from 8 a.m., and it's a particularly popular destination for breakfast at weekends. The menu offers mostly classic dishes; maybe steak and ale pie, lamb chop or sausage and mash, and daily specials and set menus are chalked up on a blackboard. The restaurant boasts period furniture, beamed ceilings and decorative antique cartoons, but don't dismiss a meal in the stone-floored bar, especially if you're after something lighter. In better weather, try the large front terrace with its colourful flower baskets.

Food serving times

Monday-Sunday:
8am-11pm

Prices

Meals: £ 14 (3 course lunch) and a la carte £ 21/33

Typical Dishes

Confit of duck leg
Grilled fillet steak
Winter berry & cinnamon crème brûlée

7mi North West of Newark by A616, 6mi past the sugar beet factory. Parking.

18 The Martins Arms

School Lane,
Colston Bassett NG12 3FD
Tel.: (01949)81361 – Fax: (01949)81039

    AE

 **Bass, Woodforde Wherry, Timothy Taylor Landlord, Jennings Cumberland, Black Dog, Spitfire**

Warm, welcoming and well run, The Martins Arms has the sort of appearance and atmosphere you'd like to expect from a village pub. Its white façade wears a cloak of creepers, while inside, the traditional décor takes in copper, brass and carpet; plus several pieces of furniture rescued from the village manor house, including a fine Jacobean fireplace. If it's a cosy corner you're after, try the candlelit snug, or for more formal service and surroundings, head for the dining room. With an appealing mix of the traditional and the more modern, the menus contain something for everyone. The owner is a keen hunter, so expect some local game; other choices might range from Ploughman's with Colston Bassett Stilton on the bar menu, to duck liver and foie gras parfait on the à la carte. The large, neatly lawned garden provides a pleasant setting for al fresco dining should the sun decide to spread its love as far north as Nottinghamshire.

Food serving times

Monday-Saturday:
12pm-1.45pm, 7pm-9.30pm

Sunday: 12pm-2pm

Closed 25-26 December dinner

Prices

Meals: a la carte £ 30/45

Typical Dishes

Pan-seared scallops
Pan-seared sea bass
Crème brûlée

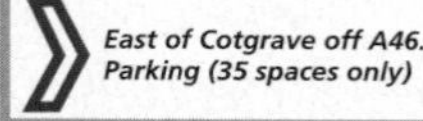

East of Cotgrave off A46.
Parking (35 spaces only)

England • East Midlands • Nottinghamshire

19 Waggon and Horses

The Turnpike,
Mansfield Rd, Halam NG22 8AE
Tel.: (01636)813109 – Fax: (01636)816228
e-mail: info@thewaggonathalam.co.uk **Website:** www.thewaggonathalam.co.uk

 **Wainwrights, Lancaster Bomber, Elma's Pound**

A simple facelift has left this small, cosy pub light, bright and up-to-date. The walls have been re-painted a pleasant shade of green, which contrasts well with the striking modern flower displays on the bar, while in place of the old cricket prints there is now a fresh floral theme. The daily blackboard menu features local meat – such as pan-fried pheasant, slow cooked lamb or pork in a kale and apple hotpot – and lots of fish, which arrives regularly from Grimsby: maybe grilled halibut steak, whole lemon sole or monkfish with creamy mussels. Main dishes are automatically accompanied by a bamboo steamer of fresh vegetables from the fields close by, for which there is commendably no charge. Another pleasant gesture from chef-owner Roy Wood is knocking a couple of pounds off the already good value set lunch menu for the local senior citizens: you could say it's like Christmas every day, well from Tuesday through to Sunday anyway.

Food serving times

Monday-Saturday:
11.30am-2.30pm,
5.30pm-9.30pm

Sunday: 11.30am-2.30pm

Closed Sunday dinner, 25-26 December and 1 January

Prices

Meals: £ 15 (3 course lunch and dinner) and a la carte £ 20/35

Typical Dishes

Seared scallops
Halibut with fennel
Chocolate & pecan tart

1.75mi West of Southwell, opposite the school. Parking.

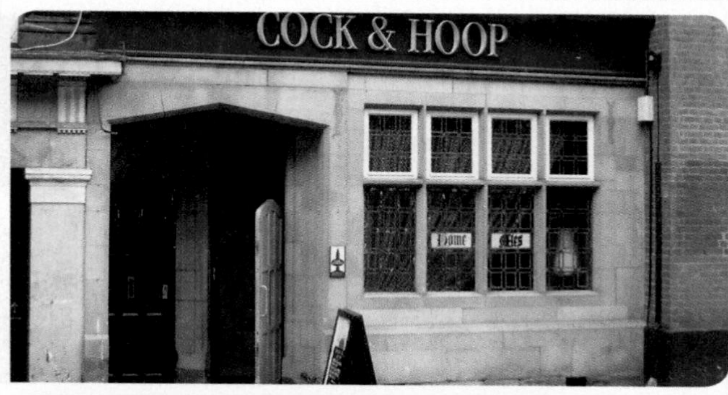

20 Cock and Hoop

29-31 High Pavement,
Nottingham NG1 1HE
Tel.: (0115)8523232 – Fax: (0115)8523223
e-mail: cockandhoop@lacemarkethotel.co.uk **Website:** www.cockandhoop.co.uk

VISA MC AE

Cock and Hoop, Fuller's London Pride, Pedigree, Timothy Taylor Landlord, Black Sheep, Notts Pale Ale

Situated opposite the Galleries of Justice in the redeveloped Lace Market quarter, and owned by the next door Lace Market Hotel, this comfortable, characterful, well-run pub is popular with hotel guests and locals alike. The attractive building dates back to 1765 and its interior is fittingly charming, with mullioned windows, wood panelled walls, open fire and a vaulted ceiling; the zinc-topped bar complete with hand pumps for real ale; softly lit and lined with assorted black and white photos. Printed and blackboard menus offer sandwiches plus all the traditional pub favourites in satisfying portions, like steak and kidney pie or sausage and mash; to follow you might find rhubarb crumble, lemon curd tart or sticky toffee pudding. Make sure that you mind your table manners – not just because this is a well-heeled sort of a place, but because there are some old prison cells in the cellar which could probably be put to good use.

Food serving times
Monday-Sunday:
12pm-10pm
Closed 25 December

Prices
Meals: a la carte £ 19/45

Typical Dishes
Beef carpaccio salad
Porterhouse steak
Rhubarb crumble

Adjacent to Lace Market Hotel. Fletchergate car park and free on-street parking in offpeak hours.

21 Exeter Arms

28 Main St,
Barrowden LE15 8EQ
Tel.: (01572)747247 – Fax: (01572)747247
e-mail: info@exeterarms.com **Website:** www.exeterarms.com

  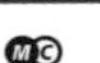 

 **Beech, Owngear, Hopgear, Bevin, IPA**

Handily placed just off the A47, this family run pub exudes much of the rural charm associated with the area close to Rutland Water. It's a 17C inn of light stone idyllically rooted in a sleepy village overlooking the green with its little pond and duck house. Inside is warm and welcoming: the yellow painted walls see to that. Beers here are a must. They come from the pub's own micro-brewery housed in an old rear barn, and you can't sup them anywhere else in the country. If you're eating you can choose a seat wherever takes your fancy, be it the stone-walled dining room or the bar with its cosy open fire. Either way, you won't forget where you are, as old photos of the pub crop up on all walls. You'll remember this hostelry, too, for its well-executed cuisine, classic dishes given an updated, international twist, with Asian influences inspiringly conspicuous. Three neat and tidy bedrooms offer pleasant country views.

Food serving times

Monday-Saturday:
12pm-2pm, 6.30pm-9pm

Sunday: 12pm-2pm

Closed Sunday dinner and November-April Monday lunch

Prices

Meals: £ 17 and a la carte £ 18/24

3 rooms: £ 75

Typical Dishes

Salmon & prawn salad
Honey duck breast
Chocolate brownies

11mi South West of Oakham by A6003 and A47. Parking.

22 The Olive Branch & Beech House

Main St,
Clipsham LE15 7SH

Tel.: (01780)410355 – Fax: (01780)410000
e-mail: info@theolivebranchpub.com **Website:** www.theolivebranchpub.com

Inspectors' favourites

 **Grainstore Olive Oil**

Very much at the heart of the community, locals are to be found at the bar of The Olive Branch sampling the real ales and soaking up the friendly atmosphere, while the shelves full of cookery books above the church pew seating will also give any newcomers a clue to the pub's gastronomic bent. Their provenance detailed on the menu, dishes might include cottage pie, langoustine ravioli or venison casserole; the kitchen here confident enough to keep things simple and let the quality ingredients speak for themselves. Don't leave without dessert; they are a speciality and definitely worth leaving room for. Six bedrooms in the delightful building across the road have equally delicious-sounding names and every extra has been thought of from homemade biscuits to a DVD player, magazines and books. Breakfast by the fire is also a treat, with freshly squeezed orange juice, and homemade everything, including the fruit compotes and the brown sauce.

Food serving times

Monday-Sunday:
12pm-2pm, 7pm-9.30pm

Closed 26 December,
1 January

Booking essential

Prices

Meals: £ 20 (lunch)
and a la carte £ 25/41

6 rooms: £ 100/200

Typical Dishes

Shallot tarte Tatin
Roast fillet of seabass
Queen of puddings

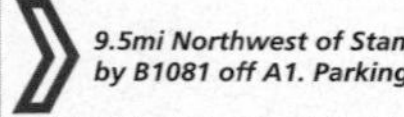

9.5mi Northwest of Stamford by B1081 off A1. Parking.

23 Finch's Arms

Ketton Rd,
Hambleton LE15 8TL

Tel.: (01572)756575 – Fax: (01572)771142
e-mail: finchsarms@talk21.com **Website:** www.finchsarms.co.uk

    AE

 **Timothy Taylor Landlord, Tetley, Abbot Ales**

With its bird's eye view of Rutland Water, this country pub is a Mecca to ornithologists and oenophiles alike. Its front is prettily framed by trees, but it's the rear terrace and garden which cause people to flock here whenever the temperature rises slightly above lukewarm. Whatever the weather, the staff maintain a sunny outlook, and there's always plenty of them around, pleased to help. The emphasis here is on seasonal, locally sourced and traceable produce, with traditional, frill-free yet flavourful dishes created using a minimal number of ingredients. Drinkers are made to feel as welcome as diners and tend to congregate in the traditional beamed bar. The garden room with its bold wallpaper and fresh flowers is more contemporary in style and has a distinctly Mediterranean feel. Six bedrooms blend French country décor with the more modern; several have stunning views over the water and one has its own balcony.

Food serving times

Monday-Saturday:
12pm-2.30pm,
6.30pm-9.30pm

Sunday: 12pm-8pm

Closed 25 December

Prices

Meals: £ 14/19
and a la carte £ 20/30

6 rooms: £ 65/75

Typical Dishes
Potted salt beef
Fillet of seabass
Iced pear parfait

3mi East of Oakham by A606.
Parking.

24 Old White Hart

51 Main Street,
Lyddington LE15 9LR
Tel.: (01572)821703 – Fax: (01572)821965
e-mail: mail@oldwhitehart.co.uk **Website:** www.oldwhitehart.co.uk

 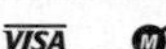

 **Timothy Taylors Golden Best, Fuller's London Pride, Greene King, Abbot**

A warm welcome awaits at the 17C Old White Hart and from the moment you step inside this country pub, with its low beams, stone walls and open fires, it's a cosy feel that envelops you. The owners are well-established and their friendly team are always around but never obtrusive. The chef-owner used to be a butcher, so you know the meat will have been carefully sourced, and whole beasts are delivered to the kitchen. Sausages are homemade and fish are also well-represented on the blackboard menu. Cooking here is classic in style but with a French slant so rump steak and grilled loin of pork share space on the menu with dishes like seared foie gras with homemade brioche. What may look like a random collection of the usual pub paraphernalia actually has deeper meaning to the owners, staff and regulars; like the pipe collection donated by a regular after he'd kicked the habit, and the dragon from a local boat race won by the staff.

Food serving times

Monday-Sunday:
12pm-2pm, 6.30pm-9pm

Closed 25 December

Closed dinner
September-April

Prices

Meals: £ 13 (3 course lunch & dinner)
and a la carte £ 21/34

9 rooms: £ 60/90

Typical Dishes
Glazed calves sweetbreads
Roast rack of lamb
Sticky toffee pudding

1.5mi south of Uppingham off A6003. By the village green. Parking.

England • East Midlands • Rutland

Wide lowland landscapes and huge skies, timber-framed houses, a frowning North Sea canvas: these are the abiding images of England's east. This region has its roots embedded in the earth and its taste buds whetted by local seafood. Some of the most renowned ales are brewed in Norfolk and Suffolk. East Anglia sees crumbling cliffs, superb mudflats and saltmarshes or enchanting medieval wool towns such as Lavenham. Areas of Outstanding Natural Beauty abound, in the Chilterns of Bedfordshire and Hertfordshire, and in Dedham Vale, life-long inspiration of Constable. Religious buildings are everywhere, from Ely Cathedral, "the Ship of the Fens", to the fine structure of Long Melford church. The ghosts of great men haunt Cambridge: Newton, Darwin, Pepys and Byron studied here, doubtless deep in thought as they tramped the wide-open spaces of Midsummer Common or Parker's Piece. Look out for Cromer crab, samphire, grilled herring, Suffolk pork casserole and the hearty Bedfordshire Clanger.

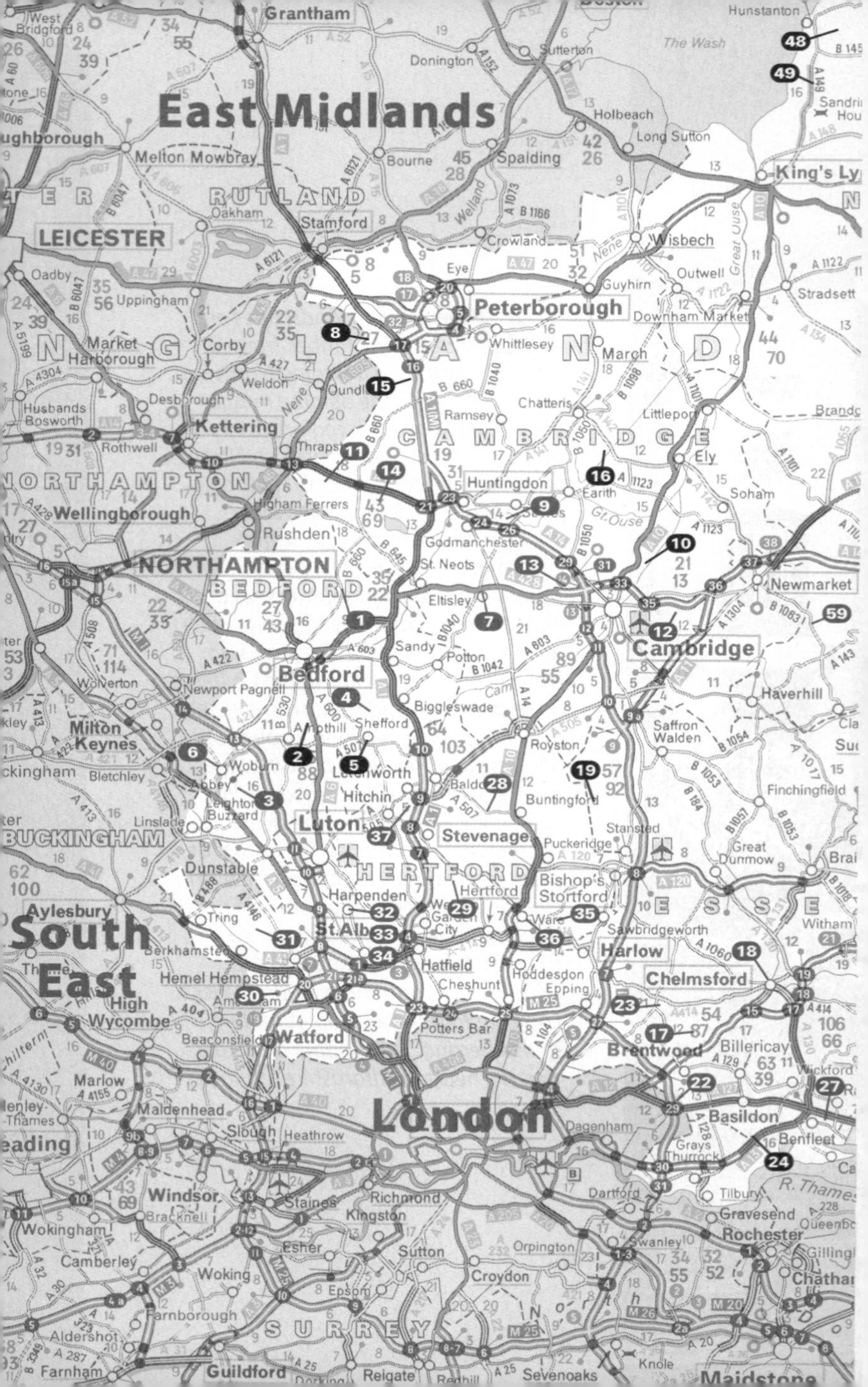

East Midlands
Grantham
West Bridgford
Donington
Sutterton
Hunstanton
The Wash
Holbeach
Long Sutton
Sandringham House
Loughborough
Melton Mowbray
Bourne
Spalding
King's Lynn
RUTLAND
Oakham
Stamford
Welland
Crowland
LEICESTER
Wisbech
Nene
Outwell
Great Ouse
Stradsett
Oadby
Uppingham
Eye
Guyhirn
Peterborough
Downham Market
Whittlesey
Market Harborough
Corby
March
Weldon
Oundle
Desborough
Husbands Bosworth
Kettering
Rothwell
Ramsey
Chatteris
Littleport
Brandon
Thrapston
CAMBRIDGE
Ely
NORTHAMPTON
Huntingdon
Earith
Soham
Wellingborough
Higham Ferrers
Rushden
Godmanchester
Gt. Ouse
St. Neots
Newmarket
BEDFORD
Eltisley
Cambridge
Sandy
Potton
Bedford
Newport Pagnell
Wolverton
Biggleswade
Haverhill
Milton Keynes
Ampthill
Shefford
Saffron Walden
Royston
Bletchley
Woburn Abbey
Baldock
Buntingford
Finchingfield
Leighton Buzzard
Hitchin
Linslade
Luton
Stevenage
Stansted
Great Dunmow
BUCKINGHAM
Puckeridge
Dunstable
HERTFORD
Bishop's Stortford
Harpenden
Hertford
Ware
Sawbridgeworth
Witham
Aylesbury
Tring
St. Albans
South East
Berkhamsted
Hatfield
Harlow
Chelmsford
Hemel Hempstead
Hoddesdon
Epping
Cheshunt
High Wycombe
Amersham
Potters Bar
Brentwood
Billericay
Beaconsfield
Watford
Marlow
Wickford
Henley-on-Thames
Maidenhead
London
Basildon
Dagenham
Benfleet
Reading
Slough
Heathrow
Grays Thurrock
Windsor
Tilbury
R. Thames
Richmond
Dartford
Wokingham
Bracknell
Staines
Kingston
Gravesend
Rochester
Esher
Swanley
Camberley
Sutton
Orpington
Woking
Croydon
Chatham
Epsom
Farnborough
Aldershot
SURREY
Farnham
Guildford
Reigate
Redhill
Sevenoaks
Knole
Maidstone

Wells-next-the-Sea
Sheringham
Cromer
Blakeney
Holt
Mundesley
Fakenham
North Walsham
Guist
Aylsham
Low Street
NORFOLK
East Dereham
Swaffham
Bure
Acle
Great Yarmouth
NORWICH
Wymondham
Watton
Gorleston-on-Sea
Yare
Mundford
Attleborough
Lowestoft
Bungay
Beccles
Thetford
Harleston
Waveney
EAST OF ENGLAND
Halesworth
Southwold
Ixworth
Dennington
Yoxford
Bury St. Edmunds
Saxmundham
Leiston
SUFFOLK
Aldeburgh
Lavenham
IPSWICH
Woodbridge
Hadleigh
Halstead
Felixstowe
Harwich
Esbjerg
Hoek van Holland
Cuxhaven
The Naze
Colchester
Walton-on-the-Naze
Frinton-on-Sea
Brightlingsea
W. Mersea
Clacton-on-Sea
Maldon
Bradwell-on-Sea
Burnham-on-Crouch
Foulness Point
Southend-on-Sea
Grain
Sheerness
Isle of Sheppey
Leysdown-on-Sea
Birchington
Margate
Herne Bay
North Foreland
Whitstable
Sittingbourne
Broadstairs
Ramsgate
South East
Sandwich

1 The Plough at Bolnhurst

Kimbolton Rd,
Bolnhurst MK44 2EX
Tel.: (01234)376274
e-mail: theplough@bolnhurst.com **Website:** www.bolnhurst.com

Potton Brewery Local Village Bike, Adnams, Cottage Brewery Champflower Ale, JMB Ockham Ale

Real ale on tap, a menu teeming with tasty dishes; smooth, assured service and a vibrant yet relaxed atmosphere - The Plough is a pub with it all. The locals patently agree, for this place is often packed to the proverbial rafters, but luckily there's a garden and smart terrace to help take the summer-day strain. Originally dating back to Tudor times, the pub was fully restored to its current whitewashed splendour after a fire some decades ago. Divided into bar and dining room, the interior is no less inviting, and its thick walls, low beams and open fires create a warm, intimate feel. The menu changes according to the seasons, and there's something here for everyone, from simple snacks like devils on horseback or roast chorizo, to pub favourites like ploughman's or free range bangers with colcannon, as well as more elaborate offerings such as foie gras with shallot confit and black pudding or roast English red leg partridge.

Food serving times

Tuesday-Saturday:
12pm-2pm, 6.30pm-9.30pm

Sunday: 12pm-2pm

Closed 31 December and 2 weeks in January

Prices

Meals: £ 17 (3 course lunch) and a la carte £ 26/35

Typical Dishes

Marinated herrings
Roast belly of pork
Baked rice pudding

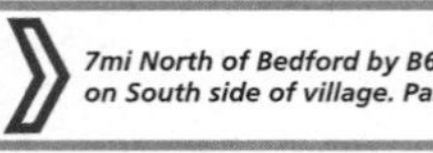

7mi North of Bedford by B660, on South side of village. Parking.

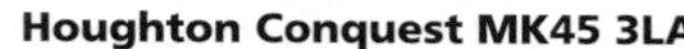

2 Knife and Cleaver

The Grove,
Houghton Conquest MK45 3LA
Tel.: (01234)740387 – Fax: (01234)740900
e-mail: info@knifeandcleaver.com **Website:** www.knifeandcleaver.com

 **Batemans XB, Potton Brewery Village Bike**

Personally and warmly run by long-established owners, the unusual-looking 17C Knife and Cleaver is a cut above the norm and great place to come for a meal. Situated opposite the medieval All Saints Church, it has a snug bar complete with squishy sofas and Jacobean oak panelling reputedly from nearby Houghton House, a small former darts room with a few tables at which you can munch on lighter snacks, plus a spacious, more formal conservatory overlooking the pretty rear garden. Seasonal, daily-changing menus present a wide selection of appealing dishes, with the emphasis firmly on fresh fish. Whole lobsters come flavoured according to this week's serving suggestion; you can indulge in a seafood platter, a classic Dover sole or sea bass fillet, and there are several meat and vegetarian options too. The converted stables house nine homely bedrooms, while the reasonable prices ensure that staying overnight won't break the bank.

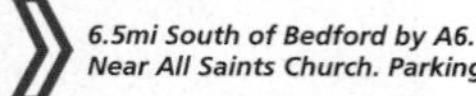

6.5mi South of Bedford by A6. Near All Saints Church. Parking.

Food serving times

Sunday-Friday:
12pm-2.30pm, 7pm-9.30pm

Saturday: 7pm-9.30pm

Closed 27-31 December

Set price dinner Monday-Friday only; a la carte menu Monday-Saturday only

Prices

Meals: £ 17/24
and a la carte £ 22/38

9 rooms: £ 75/89

Typical Dishes

Deep fried tiger prawns
Roast shoulder of lamb
Cheesecake with blueberry sauce

3 The Red Lion

Toddington Rd,
Milton Bryan MK17 9HS
Tel.: (01525)210044
e-mail: paul@redlion-miltonbryan.co.uk **Website:** www.redlion-miltonbryan.co.uk

 **Greene King IPA, Abbot Ale**

The Red Lion is not the sort of place you come across by chance, and even when you're looking for it, it can be difficult to find. But the search is worth it - and getting lost in and around Woburn or in the surrounding country lanes is no hardship either. Lunch can be eaten in the bar, with its country-style seating and stone floors, or in the larger restaurant area, and both the lunch and dinner menus contain lots of choice. All the old favourites are here; hearty and wholesome dishes such as lasagne, steak and chips and sausage and mash, plus popular puddings like spotted dick and sticky toffee pudding, all freshly prepared, and well-presented, with sandwiches and daily-changing fish specials also available at lunch. Hanging baskets bring a blaze of colour to the outside of this charming red-brick pub in summer, and on a hot day, it's a delight to eat to the sound of birdsong on the patio terrace or in the garden.

Food serving times

Monday-Saturday:
12pm-2.3pm, 7pm-9.30pm

Sunday: 12pm-2.30pm

Closed 25-26 and
31 December, 1 January

Closed Monday in winter

Prices

Meals: a la carte £ 20/33

Typical Dishes

Onion & tomato tartlet

Bellly of pork

Sticky toffee pudding

Milton Bryan is South of Woburn by A4012. Parking.

4 Hare & Hounds

The Village, Old Warden SG18 9HQ
Tel.: (01767)627225 – Fax: (01767)627588
e-mail: thehareandhounds@hotmail.co.uk
Website: www.hareandhoundsoldwarden.co.uk

 **Youngs Bitter, Charles Wells IPA and Bombardier, Old Speckled Hen**

One of the highlights of this picture postcard village on the Shuttleworth estate, the Hare and Hounds has immense charm and style. Lounge in front of a blazing open fire in one of the squashy, leather seats in the bar, or laze the day away outside in the mature garden – you're welcome here for anything from a drink to a three course meal, but if you do pop in for a pint, you may well find yourself tempted to stay for food. The British menu has been compiled with care and understanding, and provides a good range of options to suit all tastes. Where possible, ingredients have been sourced locally and dishes change regularly to reflect what's fresh and in season. Choices might include Shuttleworth belly of pork, lemon sole or braised wild rabbit, and the chef even produces his own homemade range of goods including oils, chutneys and preserves. Service is attentive, and the atmosphere warm and friendly.

Food serving times

Monday-Saturday:
12pm-2pm, 6.30pm-9.30pm

Sunday: 12pm-3.30pm

Closed 25 December

Closed mondays except Bank Holidays

Prices

Meals: a la carte £ 20/28

Typical Dishes

Tempura tiger prawns
Scottish sirloin steak
Caramelised lemon tart

3.5mi West of Biggleswade by A6001 off B658. Parking and at Village hall.

5 The Black Horse

Ireland,
Shefford SG17 5QL
Tel.: (01462)811398 – Fax: (01462)817238
e-mail: etaverns@aol.com **Website:** www.blackhorseireland.com

Inspectors' favourites

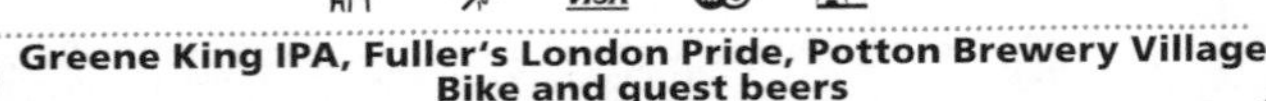

Greene King IPA, Fuller's London Pride, Potton Brewery Village Bike and guest beers

Situated in Ireland, - Ireland in Bedfordshire, not the Emerald Isle - The Black Horse is a traditional 17C village inn, boasting original feature fireplaces, polished wooden tables and comfy banquettes. The smart country style is in evidence in the beamed bar through to the adjacent dining area and the rear extension, while the attractive gardens have bench seating and a patio for use in good weather. When it comes to the food, plan ahead, since it's likely you'll only need two courses and you might not want to miss out on dessert. The seasonally-changing menus have a hearty base, with local suppliers very much in evidence, so dishes might include Bedfordshire pork and ale sausages or 31 day hung rib eye steak from the griddle. Fish often feature, and more unusual offerings might mean tucking into creole chicken, salmon and cod saltimbocca or lime leaves, aduki and borlotti croquettes.Two simple bedrooms are accessed from the garden.

Food serving times

Monday-Saturday:
12pm-2.45pm,
6.30pm-10.30pm

Sunday: 12pm-2.45pm

Closed 25-26 December, 1 January

Prices

Meals: a la carte £ 19/30

2 rooms: £ 55

Typical Dishes

Potted crab
Medallion of Cornish lamb
Sticky toffee pudding

1.75mi Northwest of Shefford by B658 and Ireland Rd. Parking.

6 The Birch

20 Newport Rd,
Woburn MK17 9HX
Tel.: (01525)290295 – Fax: (01525)290899
e-mail: etaverns@aol.com **Website:** www.birchwoburn.com

    AE

 **Fuller's London Pride, Adnams**

If you've spent the day playing golf, exploring the Abbey, or having your wing mirrors stolen by the monkeys at the safari park, you'll probably be in need of refreshment come dinner time. Plenty of others will have had the same idea, however, so it would be wise to book ahead if you want a table at The Birch. It's a well-run establishment - and needs to be given the numbers it attracts – but you get the feeling the staff know exactly what they are doing. The small bar serves a decent selection of real ales and you can sit up high here on a stool or lie low on one of the cosy sofas. The main dining room contains well-spaced wooden tables, and the large conservatory is split onto two levels, with Tim Bulmer sketches on the walls. The extensive menu has a dish to suit every taste and appetite, but it is the grill which really impresses, serving fresh meat and fish ordered by the ounce and cooked to your idea of perfection.

Food serving times

Monday-Saturday:
12pm-2.45pm,
6.30pm-10.30pm

Sunday: 12pm-2.45pm

Closed 25-26 December,
1 January

Booking essential

Prices

Meals: a la carte £ 19/30

Typical Dishes

House smoked venison
Fillets of seabass
Raspberry meringue soufflé

0.5mi North on A5130. Parking.

7 The Eltisley

2 The Green,
Eltisley PE19 6TG
Tel.: (01480)880308
e-mail: theeltisley@btconnect.com **Website:** www.theeltisley.co.uk

Old Speckled Hen, Wells Bombardier, Wells Eagle IPA

In a mere six weeks this traditional country inn overlooking the village green morphed into a chic and stylish gastro-pub. At first glance you would imagine that it's a strictly dining affair but the contemporary bar is equally as welcoming to drinkers as to diners, who can watch their dishes being prepared from the carefully placed windows in the snug. For a more formal occasion head through to the restaurant, where grey walls meet wood and tile flooring, and bold designs are offset by swanky chandeliers. Large parties should ask for the "Wurlitzer", a stylish high-backed semi-circular banquette, while for summer dining the smart new terrace is ideal. Cooking is simple, unfussy and relies on quality local ingredients to speak for themselves; meat is from nearby farms, vegetables from the allotment at their sister pub the "Hare and Hounds", and everything from the bread and pasta through to the desserts and ice cream is homemade.

Food serving times

Tuesday-Saturday:
12pm-2.30pm, 6pm-9pm

Sunday: 12pm-3.30pm

Prices

Meals: a la carte £ 20/30

Typical Dishes

Roast goats cheese
Braised wild boar
Vanilla crème brûlée

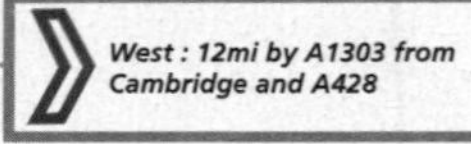

West : 12mi by A1303 from Cambridge and A428

8 The Crown Inn

8 Duck St,
Elton PE8 6RQ
Tel.: (01832)280232
e-mail: inncrown@googlemail.com **Website:** www.thecrowninn.org

  AE

Golden Crown Bitter, Greene King IPA and weekly changing guest bitters such as Timothy Taylor, Deuchars IPA

If you were to dream up the perfect location for a village inn, it would probably resemble the beautiful parish of Elton, all honey stone houses and well-trimmed green – the thatched roof and inglenook fireplace of the 17C Crown Inn blending in superbly. Sit in the open main bar, the sizeable front dining room, the rear conservatory, or in brighter weather, the front terrace, which makes a delightful spot to try some of the many, frequently changing, real ales on offer. Food is traditional in the main; you might try steak and ale pie, sausage and mash or the ever popular fish and chips - but there's a touch of Italy here too in the form of dishes such as tagliatelli, risotto or lasagne, which all arrive in healthy portions. Lunchtime sees lighter dishes like omelettes and sandwiches up for grabs and the daily-changing blackboard menu expands your choice still further. Bedrooms are smart and individually styled, with spacious bathrooms.

Food serving times

Tuesday-Saturday:
12pm-2pm, 6.30pm-8.45pm

Sunday: 12pm-3pm

Closed 10 days from 1 January

Prices

Meals: a la carte £ 20/33

4 rooms: £ 60/90

Typical Dishes

Chicken liver parfait
Seabass & mullet risotto
Elton swan profiteroles

6mi Southwest of Peterborough by A1139, A605 and minor road North. Parking and on village green opposite.

9 The Cock

47 High St,
Hemingford Grey PE28 9BJ
Tel.: (01480)463609 – Fax: (01480)461747
e-mail: cock@cambscuisine.com **Website:** www.cambscuisine.com

Inspectors' favourites

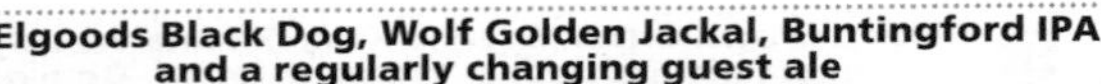

Elgoods Black Dog, Wolf Golden Jackal, Buntingford IPA and a regularly changing guest ale

The Cock cocks a snook at most other Huntingdon hostelries and is the place to come if you are after a relaxing meal in a country pub. Centrally located, this busy 17C pub serves local ales and has kept the feel of the village local, with a split-level bar specifically for drinkers on one side, and a spacious, L-shaped dining room on the other. Rustic in feel, it has polished wood floors and an open fire, and is brightened by oil paintings – available to take home with you for the right price. The menus provide plenty of choice, from a 2 course lunch menu to a full à la carte and daily-changing fish specials. Dishes range from Jerusalem artichoke and truffle risotto to sirloin steak, but the best choice would have to come from the sausage board; a kind of mix and match between differently flavoured homemade sausages and a similarly diverse choice of mashed potato and sauces.

Food serving times

Monday-Saturday:
12pm-2.30pm,
6.30pm-9.30pm

Sunday:12pm-3pm,
6.30pm-8.30pm

Prices

Meals: £ 15 (3 course lunch) and a la carte £ 21/25

Typical Dishes

Potted ham hock
Roast saddle of lamb
Blood orange tartlet

5mi Southeast of Huntingdon by A1198 off A14. Parking.

10 Crown and Punchbowl

High St, Horningsea CB25 9JG
Tel.: (01223)860643 – Fax: (01223)441814
e-mail: info@the crownandpunchbowl.co.uk
Website: www.thecrownandpunchbowl.co.uk

 **Hobsons Choice**

You won't find locals passing the time of day with a pint at the bar in the Crown and Punchbowl. Not because the locals don't patronize the place, but because there is no bar here - which makes it a weird kind of pub, if you think about it. What it does have is plenty of snug pubby charm, with rustic walls, wooden floors, open fires - and beamed ceilings low enough to present a danger to anyone over 5ft 5". Located next to a pretty church and graveyard, the pub is actually a blend of two buildings; one dating from the 17C, the other from the 19C, and inside, there are two main dining areas as well as a small private dining room for parties. Food is local, seasonal and appealing, with choices like steak and chips and confit duck leg on the à la carte, supplemented by fish specials and mix and match homemade sausage and mash, which are chalked up on blackboards. Five modern, spacious and relaxing bedrooms complete the picture.

Food serving times

Monday-Saturday:
12pm-2.30pm, 6.30pm-9pm

Sunday: 12pm-2.30pm

Prices

Meals: a la carte £ 15/40

5 rooms: £ 75/95

Typical Dishes
Pan-fried scallops
Fillet of seabass
Chocolate brownie

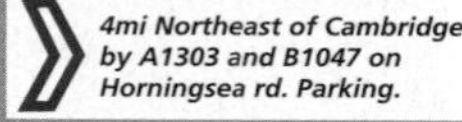
4mi Northeast of Cambridge by A1303 and B1047 on Horningsea rd. Parking.

England • East of England • Cambridgeshire

11 The Pheasant

Village Loop Road,
Keyston PE28 0RE
Tel.: (01832)710241
e-mail: info@thepheasant-keyston.co.uk **Website:** www.thepheasant-keyston.co.uk

Inspectors' favourites

    VISA AE

Adnams and rotating guest beers - Nethergate, Grainstore, Potton

If you're looking for a dining experience that reaches way above your average, this charming thatched inn hidden away in a sleepy hamlet is well worth searching out. Run by a husband and wife team, he oversees in the kitchen, while she heads the friendly serving team. The building's full of character, with cosy sofas set beside the fire in the timbered bar and a more formal dining room with walls adorned with hunting prints. For summer, however, the best seats in the house would have to be in the delightful rear garden. The daily changing menu provides a good choice of dishes, which are made from local, seasonal ingredients; they might include pot roast rabbit, crisp hake or new season's rump of lamb. For those who don't know their hairy bittercress from their hedge sorrel or their rémoulade from their rouille, a glossary of terms is provided, as is a list of favoured suppliers. There's also an excellent selection of wines by the glass.

Food serving times

Tuesday-Saturday:
12pm-2.30pm,
6.30pm-9.30pm

Sunday: 12pm-2.30pm

Booking essential

Prices

Meals: £ 18 (set price lunch) and a la carte £ 24/42

Typical Dishes

Fish soup
Braised pigs trotter
Crème brûlée

3.5mi Southeast of Thrapstone by A14 on B663. Parking.

12 The Hole in the Wall

2 High St,
Little Wilbraham CB21 5JY
Tel.: (01223)812282
Website: www.the-holeinthewall.com

 **Woodfordes Wherry, Nelsons Revenge, Milton Jupiter**

A remotely set, 15C pub serving serious food – and not a cash machine in sight. Its name actually comes from when field workers used to leave their tankards at the pub on the way to work via a hole in the wall, allowing them to pick up their beer on the way home. With a 600 year history, you'd expect the building to have its fair share of charm, and it doesn't disappoint. Exposed beams rest overhead, and in winter, the brightly burning log fires provide the only source of warmth since there's no central heating. Between them, the team here have immense experience and the confident kitchen produces good value, flavoursome British dishes using seasonal ingredients in classical ways; so you might try 12 hour pickled brisket with oxtail, sea trout with Jersey Royals or honey-roasted poussin. Enduringly popular and mightily tasty puddings could include warm ginger cake, Eve's pudding or hot chocolate fondant.

Food serving times

Tuesday-Saturday:
12pm-2pm, 7pm-9pm

Sunday: 12pm-2pm

Closed 25 December and 2 weeks in January

Prices

Meals: a la carte £ 21/30

Typical Dishes

Wild rabbit
Norfolk trout
Burnt "Trinity" Cambridgeshire cream

5mi East of Cambridge by A1303 and minor road South. Parking.

13 The Three Horseshoes

High St,
Madingley CB4 8SA
Tel.: (01954)210221 – Fax: (01954)212043
e-mail: 3hs@btconnect.com **Website:** www.thethreehorseshoesmadingley.com

 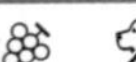   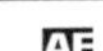

 **Adnams Southwold, Cambridge Boat House Bitter**

Swap the bustle of Cambridge City centre for the tranquillity of Madingley for a few hours and you'll not want to go back. Just a few miles out of town, this delightful thatched inn makes a picturesque location for lunch or dinner – get out of driving duties and you can also take advantage of the local ales or the superb selection of wines on offer. The same menu is served throughout, so you can be inspired by the food-themed pictures in the snug, fire-warmed bar or dine in a more formal fashion at one of the dressed tables in the conservatory / dining room. The weekly-changing à la carte offers seasonal Italian food made with the best of local produce; imaginative dishes and clean flavours run through from the bruschetta and the primi piatti to the dolce and the gelato. Set 2, 3 and 5 course menus are a good way to keep a firm hold on those purse-strings if you're on a budget. Professional, unobtrusive service completes the picture.

Food serving times

Monday-Friday:
12pm-2pm, 6.30pm-9.30pm

Saturday:
12pm-2.30pm,
6.30pm-9.30pm

Sunday:
12pm-2.30pm, 6pm-8pm

Closed 1-2 January

Prices

Meals: £ 20 (3 course lunch & dinner)
and a la carte £ 18/40

Typical Dishes

Plate of cold meats
Aberdeen rib-eye steak
Chocolae truffle cake

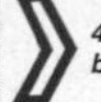

4.5mi West of Cambridge by A1303. Parking.

14 The George Inn

5 High St,
Spaldwick PE28 0TD
Tel.: (01480)890293 – Fax: (01480)896847
e-mail: info@georgeofspaldwick.co.uk **Website:** www.georgeofspaldwick.co.uk

 **Adnams Broadside, Greene King IPA, Youngs Special**

Contemporary meets old world charm at this distinctive, yellow-painted pub, its spacious, stylish interior balanced out by a host of traditional features, such as stone floors, thick walls and exposed ceiling timbers. Bag yourself a leather sofa in the roomy bar and get comfortable by one of the coffee tables; the blackboard informs you of what's on offer food-wise, and an eclectic bunch of dishes there are too. Hearty favourites like sausage and mash and shepherd's pie will put paid to the hunger pangs at lunch, while in the evening, you can choose between universally appealing dishes like coq au vin, roast guinea fowl and sirloin steak. Specials change daily, and the à la carte to match the season. The cosy front seats are a popular place to hang, while the two characterful dining areas situated in the original 15C area of the pub provide more formal dining for when the occasion demands it.

Food serving times
Monday-Sunday:
12pm-2.30pm, 6pm-9.30pm

Prices
Meals: a la carte £ 23/33

Typical Dishes
Baked figs and lentils
Pan seared seabass fillet
Peppered pineapple fritters

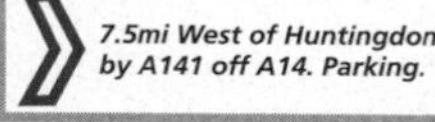
7.5mi West of Huntingdon by A141 off A14. Parking.

England • East of England • Cambridgeshire

15 Village Bar (at Bell Inn)

Great North Rd,
Stilton PE7 3RA

Tel.: (01733)241066 – Fax: (01733)245173
e-mail: reception@thebellstilton.co.uk **Website:** www.thebellstilton.co.uk

Greene King IPA, Greene King Abott, J H B, Fuller's London Pride, Crop Circle, Brewers Gold, Harvest

Stilton? Mmmmm. That name rings a bell. Just two minutes from the busy A1, and yet a world away, this striking 16C stone building dominates the village in which it sits. With its solid stone floor, open fire and rough wooden tables, the charming bar is the hub of activity and, thanks to the village's reputation as the birthplace of Stilton, is filled with cheesy memorabilia including an ornamental cheese press. Although the bistro shares a menu with the bar, the latter is the more atmospheric place to sit – just make sure that you avoid the window seats, as you might cheesed off with the draughts. Whilst there is the odd international influence, most dishes are hearty, filling and close to home, as pub dishes should be. The menu also offers several Stilton-based recipes, including soups and dressings, but if you're crackers about cheese, surely nothing can beat a mature hunk of the stuff all by itself.

Food serving times

Monday-Sunday:
12pm-2pm, 7pm-9.30pm

Closed 25 December, dinner 26 December, dinner 1 January

Prices

Meals: £ 27 and a la carte £ 19/33

22 rooms: £ 74/101

Typical Dishes

Stilton and hazelnut paté
Devilled calves kidneys
Pear & pomegranate clafoutis

4mi South of Peterborough by A15; in centre of village. Parking.

16 The Anchor Inn

Sutton Gault CB6 2BD
Tel.: (01353)778537 – Fax: (01353)776180
e-mail: anchorinn@popmail.bta.com **Website:** www.anchor-inn-restaurant.co.uk

City of Cambridge Brewery : Hobsons Choice, Boathouse Bitter

This charming inn, built on reclaimed marshland on the western edge of the Isle of Ely, was originally constructed in 1650 to house the workers who were digging up the Old and New Bedford Rivers. The previous chef and manager are now the owners, and have made some positive changes whilst retaining the essential character of the pub. There are three main rooms in which to dine, and scrubbed wooden tables and deep panelling reflect the flickering of candlelight in the evenings. An eclectic range of dishes is served, including old favourites such as lamb shank and supreme of chicken. East Anglian produce, such as venison from the Denham estate and Sutton sausages, is used wherever possible, and daily specials feature mainly fish. Sit out on the terrace and watch the beautiful sunset light up the sky, which seems to stretch forever over the fens, before retiring to one of the four comfortable bedrooms; the front-facing twin is the best.

Food serving times

Monday-Friday:
12pm-2pm, 7pm-9pm

Saturday:
12pm-2pm, 6.30pm-9.30pm

Sunday:
12pm-2.30pm,
6.30pm-9.30pm

Prices

Meals: £ 16 (lunch)
and a la carte £ 20/30

4 rooms: £ 60/155

Typical Dishes

Wild boar ham
Stuffed pork tenderloin
Mulled wine pear

Off B1381; follow signs to Sutton Gault from Sutton village. Pub is near the New Bedford River. Parking.

17 The Leather Bottle

The Green,
Blackmore CM4 0RL
Tel.: (01277)823538
e-mail: leatherbottle@tiscali.co.uk **Website:** www.theleatherbottle.net

 **Adnams, Skull Splitter, Directors, Woodforde Wherry, Cactus Jack, Timothy Taylor Landlord and guest beers**

If you're anywhere near the picturesque village of Blackmore and are wanting a good meal, then the best advice would be to hit the bottle – the Leather Bottle. The pub dates from the 1750s and overlooks the village green - known as Horsefayre Green – where horse fairs used to be held when Blackmore was an old centre for the leather trade in the 19C. The pub is divided into two, with a bar on one side and a dining area and conservatory on the other. The flagstoned bar serves a selection of real ales and is cosy and relaxing, with an open fire, while the conservatory, with its wooden floor and stylish leather chairs, has an airy, natural feel and overlooks the rear garden. The all-encompassing seasonal menu has a traditional British base with European influences, and sometimes involves the odd Asian dish too. The set two-course lunch menus are particularly popular and a traditional roast is served on Sundays.

Food serving times
Monday-Saturday:
12pm-2pm, 7pm-9pm
Sunday: 12pm-2pm
Closed Sunday dinner

Prices
Meals: £ 10 (2 course lunch) and a la carte £ 19/26

Typical Dishes
Crispy duck roulade
Wild seabass
Chocolate fondant

2.75mi Southeast of High Ongar by A414. Parking in front of the pub.

18 The Alma

37 Arbour Lane,
Chelmsford CM1 7RG

Tel.: (01245)256783 – Fax: (01245)256793
e-mail: alma@eyho.co.uk **Website:** www.eyho.co.uk/alma

 **Greene King IPA and guest beers**

The bright yellow exterior of The Alma shines like a beacon to the people of Cheltenham and beyond, as if to say "there's good food to be had here." Inside it's smart and contemporary, with a welcoming feel and plenty of character - sit in the spacious front bar, where the solid walls, open fires, wood pillars and beams help to create a rustic feel, or head instead for the more formal rear dining room, with its stylish high backed leather chairs and polished wood tables. The wide ranging menu contains a mix of British and European dishes, with choices such as carpaccio of beef, breast of duck or sesame tuna loin, as well as healthy portions of pub favourites like sausage and mash or liver and bacon served in the bar. When the sun pokes its head out from behind the clouds, there's a rush for the terrace, whilst the flat screen TV inside panders to sporting types. A keen young team provide polished service.

Food serving times

Monday-Saturday:
12pm-2.30pm, 6pm-9.30pm

Sunday: 12pm-8pm

Closed 25-26 December

Prices

Meals: a la carte £ 18/26

Typical Dishes

Pressed ham hock terrine

Roast pork belly

Baked chocolate cheesecake

East of town centre; off northside of Springfield Road (A1099). Parking.

19 The Cricketers

Clavering CB11 4QT

Tel.: (01799)550442 – Fax: (01799)550882

e-mail: info@thecricketers.co.uk **Website:** www.thecricketers.co.uk

AE

 **Adnams, Adnams Broadside, Greene King IPA**

This may be the hallowed ground where Jamie Oliver first learned to chop an onion, but, having been here since 1976, his parents have gained quite a following of their own, especially among the locals. The 16C pub has a very traditional feel, with its low ceilings, beams and velour banquettes, and if you're staying the night there's a good selection of bedrooms to choose from - those in the pavilion are cottagey in style, while those in the courtyard are more modern. The separate bar and restaurant menus, plus the vast array of daily specials ensure that there's plenty of choice – and not a turkey twizzler in sight. The seasonal menu offers a refreshing mix of classic and modern dishes, all homemade from quality, locally sourced produce. There's a strong Italian leaning, so you'll find plenty of pastas and risottos as well as choices such as slow braised wild rabbit, half a roasted local duck or even a spicy vegetable biriani. Pukka.

Food serving times

Monday-Sunday:
12pm-2pm, 6.30pm-9.30pm

Closed 25-26 December

Prices

Meals: £ 30 (3 course dinner) and a la carte £ 20/30

14 rooms: £ 65/110

Typical Dishes

Prawn & avocado tian

Rack of Suffolk lamb

Apple & lemon thyme tart Tatin

On B1038; Southwest of Saffron Walden. Parking.

20 The Sun Inn

High St,
Dedham CO7 6DF
Tel.: (01206)323351

e-mail: office@thesuninndedham.com **Website:** www.thesuninndedham.com

VISA MC

Adnams Broadside, Brewers Gold, Earl Sohams Victoria Bitter, Whitstables Indian Pale Ale

The Sun Inn is one of those rare, old-fashioned village locals where everyone knows everyone else, but if you're not a regular, don't let that put you off - they're a friendly bunch in this part of the world. While its exterior is painted a modern and fittingly sunny shade of yellow, this pub's characterful timbered interior is a reminder of its 15C origins. Open fires keep punters toasty, and photos of local history line the walls. The rustic, frequently-changing menu has a real Mediterranean base with strong leanings towards Italy, but there are also some more robust dishes for the more traditionally-minded. Locally grown fruit and vegetables are sold in the pub's own shop, "Victoria's Plums," and old-style country charm meets modernity in the comfortable bedrooms. Go for a stroll around the beautifully picturesque village or along the River Stour before sundown, and behold the views that so inspired Constable.

Food serving times

Monday-Thursday:
12-2.30pm, 6.30pm-9.30pm
Friday: 10pm
Saturday:
12pm-3pm, 6.30pm-10pm
Sunday: 9.30pm
Closed 25, 26, 31 December

Prices

Meals: £ 25 and a la carte £ 22/27

5 rooms: £ 65/130

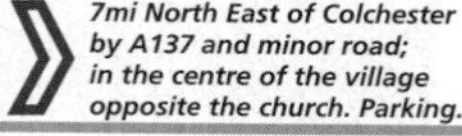

7mi North East of Colchester by A137 and minor road; in the centre of the village opposite the church. Parking.

Great Henny

Henny Swan

21 Henny Swan

Henny St,
Great Henny CO10 7LS
Tel.: (01787)269238
e-mail: harry@hennyswan.com **Website:** www.hennyswan.com

   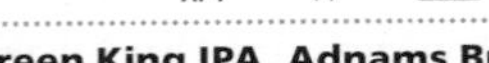

Green King IPA, Adnams Broadside, Nethergate

This converted barge house, now totally refurbished, is run by experienced ex-hoteliers and has a distinctive, contemporary feel to it. The L-shaped, beamed bar with its wood burning stove and modern artwork, is full of comfy sofas and armchairs, whilst the dining room is more bright and airy, with two sets of French windows leading out onto a large terrace. The best place to sit in fine weather is the lawn across the lane, from where you can watch the River Stour flow slowly past, while the willows sway gently from side to side in the breeze. Barbeques are unsurprisingly popular here in the summer, and the occasional band also fills the Essex evening air with the mellow sound of jazz. The diverse, fairly-priced menu has a Mediterranean base but offers something for everyone. Dishes range from grilled haloumi cheese to aubergine au gratin, but there are also choices such as steak, Thai-style fishcakes and lunchtime baguettes too.

Food serving times

Monday-Sunday:
12pm-2.30pm,
6.30pm-9.30pm

Closed Sunday dinner, closed November-April Monday

Prices

Meals: £ 11 and a la carte £ 19/26

Typical Dishes

Grilled whole sardines
Rump of Lamb
Sticky toffee pudding

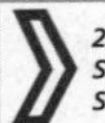

2mi South of Sudbury by A131 South West and a minor road South. Parking.

22 The Headley

The Common,
Great Warley CM13 3HS
Tel.: (01277)216104
e-mail: reservations@theheadley.co.uk **Website:** www.theheadley.co.uk

  VISA

 **Adnams**

From the outside it may not look like your stereotypical pub but with solid wood tables, comfy leather sofas and warm, welcoming fires inside – not to mention good food and drink – it definitely measures up. Split over two floors and boasting a small terrace for al fresco dining, there's plenty of choice when it comes to places to sit, so you can enjoy a different experience each time you come. The chef enjoys supporting local trades and makes the most of the produce that is grown or reared in the area around him; he even hosts a Farmers' market every second Saturday of the month to bring local producers together. As you might expect the menu features lots of regional produce, and there's always plenty of fish to be found; dishes may include sautéed pork belly, wild boar toad in the hole, grilled rainbow trout or sautéed sea bass. From Tuesday – Friday there's also a good value set lunch menu that comes complete with a glass of wine.

Food serving times
Tuesday-Saturday:
12pm-3pm, 6pm-9.30pm
Sunday: 12pm-5pm

Prices
Meals: a la carte £ 22/26

Typical Dishes
Seared scallops
Braised pork belly
Pear crumble

2mi South West of Brentwood by B186. Parking.

23 The Wheatsheaf

King St,
High Ongar CM5 9NS
Tel.: (01277)822220
Website: www.thewheatsheafbrasserie.co.uk

 **No real ales offered**

Not really a pub, but not quite a restaurant either, The Wheatsheaf would probably best be classed as a pestaurant, or perhaps a restapub. Whatever you want to call it, it's certainly a charming place and new, experienced owners are running a tight ship, with very friendly, staff and efficient service. Three stylishly furnished dining areas have varnished wood floors, semi-panelled cream walls, banquette window seating and unique, kidney-shaped tables. There's a more intimate room at the rear, as well as a fully carpeted snug. You might have to ponder over the menus awhile, given the large choice they provide; traditional, seasonal dishes form the base, while influences come from all over and flavours are well-combined. When the sun decides to put in appearance, seats in the spacious rear garden and terrace begin to look very appealing, but wherever you sit, word about The Wheatsheaf has got round, so booking is essential.

Food serving times

Tuesday-Saturday:
12pm-2.30pm, 6.30pm-late

Sunday: 12pm-2.30pm

Closed 26-30 December, Sunday dinner and Monday

Booking essential

Prices

Meals: a la carte £ 23/33

Typical Dishes

Seared pigeon breast
Lamb cutlets
Baileys chocolate fondant

2mi East by A414 on Blackmore rd. Parking.

24 The Bell

High Rd,
Horndon-on-the-Hill SS17 8LD
Tel.: (01375)642463 – Fax: (01375)361611
e-mail: joanne@bell-inn.co.uk **Website:** www.bell-inn.co.uk

It has oft-times been heard tell / If thy hunger thy need quell / It would plainly do thee well / To get thee straight down to The Bell. The current owners' family have been behind the bar of this busy Essex pub now for nigh on 50 years; a long time in the world of pub ownership, but a mere drop in the ocean compared to how long the pub has been standing. Construction began in the 15C and its country-style décor reflects this with open fires flickering in the grate and original beams hanging overhead. The characterful décor also continues in the charming period bedrooms, named after famous mistresses such as Anne Boleyn and Lady Hamilton; their decoration and furnishings inspired by their famous names. The wide-ranging blackboard menu includes lots of daily specials and has something for everyone, from the more traditional sausage and mash / steak and chips combos to dishes such as tuna Niçoise.

Food serving times

Monday-Saturday:
12pm-1.45pm,
6.30pm-9.45pm

Sunday:
12pm-2pm, 7pm-9.45pm

Closed 25-26 December and bank holiday Mondays

Prices

Meals: a la carte £ 22/31

15 rooms: £ 65/104

Typical Dishes

Mushroom risotto
Halibut fillet
Pistachio & hazelnut profiteroles

3mi Northeast of Grays by A1013 off A13. Parking.

England • East of England • Essex

25 The Mistley Thorn

High Street,
Mistley CO11 1HE
Tel.: (01206)392821 – Fax: (01206)390122
e-mail: info@mistleythorn.com **Website:** www.mistleythorn.com

Inspectors' favourites

VISA MC

Adnams, Mersea Island Bitter

This Georgian inn is reputedly the spot where Witchfinder General Matthew Hopkins lived and held his trials in the 17C. Happily, nowadays, you won't get thrown into the ornamental swan pond to see if you float, but you will get a warm, friendly welcome from the enthusiastic young staff, and a good value, quality meal to boot. The Californian owner knows her food and runs a cookery school called "The Mistley Kitchen" when not hard at work at the Thorn. The first rule of good cooking is to use good produce, and that maxim certainly applies here. The daily-changing menus have an emphasis on fresh fish and seafood, and the well-sourced ingredients are seasonal, local and organic. A similar simplicity informs the décor here; with open fires, half-timbered walls and local art for sale on the walls, the feel of the place is contemporary, yet down to earth. Bedrooms are cosy and well-maintained, and two of them overlook the River Stour.

Food serving times

Monday-Friday:
12pm-2.30pm,
6.30pm-9.30pm

Saturday-Sunday:
12pm-9.30pm

Closed 25 December

Prices

Meals: £ 15 (lunch)
and a la carte £ 14/23

5 rooms: £ 75/105

Typical Dishes

Seafood platter
Spiced tuna
Chocolate & hazelnut cake

9mi North East of Colchester by A137 and B1352; not far from Mistley Towers. Parking.

26 The Compasses at Pattiswick

Compasses Rd, Pattiswick CM77 8BG
Tel.: (01376)561322 – Fax: (01376)564343
e-mail: info@thecompassesatpattiswick.co.uk
Website: www.thecompassesatpattiswick.co.uk

 VISA MC

Woodeforde Wherry, Adnams Explorer and weekly changing guest beer

Set in the Essex countryside, this pub started life as two estate workers' cottages and despite its updated interior, still manages to hold onto its country roots. In colder months you can choose between a spacious, rustic bar boasting cosy leather sofas and warming fires or a dining room decorated with Hugo Fircks artwork; while in summer, the pleasant terrace and extensive gardens provide the perfect spot. Popular with locals, hikers and visitors alike, this pub is often deservedly busy – due partially to the quality of the food and partially to the friendly service and watchful eye of the owner. Staying true to the pub's country feel, menus feature simple, hearty dishes made from local produce; the game coming courtesy of the surrounding Holifield Estate. With light bites, a set menu and an à la carte, lunch can be anything from a sandwich to a four course meal; while, retaining the latter two menus, dinner remains more substantial.

Food serving times
Monday-Sunday:
12pm-2.45pm, 6pm-9.30-pm

Prices
Meals: a la carte £ 19/30

Typical Dishes
Fresh crab with avocado
Pan fried seabass
Knickerbocker glory

4mi West of Braintree by A120 and a minor road North. Parking.

27 The Woodmans Arms

Rayleigh Rd,
Thundersley SS7 3TA
Tel.: (01268)775799 – Fax: (01268)590689
e-mail: thewoodman@hotmail.co.uk **Website:** www.thewoodmansarms.co.uk

 **Adnams, Greene King IPA, Broadside**

The Woodmans Arms is something of a desert oasis. In an area crying out for a stylish venue to eat and drink, it ticks a lot of the right boxes. Set on a busy main road – admittedly not the most attractive location – it's a Victorian stalwart that's been modernised to a good standard, with etched and frosted bay windows and smart, wood-furnished al fresco terraces. A snazzy little lounge bar with squashy brown leather sofas and low tables is reserved for drinkers. The remainder of the pub is given over to diners, and locals are making the most of the stylish modern surroundings: each area is separated by screens and highlighted by warm modern colours. There are some old photos of the pub as it was in its former days. The good-sized menu sees some international flavours mingling alongside the mainly British selection and dishes might include rack of lamb, liver and bacon or paella, supplemented by daily specials.

Food serving times
Monday-Sunday:
12pm-9pm

Prices
Meals: a la carte £ 18/22

Typical Dishes
Chicken & mushroom terrine
Pan-fried seabass
Apple crumble

Between Basildon and Southend-on-Sea off A127. Parking.

28 The Bull of Cottered

Cottered SG9 9QP
Tel.: (01763)281243
e-mail: cordell39@btinternet.com

 **Greeene King IPA and Abbot Ale**

A popular stop-off point for travellers on their way to Stansted airport, this well-established pub is quite a picture in the summer months, when its flower baskets and tubs create a riot of colour out front. Inside, it's tradition all the way, with polished horse brasses, classic wooden furniture, crackling log fires and a tidy, homely feel. The menu follows suit, offering real pub food like calves liver, steak and kidney pie, rack of lamb or Ploughman's; with light lunches, more substantial meals, salads, burgers and Sunday roast all covered, and accompanied by a specials board and a cheese trolley. The rear dining room is a popular spot, as is the coveted alcove table in the front bar, while out the back a veritable suntrap encourages al fresco dining when the weather acquiesces. Popular music nights add spice to the winter months; so slip on your blue suede shoes, say thank you for the music and get ready to shake, rattle and roll.

6mi Southeast of Baldock by A507; in the centre of the village. Parking at the front of the pub.

Food serving times
Monday-Sunday:
12pm-2pm, 6.30pm-9.30pm

Prices
Meals: a la carte £ 17/33

Typical Dishes
Devon crab
Calves liver
Chocolate truffle torte

29 The Tilbury

Watton Rd,
Datchworth SG3 6TB
Tel.: (01438)815550 – Fax: (01438)718340
e-mail: info@thetilbury.co.uk **Website:** www.thetilbury.co.uk

 **Brakspear Best, Oxford Gold**

Owned by two local boys – one of whom you might recognise as TV chef, Paul Bloxham – and run by an experienced young team, this popular red brick pub places food firmly at its centre. Cookery school events span the globe and future plans include barbeques, a range of homemade produce and open air films with a meal. Seasonal and honest, the well executed, flavoursome dishes on the modern European menu reflect the team's commitment to sourcing first class produce from local farms. They're gaining quite a reputation for fish on Fridays and Saturdays, when the best available lobster, monkfish, bream and oysters are bought from the day boats in Cornwall – and it's great to see a pub paying as much attention to its choice of beer as its wine. The pub has a fresh, modern look, with an earthy green colour scheme and contemporary oils for sale on the walls. There's a pleasant terrace and garden - and a petanque court should the urge grab you.

Food serving times

Tuesday-Saturday:
12pm-3pm, 6pm-late

Sunday: 12pm-3pm

Closed 25-26 December, 1 January and some Bank Holidays

Prices

Meals: £ 16 (lunch)
and a la carte £ 18/33

Typical Dishes

Home-cured duck pastrami
Tilbury plate of pig
Raspberry & lemon parfait

South East : 4mi by A602 from Stevenage and minor road South

30 The Bricklayers Arms

Hogpits Bottom,
Flaunden HP3 0PH

Tel.: (01442)833322 – Fax: (01442)834841
e-mail: goodfood@bricklayersarms.com **Website:** www.bricklayersarms.com

Fuller's London Pride, Tring Jack o'Legs, Timothy Taylor Landlord, Greene King IPA

Take a map with you on your trip to The Bricklayers Arms, or you may well end up getting lost among the leafy lanes of Hertfordshire. Situated in the enchantingly named, "Hogpits Bottom," this charming, brick built 18C pub used to be three cottages, and original features include the slate roof, wooden beams and low ceilings. The spacious main bar is the best place to sit, with its exposed brick walls, country-style prints and well-spaced tables, but there is also a slightly more formal dining room too. The French chef is passionate about the freshness of his food, and the team here grow a lot of their vegetables and soft fruit on their own north London smallholding. Unsurprisingly, the menu is grounded in French classics, so you might find foie gras and snails on the menu alongside more English dishes such as steak and kidney pie as well as home-smoked fish and meats. Book ahead to avoid disappointment, especially at weekends.

4mi North of Rickmansworth by A404 and a minor road North. Parking.

Food serving times

Monday-Saturday:
12pm-2.30pm,
6.30pm-9.30pm

Sunday:
12pm-3.30pm, 6.30-8.30pm

Prices

Meals: a la carte £ 23/34

Typical Dishes

Eggs Meurette
Chicken breast
Rhubarb cream & shortbread

31 The Alford Arms

Frithsden HP1 3DD
Tel.: (01442)864480 – Fax: (01442)876893
e-mail: info@alfordarmsfrithsden.co.uk **Website:** www.alfordarmsfrithsden.co.uk

Marstons Pedigree, Flowers Original, Brakspears, Marlow Rebellion IPA

When you are searching for a seat on the front terrace on a summer's afternoon, it might seem to you as if the whole of Hertfordshire has heard about this pub. Certainly, its reputation for good food has spread further than the quiet hamlet in which it is situated and you'll need to arrive early, book a table or preferably both if you want to guarantee yourself a space in the car park as well as a meal. Although there is also a more formal rear dining room, it's best to eat at one of the chunky wooden tables in the front bar, with its wooden and tiled floor and small open fire. Bubbly, casually-attired young staff serve a real mix of diners, from local businesspeople to walkers and cyclists, as well as those simply popping in for a pint of local ale. Moroccan bean tagine, pigeon and calamari might be included on the frequently changing menu; portions suit particularly healthy appetites so a main course is all you really need.

Food serving times

Monday-Friday:
12pm-2.30pm, 7pm-10pm

Saturday:
12pm-3pm, 7pm-10pm

Sunday:
12pm-4pm, 7pm-10pm

Closed 25-26 December

Prices

Meals: a la carte £ 20/29

Typical Dishes

Smoked bacon & poached egg
Oxfordshire pork belly
Baked fig clafoutis

4.5mi Northwest of Hemel Hempstead by A4146. By the village green. Parking.

The Fox

469 Luton Rd,
Kinsbourne Green, Harpenden AL5 3QE
Tel.: (01582)713817
Website: www.thefoxharpenden.co.uk

 **Timothy Taylor Landlord**

This pub has a country feel, with exposed wood, thick chunky beams and similarly solid wood tables, but beware - once you've snuggled up in one of the comfy leather sofas next to the fire in the sitting room, you might not want to move. Come summer, the decked terrace is the scene of many al fresco meals and with its popular menu and relaxed, friendly atmosphere, The Fox cunningly attracts more than its fair share of customers. The menu is divided up into different sections: sharing plates, such as tapas and mezze, little dishes such as crab cake, scallops or soup; leaves, fired pizzas, pasta, stove and grill, as well as the popular rotisserie – and all supplemented with daily specials, so there's bound to be something to whet your appetite. Staff are courteous and efficient, and there's no danger you'll struggle to locate service when you need it, since they all wear T-shirts with the pub's name emblazoned across the front.

Food serving times

Monday-Saturday:
12pm-3pm, 6pm-10pm

Sunday:
12pm-2.30pm, 6pm-9.30pm

Prices

Meals: a la carte £ 19/34

Typical Dishes

Onion tart
Fish & chips
Apple & strawberry crumble

5mi North of St Albans by A1081.
Parking.

33 The Three Horseshoes

136 East Common,
Harpenden AL5 1AW
Tel.: (01582)713953
e-mail: threehorseshoes@spiceinns.co.uk **Website:** www.3horseshoes.net

 **Guest beers**

Tucked away down a lane past a golf course, in a peaceful corner of North Hertfordshire, The Three Horseshoes is a pub you're unlikely to come across by chance. Hidden away it may be, but that doesn't stop it from being a popular place, so make sure you arrive early, especially as it heads towards the weekend, for they often end up having to turn people away. Inside, it's a touch cramped, so perhaps not the ideal place to bring a claustrophobe on a first date, but its low ceiling is part of its 18C charm, and its solid wood floors, open fire and squashy sofas complete the country style picture. The interior may be small but the menu is huge, offering an eclectic mix of dishes ranging from steak or risotto to green Thai monkfish curry, rare grilled ostrich or fillet of pork stuffed with prunes. Cooking is confident, satisfying and tasty, its flavours enhanced by herbs from the pub's very own herb garden.

Food serving times

Monday-Saturday:
12pm-2.30pm, 6pm-9.30pm

Sunday: 12pm-2.30pm

Closed Sunday dinner

Prices

Meals: a la carte £ 25/45

Typical Dishes

Crayfish risotto
Fillet of seabass
British & continental cheese board

5mi North of St Albans by A1081. Parking.

34 The White Horse

Hatching Green,
Harpenden AL5 2JW
Tel.: (01582)469290
e-mail: twh@atouchofnovelli.com **Website:** www.atouchofnovelli.com

    AE

 **Adnams Bitter**

An appealing, whitewashed pub, close to the pretty village green, its small bar boasts an original 17C wooden parquet floor and open log fire, while the dining room has the feel of a restaurant, with exposed beams, wooden tables and semi-open kitchen. Two first floor dining rooms are available for private parties, and the large terrace is very popular in the summer, when outdoor cooking becomes an integral part of proceedings – but no bookings are taken here, so arrive early to bag a seat. The White Horse is part-owned by Jean-Christophe Novelli, and his influence is clear to see on the menu, with distinctive dishes such as liver terrine "Maman Novelli" or gigolette of spit-roast Anjou pigeon alongside 21 day aged local beef fillet or roasted veal sweetbreads; desserts such as baked Camembert with Armagnac prunes or Granny Smith tarte Tatin to round things off. A well-versed team provide polished and professional service.

Food serving times
Monday-Saturday:
12pm-2.30pm, 6pm-9.30pm

Sunday: 12pm-4.30pm

Closed 25 December

Prices
Meals: £ 20 (3 course lunch) and a la carte £ 24/33

Typical Dishes
Bresaola of Aylesbury duck
Pan-fried pigeon
Chocolate St Emilion

5mi North of St Albans by A1081.
Parking.

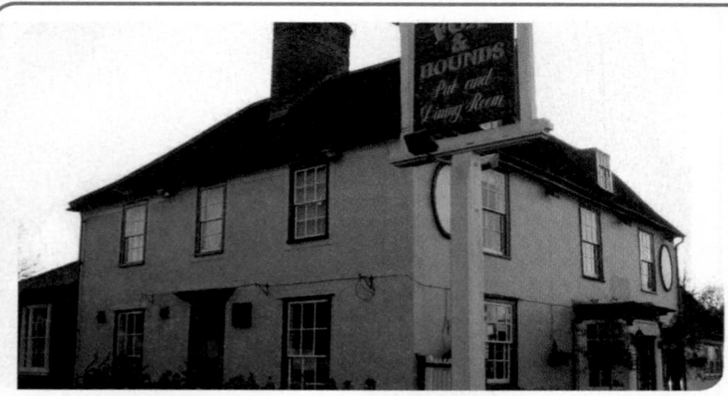

35 Fox and Hounds

2 High St, Hunsdon SG12 8NH
Tel.: (01279)843999 – Fax: (01279)841092
e-mail: info@foxandhounds-hunsdon.co.uk
Website: www.foxandhounds-hunsdon.co.uk

Adnams Bitter, Adnams Broadside; and guest ales Red Squirrel Brewery, Saffron Brewery

The first thing that strikes you about the Fox and Hounds on your approach through this pretty village is its large garden and terrace; providing plenty of room for any children in your party to burn off excess energy. If you're heading inside, the spacious rear dining room is the best place to sit, the vast array of cookery books, its high ceiling and semi-panelled walls all contributing their part to its delightfully stylish feel, while the rustic bar has lots of cosy, low level seating perfect for lounging. The chef-owner has an impressive CV and a sound culinary understanding; his philosophy being to buy the best seasonal and local ingredients, and to treat them simply, cooking with style and understanding. The menu changes daily, but dishes on offer might range from Spanish charcuterie and olives to sausage and mash, via lamb's kidneys, beer battered squid with aioli or slow roast belly of organic pork.

Food serving times

Tuesday-Sunday:
12pm-3pm, 6.30pm-10pm

Closed Sunday dinner and Monday (except Bank Holiday lunch)

Prices

Meals: £ 16/18
and a la carte £ 21/30

Typical Dishes

Crab salad
Sauté of rabbit
Treacle tart

5mi East of Ware by B1004 to Widford and B180 South. Parking.

36 Jacoby's

Churchgate House,
15 West St, Ware SG12 9EE
Tel.: (01920)469181 – Fax: (01920)469182
e-mail: info@jacobys.co.uk **Website:** www.jacobys.co.uk

 **No real ales offered**

Since the 16C Churchgate House has played host to everything from a bakery to a motorcycle repair shop and having stood empty for nearly ten years, it took the new owners nearly 16 months to bring it out of disrepair. As the second oldest building in Ware it has a Grade II listing, and a sympathetic refit has managed to retain much of its original charm. Modern furnishings sit comfortably alongside exposed brick and woodwork, and there's a relaxed, friendly buzz in the air. The spacious, rustic bar and continental style pavement terrace offer light meals such as wraps, salads and tartlets, while the peaceful upstairs restaurant provides a more substantial selection. Here you might find oriental or meze platters, crispy tiger prawns or deep-fried brie, followed by salmon Teriyaki brochette, crusted sea bass or slow cooked lamb shank; white chocolate crème brûlée, baked lemon tart or honeycomb parfait might finish off the experience.

Food serving times
Monday-Sunday:
12pm-3pm, 6pm-11pm

Prices
Meals: £ 10/13
and a la carte £ 20/30

Typical Dishes
Thai crab cake
Crusted seabass
Hot chocolate mousse

In the town centre, just off the High St. Public car park in High St.

37 The Fox

Willian SG6 2AE

Tel.: (01462)480233 – Fax: (01462)676966

e-mail: info@foxatwillian.co.uk **Website:** www.foxatwillian.co.uk

Woodforde Wherry, Adnams Best Bitter, Fuller's London Pride and one weekly changing guest beer

Built in 1750, this pub did not acquire its current moniker until 1902, due to its proximity to the hunt kennels - having previously gone under the names of The Orange Tree and the Dinsdale Arms. These days, its bar has a smart, modern feel, with a wooden floor and artwork by local artists - plus a plasma screen TV, if you prefer the sort of pictures that move. Head for the rattan chairs if you're eating in the bar – or for a more formal feel, try the roomy rear dining room. The regularly-changing menu has a seafood base, with mussels, oysters and fresh fish delivered in from north Norfolk. Meat and vegetables are sourced locally, and dishes on offer might include tiger prawns, sage and pork boudin blanc or fillet of ostrich with stir fried noodles. "The Fox Slate" is a great choice at lunchtime, with squid, smoked salmon, hummus, olives and the like for two to share. A small outer terrace and pleasant service complete the picture.

Food serving times

Monday-Saturday:
12pm-2pm, 6.30pm-9.15pm

Sunday: 12pm-3pm

Closed Sunday dinner

Prices

Meals: a la carte £ 25/50

Typical Dishes

Smoked salmon

Roast belly of pork

Doughnuts with rhubarb compote

3mi North East of Hitchin by A505 and side road. Parking.

38 Kings Head

Harts Lane,
Bawburgh NR9 3LS
Tel.: (01603)744977 – Fax: (01603)744990
e-mail: jandncatering@hotmail.co.uk **Website:** www.kingshead-bawburgh.co.uk

Woodforde Wherry, Adnams Bitter, Adnams Broadside

Only a short drive out of Norwich but already well into the countryside, this traditional place has plumped for Edward VII as its royal figurehead, the under-represented pub monarch perhaps getting the nod here for his generous appetite and his Sandringham connections. The old bon vivant would be baffled by the fruit machines, but drawn instinctively to the casual but comfortable dining room leading off from one side of the main bar. The daily changing menu blends modern European with traditional dishes: an equal mix of traditional and modern recipes might offer anything from ½ pint of prawns or sweet chilli chicken ciabatta to saffron, pea and mint risotto, homemade steak and mushroom pudding or seared red snapper. Once the woodburning stove is fired up on winter afternoons, it's also pleasant enough for a quiet pint.

Food serving times

Monday-Sunday:
12pm-2pm, 6pm-9pm

Closed 26 December, dinner 25 December and 1 January, Sunday dinner and Monday

Prices

Meals: £ 16 and a la carte £ 26/32

Typical Dishes

Pan-seared scallops
Moroccan marinated chicken
Chocolate cheesecake

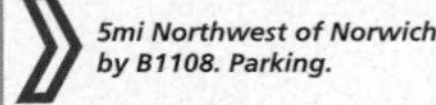

5mi Northwest of Norwich by B1108. Parking.

England • East of England • Norfolk

39 The White Horse

4 High St,
Blakeney NR25 7AL

Tel.: (01263)740574 – Fax: (01263)741303
e-mail: info@blakeneywhitehorse.co.uk **Website:** www.blakeneywhitehorse.co.uk

Adnams Broadside, Woodforde, Yetmans

Estuary, saltings, quayside, and a gaggle of tourists from the Capital make up much of the character of 21C Blakeney. It's further defined by this popular part-17C pub of flint-and-brick which draws in the locals and weekenders a-plenty. They gather round a split-level bar and sup good real ale at wooden tables, chairs and banquettes – an appealing conservatory provides a smart alternative. Go to the rear, to the former stables, to eat: the food is proudly local in nature and naturally enough, seafood is the staple here. For those not climbing back into their 4X4s, there's the option of small, cosy bedrooms.

Food serving times

Monday-Sunday:
12pm-2.15pm, 6pm-9.30pm

Closed 25 December

Prices

Meals: £ 20/32

9 rooms: £ 80/140

Typical Dishes

Pork tenderloin salad
Guinea fowl
Roasted bananito

Off A149 following signs for the Quay, beside the church. Parking.

40 The White Horse

Brancaster Staithe PE31 8BY
Tel.: (01485)210262 – Fax: (01485)210930
e-mail: reception@whitehorsebrancaster.co.uk
Website: www.whitehorsebrancaster.co.uk

  VISA 

Woodforde Wherry, Adnam Best Bitter, Fuller's London Pride, Timothy Taylor Landlord

With glorious views over the Brancaster Marshes and Scolt Head Island, a seat on this village pub's sunny back terrace or in the spacious rear conservatory is a must. If the tables here are all taken, then the landscaped front terrace may not have the views, but it's got the parasols, the heaters and the lights to make up for it. From the outside, the pub looks like an extended house, but venture inside and you'll find a proper bar at the front, complete with bar billiards and historic photos of Brancaster. Foodwise, the oft-changing menus provide ample choice, with a seafood slant that takes in local Cromer crab, Brancaster oysters, mussels and fish from the boats at the end of the car park. The pub's popularity means that service can sometimes suffer under the strain but with the coastal views to provide a distraction you might not even notice. For those who'd like to extend their stay, bedrooms are comfy; two have their own terrace.

Food serving times
Monday-Sunday:
12pm-2pm, 6.30pm-9pm

Prices
Meals: a la carte £ 25/36
15 rooms: £ 75/128

Typical Dishes
Mussels in white wine
Steamed fillet of cod
White Horse lemon tart

On A149 Hunstanton to Wells Rd.
Parking

Burnham Market

41 The Hoste Arms

The Green,
Burnham Market PE31 8HD
Tel.: (01328)738777 – Fax: (01328)730103
e-mail: reception@hostearms.co.uk **Website:** www.hostearms.co.uk

 **Adnams, Woodforde Wherry, Nelson's Revenge**

The popularity of this coaching inn has almost come to define the charming north Norfolk town of Burnham Market: set on the picturesque Green, its 17C quirks have been fully restored; in startling contrast, there's an intriguing wing decorated in Zulu style, and a Moroccan garden terrace. The bar is an invariably bustling place, and the sound of champagne corks popping is not uncommon; you'll find similar levels of volume and bonhomie in the restaurant. The staff respond well to being busy, and are invariably attentive and friendly, with good attention to detail. Fairly-priced menus offer a mix of global styles, with much local produce in evidence; dishes might include braised pork belly, caramelised escalope of foie gras, roast quail or homemade steamed steak and kidney pudding. There's an excellent wine selection featuring 180 bins.

Food serving times
Monday-Sunday:
7.30am-10am, 12pm-2pm, 6pm-9pm

Prices
Meals: a la carte £ 19/29
35 rooms: £ 95/220

Typical Dishes
Oriental salmon fishcake
Breast of Gressingham duck
Raspberry bavarois

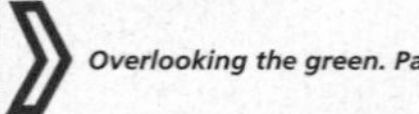
Overlooking the green. Parking.

42 The Lord Nelson

Walsingham Rd,
Burnham Thorpe PE31 8HL

Tel.: (01328)738241 – Fax: (01328)738241

e-mail: enquiries@nelsonslocal.co.uk **Website:** www.nelsonslocal.co.uk

  MC

 **Woodforde Wherry, Greene King, Abbot Ale, Nelson's Blood Bitter**

Named in honour of Burnham Thorpe's most illustrious son, and perhaps Britain's first modern celebrity, this 17C inn honours the Victor of the Nile with just enough in the way of pictures and memorabilia: too much swashbuckling nauticalia would clutter up this shipshape little place. Three low-ceilinged parlours, one with a Battle of Trafalgar mural, lead off from a firelit taproom with a tiny cubby-hole of a bar: the landlord opens up the timbered barn, with chunky pine tables and benches, if the pub itself starts to feel overcrowded. Simple, fresh, good-value dishes, both classic and modern, could include steak and kidney pudding, veal kidneys in a Dijonnaise sauce or swordfish with crab, cream and vodka sauce.

Food serving times

Tuesday-Friday:
12pm-2pm, 6pm-9pm

Saturday-Sunday:
12pm-2.30pm, 6pm-9pm

Closed Monday (except school holidays and half term holidays)

Prices

Meals: £ 20 (dinner) and a la carte £ 19/34

Typical Dishes

Asparagus "Flamande"
Pan-roasted fillet of duck
Traditional bread & butter pudding

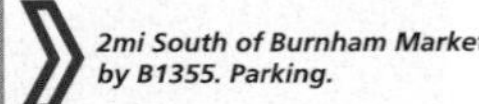

2mi South of Burnham Market by B1355. Parking.

43 The George

High St,
Cley-next-the-Sea NR25 7RN
Tel.: (01263)740652 – Fax: (01263)741275
e-mail: info@thegeorgehotelatcley.co.uk **Website:** www.thegeorgehotelatcley.co.uk

 VISA MC

Woodfordes, Adnams, Yetmans

There are two imposing buildings in Cley: the famous windmill which can be viewed from miles around, and the rather grand-looking George, its red-brick Victorian/Edwardian façade providing a solid security to this charming little coastal village. Etched frosted windows and plenty of hanging baskets add lustre to the ornate exterior. Inside, there's an individual style to the place. Three rooms are divided into a bar and two dining areas, decorated in warm coloured wallpapers, and enhanced by wood-burning stoves. A large book on a brass pulpit records bird sightings from the nearby bar: whether these are influenced by pints consumed, you decide! Weighty menus make great use of local mussels and oysters, while the village smokehouse supplies other seafood. Rustic modern British cooking is tasty and accomplished. Bedrooms come in various configurations: the superior version, on the top floor, has finer views over the marshes.

Food serving times

Monday-Sunday:
12pm-2.15pm, 6.30pm-9pm

Closed 25 December

Prices

Meals: a la carte £ 15/25

12 rooms: £ 40/130

Typical Dishes

Escalope tenderloin pork bruschetta
Steamed hake fillet
Lemon tart

12mi West of Cromer by A149. Parking.

44 King's Head

26 Wroxham Rd,
Coltishall NR12 7EA
Tel.: (01603)737426 – Fax: (01603)266113

 **Adnams Best, Fuller's London Pride, Broadland Harvest**

One of the nicest things about this rather ordinary looking pub in deepest Norfolk is its attractive setting – diners with window tables can look out onto the meandering River Bure. Elsewhere within, a relaxed air pervades. Open fires crackle beneath solid timbers and pieces of fishing and boating memorabilia hang from the ceiling, lending a particularly atmospheric air at night: meals can be ordered in the bar as well as the dining room. Seafood specialities take pride of place with the Norfolk catch freshly served each day or, as an alternative to fish, chef's special meat dishes.

Food serving times

Monday-Sunday:
12pm-2pm, 7pm-9.30pm

Closed dinner 26 December and 1 January

Prices

Meals: £ 11 (3 course lunch) and a la carte £ 23/35

Typical Dishes

Herring roes
Duck Marco Polo
Beignet soufflé

7mi North of Norwich on B1150.
Parking.

45 The Saracen's Head

Wolterton, Erpingham NR11 7LX
Tel.: (01263)768909 – Fax: (01263)768993
e-mail: saracenshead@wolterton.freeserve.co.uk
Website: www.saracenshead-norfolk.co.uk

    AE

 **Adnams Best, Woodforde Wherry**

Charmingly faded and quirky by turns, this individualistic 19C former coaching inn is in the middle of nowhere and loses nothing by its isolation. It contains an impressive walled garden and courtyard set back from two busy, bustling bar rooms and a boldly red-painted parlour filled with odd pictures, bric-a-brac and little wooden tables and chairs with plastic tablecloths. Traditional dishes come dressed in local ingredients such as mussels from Morston and crab from Cromer: unpretentious, country dishes that draw in regular shoals of satisfied customers from miles around. Bright, modest bedrooms nevertheless share the long-standing owner's mild and endearing eccentricity.

Food serving times

Monday-Sunday:
12.30pm-2pm, 7.30pm-9pm

Closed 25 December and dinner 26 December

Prices

Meals: £ 10 (lunch) and a la carte £ 24/32

6 rooms: £ 50/90

Typical Dishes

Game and cranberry terrine

Seared scallops

Brown bread and butter pudding

West 1.5mi on Wolterton Hall rd. Parking.

46 The Hunny Bell

The Green,
Melton Constable NR24 2AA
Tel.: (01263)712300
e-mail: hunnybell@animalinns.co.uk **Website:** www.thehunnybell.co.uk

Inspectors' favourites

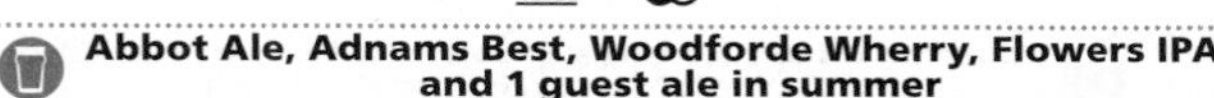

Abbot Ale, Adnams Best, Woodforde Wherry, Flowers IPA and 1 guest ale in summer

Following a loving renovation, this whitewashed pub looks the bee's knees, boasting a smart country interior, slab stone flooring and restored wooden beams. You have to be quick to get a table, with only a handful in the main bar and even fewer in the next room, but there are plans to renovate the restaurant soon and with more tables the atmosphere will be buzzing in no time. As country cousin to the slightly eccentric Wildebeest Arms and two other eateries, the owners' collective experience shines through, resulting in a seasonal, keenly priced menu that's modern-European meets traditional pub. For main course you might find local pork sausages, Norfolk beer battered cod, sage roast chicken breast or 28 day aged sirloin steak; whilst at either end of the meal the chef proudly presents homemade breads and sorbets. This new addition to the Animal Inns family is as sound as a bell and "Hunny" is sure to be the buzz word for miles around.

Food serving times

Monday-Saturday:
12pm-2.15pm, 6pm-9pm

Sunday:
12pm-2.15pm, 6pm-8.30pm

Prices

Meals: a la carte £ 15/29

Typical Dishes

Chicken liver parfait
Steak & chips
Chocolate & orange torte

South : 2.5mi by B1149 from Holt

47 The Walpole Arms

The Common,
Itteringham NR11 7AR
Tel.: (01263)587258 – Fax: (01263)587074
e-mail: goodfood@thewalpolearms.co.uk **Website:** www.thewalpolearms.co.uk

Inspectors' favourites

 VISA

Adnams Bitter, Adnams Broadside, Woodforde Wherry, Golden Jackal, Walpole Ale

Blickling Hall sets an awesome architectural benchmark in this part of Norfolk; in its more modest way, the nearby part-18C Walpole Arms reaches out in empathy. It's hugely characterful and inviting, with a warm ambiance, roaring fires, exposed brick walls and heavy timbers marking out the bar as a great place for modern dining. New, varied menus are devised daily; the accomplished kitchen interweaves Italian and Spanish ideas. Extensive use is made of local and seasonal ingredients; the owners heartily take on board recommendations from their fishmonger and game supplier. There's a more formal restaurant beyond the bar, but no let-up on the character front, with linen-clad tables and exposed roof trusses lending it an appealing air. Wednesday night is quiz night.

Food serving times

Monday-Saturday:
12pm-2pm, 7pm-9pm

Sunday: 12pm-2pm

Closed 25 December and Sunday dinner

Prices

Meals: a la carte £ 20/28

Typical Dishes

Sicilian style escabeche
Warm salad of pigeon
White rum baba

5mi Northwest of Aylsham by B1354. Signed The Common. Parking.

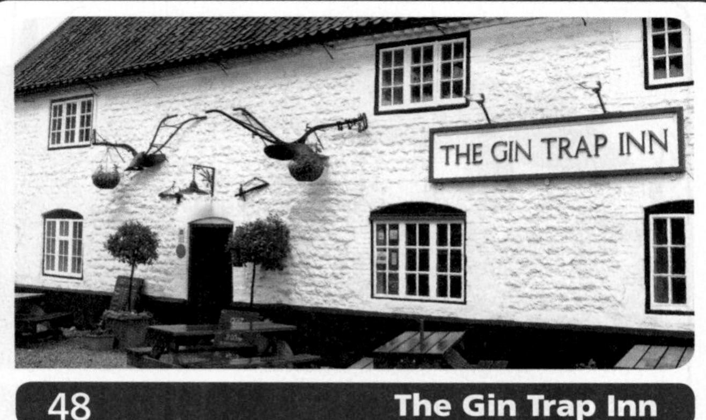

48 The Gin Trap Inn

6 High St,
Ringstead PE36 5JU
Tel.: (01485)525264
e-mail: thegintrap@hotmail.co.uk **Website:** www.gintrapinn.co.uk

Inspectors' favourites

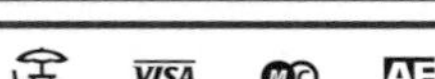

Adnams Bitter, Woodforde Wherry and guests ales - Abbot, Elgoods

Two ploughs hanging on the front walls of this attractive whitewashed inn remind you of its 17C origins, as does the cosy front bar with its traditional quarry tile floor, wood burner and beams. Locals still congregate here with their dogs, but it's no longer packed with gin traps, as once was the case; the link to the pub's name now provided by the more modern juniper berry logo. Another contemporary addition is the spacious wood-floored conservatory with its stylish wood tables and leather-effect chairs, which overlooks the garden; and the traditional and the more modern mix successfully in food terms too, the blackboard menu offering favourites such as fish and chips and sausage and mash while the à la carte features such delights as roasted quail or handmade saffron pasta. Dishes are well-presented, flavoursome and good value - and if you're staying over, bedrooms boast wrought iron beds and roll top baths.

Food serving times

Monday-Thursday:
12pm-2pm, 6pm-9pm

Friday:
12pm-2pm, 6pm-9.30pm

Saturday:
12pm-2.30pm, 6pm-9.30pm

Sunday:
12pm-2.30pm, 6pm-9pm

Prices

Meals: a la carte £ 19/27

3 rooms: £ 49/140

Typical Dishes

Pressed chicken

Loch Duart salmon fillet

Sticky toffee pudding

3,25 miles East of Hunstanton byA149. Parking.

49 The Rose and Crown

Old Church Rd, Snettisham PE31 7NE
Tel.: (01485)541382 – Fax: (01485)543172
e-mail: info@roseandcrownsnettisham.co.uk
Website: www.roseandcrownsnettisham.co.uk

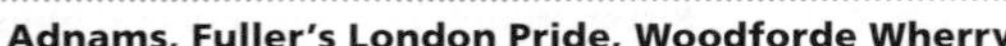
Adnams, Fuller's London Pride, Woodforde Wherry

First-time guests may struggle to get their bearings in this maze of cosy rustic bars and vibrant contemporary dining rooms, where quirky details and bric-a-brac abound. Each area has its own style and atmosphere, so you're sure to find somewhere that you love; dark wood chairs and antique looking tables furnish one room, while the next features chunky pine tables, high-backed leather chairs and brightly painted walls. The produce here is definitely local, with meat supplied by nearby farms, fish delivered daily from King's Lynn or Lowestoft and game coming courtesy of one of the regulars. Despite the British ingredients, the menu isn't restricted to classic English cooking. In fact, there's hardly a country that doesn't feature here; you might find Italian platters, Chinese or Japanese starters, and Moroccan, Thai or French main courses. Bedrooms are individually styled in a range of colours, some are modern and others more classic.

Food serving times

Monday-Thursday:
12pm-2pm, 6.30pm-9pm

Friday:
12pm-2pm, 6.30pm-9.30pm

Saturday-Sunday:
12pm-2.30pm, 6.30pm-9.30pm (Sunday 9pm)

Prices

Meals: a la carte £ 20/25

16 rooms: £ 70/110

Typical Dishes

Welsh rarebit
Braised oxtail
Coffee crème brûlée

11mi North of King's Lynn by A149. Parking.

50 Wildebeest Arms

82-86 Norwich Rd,
Stoke Holy Cross NR14 8QJ
Tel.: (01508)492497 – Fax: (01508)494946
e-mail: wildebeest@animalinns.co.uk **Website:** www.thewildebeestarms.co.uk

  VISA  AE

 **Adnams**

With a name like the Wildebeest Arms, you know that this is not going to be just another run-of the-mill pub. Yes, it has the rustic beams and the wood floors, but the deep yellow-coloured walls, African carvings and tree-trunk tables mean that at heart it's more savannah than tequila slammer.
An open-plan space with a central bar and an open kitchen, it still manages to feel extremely cosy, there are picnic tables in the garden, and service is bright and attentive. The set lunch and dinner menus offer ample choice and great value for money, while the contemporary and inventive à la carte proposes tasty, well-presented, restaurant-style dishes, which vary according to what's in season. Busy both with locals and visitors, booking here is essential – but if you can't get a table, the owner does own two more eateries in the area. Refurbishment is imminent, so, if all goes according to plan, this beast will soon be looking as good as a gnu.

Food serving times

Monday-Saturday:
12pm-2pm, 7pm-10pm

Sunday:
12.30pm-2pm, 7pm-10pm

Closed 25-26 December

Prices

Meals: £ 17/19
and a la carte £ 22/34

Typical Dishes

Smoked salmon mousse
Roast Gressingham duck
Custard & nutmeg tart

5.75mi South of Norwich by A140.
Parking.

England • East of England • Norfolk

51 The Globe Inn

The Buttlands,
Wells-next-the-Sea NR23 1EU
Tel.: (01328)710206 – Fax: (01328)713249
e-mail: globe@holkham.co.uk **Website:** www.globeatwells.co.uk

Adnams Best and Broadside, Woodforde Wherry and Nelson's Revenge

Overlooking a leafy Georgian square and only a five minute stroll from the harbour – where the local fishermen set out for their daily inshore catch – this pub is situated in an idyllic location. Nearby Holkham beach and Nature Reserve provide some peaceful distractions but it's equally as pleasant to sit in the sun-filled courtyards of the inn. Inside, the characterful bar boasts exposed brick walls, an open fire and plenty of charm, while to the rear, the restaurant has a lighter, brighter feel. The classical menu offers something for everyone, featuring a selection of lighter dishes such as sandwiches and pies, through to more substantial ones, such as fish or steaks. Specials change daily in line with the latest seasonal produce and ingredients are always sourced from the nearby seas, farms and Estates. Bedrooms are light, airy and modern and come with the choice of a full English breakfast, eggs Benedict or Cley smoked haddock.

Food serving times
Monday-Sunday:
12pm-2.30pm, 7pm-9pm

Prices
Meals: a la carte £ 18/24
7 rooms: £ 85/110

18mi East of Hunstanton by A149. Parking restrictions around the Buttlands.

52 The Wiveton Bell

Blakeney Rd,
Wiveton NR25 7TL
Tel.: (01263)740101
Website: www.wivetonbell.com

Yetmans, Adnams Broadside, Woodforde Wherry

Surrounded by the local salt marshes and nearby nature reserves, this pub is situated in a beautiful area and is ideal for walkers following the Norfolk coastal path. The neatly-kept garden provides an attractive flower display by day, whilst at night it's a fantastic setting for stargazing. Following a dramatic renovation, the inside of this pub is comfortable and up-to-date, with a pleasant bar giving way to a light and airy conservatory; host to a convivial atmosphere and bright, efficient service. You can choose from salads and light meals or the traditional à la carte menu, where a few international influences appear alongside the mainly British selection; you might find Thai fish cakes or chicken Dansak next to Briston pork belly or fisherman's pie. On either side of the property, the charming rooms come complete with a continental tuckbox, so if you're feeling lazy you can keep your PJs on and have breakfast in bed.

Food serving times

Monday-Saturday:
12pm-2.15pm, 6pm-9.15pm

Sunday:
12pm-3pm, 6pm-8pm

Prices

Meals: a la carte £ 19/28

2 rooms: £ 82/130

Typical Dishes

Thai fish cake
Pork belly
Selection of local cheeses

Southeast 1m by A149 on Wiveton Rd from Blakeney.

53 The Bildeston Crown

104 High Street,
Bildeston IP7 7EB

Tel.: (01449)740510 – Fax: (01449)741843

e-mail: info@thebildestoncrown.co.uk **Website:** www.thebildestoncrown.co.uk

Inspectors' favourites

 **Adnams, Greene King, Mauldons**

15C origins, a part-timber frontage and a smart yellow finish announce this extremely popular hostelry in the heart of Suffolk. Smart modern styling mixes well with the traditional appeal of the exterior, as exemplified by the bar area, where delightful inglenook, beams and heavy wood furniture evolve into comfy sofas in an adjacent room. The old and the new also rub shoulders in the dining room – the whole pub boasts a well-integrated feel. Locals enjoy a drink in the popular bar, and if you choose, you can eat here as well as sup. Good-sized menus are of two types: the Crown Classic, which is mainly traditional, or the dinner menu, which offers more elaborate temptations. Overnighters have made a sound choice: bedrooms are very strong here: individually styled, they merge pleasant traditional features with up-to-date facilities like Wi-Fi.

Food serving times

Monday-Sunday:
12pm-3pm, 7pm-10pm

Prices

Meals: £ 20 (3 course lunch/dinner) and a la carte £ 28/38

12 rooms: £ 80/220

Typical Dishes

Smoked haddock velouté

Poached & roasted rump of veal

Lemon posset

9mi Northeast of Sudbury by B1115. Parking.

54 Queen's Head

The Street,
Bramfield IP19 9HT
Tel.: (01986)784214
e-mail: qhbfield@aol.com **Website:** www.queensheadbramfield.co.uk

Adnams Bitter, Adnams Broadside

In the heart of the village of Bramfield, near the edge of the Suffolk coast, lies this well-run, cream-washed roadside pub. In winter, take a seat in the high-raftered main room and warm yourself by the huge log fireplace. In summer, sit in the conservatory or in the beautiful terraced gardens and enjoy one of the homemade ice creams on offer. These and other delicious puddings are by no means the only homemade food to be had here; on the contrary. An eclectic menu draws on locally sourced food and organic farm produce, including rare-breed meats, and it is not unusual to see on the menu the name of the farm from which the principle ingredients of a dish have come. The beamed interior with its wood and flagstone flooring reflects the age of this long-standing pub. After you've eaten, a wander around the equally historic thatched church next door with its unusual detached round tower is a must.

Food serving times
Monday-Saturday:
12pm-2pm, 6.30pm-9.15pm
Sunday:
12pm-2pm, 7pm-9pm
Closed 26 December

Prices
Meals: a la carte £ 16/26

Typical Dishes
Dates wrapped in bacon
Pork loin steak
Tunisian orange & almond cake

3mi South of Halesworth on A144.
Parking.

55 The Buxhall Crown

Mill Road,
Buxhall IP14 3DW
Tel.: (01449)736521
e-mail: trevor@thebuxhallcrown.co.uk **Website:** www.thebuxhallcrown.co.uk

 **Green King IPA, Tindalls Best, Cox Holbrook, Woodfordes Wherry**

Two buildings join to make this pub; one of them dates from 17C, the other's birth date nobody knows – but what is known is that at one time it housed both a butcher and a piggery. You might well feel a compulsion to piggery yourself when you peruse the menu at The Buxhall Crown. Dishes might range from mussels or prawns to venison casserole or lambs hearts stuffed with sausage meat, the quality of the cooking helped by the use of superior local produce, including some sumptuous beef, which makes the steak a good choice for a main course. You can eat in either side of the pub, or outside at wooden tables on the impressively lit, heated and sheltered terrace. The left side is the more cosy and characterful, with wattle and daub walls, heavy wood beams and an inglenook fireplace, while the right hand side, where photos of the village and the pub line the walls, is lighter and more contemporary in style.

Food serving times

Tuesday-Saturday:
12pm-2pm, 6.30pm-9pm

Sunday: 12pm-2pm

Closed for food 25-26 December (open for drinks 12pm-2pm)

Prices

Meals: a la carte £ 21/30

Typical Dishes
Seared pigeon
Pan-fried sea bream
Vanilla pannacotta

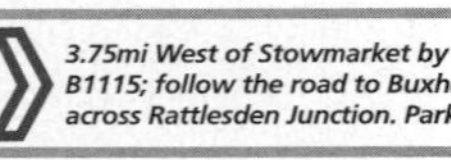

3.75mi West of Stowmarket by B1115; follow the road to Buxhall across Rattlesden Junction. Parking.

56 The Beehive

The Street,
Horringer IP29 5SN
Tel.: (01284)735260 – Fax: (01284)735532

 **Green King IPA, Abbot Ale, Old Speckled Hen**

Staggeringly rich and deeply eccentric, even by the standards of the Regency gentry, the 4th Earl of Bristol spared no expense on Ickworth House and its Italianate gardens, now owned by the National Trust. His ideal local would probably have been a neoclassical gastro-folly, but The Beehive, just down the road, brings us back down to earth in the very best sense. An attractive, traditional brick and flint house, its old timbers and flagstones set off nicely with a bright, modern décor, it always seems to have one last inviting corner waiting and an old wooden table free. A good-sized blackboard menu, with its share of lighter dishes, combines predominantly British themes with a subtle taste for the modern and the exotic – perhaps His Lordship would have approved after all. Well run by long-standing landlords.

Food serving times

Monday-Saturday:
12pm-2pm, 7pm-9.30pm

Sunday: 12pm-2pm

Closed 25-26 December

Prices

Meals: a la carte £ 20/28

Typical Dishes

Smoked haddock chowder

Slow roast belly of pork

Apricot bread & butter pudding

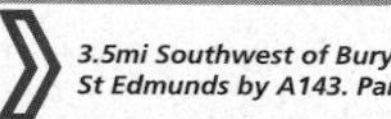

3.5mi Southwest of Bury St Edmunds by A143. Parking.

57 The Angel

Market Pl,
Lavenham CO10 9QZ

Tel.: (01787)247388 – Fax: (01787)248344
e-mail: angel@maypolehotels.com **Website:** www.maypolehotels.com

Nethergate Bitter, Adnams, Greene King IPA, Woodforde Wherry

History's timbered face appears at every turn in the gorgeous old town of Lavenham, and the Angel wears one of its more delightful countenances. This charming inn has stood in the market square since 1420 and receives a never-ending stream of curious tourists and relaxed locals. There's a pubby bar with several dining areas including lots of timbers, simple wooden tables and a log fire. On the first floor is the Solar, which contains a rare fully pargetted ceiling constructed in the early 1600s, featuring the remains of early wall paintings on some of its beams. This has great views of the Guildhall and Church and is now a residents' sitting room. Hearty, varied menus employ seasonal, local produce, while well-kept bedrooms provide effortlessly comfortable accommodation.

Food serving times

Monday-Sunday:
12pm-2.15pm, 6.45pm-9.15pm

Closed 25-26 December

Prices

Meals: a la carte £ 16/25

8 rooms: £ 60/120

Typical Dishes

Smoked salmon & crayfish salad

Steak & ale pie

Steamed syrup sponge

6mi North of Sudbury by B1115 and B1071; in town centre. Parking.

58 The Ship Inn

Church Lane,
Levington IP10 0LQ
Tel.: (01473)659573

Greene King IPA, Adnams Best and Broadside

In an age of rebranding, some pub names still go deeper. The salt of the Suffolk marshes is in the very timbers of this part 14C thatched inn, which stands in sight of the estuary. Though built from the broken-up hulks on the coast and full of seafaring pictures, curiosities and keepsakes, it now feels just too neat and cosy ever to have been a smugglers' haunt, but read the old newspaper cutting on the wall and you'll find the atmosphere of excisemen and contraband hangs about you a little more thickly. Relaxed, smiling and attentive service recalls you to the present for an appetizing menu with a good balance tilted in favour of the traditional: seafood includes Cromer crab and fresh griddled plaice with crispy salad. Save a space for homemade puddings like apple and rosemary crumble with custard.

Food serving times

Monday-Saturday:
12pm-2pm, 6.30pm-9.30pm

Sunday:
12pm-3pm, 6.30pm-9.30pm

Closed 25-26 December, dinner 31 December

Prices

Meals: a la carte £ 18/25

Typical Dishes

Tian of avocado, prawns & crayfish
Roast Welsh lamb rump
Pear & frangipane tart

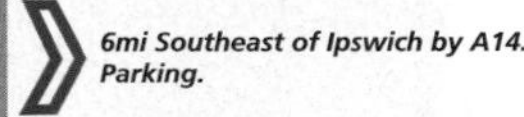
6mi Southeast of Ipswich by A14. Parking.

59 The Star Inn

The Street,
Lidgate CB8 9PP
Tel.: (01638)500275 – Fax: (01638)500275

Greene King IPA, Abbot, Ruddles, Guinness, Fosters, Kronenbourg

This part 16C village inn may just prove the point: any fusion of traditions will work if you understand both well enough. Its three intimate rooms and snugs are full of restful, old-English charm, braced with ancient beams worn smooth and warmed by drowsy inglenooks. Absolutely the last place, in fact, that you would expect to find sparklingly fresh Iberian cooking. The day's menu comes on blackboards that offer a good variety of simply stated Spanish and Mediterranean dishes. Even locally sourced wild boar and venison are prepared to authentic recipes: at once hearty, piquant and satisfyingly different. Suffolk summers seldom feel properly continental: even so, the terraced garden is very pleasant once the weather finally gets it right.

Food serving times

Monday-Saturday, 12pm-2.30pm, 7pm-10pm

Sunday: 12pm-2.30pm

Closed 25-26 December, 1 January

Spanish

Prices

Meals: a la carte £ 28/32

Typical Dishes
Moules marinières
Wild boar
Lemon tart

7mi southeast of Newmarket on B1063. Parking.

60 The Swan

The Street,
Monks Eleigh IP7 7AU
Tel.: (01449)741391
e-mail: swan@monkseleigh.com **Website:** www.monkseleigh.com

 **Adnams Best, Adnams Broadside**

Boasting honey yellow walls and a charming thatched roof, this attractive building is more "destination dining pub" than local village boozer – although that doesn't mean that drinkers aren't welcome. Set on the main road of pretty Monks Eleigh, it displays a seamless mix of old and new: your first step inside reveals a fresh, modern feel but if you take a closer look many original features can still be found. For special occasions there's a characterful private dining room and when weather permits, you can eat on the small side terrace. The friendly and very experienced chef-owner has a background in Italian cuisine and a strong passion for local produce. Menus change daily and comprise of a good selection of classic and more refined pub dishes, as well as some more Italian influences; you might find duck breast, fillet steak or braised lamb alongside cannelloni or lasagne. Everything is homemade, from the bread to the ice cream.

Food serving times

Wednesday-Sunday:
12pm-2pm, 7pm-9pm

Closed 25-26 December and 1 January and 1 week in summer

Prices

Meals: £ 19 and a la carte £ 20/35

3.5mi Southeast of Lavenham on A1141.

61 King's Head Inn

Front Street,
Orford IP12 2LW

Tel.: (01394)450271

e-mail: info@crownandcastle.co.uk **Website:** www.kingshead-orford-suffolk.co.uk

VISA 

Adnams : Bitter, Broadside, Explorer

The King's Head Inn is a proper, honest English pub, with no pretence to be anything but. Decked out in heraldic prints and banners and kingly furnishings fitting to its name, it boasts 16C origins and a history of smuggling. The bar is traditional in décor, with wooden tables and an open fired stove, but the best place to sit if you're eating is in the large dining room. A proper pub needs proper pub food and the King's Head Inn doesn't disappoint. Fit for a pauper rather than a king – but in the nicest possible sense - the cooking is down to earth but still eminently worthy, so ham and eggs means local cured ham and free range eggs, the scampi is real, whole and home battered, and sandwiches are "doorstops." Puddings are also commendably classic, and choices might include rice pudding, apple crumble or treacle tart; all washed down with a good selection of real ales and wines. Spacious bedrooms are well furnished and comfortable.

Food serving times

Monday-Saturday:
12pm-2.30pm, 6.30pm-9pm

Sunday:
12pm-3pm, 7pm-9pm

Prices

Meals: a la carte £ 18/24

4 rooms: £ 54/95

12mi East of Woodbridge by A1152 and B1084. Parking.

62 The Duke's Head

Slugg's Lane,
Somerleyton NR32 5QR

Tel.: (01502)730281

e-mail: dukeshead@somerleyton.co.uk **Website:** www.somerleyton.co.uk

 **Greene King, Adnams, Oulton Ales, Green Jack, Woodforde, Crouch Vale**

Up the coast and inland a bit from Lowestoft stands one of Suffolk's finest stately homes, Somerleyton Hall, and its watering hole has a friendly and welcoming feel about it. Located in the unfortunate sounding Slugg's Lane, it's not the prettiest of pubs, but its setting, down by the river, and its super sun-drenched terrace, enhance the feeling that all is not lost. The characterful interior is thronged with locals and visitors to the Hall, and there are regular live music evenings as well as "big screen" events. A spacious, simply furnished restaurant stands by the bar, and this is home to some appetising grub at very digestible prices. Simply prepared, well executed dishes are full of tasty, fresh ingredients originating from, or around, the estate, with Cromer crab and brown shrimps a couple of tasty possibilities.

Food serving times

Monday-Friday:
11.30am-3pm, 5.30pm-11pm

Saturday-Sunday:
12pm-11pm

Bar snacks all day

Prices

Meals: a la carte £ 20/40

Typical Dishes

Ham hock terrine

Somerleyton rump of lamb

Warm treacle pudding

6mi Northwest of Lowestoft by B1074. Parking.

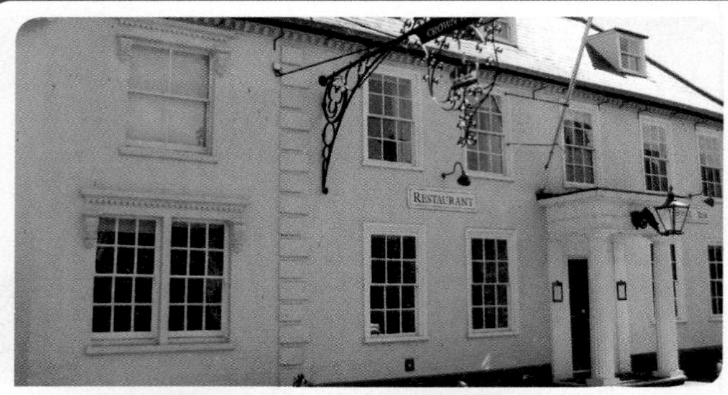

63 The Crown

90 High St,
Southwold IP18 6DP

Tel.: (01502)722275 – Fax: (01502)727263
e-mail: crown.hotel@adnams.co.uk **Website:** www.adnams.co.uk

Inspectors' favourites

VISA

Adnams - Bitter, Broadside, Explorer, Regatta, East Green

The sophisticated elegance of The Crown sits easily within the beguiling surrounds of delightful Southwold. Its mellow yellow tones have graced the high street for many a year, standing proudly adjacent to the Adnams Sole Bay brewery. This smart, intimate old coaching inn is the ideal stopping off point for a pint with the Suffolk locals in the compact oak-panelled rear bar where, not surprisingly, a nautical edge permeates. Get to the front bar early if you want to bag a seat for dining: it can get packed in there. Or choose a more formal option in the intimate, linen-clad restaurant. The same daily changing menu is served throughout: a well-established and well-prepared mix of modern and more classical dishes, which find favour with East Anglians and the metropolitan influx alike. Individually styled bedrooms.

Food serving times

Monday-Sunday:
12pm-2.30pm, 6pm-9.30pm

Prices

Meals: a la carte £ 24/33

14 rooms: £ 86/232

Typical Dishes

Roast quail
Dingley Dell pork
Trio of rhubarb

In the town centre. Parking.

64 The Randolph

41 Wangford Rd,
Reydon, Southwold IP18 6PZ

Tel.: (01502)723603 – Fax: (01502)722194
e-mail: reception@therandolph.co.uk **Website:** www.therandolph.co.uk

 **Adnams Bitter, Adnams Broadside**

Following a bracing walk along the beach at the charming town of Southwold, you might want to head inland slightly to the equally charming but quieter village of Reydon. All that sea air will have given you an appetite, so what better than a meal at The Randolph? Named after the father of Sir Winston Churchill, its Victorian façade is suitably grand, while the interior has been renovated in a bright, contemporary style. Take a seat in the garden or settle into one of the comfy sofas in the light, airy bar area for a pre-dinner drink courtesy of the local Adnams brewery, before moving into the larger dining area to tuck into the hearty yet modern food, ranging from sandwiches through to steaks with plenty of fresh fish in between. If you're staying the night in one of the spacious, well-kept rooms, the knowledge that you've got good value for money is bound to help you sleep particularly well.

Food serving times

Monday-Sunday:
12pm-2pm, 6.30pm-9pm

Prices

Meals: a la carte £ 21/28

10 rooms: £ 60/100

Typical Dishes

Gruyère cheese tart
Fillet of seabass
Sticky gingerbread pudding

Stoke-by-Nayland

65 The Crown

Stoke-by-Nayland CO6 4SE
Tel.: (01206)262001 – Fax: (01206)264026
e-mail: thecrown@eoinns.co.uk **Website:** www.eoinns.co.uk

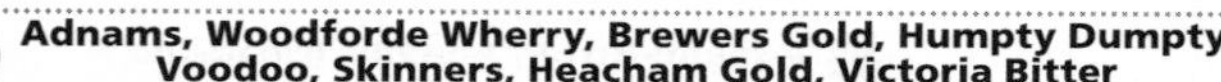

Adnams, Woodforde Wherry, Brewers Gold, Humpty Dumpty, Voodoo, Skinners, Heacham Gold, Victoria Bitter

"1530" is stamped on the outside of this promising-looking pub, but its comfortable and stylish interior – with a mis-match of sofas, leather armchairs and farmhouse chairs at broad tables – owes much to a recent sympathetic refit. Such is its local reputation that several spacious dining rooms soon fill with a mix of couples, friends and families, particularly for long lunches at weekends and holidays, so booking really is a must. With a new menu every fortnight, the hearty cooking keeps pace with the seasons and brings a regional touch to a couple of daily specials – plus a catch of the day – and a wider range of surefire gastropub classics: a handful of these come in either starter or main portions. To accompany your meal there's an interesting selection of wines for sale in their on site shop, as well as some delicious homemade chocolates. Bedrooms are expected soon.

Food serving times

Monday-Thursday:
12pm-2.30pm, 6pm-9.30pm

Friday-Saturday:
12pm-2.30pm, 6pm-10pm

Sunday: 12pm-9pm

Closed 25-26 December

Booking essential

Traditional

Prices

Meals: a la carte £ 20/34

Typical Dishes

Goats cheese crostini
Salt marsh lamb rump
Hot jam doughnuts

Village centre at the junction of B1068 and B1087. Parking.

66 The Anchor

Main St,
Walberswick IP18 6UA
Tel.: (01502)722112 – Fax: (01502)724464
e-mail: info@anchoratwalberswick.com **Website:** www.anchoratwalberswick.com

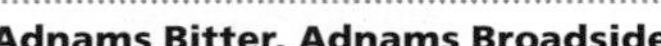

Adnams Bitter, Adnams Broadside

Drop anchor in this unspoilt area of Suffolk coastline and head for the main street of Walberswick, the less celebrated neighbour of trendy Southwold. Here you will find a large pub garden and terrace, looking out over allotments to a sandy bank and the sea beyond. The World Crabbing Championships are an ideal time to visit as the town really comes alive but you will receive a warm welcome here whatever the time of year. Cooking is hearty, unfussy and full of flavour, with local or homemade produce being used wherever possible. Seafood features highly and you can usually find West Mersea oysters or Brancaster mussels alongside fish from the Aldeburgh day boats. Sophie is often seen to pop her head out of the kitchen to passionately describe her specials, while Mark spends more of his time in the cellar, matching each of her dishes to a beer and wine from his seriously impressive collection. Bedrooms aren't currently recommendable.

Food serving times
Monday-Sunday:
12pm-3pm, 6pm-9pm

Prices
Meals: a la carte £ 16/25

Typical Dishes
Fish soup
Braised ox cheek
Hot chocolate pudding

3.5mi East of A12 on B1387 by Corporation Marshes. Parking.

Twenty-first century London may truly be called the definitive world city. Time zones radiate from Greenwich, and global finances zap round the Square Mile, while a vast smorgasbord of restaurants is the equal of anywhere on the planet. A stunning diversity of population now calls the capital its home, mixing and matching its time between the urban sprawl and enviable acres of green open space. From Roman settlement to banking centre to capital of a 19C empire, London's pulse has rarely missed a beat. Along the way, expansion has gobbled up surrounding villages, a piecemeal cocktail with its ingredients stirred to create the likes of Kensington and Chelsea, Highgate and Hampstead, Twickenham and Richmond. Apart from the great range of restaurants, London boasts over three and a half thousand pubs, many of which now see accomplished, creative cooking as an integral part of their existence and appeal. And you can find them sprinkled right the way across from zones one to five…

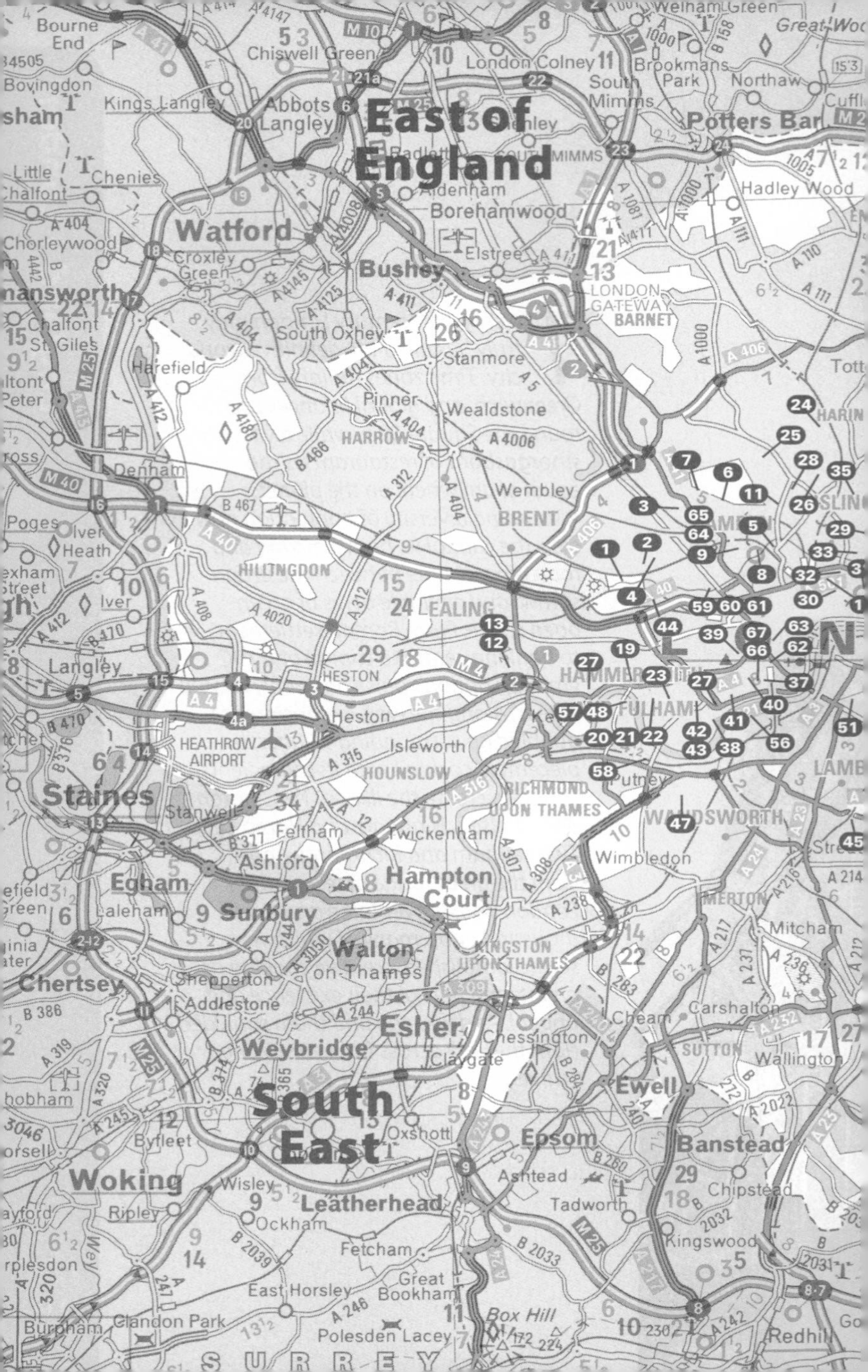

East of England
South East
SURREY
Bourne End
Bovingdon
Kings Langley
Chiswell Green
Abbots Langley
London Colney
Welham Green
Brookmans Park
South Mimms
Potters Bar
Northaw
Hadley Wood
Little Chalfont
Chenies
Chorleywood
Watford
Croxley Green
Radlett
Aldenham
Borehamwood
Elstree
Bushey
LONDON GATEWAY
BARNET
Chalfont St Giles
Harefield
South Oxhey
Stanmore
Pinner
Wealdstone
HARROW
Wembley
BRENT
Denham
Iver Heath
Iver
Langley
HILLINGDON
EALING
HESTON
Heston
HAMMERSMITH
FULHAM
HEATHROW AIRPORT
Isleworth
HOUNSLOW
Staines
Stanwell
Feltham
Twickenham
RICHMOND UPON THAMES
Putney
WANDSWORTH
Ashford
Egham
Sunbury
Hampton Court
Wimbledon
Laleham
Walton-on-Thames
KINGSTON UPON THAMES
MERTON
Mitcham
Chertsey
Shepperton
Addlestone
Esher
Chessington
Cheam
Carshalton
SUTTON
Wallington
Weybridge
Claygate
Ewell
Cobham
Byfleet
Oxshott
Epsom
Banstead
Woking
Wisley
Ashtead
Chipstead
Ripley
Leatherhead
Tadworth
Ockham
Fetcham
Kingswood
Great Bookham
East Horsley
Burpham
Clandon Park
Box Hill
Polesden Lacey
Redhill
M 25
M 40
M 4
M 1
M 10

East of England
London
South East
Cheshunt
Epping
High Ongar
N. Weald Bassett
Chipping Ongar
Blackmore
Fryerning
Ingatestone
Theydon Bois
Waltham Abbey
Epping Forest
Loughton
Abridge
Pilgrims Hatch
Brentwood
Ingrave
Stapleford Abbotts
Chigwell
Waltham
Redbridge
Havering
Hornchurch
Upminster
Ilford
Barking and Dagenham
Hackney
Tower Hamlets
Newham
Beckton
Bulphan
South Ockendon
Aveley
Thurrock
Woolwich
Greenwich
Blackwall Tunnel
Erith
Bexley
Dartford Crossing
Grays Thurrock
Northfleet
Tilbury
Dartford
Swanscombe
Lewisham
Sydenham
Sidcup
Wilmington
Darenth
Istead Rise
Longfield
Swanley
Hartley
Farningham
Meopham
Bromley
West Wickham
Croydon
Orpington
Eynsford
Ash
West Kingsdown
New Addington
Biggin Hill
Otford
Wrotham
Warlingham
North Downs
Ightham
Woldingham
Borough Green
W. Malling
Caterham
Sundridge
Sevenoaks
Mereworth
Westerham
Knole
Ightham Mote
Shipbourne
Limpsfield
Chartwell
Oxted
Crockham

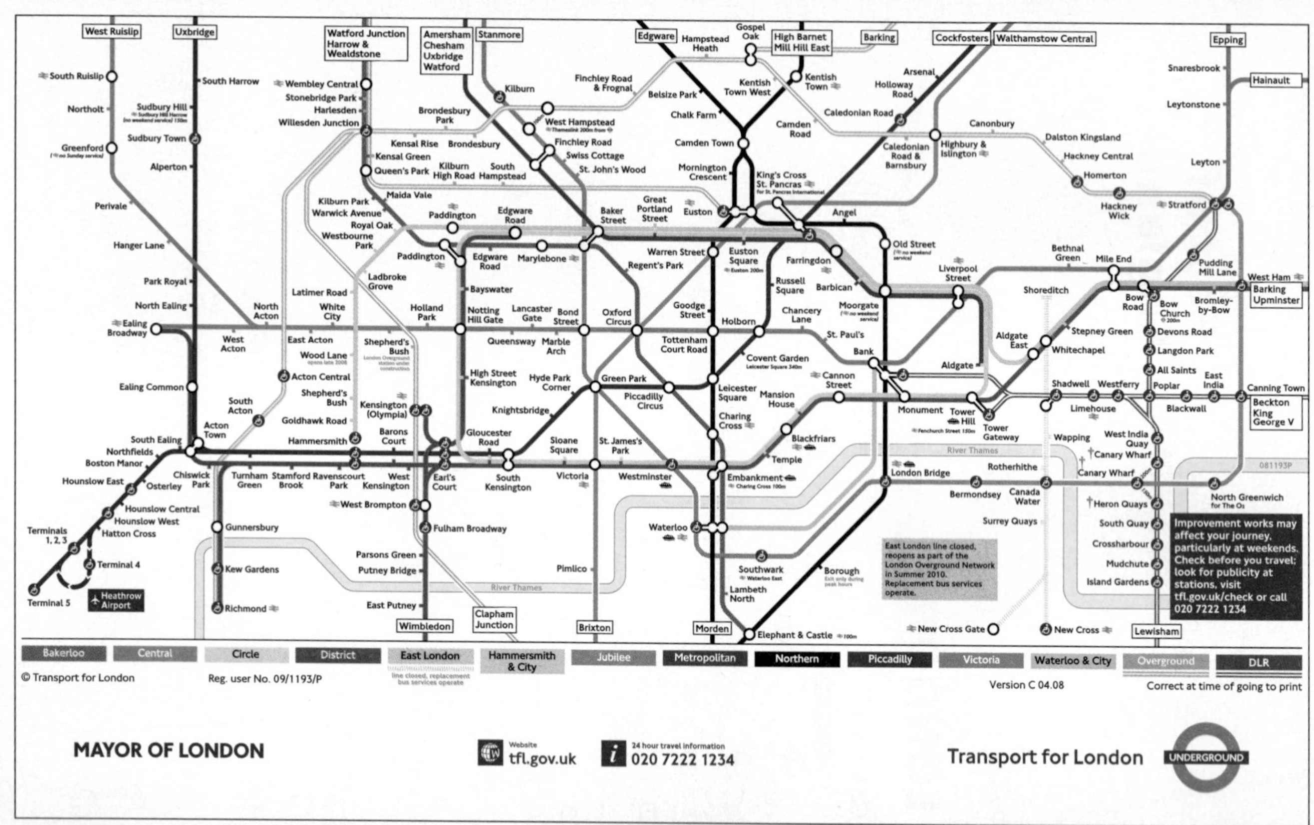
West Ruislip
Uxbridge
Watford Junction
Harrow & Wealdstone
Amersham
Chesham
Uxbridge
Watford
Stanmore
Edgware
Hampstead Heath
Gospel Oak
High Barnet
Mill Hill East
Barking
Cockfosters
Walthamstow Central
Epping
Hainault
South Ruislip
Northolt
Greenford
Perivale
Hanger Lane
Park Royal
North Ealing
Ealing Broadway
Ealing Common
South Ealing
Northfields
Boston Manor
Hounslow East
Osterley
Hounslow Central
Hounslow West
Hatton Cross
Terminals 1, 2, 3
Terminal 4
Terminal 5
Heathrow Airport
South Harrow
Sudbury Hill
Sudbury Town
Alperton
Acton Town
Chiswick Park
Turnham Green
Stamford Brook
Ravenscourt Park
West Kensington
Earl's Court
Gunnersbury
Kew Gardens
Richmond
South Acton
Acton Central
West Acton
North Acton
East Acton
White City
Latimer Road
Wood Lane
Shepherd's Bush
Goldhawk Road
Hammersmith
Barons Court
Kensington (Olympia)
West Brompton
Fulham Broadway
Parsons Green
Putney Bridge
East Putney
Wimbledon
Clapham Junction
Wembley Central
Stonebridge Park
Harlesden
Willesden Junction
Kensal Green
Queen's Park
Kensal Rise
Brondesbury
Brondesbury Park
Kilburn High Road
South Hampstead
Kilburn
West Hampstead
Finchley Road
Swiss Cottage
St. John's Wood
Finchley Road & Frognal
Kilburn Park
Maida Vale
Warwick Avenue
Royal Oak
Westbourne Park
Ladbroke Grove
Paddington
Edgware Road
Marylebone
Baker Street
Bayswater
Notting Hill Gate
Holland Park
Queensway
Lancaster Gate
Marble Arch
Bond Street
High Street Kensington
Hyde Park Corner
Knightsbridge
Gloucester Road
South Kensington
Sloane Square
Victoria
St. James's Park
Westminster
Pimlico
Brixton
Great Portland Street
Regent's Park
Oxford Circus
Green Park
Piccadilly Circus
Warren Street
Euston
Euston Square
Goodge Street
Tottenham Court Road
Holborn
Covent Garden
Leicester Square
Charing Cross
Embankment
Waterloo
Southwark
Lambeth North
Morden
Elephant & Castle
Borough
Belsize Park
Chalk Farm
Kentish Town West
Kentish Town
Camden Town
Camden Road
Mornington Crescent
King's Cross St. Pancras
Caledonian Road
Caledonian Road & Barnsbury
Holloway Road
Arsenal
Highbury & Islington
Canonbury
Dalston Kingsland
Hackney Central
Homerton
Hackney Wick
Angel
Old Street
Farringdon
Barbican
Russell Square
Chancery Lane
St. Paul's
Moorgate
Liverpool Street
Bank
Cannon Street
Mansion House
Blackfriars
Temple
Monument
Tower Hill
Tower Gateway
Aldgate
Aldgate East
Whitechapel
Shoreditch
Bethnal Green
Mile End
Stepney Green
Bow Road
Bow Church
Devons Road
Langdon Park
All Saints
Poplar
East India
Blackwall
Canning Town
Beckton
King George V
Bromley-by-Bow
Pudding Mill Lane
Stratford
West Ham
Barking
Upminster
Leyton
Leytonstone
Snaresbrook
Shadwell
Westferry
Limehouse
Wapping
West India Quay
Canary Wharf
Rotherhithe
Canada Water
Surrey Quays
Bermondsey
London Bridge
Heron Quays
South Quay
Crossharbour
Mudchute
Island Gardens
North Greenwich
for The O2
New Cross Gate
New Cross
Lewisham
River Thames
East London line closed, reopens as part of the London Overground Network in Summer 2010. Replacement bus services operate.
Improvement works may affect your journey, particularly at weekends. Check before you travel; look for publicity at stations, visit tfl.gov.uk/check or call 020 7222 1234
081193P
Bakerloo
Central
Circle
District
East London
line closed, replacement bus services operate
Hammersmith & City
Jubilee
Metropolitan
Northern
Piccadilly
Victoria
Waterloo & City
Overground
DLR
© Transport for London
Reg. user No. 09/1193/P
Version C 04.08
Correct at time of going to print
MAYOR OF LONDON
Website
tfl.gov.uk
24 hour travel information
020 7222 1234
Transport for London
UNDERGROUND

1 Paradise by way of Kensal Green

19 Kilburn Lane,
Brent W10 4AE
Tel.: (020)89690098 – Fax: (020)89698830
Website: www.theparadise.co.uk

  AE

 **Spitfire**

"For there is good news yet to hear and fine things to be seen / before we go to Paradise by way of Kensal Green", so ended a poem by G.K Chesterton, writer, philosopher, theologian and vegetarian-loather; the pub is doing its bit by reminding us that there's more to the local area than the cemetery. It's certainly eye-catching as it has been kitted out in an appealingly bohemian style with mismatched furniture, Murano chandeliers, old portraits and even the odd birdcage. Burlesque shows, comedy and music nights all happen upstairs. The bar menu is available during the day and covers most bases, from Welsh rarebit to plates of charcuterie but it's in the evening in the restaurant when the kitchen puts on its show. Mostly British ingredients come with enduring partners, like asparagus with butter, York ham with Cumberland sauce and lemon sole with Jersey Royals. Portions are man-sized and service is good-natured and natural.

Food serving times

Monday-Friday:
6.30pm-10.30pm

Saturday:
4pm-10.30pm (bar snacks)

Sunday: 12pm-8pm

Closed 25-26 December,
1 January

Prices

Meals: a la carte £ 23/30

Typical Dishes
Ham hock terrine
Goosnargh chicken
Knickerbocker glory

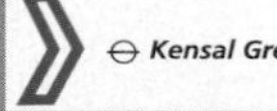 ⊖ *Kensal Green*

2 The Greyhound

64-66 Chamberlayne Road,
Kensal Rise NW10 3JJ
Tel.: (020)89698080 – Fax: (020)89698081
e-mail: thegreyhound@needtoeat.co.uk

 **Adnams Explorer and guest ales**

On the left you have the bar, decorated with assorted sporting memorabilia and black and white photos of everyone from Samuel Beckett to Ronnie Wood. There's a blackboard menu on the wall which is served throughout the place, including the slightly more formally dressed dining room which occupies the right side room. This has an almost Edwardian feel with its green walls, mirrors, leather seating, mounted animals and old adverts. The flowers on each table brighten it all up and there's a pleasant enclosed terrace at the back. The menu covers all points, from the burger, steak or haddock in an Adnam's beer batter to dishes where a lighter touch is required such as sea bass with lentils. Pâtés are robust and come with homemade piccalilli, the chicken is free range, fish comes daily from Cornwall and vegetarians are looked after (if they can avert their eyes from the taxidermy). There are over a dozen wines available by the glass.

Food serving times

Monday-Friday:
12.30pm-3pm,
6.30pm-10.30pm

Saturday:
12.30pm-4pm,
6.30pm-10.30pm

Sunday: 12.30pm-8pm

Closed 25 December, 1 January

Prices

Meals: £ 18 and a la carte £ 20/25

Typical Dishes

Smoked goose breast
Rock fish fillets
Apple & rhubarb crumble

 ⊖ *Kensal Green* 

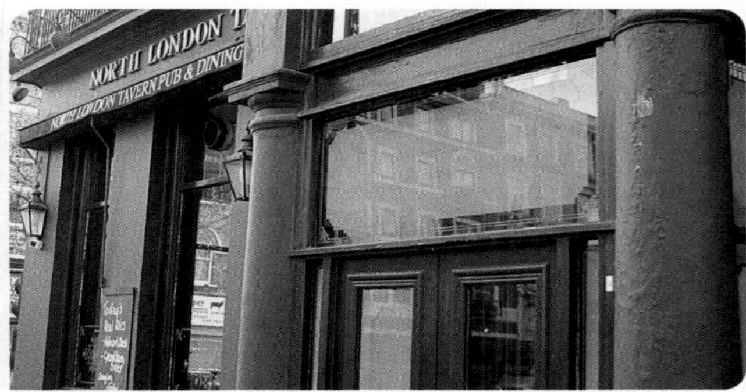

3 North London Tavern

375 Kilburn High Rd,
Kilburn NW6 7QB

Tel.: (020)76256634 – Fax: (020)73722723

e-mail: northlondontavern@realpubs.co.uk **Website:** www.realpubs.co.uk

  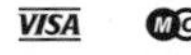

 **Timothy Taylor Landlord, Adnams Bitter, Nethergate Umbel Ale, Wooden Hand Bucaneer, Deuchars, Brains SA**

It may look as though it's bursting at the seams but those groups huddled together outside are usually just the smokers out for a quick gasper. That being said, the bar is a popular local spot. The dining room is separated from the bar by a red curtain and glass panelling and it too can quickly fill up. Old church seats, mismatched tables, high ceilings and chandeliers add a little gothic character and there are photos of old Kilburn on the walls. Lunch is a simpler affair in the bar but at dinner the printed menu, which is rather needlessly repeated verbatim on a large blackboard, offers a comprehensive selection of gastropub greatest hits, from belly pork to rib-eye, tuna niçoise to apple crumble, plus a couple of veggie options. The crusty bread is terrific and each dish arrives fully garnished and appetisingly presented on a big white plate. There's a whole roast beast at weekends and the wine list keeps things mostly under £20.

Food serving times

Monday: 6.30pm-10.30pm

Tuesday-Friday:
12pm-3.30pm,
6.30pm-10.30pm

Saturday: 12pm-4.30pm,
6.30pm-10.30pm

Sunday: 12pm-9.30pm

Closed 25 December

Bar lunch Monday-Friday

Prices

Meals: a la carte £ 23/27

Typical Dishes

Roast boned stuffed quail

Pan-fried gilt head bream

Brioche & raisin butter pudding

 ⊖ *Kilburn.*

4 The Salusbury

50-52 Salusbury Road,
Queen's Park NW6 6NN
Tel.: (020)73283286
e-mail: thesalusbury@london.com

 **Adnam's Broadside, Adnam's Bitter**

Salusbury Road is becoming quite a foodie quarter. There's a Sunday farmers' market up the road, plenty of local cafés and The Salusbury Pub & Dining Room whose success is evident by the presence of their own food store a couple of doors down. Two large aubergine coloured canopies highlight the location; one emblazoned with "pub" the other with "dining room" although you have to pass through the permanently busy former to get to the equally popular latter. Mirrors and large tables make the room seem bigger but the style is pleasantly higgledy and the occasional shared table contributes to the general bonhomie. The cooking, though, is more restaurant than pub and the menu has a distinct Italian accent. Good quality bread and olive oil set things off and the assorted pasta dishes come as either starters or mains. Flavours are pronounced, ingredients good and portions generous. It's also well worth leaving trouser space for dessert.

Food serving times

Monday: 7pm-10.15pm

Tuesday-Saturday:
12.30pm-3.30pm,
7pm-10.15pm

Sunday:
12.30pm-3.30pm, 7pm-10pm

Closed 25 December,
1 January

Prices

Meals: a la carte £ 22/29

Typical Dishes

Papardelle with swordfish

Monkfish & seafood cartoccio

Orange crème brûlée

 ⊖ *Queen's Park.* 

5 Prince Albert

163 Royal College St,
Camden Town NW1 0SG

Tel.: (020)74850270 – Fax: (020)77135994

e-mail: info@princealbertcamden.com **Website:** www.princealbertcamden.com

Black Sheep, Adnams, Brewers Gold, JHB, Spriggan Ale, GFB, Tawny Owl, Oregon Best

Albert had only been Prince Consort for three years when this pub opened in 1843. In 1863 work began down the road on St Pancras and it now seems highly appropriate that the re-opening of this Gothic Victorian masterpiece has coincided with the rebirth of the pub. The Prince Albert has kept much of its character but now comes with an appealing neighbourhood feel coupled with a welcoming atmosphere. The lunch menu of open sandwiches, catch of the day with hand-cut chips or offerings like guinea fowl or matured rib-eye is served throughout the pub but in the evening the upstairs restaurant gets its own menu. Decent olives and homemade soda bread are on hand while choosing from a selection of satisfyingly filling dishes, where freshness and traceability are given every respect. The wine list is on the back of the menu and offers over a dozen labels by the glass and plenty of choice for under £20.

Food serving times

Monday-Sunday:
12pm-3pm, 6.30pm-10pm

Closed 25-26 December

Prices

Meals: £ 17/22
and a la carte £ 23/33

Typical Dishes

Braised globe artichoke
Roast Guinea fowl
Hot chocolate fondant

 ⊖ *Camden Town* 

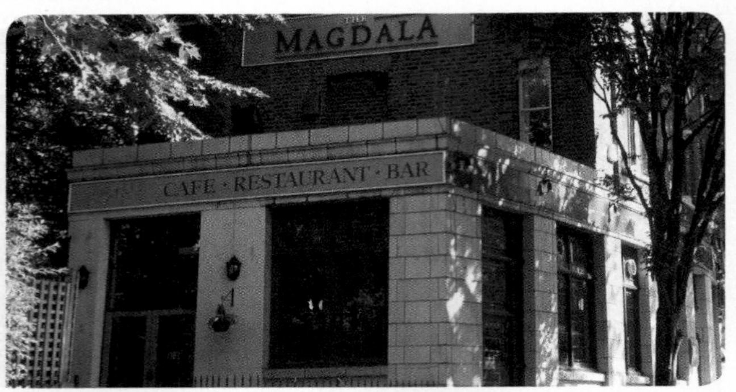

6 The Magdala

2A South Hill Park,
Hampstead NW3 2SB

Tel.: (020)74352503 – Fax: (020)74356167
e-mail: themagdala@hotmail.co.uk **Website:** www.the-magdala.com

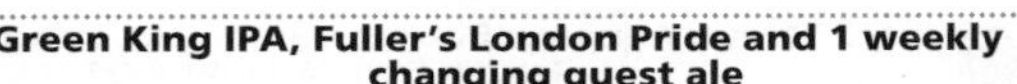

Green King IPA, Fuller's London Pride and 1 weekly changing guest ale

The Magdala has its place in history as it was outside this pub where Ruth Ellis shot her paramour in 1955. She was the last woman to be hanged in Britain and her case contributed to the eventual abolition of the death penalty. To its credit, the pub doesn't let this episode define it but instead concentrates on its community feel, general air of friendliness and decent food. The owner worked here for several years before buying it in 2007 and she certainly keeps her eye on the ball. As you walk in, it's a right turn for drinking and left for eating. The latter comes from a concise but balanced menu, with its heart and influences mostly within the British Isles. There are also interesting snacks and sharing plates, like assorted antipasti, on the supplementary blackboard. Wisely, no great risks are taken in preparation; this is about decent pub food. The menu lengthens at weekends when the upstairs room comes into play.

Food serving times
Monday-Friday:
12pm-2.30pm, 6pm-10pm
Saturday: 12pm-10pm
Sunday: 12pm-9.30pm

Prices
Meals: a la carte £ 18/26

Typical Dishes
Rabbit & duck terrine
Seabass fillet
Coconut crème brûlée

⊖ *Belsize Park*

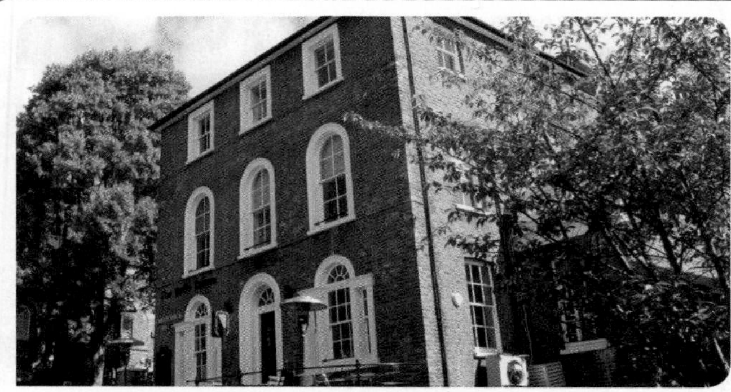

7 The Wells

30 Well Walk,
Hampstead NW3 1BX
Tel.: (020)77943785 – Fax: (020)77946817
e-mail: info@thewellshampstead.co.uk **Website:** www.thewellshampstead.co.uk

 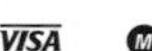

 **Adnams Broadside, Black Sheep**

Owned by Beth Coventry, the sister of restaurant critic Fay Maschler, The Wells is somewhere in between a restaurant and a pub. But whatever you consider it to be, one thing for sure is that it's in a grand old spot and adds to the mystery of why there are not more places to eat in Hampstead. It's equi-distant from the Heath and the High Street so whether you've been walking or shopping The Wells makes an ideal stopping-off point and the villagey atmosphere makes you feel that you're miles from London. The ground floor is the pubbier part, with a well chosen menu of dishes that go well with beer, but it can be a bit of a bun-fight, especially in summer and at weekends. Upstairs is an altogether more composed affair but one that still has considerable charm. Muscular gastropub offerings like ham hock terrine or Cumberland sausage with onion gravy sit alongside others whose origins may be more Mediterranean and perhaps even Asian.

Food serving times
Monday-Friday:
12pm-3pm, 6pm-10pm
Saturday:
12pm-4pm, 7pm-10pm
Sunday:
12pm-4pm, 7pm-9.30pm
Closed 1 January

Prices
Meals: a la carte £ 25/35

Typical Dishes
Pan-fried scallops
Salt marsh lamb rump
Apple & rhubarb crumble

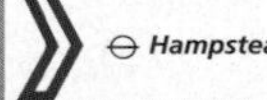

⊖ Hampstead

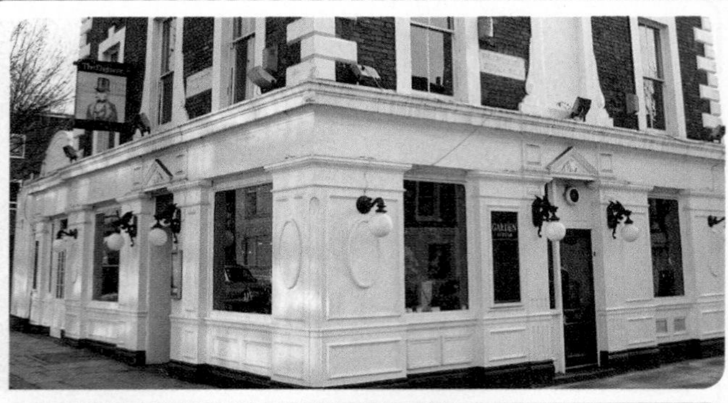

8 The Engineer

65 Gloucester Ave,
Primrose Hill NW1 8JH

Tel.: (020)77220950 – Fax: (020)74830592
e-mail: info@the-engineer.com **Website:** www.the-engineer.com

 **Bombardier, Hook Norton**

Über cool staff in T-shirts and jeans provide enthusiastic service in this pleasant part of town and a convivial, relaxing ambience prevails. The striking, part-stuccoed building is rumoured to have been built by Isambard Kingdom Brunel, and inside, the décor is contemporary and relaxing. The open bar has a light, airy feel to it, with tables not too closely spaced. The menu's the same whether you're in the bar, in the arty dining room or outside in the popular, plant-filled terrace, and it's an all day affair, with people coming in for breakfast, lunch and dinner. Food is well-sourced and boldly flavoured, with eclectic influences from Europe to the Pacific Rim, and choices might include salt and pepper tofu or tequila cured organic salmon. The chefs are well-established and take pride in their work - and it shows. People come in especially for the organic cheeseburger and the fabulous baker fries.

Food serving times

Monday-Friday:
9am-11.30am, 12pm-3pm, 7pm-11pm

Saturday: 9am-12pm, 12.30pm-4pm, 7pm-11pm

Sunday: 9am-12pm, 12.30-4pm, 7pm-10.30pm

Closed 25-28 December

Prices

Meals: a la carte £ 30/60

Typical Dishes

Sun-cured salmon

Grilled pork chop

Gingerbread & lemon cheesecake

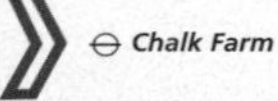

⊖ *Chalk Farm*

9 The Queens

49 Regent's Park Rd,
Primrose Hill NW1 8XD
Tel.: (020)75860408 – Fax: (020)75865677
e-mail: thequeens@geronimo-inns.co.uk **Website:** www.geronimo-inns.co.uk

VISA MC AE

 **Youngs, Youngs Special, Wells Bombardier**

The Queens will have a place in the annals of gastropub history, as it was one of the pioneers in bringing decent food into an environment hitherto resistant to change and proved that a local pub with good food was not an oxymoron. Its location on Primrose Hill's main drag and alongside the grassy knoll is clearly another attraction and the balcony terrace is a sought after summer spot. The whole place was stripped down and done up in 2006 but the narrow ground floor bar remains an established local meeting point, with the footie on TV in the corner. Head upstairs and you'll find a warm and welcoming dining room, prettily decorated in green. More importantly, the food is just the sort you'd want to find in a pub. Cassoulet, terrines, pies of the shepherd or fish variety are all there in generous portions and dishes come with an interesting selection of sides. Wine prices are kept low and there's plenty on offer by the glass.

Food serving times

Monday-Saturday:
12pm-3pm, 6pm-10pm

Sunday: 12pm-8pm

Closed 25 December

Prices

Meals: a la carte £ 18/29

Typical Dishes

Ham hock terrine
Char-grilled Welsh lamb
Sticky toffee pudding

⊖ *Chalk Farm*

10 Norfolk Arms

28 Leigh Street,
St Pancras WC1H 9EP
Tel.: (020)73883937
e-mail: info@norfolkarms.co.uk **Website:** www.norfolkarms.co.uk

VISA MC AE

 **Greene King IPA, Theakstons**

A onetime drinkers' paradise, the transformation of The Norfolk Arms to a North London gastropub has been as welcome as it has been absolute. The bench-strewn exterior is beautifully tiled and the inside is just as charming, with ornate ceiling squares, raw plaster walls and tables neatly laid with teacloth napkins. Dried peppers, chillies and strings of onions hang from the walls and light fittings, and the cured hams and salami that decorate the bar can be sized to order by the chef. On the menu you will find some British dishes, but it's heavily influenced by the Mediterranean and particularly Spain, and dominated by tapas. Quirky touches include food served in ceramic dishes (they say it retains the flavour), and the lack of traditional course divisions on the menu. Wines are taken seriously here and have their own blackboard to prove it. The private room upstairs is great for candle-lit tapas-sharing parties.

Food serving times

Monday-Sunday:
12pm-3pm, 6.30pm-10.15pm

Closed 25-26 December,
1 January

Prices

Meals: a la carte £ 19/22

Typical Dishes

Mixed vegetable mezze
Basque fish stew
Poached pear

⊖ Russell Square. Parking meters in the street.

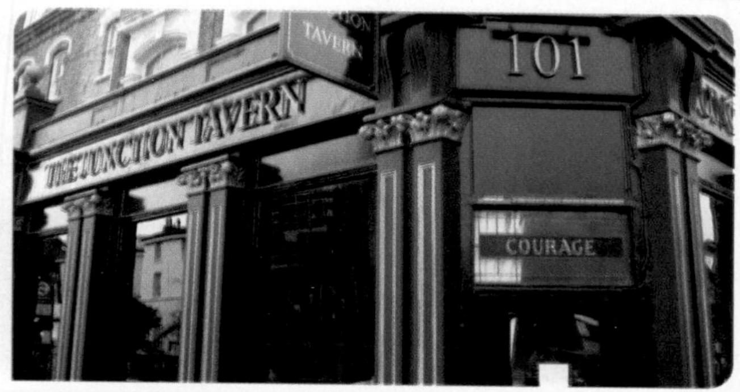

11 Junction Tavern

101 Fortess Rd,
Tufnell Park NW5 1AG
Tel.: (020)74859400 – Fax: (020)74859401
Website: www.junctiontavern.co.uk

Deuchar IPA and 15 guest beers per week from independent brewers

An immense pub a short walk from Tufnell Park Tube; with its brass cock glinting in the sun, you can't miss The Junction, and nor would you want to. Inside, it's just as impressive; painted ox blood red, with rich wood panelling, large windows and high ceilings. With a conservatory, dining room and terrace as well as the bar, there's plenty of space to accommodate the young crowds who gather here, and service is relaxed and efficient.The choice on the daily-changing menu is as eclectic as the range of cookbooks propped up at one end of the open kitchen. Wholesome and bold, choices might include wild mushroom and spinach crepes or dukkah crusted tofu - and the chunky chips deserve a special mention. An ale pub at heart, the weekly-changing selection here boasts a menu all of its own. Ale lovers also congregate several times a year for a beer festival, when pints are poured straight from the mass of barrels lined up inside.

Food serving times

Monday-Friday:
12pm-3pm, 6.30pm-10.30pm

Saturday:
12pm-4pm, 6.30pm-10.30pm

Sunday:
12pm-4pm, 6.30pm-9.30pm

Closed 24-26 December, 1 January

Prices

Meals: a la carte £ 22/30

Typical Dishes
Pan-fried duck livers
Baked sea bream
Vanilla pannacotta

⊖ *Tufnell Park*

12 The Bollo

13-15 Bollo Lane,
Acton Green W4 5LR

Tel.: (020)89946037

e-mail: thebollohouse@btconnect.com **Website:** www.thebollohouse.co.uk

 **IPA, Abbot**

You'll find this handsome tavern is at its best on bright summer days, when a buoyant crowd of drinkers and diners fill the spacious bar and make themselves at home on the terrace. But on those days and weeks without the sun, The Bollo still provides a warm and welcoming environment, even to those who don't live in the immediate neighbourhood. There's a slightly smarter rear dining room – its wood panelling, burgundy walls and tan leather banquettes rather suit the pub's Victorian dimensions – but the full menu is served throughout. A core of suitably generous gastropub favourites, from lamb burgers to 28 day aged steaks, need no introduction, but the regularly changing menu finds room for plenty of seasonal ingredients to put in their yearly appearances. Sunday roasts will leave you appropriate somnolent for the afternoon, especially if followed by one of the puddings that come primarily from the comfort-food school of culinary arts.

Food serving times

Monday-Sunday:
12pm-10.30pm

Closed 25 December

Prices

Meals: a la carte £ 20/35

Typical Dishes

Suffolk asparagus
Grilled seabass
Blueberry Bakewell tart

 ⊖ *Chiswick Park*

13 Duke of Sussex

75 South Parade,
Acton Green W4 5LF
Tel.: (020)87428801
e-mail: michael-buurman@yahoo.co.uk

Moorhouse Premier, Timothy Taylor, Bath Ales, Youngs, Proper Job

This grand old Victorian Duke has been given a new lease of life by an enthusiastic pair of experienced gastropub specialists. They've taken a long lease on the place, done it all up and, most importantly, introduced some very appealing menus. A hospitable atmosphere reigns throughout, but the best place to eat is in the back room, which was once a variety theatre and comes complete with proscenium arch, chandeliers and ornate plasterwork. The menu's printed daily and the Spanish influence highlights where the chef's passions lie. Rustic and satisfying stews, whether fish or fabada, suit the environment perfectly, as does a plate of Spanish cured meats or a tortilla; there are often dishes designed for sharing and on some evenings the kitchen might roast a whole suckling pig, which they start dishing out at around 7.30 – but when it's gone, it's gone. The wine list is short but affordable, with plenty available by the glass or carafe.

Food serving times
Monday-Sunday:
12pm-10.30pm

Mediterranean

Prices
Meals: a la carte £ 21/24

Typical Dishes
Pressed ox tongue
Salt beef & dumplings
Blackberry & apple crumble

⊖ *Chiswick Park*

14 Cat & Mutton

76 Broadway Market,
Hackney E8 4QJ

Tel.: (020)72545599 – Fax: (020)72542797
e-mail: catandmutton@yahoo.co.uk **Website:** www.catandmutton.co.uk

VISA  AE

 **Adnams, Timothy Taylor Landlord**

The Cat and Mutton is your typical early Victorian corner pub with a bona fide London feel; it's a drinking pub that does decent food, rather than an eating one that reluctantly serves drinks. The ground floor can take a hammering with the after-work crowd and it has a rough and ready vibe, with exposed brick walls and a resolute lack of decorative embellishment save for a solitary picture of a cat and, unsurprisingly, a leg of mutton. Such uncompromising surroundings make it an unlikely spot in which to find decent food but that's exactly what the Cat and Mutton delivers, although this still may not be the best choice for that romantic dinner à deux. The blackboard menu offers around five choices per course, which could include anything from chilli squid to a decent steak. The open plan kitchen uses some ingredients garnered from the local market and the cooking is full-bodied and satisfying. The room upstairs is used at weekends.

Food serving times

Monday: 6.30pm-10pm

Tuesday-Saturday:
12pm-3pm, 6.30pm-10pm

Sunday: 12pm-3pm

Closed 25-26 December and 1 January

British

Prices

Meals: £ 15 (weekday dinner) and a la carte £ 21/33

Typical Dishes

Steamed mussels
Scottish sirloin
Rhubarb & sherry trifle

⊖ Bethnal Green Parking Pay and Display in Broadway Market.

15 The Empress of India

130 Lauriston Road,
Victoria Park, Hackney E9 7LH
Tel.: (020)85335123 – Fax: (020)74042250
e-mail: info@theempressofindia.com **Website:** www.theempressofindia.com

VISA MC AE

Fuller's London Pride, Timothy Taylor Landlord, Adnams Broadside and Mean Time Pale Ale

Fancy a cup of tea? No, not a cuppa from the greasy spoon, but an aromatic infusion from the excellent afternoon tea menu at the eminently named Empress, just around the corner from Victoria Park. The building dates from the 1880s and pays homage to said title-bearer, Queen Victoria and her era, but has enjoyed various past incarnations as a nightclub, a print works and a floristry training school. Now a smart, open plan pub with the emphasis firmly on dining, it's brightly lit with high ceilings, mosaic flooring, red leather banquettes and eye-catching murals picturing Indian scenes; young and enthusiastic serving staff complete the look. The seasonally-evolving menu is classically based with some Mediterranean influences, and blends the robust with the more refined. The patrons use rare breeds for their meats and poultry, and these can often be temptingly seen and smelt cooking on the rotisserie.

Food serving times

Monday-Friday:
12pm-3pm, 6pm-10pm

Saturday:
12pm-3pm, 9pm-11.30pm

Sunday:
9am-4pm, 6.30-9.30pm

Closed 25-26 December

Prices

Meals: £ 25 and a la carte £ 19/33

Typical Dishes
Hot smoked salmon
Veal osso bucco
Apple & almond bread & butter pudding

⊖ Mile End Parking in neighbouring side streets.

16 Prince Arthur

95 Forest Road, Hackney E8 3BH

Tel.: (020)72499996 – Fax: (020)72497074

e-mail: info@theprincearthurlondonfields.com

Website: www.theprincearthurlondonfields.com

Fuller's London Pride, Deuchars IPA

The Prince Arthur is less gastropub, more your favourite intimate little local serving proper pub grub. Much of the old character remains but the owners, brothers Tom & Ed Martin, have added some ironic touches, from stuffed animals to a collection of saucy seaside postcards. It is also still a pub for local people, with the occasional Martin Amis enthusiast thrown in for good measure. The menu matches the surroundings in its lack of pretension. Soup comes with crusty bread, prawns come by the pint and pub classics, like cottage pie and apple crumble, are always to be found. There are also hearty lamb shanks and saddles of rabbit for the more adventurous. Desserts should really be written as "puddings" as they are of the weigh-you-down-but-make-you-feel-good variety. That being said, the deep-fried jam sandwich with carnation milk ice cream appears to be more of an attention-grabber than a culinary breakthrough.

Food serving times

Monday-Thursday:
6pm-10pm

Friday-Sunday:
12pm-4.30pm, 6pm-10pm

Prices

Meals: a la carte £ 20/27

Typical Dishes

Guinea fowl terrine

Darne of sea trout

Deep-fried jam sandwich

⊖ *Bethnal Green*

17 The Fox

28 Paul St, Shoreditch EC2A 4LB
Tel.: (020)77295708
e-mail: thefoxpublichouse@thefoxpublichouse.com
Website: www.thefoxpublichouse.com

 **Bombardier, Harveys Best Bitter,**

The Fox changed hands towards the end of 2006 but the new owners have wisely not interfered too much with the winning formula. For one thing, it still has that relaxed and lived-in feel despite the fresh coat of paint and the upstairs dining room continues to boast a sense of Victorian decorum in contrast to the animated bar downstairs. Now, though, the menu is slightly longer and is available throughout both floors, although the upstairs is still the best place to eat in – even the terrace is spoiled somewhat by the presence of an extractor fan. The kitchen knows its way around an animal and much of the cooking is red blooded – quite literally so if you order the onglet or ox heart. Many of the dishes come with a satisfyingly rustic edge and this no-nonsense approach married with seasonal pertinence keeps the flavours honest and to the fore. The service comes nicely paced and reassuringly knowledgeable.

Food serving times

Monday-Friday:
12pm-3pm, 6pm-10pm

Saturday: 6pm-10pm

Sunday: 12pm-3pm

Closed one week Christmas to New Year

Prices

Meals: a la carte £ 19/25

Typical Dishes

Rabbit rillettes
Smoked haddock
Steamed marmalade sponge

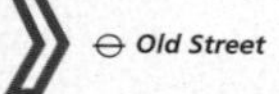 ⊖ *Old Street*

18 The Princess

76-78 Paul St,
Shoreditch EC2A 4NE
Tel.: (020)77299270
e-mail: princesspub@gmail.com

 VISA MC AE

 **Timothy Taylor, Fuller's London Pride**

A traditional Victorian pub which has travelled the modernist path of others within this trendy postcode, The Princess announces its gastro credentials atop an iron staircase within an eye-catchingly stylish first floor setting. Here you'll find bold wallpaper, oil paintings, sash windows and very comfortable leather cushioned chairs arranged at dark wooden tables. Rather than a lengthy list of dishes, chef concentrates on a concise menu, and the choice is invariably interesting and original. And well priced, to boot. The style is international, with Mediterranean combinations particularly to the fore. Waiters are friendly and efficient, and obviously used to being busy. This is a well-run pub that's strong in every aspect, and great to visit after a trip to nearby Spitalfields Market or Columbia Road flower market.

Food serving times

Sunday-Friday:
12.30pm-3pm, 6.30pm-10pm

Saturday: 6.30pm-10pm

Closed 24 December-
1 January and Bank
Holidays

Prices

Meals: a la carte £ 25/30

Typical Dishes

Linguine with roast fennel

BBQ lemon chicken

Chocolate & hazelnut fondant

⊖ Old Street Parking meters outside in the street.

19 The Farm

18 Farm Lane,
Fulham SW6 1PP
Tel.: (020)73813331
e-mail: info@thefarmfulham.co.uk **Website:** www.thefarmfulham.co.uk

  VISA MC AE

 **Old Speckled Hen**

This inner-city farm is somewhat hidden away behind Fulham Road but this just makes you feel more like a local when you find it. The austerity suggested by the semi-industrial looking red brick façade is tempered by the warming fireplaces within. The same food is served throughout, so you can eat either in the relaxed bar area or head through to the altogether more stylish restaurant. The menu displays its ambition and international credentials through dishes such as black pudding with foie gras or duck cassoulet with Toulouse sausage but there are also more traditionally British dishes such as smoked salmon and Dover sole; if you've only time for a fleeting visit then there's always some lighter bites, which could include meze, mini Cumberland sausages or cheese and chutney. The strength of the kitchen lies in the astute sourcing and preparation of the meat dishes, particularly the very tender beef.

Food serving times
Monday-Sunday:
11am-10.30pm
Closed 25 December

Prices
Meals: a la carte £ 25/40

Typical Dishes
Fish bisque & rouille
Grilled rib eye steak
Pannacotta

⊖ ***Fulham Broadway Parking meters in the street.***

20 Anglesea Arms

35 Wingate Rd,
Hammersmith W6 0UR

Tel.: (020)87491291 – Fax: (020)87491254

e-mail: anglesea.events@gmail.com **Website:** www.angleseaarms.co.uk

 **Deuchars IPA, Timothy Taylor Landlord, Fuller's London Pride, Adnams Broadside, Summer Lightning, St Austell Tribute**

If, for some reason, you need another excuse to visit a pub then just remember that they can always provide a little local history. The Marquess of Anglesea was Wellington's Number Two at Waterloo – where he lost his leg – and many of the surrounding streets are named after the Duke. The pub dates back to 1909 and the builders responsible for many of the charming properties in those streets were housed in the pub. Today it continues to provide sustenance to many a local dweller or worker and does so in a friendly, laid-back manner. The blackboard menu changes in parts twice daily and the cooking is gutsy and wholesome. Oysters are a regular feature and what The Marquess would have made of seeing French classics like Beef Bourguignon on the menu doesn't bear considering. The same menu is served throughout so you can sit in the glass-roofed restaurant with the open kitchen or the characterful bar with its dark panelling and fireplaces.

Food serving times

Monday: 12.30pm-2.45pm, 7pm-10pm

Tuesday-Friday: 12.30pm-2.45pm, 7pm-10.30pm

Saturday: 12.30pm-3pm, 7pm-10.30pm

Sunday: 12.30pm-3.30pm, 7pm-10pm

Closed 23-27 December

Bookings not accepted

Prices Meals: a la carte £ 15/35

Typical Dishes

Duck liver parfait

Braised beef brisket

Norfolk apple treacle tart

 ⊖ *Ravenscourt Park* 

21 Carpenter's Arms

91 Black Lion Lane,
Hammersmith W6 9BG
Tel.: (020)87418386 – Fax: (020)87416437
e-mail: info@carpentersarms-info

 **Adnams**

Pubs come in all sorts of shapes, sizes and guises; the Carpenter's Arms is from the "doesn't actually look much like a pub" school of pub. It has changed its name a few times over the years and even spent time as a French brasserie but now, under the same ownership as Chelsea's Pig's Ear, it appears to have found its niche. Decoratively it's as understated as the exterior but there's lots of natural light and a small terrace at the back. The place attracts a younger clientele and the service is smart and sensible. The cooking continues this theme of unpretentiousness; menus are intelligently written and combinations are never too unusual. Dishes are a mix of stout British ingredients, like liver, eel, rabbit or duck, enlivened by more worldly accompaniments such as gnocchi or ricotta; the seasonal vegetables are a particular strength. Expect the food to arrive in generous dimensions – this is, after all, a pub. Really.

Food serving times
Monday-Friday:
12pm-2.30pm, 6.30pm-10pm
Saturday:
12.30pm-3pm, 7pm-10pm
Sunday:
12.30pm-4pm, 7.30pm-9pm
Closed 25 December, 1 January

Prices
Meals: a la carte £ 22/35

Typical Dishes
Mutton & vegetable broth
Roast fillet of halibut
Pumpkin Bakewell tart

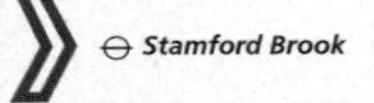
⊖ *Stamford Brook*

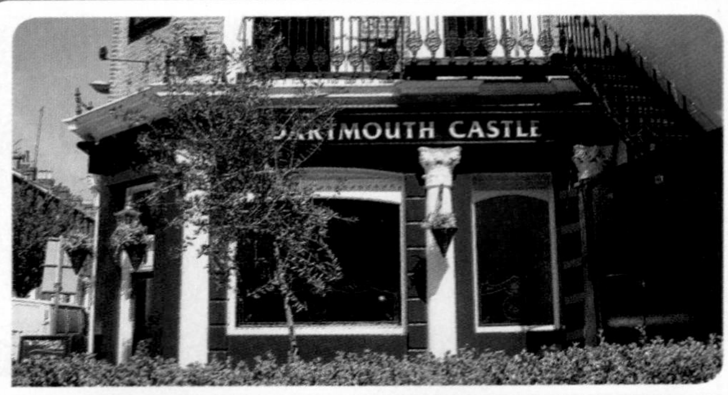

22 The Dartmouth Castle

26 Glenthorne Road,
Hammersmith W6 0LS

Tel.: (020)87483614 – Fax: (020)87483619

e-mail: dartmouth.castle@btconnect.com **Website:** www.thedartmouthcastle.co.uk

Fuller's London Pride and guests ales such as Timothy Taylor Landlord, Deuchars Caledonian IPA

Samuel Johnson once remarked "there is no private house in which people can enjoy themselves so well as at a capital tavern". He would have been taken with The Dartmouth Castle: customers are positively encouraged to dwell; there are board games available and cask ales change regularly and sometimes feature popular requests from the regulars. What would be alien to him would be the food: one of the owners has spent time in California and France and the monthly changing menu has a decidedly sunny disposition. The influences from the Mediterranean and southern Europe are evident throughout, with the likes of Tunisian lamb, assorted pastas, roast vegetables, thyme, tomatoes and fishy stews like caldeirada all featuring. Good bread with olive oil starts it all off and dishes arrive with appetisingly unfussy presentation. This is a no-nonsense, simply furnished, hospitable pub that serves distinctly pleasing food.

Food serving times

Monday-Saturday:
12pm-3pm, 6pm-10pm

Sunday: 12pm-9.30pm

Closed 24 December to 1 January, first Monday in August

Mediterranean

Prices

Meals: a la carte £ 18/27

Typical Dishes

Goats cheese & squash tart

Grilled Tuscan sausages

Chocolate & almond cake

⊖ Hammersmith

23 The Havelock Tavern

57 Masbro Rd,
Brook Green, Shepherd's Bush W14 0LS
Tel.: (020)76035374
e-mail: info@thehavelocktavern.co.uk **Website:** www.thehavelocktavern.co.uk

Inspectors' favourites

 **Sharps Doombar, Fullers London Pride, Adnams Bitter**

Having welcomed in a new team in early 2008, you can't be blamed for wondering if it's all change here; but, thankfully, that's not the case. As before, they don't take bookings; you have to go to the bar to place your order; and at busy times – which is pretty much after 7:30pm – you might have to wait to be served. In fact, the only thing that's really changed is that they now accept credit cards, but who's complaining about that? The real beauty of this pub is that it's true, honest and isn't afraid to hold onto its roots. Drinkers and diners rub shoulders throughout, be it on large shared tables, the pretty courtyard terrace or the picnic benches out front, while the great value blackboard menu features modern, seasonal, gutsy dishes. There are big tubs of tempting pistachios and succulent olives on the bar which make the perfect intro, but make sure you save room for a heart-warming dessert, maybe chocolate tart or summer pudding.

Food serving times
Monday-Saturday:
12.30pm-2.30pm, 7pm-10pm
Sunday:
12.30pm-3pm, 7pm-9.30pm
Closed 25 December
Bookings not accepted

Prices
Meals: a la carte £ 19/28

Typical Dishes
Duck liver salad
Grilled mackerel fillets
Lemon & blueberry pannacotta

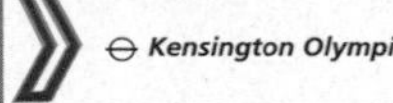
⊖ *Kensington Olympia*

24 The Queens Pub and Dining Room

26 Broadway Parade,
Crouch End N8 9DE

Tel.: (020)83402031

e-mail: queens@foodandfuel.co.uk **Website:** www.thequeenscrouchend.co.uk

Wells Bombardier, Eagle IPA and weekly changing guest ales

This classic Victorian pub was once known more for the fighting than the food but the 2006 makeover ensures that the closest thing now to an episode of EastEnders is the occasional presence of a cast member or two. The young owners have kept the eye-catching Victoriana, from the mahogany panelling and ornate plasterwork to the stained glass windows and wrought iron but the presence of a separate dining room shows where the emphasis now lies. The menu changes daily and food is served all day. It's a confident kitchen, offering a mix of modern British with plenty of Mediterranean influence so the sausages that come with the mash may include Toulouse as well as wild boar, and apple crumble might arrive with pistachio ice cream. There's a cocktail of the week and an accessible wine list with plenty available by the glass or carafe; non-drinkers are not ignored – there's home-made lemonade to stir childhood memories in many.

Food serving times

Monday-Saturday: 12pm-10pm

Sunday: 12pm-9pm

Prices

Meals: a la carte £ 15/28

Typical Dishes

Crispy pork belly
Roast cod
Sticky toffee pudding

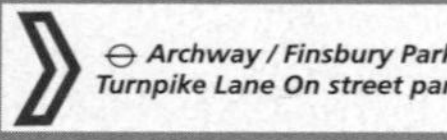

⊖ Archway / Finsbury Park / Turnpike Lane On street parking.

25 The Bull

13 North Hill,
Highgate N6 4AB
Tel.: (0845)4565033 – Fax: (0845)4565034
e-mail: info@inthebull.biz **Website:** www.themeredithgroup.co.uk

1 guest ale changing weekly - Youngs, Adnams, Wells Bombardier

If the first thing you notice is a drinks trolley then you know you're not in your, or anyone else's, local boozer. The Bull is part of the Meredith Group, along with The House and The Running Footman, and they only deal in your proper foodie pubs. The open kitchen puts the chefs on view and their food is mostly modern European, with a dominant French gene running through it; their home-baked breads are a real speciality of the house. Dishes are seasonally pertinent and the construction, ingredients and execution are aimed more at the "serious" end of the dining pub scale, although there is a good value lunch menu to accompany the à la carte. Those who have a boat they wish to push out will find their task aided by the wine list, which does also offer sufficient numbers of affordable bottles. Weekends welcome a more family atmosphere, where brunch is offered. The room is bright, service is on the ball and Thursday night is music night.

Food serving times
Monday-Saturday:
12pm-2.30pm, 6pm-10.30pm
Sunday:
12pm-4pm, 6.30pm-10pm
Closed 26 December or 1 January

Prices
Meals: £ 18 (lunch) and a la carte £ 28/35

Typical Dishes
Spiced quail
Roast Barbary duck breast
Rhubarb & custard

⊖ Highgate Free parking on road outside pub.

26 The Old Dairy

1-3 Crouch Hill,
Stroud Green N4 4AP

Tel.: (020)72633337 – Fax: (020)75611851
e-mail: theolddairy@realpubs.co.uk **Website:** www.realpubs.co.uk

Flowers IPA, Moorhouse Black Car, Adnams Regatta

Of all the new pub conversions around, there can be few as characterful as The Old Dairy. Dating from 1890, the picture panels among the original red bricks and steel girders illustrate the listed building's former use when owned by Friern Manor Dairy Company. Despite the renovation and the locale's increasing gentrification, the pub has kept itself at the heart of the community by investing as much effort in the bar – which occupies quite a space – as it has in the dining room and the period photos of the area on the walls also help. The locals have certainly taken to the place and any background music is soon drowned out by the sound of contented customers. The cooking is bold and honest and how nice it is that dishes arrive exactly as described on the menu. It's modern British with a hint of Europe. The crisp sourdough gets you started and the portions are well judged and confidently flavoured. Weekend brunches are a real hit.

Food serving times

Monday-Thursday:
6.30pm-10.30pm

Friday-Sunday:
12pm-3.30pm,
6.30pm-10.30pm

Closed 25 December

Bar snacks all day

Prices

Meals: a la carte £ 20/25

Typical Dishes

Pork & apricot terrine

Chicken stuffed with haggis

Chocolate & caraway tart

⊖ *Finsbury Park / Archway.*

27 The Devonshire

126 Devonshire Rd,
Chiswick W4 2JJ

Tel.: (020)75927962 – Fax: (020)75921603

e-mail: thedevonshire@gordonramsay.com **Website:** www.gordonramsay.com

Fuller's London Pride, Deuchars IPA

The Devonshire joined Gordon Ramsay's burgeoning pub portfolio at the end of 2007 and, like The Narrow, enjoyed almost immediate success. It's in one of those roads that's a microcosm of London: pretty Victorian terraced houses at one end of the street and '60s council housing at the other, with the pub bang on the half-way line. The striking Edwardian façade is matched by the characterful oak panelling and polished wood flooring in the bar and here you can enjoy such egalitarian treats as scotch eggs or pots of pickled cockles. If, on the other hand, you want a more structured environment then head for the neatly laid out restaurant. It has a concise and good value menu, with daily-changing specials, and propounds an appealing mix of pub classics alongside other dishes that are more West End in their pedigree. There's an "on toast" selection, which could include herring roes, as well as weekly changing soups and pies.

Food serving times

Monday-Friday:
12pm-3pm, 6pm-11pm

Saturday:
12pm-4pm, 5pm-11pm

Sunday:
12pm-4pm, 5pm-10.30pm

Closed Monday
23 December to 3 January

Prices

Meals: £ 17 (lunch)
and a la carte £ 25/28

Typical Dishes

Marinated salmon
Slow-cooked pork belly
Steamed marmalade pudding

⊖ *Turnham Green*

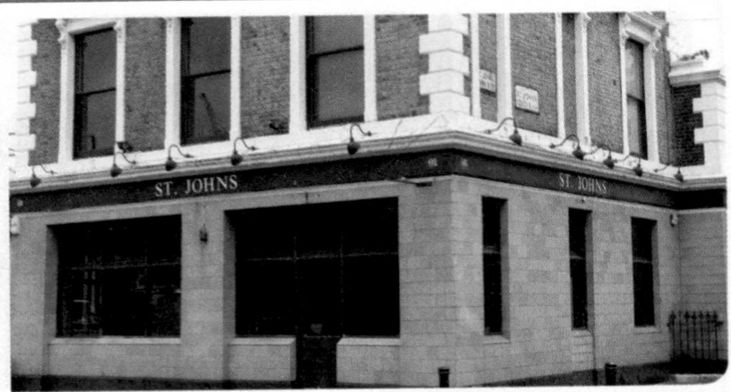

28 St John's

91 Junction Rd,
Archway N19 5QU
Tel.: (020)72721587
e-mail: st.johns@virgin.net

 **Timothy Taylor, Summer Lightning, Adnams Broadside, Brakspear Bitter**

If anywhere represents what can be achieved with imagination, enthusiasm and an eye for the bigger picture it is surely St John's. Not many years ago this was a dodgy old Archway boozer into which only the big and the brave would venture. It still looks pretty scruffy from the outside but inside it is a lively and very successful gastropub, whose fans include writers and actors from the smarter houses up the hill in Dartmouth Park. The front half is a busy bar but go through to the back (which was once the snooker hall) and you'll discover a vast and quite theatrical dining room, with a blackboard menu at both ends and one of the walls covered with pictures. The atmosphere is animated and bustling, helped along by the young staff who are chatty and obliging. The kitchen keeps the flavours to the fore, with dishes that are satisfyingly warming and gutsy in winter and lighter and more Mediterranean in the summer months.

Food serving times

Monday-Thursday: 6.30pm-11pm

Friday: 12pm-3.30pm

Saturday: 12pm-4pm

Sunday: 12pm-4pm, 6.30pm-9.30pm

Closed 25-26 December and 1 January

Prices

Meals: a la carte £ 20/32

Typical Dishes

Octopus & red wine risotto

Venison steak

Chocolate caramel tart

 ⊖ Archway 

29 The House

63-69 Canonbury Rd,
Canonbury N1 2DG
Tel.: (020)77047410 – Fax: (020)77049388
e-mail: info@inthehouse.biz **Website:** www.themeredithgroup.co.uk

Inspectors' favourites

 **Adnams**

The House is a coolly sophisticated pub, tucked away in a residential part of Islington. It effortlessly combines a laid back vibe at the bar, which adjoins a triangular shaped terrace at the front, with a more urbane atmosphere found in the nattily attired dining room. Just reading the menu provides evidence that The House has loftier culinary ambitions than many a gastropub. Indeed, a number of the kitchen's carefully composed dishes would not look out of place in restaurants sporting a higher brow and a more prosperous postcode. But it also remembers it is a pub so alongside dishes such as saddle of venison with pomegranate or sea bass with braised fennel you'll find the good old ploughman's lunch (although ploughmen are rarely seen in Islington these days) and Shepherd's Pie (ditto). Weekend breakfasts are proving a hit and are undertaken in conjunction with the local farmers' market. Check out their other pub in Highgate, The Bull.

Food serving times

Monday: 6pm-10.30pm

Tuesday-Friday:
12pm-2.30pm, 6pm-10.30pm

Saturday: 11am-3.30pm,
6pm-10.30pm

Sunday:
11am-4pm, 6.30pm-9.30pm

Closed Monday lunch

Prices

Meals: £ 18 (lunch)
and a la carte £ 26/35

Typical Dishes

Tomato Tartare

Char-grilled Angus rib of beef

Rhubarb & apple crumble

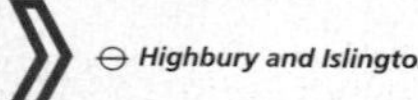

⊖ *Highbury and Islington*

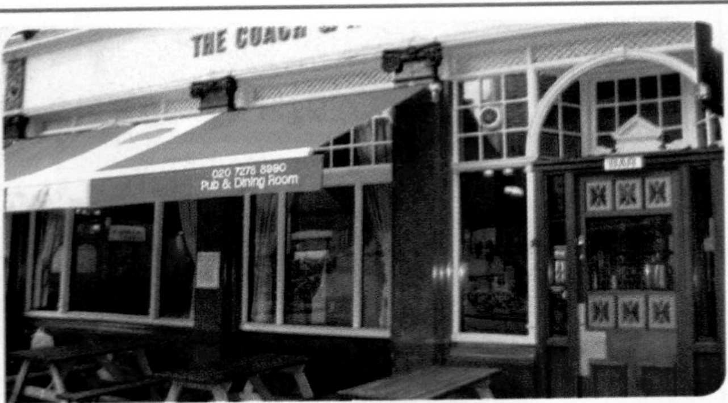

30 The Coach & Horses

26-28 Ray St,
Clerkenwell EC1R 3DJ
Tel.: (020)72788990 – Fax: (020)72781478
e-mail: info@thecoachandhorses.com **Website:** www.thecoachandhorses.com

   AE

 **Adnams Bitter, Fuller's London Pride, Timothy Taylor Landlord**

The Coach and Horses may be one of those pubs that has a palpable sense of its own Victorian heritage, with its original etched windows and panelling, but that doesn't mean it's not moving with the times. A recent refreshment of the dining room, with its tent-like ceiling and plush red walls filled with sketches and lithographs, has turned it into a very pleasant environment. Here, the near-daily changing menu is a reflection of the self-taught chef's enthusiasm for all things European, especially its sunnier Mediterranean parts. There are Spanish and Italian influences aplenty, with everything from osso bucco to polenta, chorizo to chilled soups. But our own British contribution to cuisine is not forgotten, especially in the bar where the appealing list of snacks includes Scotch eggs with mustard - surely a near perfect accompaniment to a pint. Any summer warmth provokes a stampede for the enclosed decked yard.

Food serving times

Monday-Friday:
12pm-3pm, 6pm-10pm

Saturday: 6pm-10pm

Sunday: 12pm-3pm

Closed Christmas to New Year, Easter weekend, Bank Holidays

Prices

Meals: a la carte £ 22/28

Typical Dishes

Roast field mushrooms
Morcilla Iberico
Mulled wine pear

⊖ Farringdon. Parking meters across the road.

31 The Peasant

240 St John St,
Finsbury EC1V 4PH

Tel.: (020)73367726 – Fax: (020)74901089
e-mail: gapsbairs@aol.com **Website:** www.thepeasant.co.uk

  AE

Wells Bombardier, Crouch Vale Brewers Gold, Elgoods Black Dog, Adnams Southwold Bitter

Originally called the George & Dragon, it changed to The Peasant to celebrate Wat Tyler's revolting ones of 1381 who gathered near this spot. However, what really made the name of this classic Victorian pub was its being in the vanguard of the original gastro-pub movement. To its lasting credit, the place retains a traditional pub feel, thanks largely to the busy ground floor bar, with its tiles, arched windows, high ceiling and mosaics. This is a great place for some heartening fare, from sausage and mash to plates of charcuterie or meze, to go with your beer. Upstairs, it's more your proper restaurant experience; it's quite formally laid out, with decoration courtesy of a fairground/circus theme. The huge windows still let in plenty of light but the noise levels are just a little more subdued. Here, you'll find a degree of originality in the cooking, but the kitchen is at its best when it keeps things relatively simple.

Food serving times

Monday-Sunday:
12pm-3pm, 5.30pm-11pm

Closed 25 December to 3 January

Booking essential

Prices

Meals: a la carte £ 25/40

Typical Dishes
Poached scallops
Roast pollock
Bread & butter pudding

⊖ Farringdon

32 The Well

180 St John St,
Finsbury EC1V 4JY
Tel.: (020)72519363 – Fax: (020)72539683
e-mail: drink@downthewell.co.uk **Website:** www.downthewell.co.uk

 VISA MC AE D

Speckled Hen (bottled)

Finsbury locals may not glance twice as they pass this predictable looking pub-on-a-corner in a trendy part of St John Street not unacquainted with food-and-drink destinations. But regulars in The Well know they're on to a good thing here. Big blue canopies hang out over the pavement providing shelter for drinkers at al fresco benches next to slide-open screen windows. Inside, it's small, busy and buzzing: all around is the ambience of the metropolitan gastropub with wooden floorboards, exposed brickwork and mismatched wood furniture. It's the food that lifts it above the average, with everything from the "pie of the week" to sophisticated, accomplished dishes in the modern British vein: all the fish and shellfish is from Billingsgate down the road. Downstairs a sexy lounge with fish tanks and brown sofas draws a more louche crowd.

Food serving times
Monday-Sunday:
12pm-3pm, 6pm-10.30pm
Closed 25-26 December

Prices
Meals: a la carte £ 23/30

Typical Dishes
Crispy lamb belly
Pork belly
Chocolate fondant

⊖ Farringdon NCP in Clerkenwell Rd; free parking after 6.30pm in street outside.

33 The Barnsbury

209-211 Liverpool Rd,
Islington N1 1LX
Tel.: (020)76075519 – Fax: (020)76073256
e-mail: info@thebarnsbury.co.uk **Website:** www.thebarnsbury.co.uk

Timothy Taylor Landlord, Fuller's London Pride and 1 monthly changing guest beer

It may have been spruced up a few years back but The Barnsbury is still your proper local. Hence, you'll find it on down-to-earth Liverpool Road rather than glossier Upper Street which runs parallel. The more traditional features of restored wood panelling and a large central counter contrast with contemporary touches, such as the chandeliers made from crystal wine glasses and the regularly changing local artwork. It's all very relaxed and the young staff helpful and competent. The owner, an acolyte of the Conran empire, clearly knows what he is doing. The menu will satisfy the appetites of both those who like to see recognisable British ingredients, as well as diners who prefer to see European influences on the plate. You'll find plenty of pasta, some Spanish charcuterie, Greek salads and cheeses from feta to Roquefort. British and Italian favourites feature in the desserts which come in man-size portions.

Food serving times

Monday-Sunday:
12pm-3pm, 6.30pm-10pm

Closed 25-26 December, 1 January

Prices

Meals: a la carte £ 35/45

 ⊖ *Highbury and Islington* 

34 The Drapers Arms

44 Barnsbury St,
Islington N1 1ER

Tel.: (020)76190348 – Fax: (020)76190413
e-mail: info@thedrapersarms.co.uk **Website:** www.thedrapersarms.co.uk

Adnams Explorer, Fuller's London Pride and guest ales: Beacon, Dizzy Blonde, Greene King IPA

This battleship grey pub in an oasis of leafy residential splendour must be good, because all the access streets have speed humps. Its secret appears to be in its sincerity – with its wood floors, old style furniture and huge windows; it just feels like a proper pub, albeit one with decent food. Granted, there's a more formal dining room upstairs, but the same menu is served throughout so stay downstairs for the banter in the bar, decorated with assorted drapery-themed photos. Dishes are either British in their frankness or Mediterranean in their inclination, so choose between chips and couscous, steak and risotto, and Eton mess and crème brûlée. The catch of the day can be three different fish, flavours are pronounced and natural, and dishes are heartening in their lack of pretension. There's an enclosed terrace out the back for bright spells, service is polite and friendly, and the atmosphere is lively yet relaxed.

Food serving times

Tuesday-Saturday:
12pm-3pm, 7pm-10.30pm

Sunday-Monday:
12pm-3pm, 7pm-10pm
(meals in bar only)

Closed 24-27 December,

Prices

Meals: a la carte £ 22/28

Typical Dishes

Chilled white gazpacho
Seared yellow fin tuna
Chocolate tart

⊖ *Highbury and Islington*

35 The Northgate

113 Southgate Rd,
Islington N1 3JS
Tel.: (020)73597392 – Fax: (020)73597393
e-mail: thenorthgate@hotmail.co.uk

 **Deuchars IPA and guest beers such as Fuller's London Pride**

The Northgate is a large, square Victorian pub located on a corner of, rather confusingly, Southgate Road. It may look fairly unremarkable from the outside but this was one of the first of many Islington pubs to blossom into a gastro variety. However, there remains an honesty about this place which engenders a relaxed and welcoming vibe, even when it is full-on busy - which appears to be most evenings. The front section comes decked out with the gastropub uniform of mismatched furniture and modern art, with a large central bar. There's a separate dining room at the back with a skylight and the terrace is a big draw when the sun has got his hat on. From the blackboard menu comes liberally sized plates of satisfying wholesome gastropub staples mixed with others of more ambitious provenance. Care is taken to correspond with the seasons, fish is handled particularly dextrously and all appetites are guaranteed to be sated.

Food serving times
Monday: 6.30pm-10.30pm
Tuesday-Sunday:
12pm-3pm, 6.30pm-10.30pm

Prices
Meals: a la carte £ 20/30

Typical Dishes
Pan-fried tiger prawns
Herb-battered pork fillet
Hot chocolate fondant

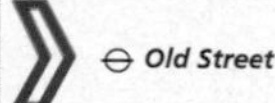
⊖ *Old Street*

36 The Admiral Codrington

17 Mossop St, Chelsea SW3 2LY
Tel.: (020)75810005 – Fax: (020)75892452
e-mail: admiral-codrington@333holdingsltd.com
Website: www.theadmiralcodrington.com

 **Black Sheep, Spitfire**

The personnel running the place may change occasionally but the local reputation of "The Cod" remains largely unaltered. Lunch can be had in the bar or the restaurant but in the evenings the locals descend and drinkers rule, so the serving of food is restricted to the dining room. This in turn becomes something of a haven of relative peace (which presumably explains the curious appearance of a cover charge). The retractable roof remains an appealing feature as does the booth seating for larger parties. The perennial favourites are never removed from the menu, like the crispy squid and fishcakes, and it's generally a pleasing mix of British and European classics, from fish pie to veal Holstein via assorted pasta dishes and a fish of the day. The kitchen appears well-drilled and organised. The private dining room upstairs is dedicated to Mac, the cartoonist, whose work adorns the walls and they've tidied up the small terrace at the side.

Food serving times

Moday-Friday:
12pm-2.30pm, 6.30pm-11pm

Saturday:
12pm-3pm, 6.30pm-11pm

Sunday:
12pm-4pm, 7pm-10pm

Closed 24-27 December

Prices

Meals: a la carte £ 25/32

Typical Dishes

Crispy squid
Roast rump of spring lamb
Pear tarte Tatin

 ⊖ *South Kensington* 

37 Builders Arms

13 Britten St,
Chelsea SW3 3TY
Tel.: (020)73499040
e-mail: buildersarms@geronimo-inns.co.uk **Website:** www.geronimo-inns.co.uk

  AE

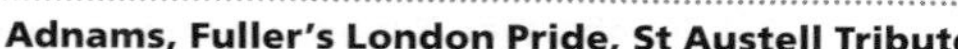
Adnams, Fuller's London Pride, St Austell Tribute

Discreetly tucked away in a residential area of Chelsea, it can be hard to park near The Builders Arms before 6.30 p.m., by which time the bar is packed to bursting with well-heeled locals. It's advisable to arrive early for dinner, anyway, since they don't take bookings; and orders are only taken at 7.15 p.m. on the dot, at which point the service swings into action like a minor military operation. Once you understand all of these unwritten rules, however, you'll find service polite and helpful. Beyond the bar, swarms congregate noisily on sofas, while diners tend to head for the stripped pine tables on the other side. Slightly less frenetic is the glass-roofed area at the back. Food here mixes gutsy, classic pub food with contemporary European dishes, and pies and fish and chips sit happily on the menu alongside salt and pepper squid with chilli dip, or steak with marrow.

Food serving times

Monday-Wednesday:
11am-11pm

Thursday-Saturday:
11am-12 midnight

Sunday: 12pm-10.30pm

Closed 25-26 December

Bookings not accepted

Prices

Meals: a la carte £ 20/35

Typical Dishes

Seared scallops
Pan-fried veal chop
Apple & rhubarb pie

⊖ South Kensington

38 Chelsea Ram

32 Burnaby St,
Chelsea SW10 0PL
Tel.: (020)73514008
e-mail: bookings@chelsearam.co.uk

 **Bombardier, Youngs, Youngs Special**

This stalwart of the London dining scene remains as popular as ever; book or arrive early for lunch as they only have 17 tables and they get snapped up quickly, particularly the two by the fire. There's full table service and whilst it all chills out a little at dinner, timings from the kitchen are generally spot-on. "Comforting classics" and "honest home-cooking" is how the chef describes his food; home-made soup comes with crusty bread, lamb chops with bubble and squeak, sausages with mash and rib-eye with dauphinoise potatoes; there are also pies and casseroles and even some mean snacks to accompany a pint. To finish, you can get a proper pudding, not a dessert, and these could include sticky banana or a crumble. The wine list is on the back of the menu and offers over 20 wines by the glass. If that isn't enough for a pub, they hold a quiz night on the first Monday of each month. All in all, they appear to have cracked the formula.

Food serving times
Monday-Saturday:
12pm-3pm, 7pm-10pm
Sunday:
12pm-4.30pm, 7pm-9pm

Prices
Meals: a la carte £ 20/27

Typical Dishes
Smoked duck breast
Smoked haddock & cod fishcakes
Bramley apple & rhubarb crumble

⊖ Gloucester Road

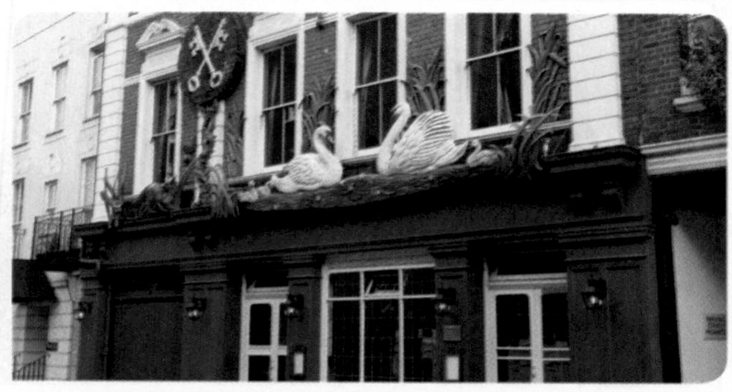

39 The Cross Keys

1 Lawrence St,
Chelsea SW3 5NB
Tel.: (020)73499111 – Fax: (020)73499333
e-mail: xkeys.nicole@hotmail.co.uk **Website:** www.thexkeys.net

   AE

 **Courage Best, Directors**

The clue is in the façade. This may be a pub with a history dating back well over 200 years, but the interior owes more to today's sense of irony and fun. The bar offers plenty of elbow room and its own menu but, beyond, one finds the glass roofed dining room. This is the centre of things and comes complete with little statues, its own tree and an eye-catching frieze of garden implements. The kitchen is more conventional in its approach that the surroundings would suggest, with food that is modern in style but robust in flavour and influences are kept largely within old Europe. So expect to find alluring sounding dishes like smoked duck with glazed figs, wild mushroom tart with pesto, lamb cutlets, coq au vin and poached pear in red wine. There are also blackboard specials to supplement the menus. The two private dining areas, in the gallery above the bar and on the top floor, come with their own eccentric touches.

Food serving times
Monday-Friday:
12pm-2.30pm, 6pm-11pm
Saturday-Sunday:
12pm-4pm, 6pm-10pm
Closed 24-25 December,
1 January, Bank Holidays

Prices
Meals: a la carte £ 25/30

Typical Dishes
Foie gras with toasted brioche
Organic breast of chicken
Crème brûlée

⊖ South Kensington Parking in Oakley Street or in Battersea Park / Albert Bridge car park.

40 Lots Road Pub & Dining Room

114 Lots Rd,
Chelsea SW10 0RJ
Tel.: (020)73526645 – Fax: (020)73764975
e-mail: lotsroad@foodandfuel.co.uk **Website:** www.lotsroadpub.com

VISA MC AE

Fuller's London Pride, Adnams, Hook Norton, Charles Wells Bombardier

If you make a decision not to pay a visit to this place based on the premise that the more people you can see through the windows, the better the pub, you'll be making a grave mistake. The high windows of this corner building give the impression that it is empty; in reality, the reverse is true. The local thirty and fortysomethings who frequent it might prefer you to think otherwise, however; that way they could keep it for themselves. What keeps them coming back time and again are the earthy pub dishes such as tasty hamburgers, lamb shanks and belly pork offered on a daily-changing menu, plus the heart-warming puddings just like Mamma used to make. The sign reads, "You haven't lived until you've tried our sticky toffee pud," and its popularity bears witness. Diligent and friendly young staff stay on the move between table and open kitchen. Thursday evenings see regular wine tastings, with bar snacks laid on.

Food serving times
Monday-Saturday:
10am-4pm, 6pm-10pm

Prices
Meals: a la carte £ 20/26

Typical Dishes
Chicken liver parfait
Cumberland sausages
Sticky toffee pudding

⊖ *Fulham Broadway*

41 The Phoenix

23 Smith St,
Chelsea SW3 4EE
Tel.: (020)77309182
e-mail: thephoenix@geronimo-inns.co.uk **Website:** www.geronimo-inns.co.uk

 VISA MC AE

 **Adnams, Fuller's London Pride**

The Phoenix may be part of an ever-expanding group of pubs but you'd never know it. It's a rather chic little number, close enough to the King's Road to be a useful pit-stop but also something of a local destination. The largest part of the pub is taken over by those very civilised locals, relaxing in the squashy sofas, enjoying a Welsh rarebit with their drinks. But work your way through to the back and you'll find the dining room, refurbished in 2008, where the murmur from the bar reminds you that you're still in a pub. Their aim is to provide pub food that's fairly priced, seasonal and, most importantly, tasty, whether that's eggs Benedict, Portland crab on toast or steak and hand-cut chips which arrive in sweet enamel pie dishes. The specials on the blackboard are precisely that and get quickly snapped up. St.George's day is proudly celebrated, there's the occasional oyster festival and regular wine and cider promotions.

Food serving times
Monday-Sunday:
12pm-2.45pm, 7pm-10pm
Closed 25-26 December

Prices
Meals: a la carte £ 15/25

Typical Dishes
Brown Portland crab
Clam & tiger prawn salad
Key lime pie

⊖ Sloane Square. Parking meters.

42 The Pig's Ear

35 Old Church St,
Chelsea SW3 5BS

Tel.: (020)73522908 – Fax: (020)73529321
e-mail: thepigsear@hotmail.co.uk **Website:** www.thepigsear.co.uk

   AE

 **Walley Pig's Ear, Old Speckled Hen**

There's a timeless feel to this relaxed, foodie pub off the King's Road and the selection of board games and newspapers make it the perfect location to while away a weekend hour or three. The owners' love of cinema and music is evident in the plethora of posters and photos, a jug of Bloody Mary takes pride of place on the bar and bottles of Bréton cider are proudly served alongside the beers and wines. It can feel as if the whole of Chelsea has come out to play downstairs, so book ahead to eat in the romantic panelled dining room, or alternatively, ask if you can commandeer the Blue Room – a cosy, curtained off area with a real fire. The menu is modern British meets the Mediterranean, with dishes like beef marrow, lamb stew and dumplings, or Cornish crab Thermidor. Charcuterie is a firm staple, there's the odd steak tartare for good measure and the splendid bread comes from The Flour Station in Battersea.

Food serving times

Monday-Sunday:
12.30pm-3.30pm,
7.30pm-11pm

Closed 10 days Christmas to New Year

A la carte menu Saturday-Sunday only

Prices

Meals: a la carte £ 30/50

Typical Dishes

Marinated herring
Haddock & octopus stew
Apple granita

⊖ *Sloane Square.*
(25 mins. on foot).

43 Swag and Tails

10-11 Fairholt St,
Knightsbridge, Chelsea SW7 1EG
Tel.: (020)75846926 – Fax: (020)75819935
e-mail: theswag@swagandtails.com **Website:** www.swagandtails.com

Adnams, Charles Wells Bombardier

The Swag and Tails is found in a quiet mews close to Harrods and is one of the prettier pubs around, with its charming display of hanging baskets. It is also one that has that welcoming atmosphere which comes from being privately owned. At the front you'll find the bar, with a log fire, panelling and those swaged and tailed drapes, while the dining area is at the rear with a conservatory extension. The kitchen clearly knows its customers and gives them a balanced selection, combining modern, Mediterranean-influenced cooking while still satisfying those who just want a decent steak sandwich. There's also a degree of sophistication in that the liver comes with pancetta and the duck is accompanied by pistachios; they also throw in the occasional Asian twist in the form of duck pancakes or spring rolls. Plates of charcuterie or Caesar salads are there for those with lighter appetites. Most of the wine comes in around £20 a bottle.

Food serving times
Monday-Friday:
12pm-3pm, 6pm-10pm
Closed Christmas-New Year, Bank Holidays, weekends

Prices
Meals: a la carte £ 22/32

Typical Dishes
Pan-seared foie gras
Slow-roasted pork belly
Belgian chocolate pot

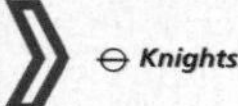

⊖ *Knightsbridge*

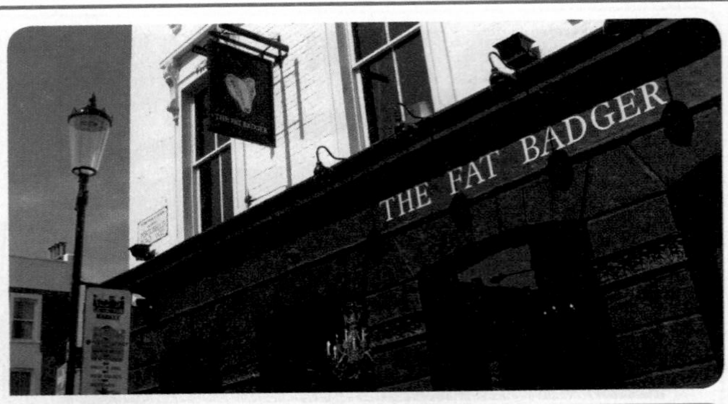

44 The Fat Badger

310 Portobello Road,
North Kensington W10 5TA

Tel.: (020)89694500 – Fax: (020)89696714

e-mail: rupert@thefatbadger.com **Website:** www.thefatbadger.com

  VISA MC AE

Timothy Taylor Landlord, Greene King IPA

There's an inevitability about pubs around Portobello Road getting the full makeover treatment and, sure enough, The Fat Badger – named after one of the owner's with a stripy barnet – is the new moniker for that old haunt, The Caernarvon Castle. It appears to be the usual set-up inside with old sofas, church seats and wood floors but those chandeliers and that intriguing wallpaper hint at something different. Sure enough, one glance at the menu reveals that there is nothing gastropub-formulaic about the cooking. The chef's philosophy is British and seasonal, with a waste-not-want-not approach to butchery. Whole beasts are delivered to the kitchen and they are not afraid of offering unfamiliar cuts; the menu is constantly changing to reflect what the suppliers deem worthy and vegetables reflect what's in season. This is real and earthy cooking. Breakfast and brunch menus also reveal that this is a kitchen with imagination and integrity.

Food serving times

Monday-Friday:
12pm-3pm, 6.30pm-10pm

Saturday:
11am-5pm, 6.30pm-10.30pm

Sunday:
12pm-5pm, 6.30pm-9pm

Closed 25-26 December

Prices

Meals: £ 15 and a la carte £ 30/50

Typical Dishes

Globe artichoke & goats cheese

Grilled bavette

Poached white pear

⊖ Ladbroke Grove. Parking meters in street; free parking after 6.30pm.

45 The Rosendale

65 Rosendale Rd,
West Dulwich SE21 8EZ
Tel.: (020)86700812 – Fax: (020)86719008
e-mail: dine@therosendale.co.uk **Website:** www.therosendale.co.uk

Inspectors' favourites

 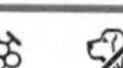   MC

 **Spitfire, Fuller's London Pride**

Included among the many things that stand out about The Rosendale are that they make their own butter, as well as their own bread, and have a wine list that is remarkable in its breadth, depth and affordability. This vast former coaching inn dates from the 1820s and has a soaring ceiling and plenty of original features. There are two menus – stay in the front bar for a grill menu with your more typical pub food or go through to the dining room at the back to find dishes of a more ambitious nature. Here this can mean that what appears on the plate is quite complicated but there is no denying the quality of the ingredients and sourcing is clearly taken seriously. Fish is delivered daily from Cornwall; farms are given name checks; they hang their own meat and smoke their own fish. This is a well run pub with a great atmosphere - there may not be many things worth enduring the South Circular for, but The Rosendale is one of them.

Food serving times

Monday:
12pm-10pm (bar grill only)

Tuesday-Friday: 12pm-10pm (bar grill only), 7pm-10pm

Saturday:
12pm-3pm, 7pm-10pm

Sunday: 12pm-4pm

Closed 1 January

Prices

Meals: £ 20 (lunch) and a la carte £ 20/28

Typical Dishes
British veal ragout
Ostrich fillet
Opera cake

 ⊖ *West Dulwich (rail)* 

The Dartmouth Arms

46 The Dartmouth Arms

7 Dartmouth Road,
Forest Hill SE23 3HN

Tel.: (020)84883117 – Fax: (020)77717230

e-mail: info@thedartmoutharms.com **Website:** www.thedartmoutharms.com

Fuller's London Pride, Charles Wells Bombardier, Brakspears

The Dartmouth Arms' position opposite Forest Hill train station meant that this was once the sort of pub whose main selling point was as somewhere to dive into for a swift one on the way home. Since its makeover in 2004 it is now the sort of place in which to spend the evening. The original double doors now open into a friendly environment with art for sale on the walls, the usual hotchpotch of furniture and an open plan kitchen. The couple running the show know what their customers want and the menu offers an appealing mix of dishes from the single sheet of A4. Many have more of a restaurant pedigree than your average pub grub but there's commendable Britishness in evidence here, as well as a healthy regard for seasonality. So expect to see Barnsley chops, asparagus, samphire and Jersey Royals at certain times. There's also some invention so you'll find the black pudding in a risotto and crab in beignets with chilli jam.

Food serving times

Monday-Saturday:
12pm-3.30pm, 6.30pm-10pm

Sunday: 12pm-9pm

Closed 25-26 December,
1 January

Prices

Meals: £ 15/18
and a la carte £ 23/31

Typical Dishes

Squid & black pudding
Shank of lamb
Apple & plum crumble

 ⊖ *Forest Hill (rail) Parking.* 

47 The Fire Stables

27-29 Church Rd,
Wimbledon SW19 5DQ
Tel.: (020)89463197 – Fax: (020)89461101
e-mail: thefirestables@youngs.co.uk **Website:** www.firestableswimbledon.co.uk

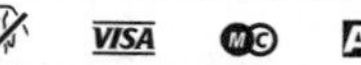

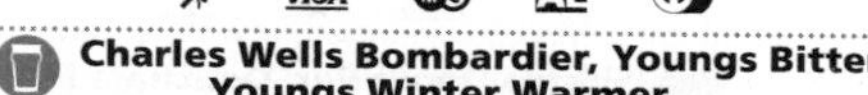

Charles Wells Bombardier, Youngs Bitter, Youngs Winter Warmer

"Gastropub" is a somewhat nebulous term to describe anywhere serving decent food in fairly casual surroundings and The Fire Stables proves that not all gastropubs were once old boozers. This may have originally been where the horses to pull the old fire engines were stabled but nowadays it calls itself a "pub and dining room" and is modish in style without being threateningly trendy. It is also the nearest place to eat when leaving the well-known local tennis courts. Whatever it is, it seems to work. You'll find a separate bar area with its own snackier menu and a long dining room at the back overlooking the garden. Lunch times appear popular with mothers with young children, while noise levels become more boisterously adult in the evenings. The menu covers all bases, from Caesar salads and burgers to more adventurous choices such as game in season and rack of lamb. Puddings are full-bodied and satisfying.

Food serving times
Monday-Sunday:
12pm-4pm, 6pm-10.30pm
Set price dinner Sunday only

Prices
Meals: £ 16/25
and a la carte £ 20/30

Typical Dishes
Chicken liver parfait
Rack of Lamb
Panacotta
with berry compote

⊖ Wimbledon

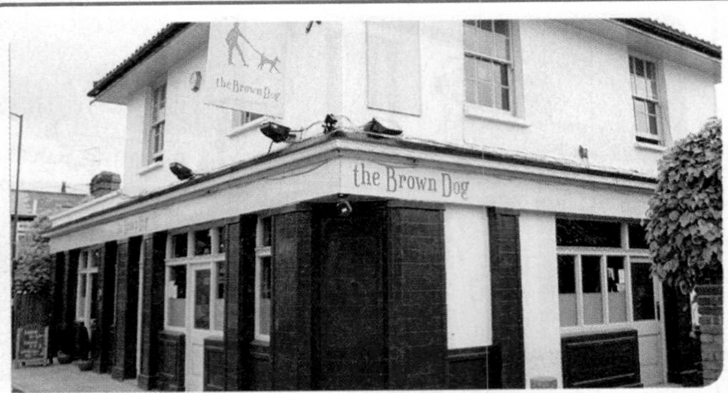

48 The Brown Dog

28 Cross Street,
Barnes SW13 0AP
Tel.: (020)83922200 – Fax: (020)83922200
Website: www.thebrowndog.co.uk

 VISA  AE

Sharps Doom Bar, Deuchars IPA

Tucked away down a veritable labyrinth of residential streets, you almost feel you might need a ball of string to help you find your way back from The Brown Dog, and are unlikely to stumble across it in passing. Locals should count themselves lucky. Décor is charmingly stylish with cast iron fireplaces and antique furniture, eclectic artwork, and bulbous space age lamps. Set around a horseshoe bar, seating is split into snug lounge and separate dining area, and a relaxed atmosphere reigns. The daily-changing, seasonal menu takes a modern slant on traditional dishes and, although concise, is well-balanced. Good value food is popular in these parts, so make sure you book in advance; and if you're driving, factor in some time to park. Why the Brown Dog? Well, when a Geordie claims, "I'm taking the dog for a walk," what he really means is, "I'm off down the pub for a bottle of Newcastle Brown Ale." And not a lot of people know that.

Food serving times

Monday-Sunday:
12pm-4pm, 7pm-10pm

Closed 25-26 December, 1 January

Prices

Meals: a la carte £ 22/33

Typical Dishes

Duck confit salad
Goats cheese & herb polenta
Mango tarte Tatin

⊖ *Barnes Bridge (rail)*

49 The Garrison

99-101 Bermondsey St,
Bermondsey SE1 3XB
Tel.: (020)70899355
e-mail: info@thegarrison.co.uk **Website:** www.thegarrison.co.uk

 **Adnams, Franziskaner, St Peter's Ale**

Close to the owners' other place, Village East, sits this part shabby-chic gastropub, part boho brasserie. Bermondsey was an area known in the 19C for its food processing as well as its tanning and the blossoming number of eateries bears witness to its bourgeoning 21C rejuvenation. The pub's full of bustle and life and the ideal venue for meeting up with friends, especially if you can snare one of the booths. If you're an even bigger party then consider hiring the downstairs room which doubles as a mini cinema. There's a refreshing wholesomeness to the cooking; there are blackboard specials, everything's homemade except for the quince paste which comes with the cheese and the menu changes every eight weeks. Dishes display this no-nonsense approach by being full in flavour and decent in size, whether that's meatloaf with purple sprouting broccoli or smoked haddock with bubble and squeak. It's all fairly priced, as is the wine list.

Food serving times
Monday-Sunday:
8am-11am, 12pm-3pm,
6pm-10pm
Closed 25-26 December,
1 January

Prices
Meals: a la carte £ 28/45

Typical Dishes
Goats cheese salad
Orkney calves liver
Apple & cinnamon crumble

⊖ *London Bridge*

50 The Hartley

64 Tower Bridge Road,
Bermondsey SE1 4TR
Tel.: (020)73947023
e-mail: enquries@thehartley.com **Website:** www.thehartley.com

 **IPA, Spindrift**

Local competition in this part of town may be a little thin on the ground but The Hartley still makes a valiant effort in flying the local gastropub flag. This red-bricked Victorian pub is also doing its bit to remember the diminishing local heritage by honouring, in name and decoration, the Hartley Jam Factory which once stood opposite and is now, predictably, a residential development. There are original posters, black and white photos and even jars of jam scattered around the place. The cooking also has a certain zesty appeal. Appetite-satisfying is the order of the day, with a refreshingly concise menu supplemented by daily-changing blackboard specials. Terrines, fishcakes and pies sit happily alongside more adventurous pork belly or swordfish dishes. The wine list is also kept quite short but is also kept affordable, with an adequate choice available by the glass. Service is relaxed and cool headed.

Food serving times
Monday-Saturday:
12pm-3pm, 6pm-10pm
Sunday: 12pm-3pm
Closed 25-26 December and Bank Holidays

Prices
Meals: a la carte £ 20/27

Typical Dishes
Pan-fried sea scallops
Marinated lamb chop
Fruit of the forest cheesecake

⊖ Borough. On street parking (meters).

51 The Anchor & Hope

36 The Cut,
Southwark SE1 8LP
Tel.: (020)79289898 – Fax: (020)79284595
e-mail: anchorandhope@btconnect.com

Youngs Ordinary, Wells Bombardier and guest ales such as Brains SA

The Anchor & Hope is always and understandably busy, due to some degree to its proximity to both Vic theatres but mostly because of his culinary reputation. The fact that they don't take reservations means that it's worth getting here early - in fact very early – to secure a table although if you're willing to share you'll be seated sooner. The owners are of the sleeve-rolled-up school and take charge of the cooking, the delivery of the dishes and the serving of drinks. The general buzz creates a noisy but highly convivial atmosphere. From the tiny kitchen they produce immensely satisfying dishes, in a rustic and earthy style, drawing on influences from St John restaurant in Islington, but at prices which make the queuing worth it. Menu descriptions are understated but infinitely appealing: crab on toast, grilled razor clams, rare roast venison with duck fat potato cake, beef on dripping toast…

Food serving times

Monday: 6pm-10.30pm

Tuesday-Saturday, 12pm-2.30pm, 6pm-10.30pm

Sunday: 12pm-2pm

Closed 2 weeks at Christmas, Easter, May Bank Holidays, last 2 weeks in August

Prices

Meals: £ 30 and a la carte £ 20/35

Typical Dishes

Grilled razor clams
Shoulder of lamb
Buttermilk pudding

⊖ Southwark. Parking in The Cut after 6.30pm.

52 The Morgan Arms

43 Morgan St,
Bow E3 5AA
Tel.: (020)89806389
e-mail: themorgan@geronimo-inns.co.uk **Website:** www.geronimo-inns.co.uk

 **Adnams Best Bitter, Timothy Taylor Landlord**

Within the sound of the Bow Bells stands this Cockney gastro-rub-a-dub; far removed from its previous life as a spit and sawdust battlecruiser. Inside, it's now all informal, shabby chic, with Chesterfields and banquettes and warm rugs on the floor. Snacks are served in the bar, but it's often noisily busy with locals, builders, students and whistles all having a tiddly, so your best bet if you're eating is to head for a Cain and Abel in the dining room. Take a butchers at the concise but constantly evolving menu; food is robust and hearty and will certainly fill your Auntie Nelly. Some dishes contain unusual ingredients and a glossary of terms is helpfully provided on a blackboard. Get yer Hampsteads around some braised pigs cheeks, devilled whitebait or oxtail ravioli. It won't matter if you don't have much sausage and mash in your sky rocket; you'll find starters for under an Ayrton and main courses for less than a Dudley.

Food serving times

Monday-Saturday:
12pm-3pm, 7pm-10pm

Sunday: 12pm-4pm

Closed 24-26 December, 1 January

Bookings not accepted

Prices

Meals: a la carte £ 20/31

Typical Dishes

Devilled whitebait
Pork belly
Sticky toffee pudding

⊖ Bow Road. Before 6.30pm parking meters in Tredegar Square; after 6.30pm outside.

53 The Gun

27 Coldharbour,
Canary Wharf E14 9NS
Tel.: (020)75155222
e-mail: info@thegundocklands.com **Website:** www.thegundocklands.com

Fuller's London Pride, Adnams Broadside

Anyone interested in seeing London's past juxtaposed with the present should get down to The Gun. This thoughtfully restored 18C pub in a cobbled street has a long connection to the river and was where Lord Nelson conducted his trysts with Lady Emma Hamilton. But sit on the terrace or in the back with the locals and the views are of the O2 Arena. Renewal and revitalisation are also reflected in the food side: the concise menu is a balanced combination of European influenced dishes, prepared with a light yet assured touch. Fish is a key component of the blackboard daily specials and comes from Billingsgate, no further than a hefty cast away. Those side dishes can push up the final bill and there are plenty of temptations on the wine list but this is a pub for those who know their food. There are jazz nights on Sundays; news that will attract and repel in equal measure but bite the bullet and get down to The Gun.

Food serving times

Monday-Friday:
12pm-3pm, 6pm-10.30pm

Saturday-Sunday:
11.30am-4pm

Closed 25-26 December

Prices

Meals: a la carte £ 27/32

Typical Dishes

Croquette of chicken
Fillet of halibut
Pear tarte Tatin

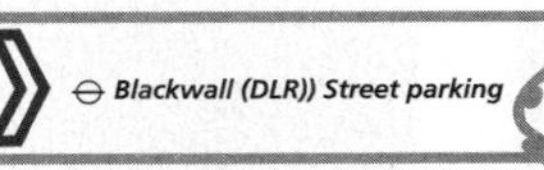

54 The Narrow

Narrow Street,
Limehouse E14 8DP
Tel.: (020)75927950 – Fax: (020)72659503
e-mail: thenarrow@gordonramsay.com **Website:** www.gordonramsay.com

Inspectors' favourites

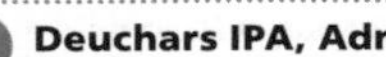 **Deuchars IPA, Adnams Explorer, Greene King Abbot Ale**

Gordon Ramsay's world or, at the very least, London domination, continued with his first foray into the world of the gastropub - and it appears he cracked it. For a start, he found a handsome pub in a grand spot: a Grade II listed former dockmaster's house on the river. He may have sympathetically restyled it, but this still feels like the genuine article, albeit one with seating in the main dining room for only 32, so getting a table is going to be the trickiest part. But the real skill and experience is there to see on the menu; expect British classics alongside dishes that will stir childhood memories for many. You'll find potted crabs, sardines on toast, salt beef, monkfish and chips; and proper puddings, not fancy desserts. As you would expect, the kitchen knows what it's doing, and what's more, the prices are competitive, although too many of the tempting but individually priced side dishes can push up the final bill.

Food serving times

Monday-Friday:
12pm-3pm, 6pm-11pm

Saturday-Sunday:
12pm-4pm, 5pm-11pm

Prices

Meals: a la carte £ 35/45

Typical Dishes

Chicken liver salad
Baked rainbow trout
Lemon & vanilla cheesecake

⊖ Limehouse (DLR) West side of inlet into Limehouse Basin. Parking.

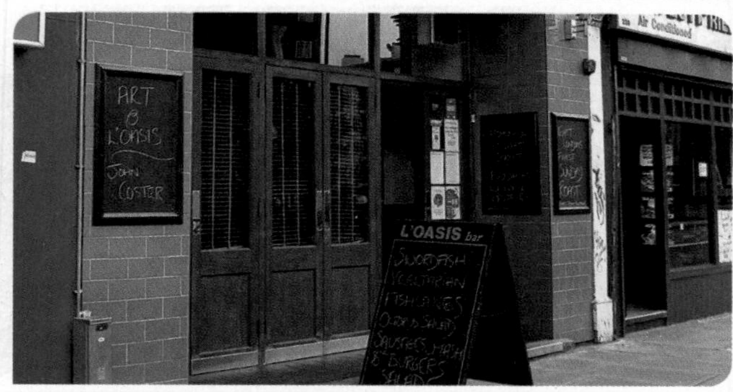

55 L'Oasis

237 Mile End Rd,
Mile End E1 4AA

Tel.: (020)77027051 – Fax: (020)72659850

e-mail: info@loasisstepney.co.uk **Website:** www.loasisstepney.co.uk

Timothy Taylor Landlord, Adnams

Fully confident in his chef's abilities, the owner of the-pub-formerly-known-as-The-Three-Crowns decided that the new name L'Oasis would perfectly reflect its role in the culinary desert that is Stepney Green. The question is: does this watering hole refresh the parts that others do not reach? The answer would have to be yes. Although it doesn't look much like a modern dining pub - more like a narrow bar with slightly dubious neighbours – the inside is cavernous and brightly lit, with wooden furniture and floors, and original features including a delightful ornamental Victorian ceiling and decorative glazed tiles. Upstairs, a bright yellow function room copes with any overflow, service is friendly and efficient and food delivery is prompt even when they are busy. Concise menus offer hearty, rustic cooking with influences from all over the world, and what dishes may lack in finesse, they more than make up for in flavour and size.

Food serving times

Monday-Sunday:
12pm-9.30pm

Closed public holidays

Prices

Meals: a la carte £ 20/33

Typical Dishes

Mezze tray
Cumberland sausage
Cranberry cheesecake

⊖ Stepney Green. Parking in main road and side street.

56 The Greyhound at Battersea

136 Battersea High St,
Battersea SW11 3JR

Tel.: (020)79787021 – Fax: (020)79780599

e-mail: eddie@savpubs.com **Website:** www.thegreyhoundatbattersea.co.uk

    AE

 **Abbot ales in bottles**

The neighbourhood may not have moved inexorably upwards as the owners imagined it would when they opened but The Greyhound still manages to attract plenty of punters, especially the ones who know their food. For this is anything but your average local - this is a real foodie pub, with prices to reflect the ambition and endeavour. The current chef is Italian and although there may be the odd ravioli or gnocchi dish, the menu stays true to the pub's philosophy of supporting artisanal producers and sourcing top quality meats like Herdwick Mutton, Black Pig pork and Galloway beef. Dishes come presented as straightforwardly as they are described and flavours are clean and distinct. The Aussie owner has also used his past experience as a sommelier to good effect: the wine list is interesting yet accessible and there are plenty of unfamiliar wines as well as a good selection by the glass. The pub itself has a contemporary yet welcoming feel.

Food serving times

Tuesday-Saturday:
12pm-3pm, 7pm-10pm

Sunday: 12pm-3pm

Closed 24 December to 1 January

Prices

Meals: £ 21 (lunch) and a la carte £ 21/33

Typical Dishes

Home smoked Alaskan salmon

Grilled Galloway beef

Sorbet & ice cream

⊖ Clapham Junction (rail) Parking in Simpson Street or Battersea High Street.

57 Prince of Wales

138 Upper Richmond Rd, Putney SW15 2SP

Tel.: (020)87881552 – Fax: (020)81800191

e-mail: info@princeofwalesputney.co.uk **Website:** www.princeofwalesputney.co.uk

 **Fuller's London Pride, Black Sheep, Aldestone Rider**

Those who decry the rise of the gastropub should have tried The Prince of Wales in its past: such was its reputation that it earned the nickname "The Prince of Darkness". Now it's a thoroughly civilised spot, thanks to its Scottish owner whose ambition was to create a "country pub in the city". The dining room at the back is the best place to sit as it has the feel of a billiard room in a Scottish Baronial hall complete with stuffed animals and deer antlers. This gives some clues as to the cooking: it is robust and British, with game featuring strongly. The kitchen tends to buy the whole beast so expect prime cuts, offal, then stews, pies, terrines and parfaits. There are often dishes for two such as cassoulet, a roast leg of venison or a beef and beer pie but those without the appetite of Desperate Dan will also find much that's appealing. As with all good pubs, it's part of the local community and Sunday night is quiz night.

Food serving times

Monday-Friday:
12pm-4pm, 6pm-10pm

Saturday-Sunday:
12pm-3pm, 6pm-10pm

Closed 25-26 December

Prices

Meals: a la carte £ 22/30

Typical Dishes

Rabbit & prune terrine
Braised ox cheek
Caramelised banana

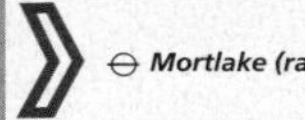

⊖ *Mortlake (rail)*

58 The Spencer Arms

237 Lower Richmond Road,
Putney SW15 1HJ

Tel.: (020)87880640 – Fax: (020)87882216

e-mail: info@thespencerarms.co.uk **Website:** www.thespencerarms.co.uk

 **Adnams Bitter, Adnams Broadside, Fuller's London Pride**

If you're not drinking, you can go for a stroll on adjacent Putney Common. If you're not strolling, you can take in the more sedentary charms of this attractive Victorian corner pub, which, on a warm day, offers visitors smart pavement seating and a pint of Fuller's London Pride. Inside, the dining pub transformation is total. Left of the main entrance is an enticing "library" area with leather sofas – lose yourself here amongst a plethora of books and games - a fireplace and plasma TV. Over the other side, the hungry are catered for in a rustic bar-cum-restaurant: scrubbed tables and mix-and-match chairs exert an old church/old school charm. Blackboard menus are concise - six starters, six mains, three puds the max - ranging from the likes of home-made soups to duck pie to Dundee cake with rhubarb compote… maybe the stroll should wait till this point.

Food serving times

Monday-Friday:
12pm-2.30pm, 6.30pm-10pm

Saturday:
12pm-3pm, 6.30pm-10pm

Sunday:
12pm-4pm, 6.30pm-10pm

Closed 25 December, 1 January

Prices

Meals: £ 24 (lunch) and a la carte £ 22/32

Typical Dishes

Guinea fowl terrine
Gressingham duck
Rice pudding

⊖ East Putney. Parking at top of Putney Common and in nearby streets.

59 Prince Alfred & Formosa Dining Room

5A Formosa St,
Bayswater and Maida Vale W9 1EE
Tel.: (020)72863287
e-mail: princealfred@youngs.co.uk **Website:** www.princealfred.co.uk

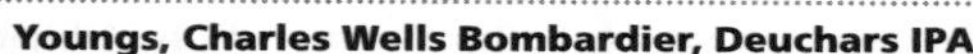

Youngs, Charles Wells Bombardier, Deuchars IPA

It is possible, if you're approaching from Warrington Crescent, to find yourself seated in the Formosa Dining Room and be virtually unaware of the pub to which it is attached. This would be a crying shame as the Prince Alfred is a magnificent Grade II listed pub which dates back to 1863. Its most striking feature, along with the etched glass, is the partitions creating individual private booths. Architectural purists may shudder at the more contemporary, almost semi-industrial, dining room which has been attached but local diners seemingly have little regard for such sensibilities and just enjoy the space. The very open open-kitchen produces satisfyingly robust gastro-pub staples of a mostly European nature. Typically, you could expect grilled sardines with rocket, followed by fillet of pork with apple and finished with a rich chocolate brownie. The wine list commendably features over thirty choices available by the glass.

Food serving times
Monday-Sunday:
12pm-3pm, 6.30pm-10pm

Prices
Meals: a la carte £ 23/33

Typical Dishes
Terrine of rabbit
Crispy pork belly
Sticky toffee pudding

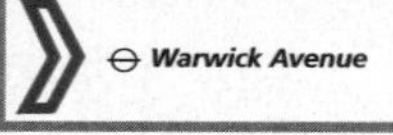

⊖ Warwick Avenue

60 The Warrington

93 Warrington Crescent,
Bayswater and Maida Vale W9 1EH
Tel.: (020)75927960 – Fax: (020)75921603
e-mail: thewarrington@gordonramsay.com **Website:** www.gordonramsay.com

   AE

Greene King IPA, Fuller's London Pride, Adnams Broadside and guest ale such as White Rabbit

Nothing upsets a community more than when their favourite pub gets a makeover and thereafter attracts interlopers from outlying postcodes. The cleverness of The Warrington, which dates from 1857, is that the Gordon Ramsay group have spent a few million on the place but the ground floor, with its art nouveau friezes, dark wood and pillars, retains its traditional flavour and remains the haunt of locals just in for a drink, a snack or a lunchtime pie. The main eating event is upstairs in the smarter but decidedly less characterful restaurant; you'd hardly know it was there as there are no signs. It is a bright room, with friendly staff who provide service that's smooth without being too ceremonial. The cooking also keeps things relatively simple and is a mix of British and French, with cullen skink or chicken and mushroom pie jostling for your attention with steak tartare or confit of duck. The wine prices are commendably competitive.

Food serving times

Monday-Thursday:
12pm-2.30pm, 6pm-10pm

Friday:
12pm-2.30pm, 6pm-10.30pm

Saturday:
12pm-4pm, 6pm-10.30pm

Sunday:
12pm-4pm, 6pm-10pm

Prices

Meals: a la carte £ 25/35

Typical Dishes

Sharpham spelt risotto
Devilled Cornish mackerel
Knickerbocker Glory

⊖ Maida Vale. Metered parking on Sutherland Avenue.

61 The Waterway

54 Formosa St,
Bayswater and Maida Vale W9 2JU
Tel.: (020)72663557 – Fax: (020)72663547
e-mail: info@thewaterway.co.uk **Website:** www.thewaterway.co.uk

 **HSB, Fuller's London Pride**

A glimpse of sun and we're all outside, so praise be for places like The Waterway. Not only does it have a large terrace but its pleasing vista takes in the canal, barges and the church spire beyond, although you have to be quick off the mark to get a spot. This is as far as from the spit and sawdust pub as it is possible to get. You'll have to fight through the throng of drinkers in the stylish bar to get through to the restaurant which is quite a swanky affair - all wood and leather, with the staff dressed all in black. The kitchen balances the tradition with the contemporary to the clear satisfaction of its customers. So, the "classics" section on the menu may include moules or burgers and there are barbecues and Sunday roasts but you'll also find more restaurant kind of dishes involving sea bass, belly pork or lamb. Puds are quite delicate little things and it's nice to see that cheese is taken seriously.

Food serving times

Monday-Friday:
12pm-3.30pm,
6.30pm-10.15pm

Saturday-Sunday:
12pm-4pm,
6.30pm-10.15pm

Prices

Meals: a la carte £ 30/40

Typical Dishes

Chorizo & black pudding
Chicken breast
Apple crumble

 ⊖ *Warwick Avenue*

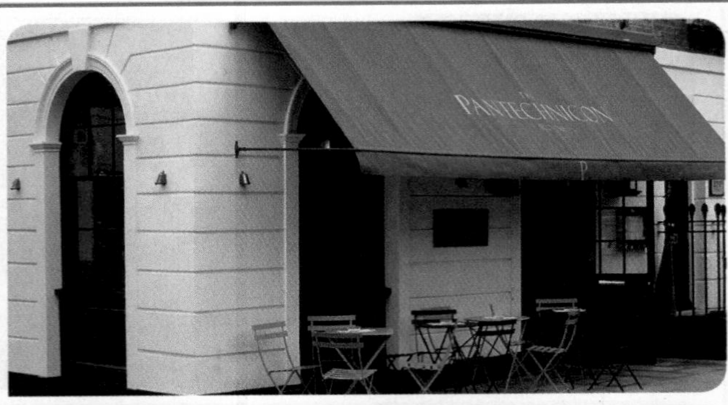

62 The Pantechnicon Rooms

10 Motcomb St,
Belgravia SW1X 8LA

Tel.: (020)77306074 – Fax: (020)77306055
e-mail: reservations@thepantechnicon.com **Website:** www.thepantechnicon.com

 **IPA, Deuchars**

It took the owners over a year to transform the distinctly unprepossessing Turks Head into this smart new pub to go with their other place nearby, The Thomas Cubitt. It's named after the art and antique repository that once graced Motcomb Street until it was destroyed by fire in 1874. A painting of that fire adorns the upstairs restaurant; this being Belgravia means the menu is a sophisticated number, with oysters, caviar and shellfish having their own sections and cocktails and champagne muscling in on the wine list. Downstairs, the menu gets tweaked slightly so that starters become "small plates" but otherwise there's little difference; influences are kept within Europe, the seafood is a strength and dishes come daintily presented. It's all very pleasant on a bright day, with light streaming in through the arched windows. The Pantechnicon and Motcomb Street look like the perfect match.

Food serving times
Monday-Friday:
12pm-11pm
Saturday-Sunday:
10am-10.30pm
Closed 25 December,
Good Friday

Prices
Meals: £ 25 (lunch)
and a la carte £ 25/50

Typical Dishes
Lobster salad
Pantechnicon fish fingers
Blueberry soufflé

 ⊖ *Knightsbridge* 

63 The Only Running Footman

5 Charles St.,
Mayfair W1J 5DF
Tel.: (020)74992988 – Fax: (020)74918162
e-mail: info@therunningfootman.biz **Website:** www.therunningfootman.biz

 **Fuller's London Pride, Charles Wells Bombardier, Youngs**

Anyone who despairs about pubs serving Thai curry should head to this charming, historic pub which re-opened in 2007 under the ownership of the group who gave us The Bull in Highgate and The House in Islington. The Union flag flying outside tells you everything about their attitude, for here our very own culinary heritage is celebrated. The ground floor is small, atmospheric and always packed – it's first-come-first-served. Here the menu really hits the bullseye: who can resist a richly satisfying Omelette Arnold Bennett for breakfast, potted shrimps for lunch or some beer-battered haddock for dinner? You can even order a sausage sarnie to take away. Upstairs you can book and it's all rather plush in comparison; the menu is more ambitious and the prices also a little loftier. You do get to order the rib of beef for two; otherwise you may just wish you were downstairs with a pork pie and piccalilli.

Food serving times
Monday-Sunday:
12pm-10.30pm

Prices
Meals: a la carte £ 29/39

Typical Dishes
Smoked eel & asparagus paté
Fish & chips
Sticky toffee pudding

 ⊖ *Green Park* 

64 Queen's Head & Artichoke

30-32 Albany St,
Regent's Park and Marylebone NW1 4EA
Tel.: (020)79166206
e-mail: info@theartichoke.net **Website:** www.theartichoke.net

VISA MC AE

 **Adnams, Marston Pedigree**

The location may be just about spot-on: bordering the park to catch the strollers and close enough to the Euston Road to get the office bods. The formula too looks like it hits the spot: modern European influenced food mixed with a large selection of "tapas" in its loosest form. Either way, the place is always jumping, with the restaurant in an upstairs room decorated in a whimsical non-theme. The pub's history includes time as a royal hunting lodge, demolition and relocation but the licence can be traced back to good Queen Bess and apparently she loved a bit of artichoke. Today's customers can all enjoy completely differing culinary experiences. One might be having pâté followed by roast lamb while their partner has chicken satay followed by red duck curry. Tapas is the nebulous term for a huge and appealing mix of small dishes where the influences take in North Africa, the Middle East as well as Europe and is offered all day.

Food serving times

Monday-Sunday:
12.30pm-3pm,
6.30pm-10.15pm

Closed 24 December-
2 January

Prices

Meals: a la carte £ 19/25

Typical Dishes

Brie tart
Grilled mackerel
Tunisian citrus cake

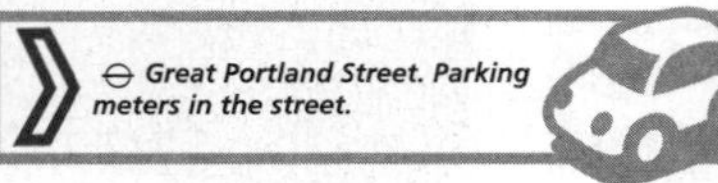
⊖ Great Portland Street. Parking meters in the street.

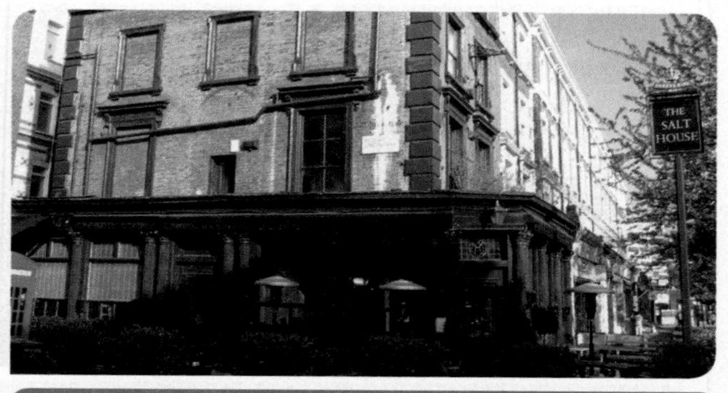

65 The Salt House

63 Abbey Road,
St John's Wood, Regent's Park and Marylebone NW8 0AE
Tel.: (020)73286626
e-mail: salthousemail@majol.co.uk **Website:** www.thesalthouse.co.uk

 **Abbot Ale, IPA**

First it was The Salt House, then The Abbey Road, then it changed back again to The Salt House. But whatever the name it has remained a reliable and inviting neighbourhood pub, with cooking that has a sunny, country feel and comes in man-size portions. The dining room's a few steps down from the bar, where the large picture windows overlook the pleasant semi-enclosed outside terrace and its style is of the relaxed, higgledy-piggledy school, with posters and lamps; some tables are dressed with tablecloths, others are nude. There's an upstairs for the weekend overflow and a snackier menu available in the bar. The bill can tot up without you noticing but there's plenty of interest in the menu, whether that's the sea bass cartoccio, the rack of lamb with sweet potatoes or the top-notch quality Scottish beef. There are always assorted pasta dishes available and more unusual offerings like rabbit casserole or honey-glazed poussin.

Food serving times
Monday-Sunday:
12pm-10.30pm

Prices
Meals: a la carte £ 20/36

Typical Dishes
3 Falmouth oysters
Salt marsh lamb
Home-made tiramisu

⊖ St John's Wood. Parking meters.

66 The Ebury

11 Pimlico Rd,
Victoria SW1W 8NA
Tel.: (020)77306784 – Fax: (020)77306149
e-mail: info@theebury.co.uk **Website:** www.theebury.co.uk

  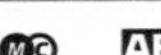

 **Fuller's London Pride**

The Ebury has become an established feature in this part of town and has done so by successfully offering both satisfyingly hearty food and by providing its customers with the choice of two different dining options. On the ground floor one finds the busy and lively brasserie/pub with floor to ceiling windows and a thrusting young crowd, with a bar that is equally adept at satisfying their demands. Ascend the oak staircase and you come upon altogether more tranquil and restful surroundings, where the added formality and pretty decorative touches help create a very soothing ambience. There's a crustacean bar, ideal for those who wish to share their food, while the main menu reads like a manifesto for modern European cooking: there's everything from foie gras, pork belly and rump of lamb to other less artery-bothering offerings like roast cod with Puy lentils and guinea fowl with root vegetables. Desserts will be hard to resist.

Food serving times

Monday-Saturday:
12pm-3.30pm,
6pm-10.30pm

Sunday:
12pm-4pm, 6pm-10pm

Closed 25 December

Prices

Meals: £ 20 (lunch)
and a la carte £ 30/45

Typical Dishes

Confit of rabbit shoulder

Roast cod with brandade

Sautéed cherry pancake

⊖ Sloane Square. On street parking after 6.30pm.

67 The Thomas Cubitt

44 Elizabeth Street,
Victoria SW1W 9PA
Tel.: (020)77306060 – Fax: (020)77306055
e-mail: reservations@thethomascubitt.co.uk **Website:** www.thethomascubitt.co.uk

Inspectors' favourites

Deuchars Bitter

This sizable Georgian pub has been converted and renamed after the famous master builder, who would have approved of its elegant and well-furnished style. There's a split personality here: downstairs is where the drinkers gather and where those wanting pie of the day can repair to rustic tables at the back. Upstairs, however, it's a different story. The dining room is divided into three, with fine period detail at every turn, including edging to the ceilings, marble fireplaces, wooden laid floor, huge floral arrangements and chic grey painted walls. For the sheer sake of a talking point, wall pictures are hung upside down! Unobtrusive service is nevertheless warm and friendly. Time is spent sourcing suppliers, and the modern British dishes are appealingly seasonal.

Food serving times

Monday-Friday:
12pm-11pm (until 3pm in Dining Room)

Saturday: 12pm-11pm

Sunday: 12pm-10.30pm

Closed 25 December, Good Friday

Prices

Meals: a la carte £ 30/60

Typical Dishes
Smoked trout & crab
Beef Wellington
Apple tart

⊖ Sloane Square. Pay and display parking in Elizabeth Street and adjoining streets.

This region cradles some of England's wildest and most dramatic scenery typified by Northumberland National Park, a landscape of rolling purple moorlands and roaring rivers bursting with salmon and trout. Kielder Forest's mighty wilderness has been called "the country's most tranquil spot" while Bill Bryson has waxed lyrical upon the glories of Durham Cathedral. Those who love the wind in their hair are equally effusive about the eleven-mile footpath that accompanies the pounding waves of Durham's Heritage Coast; further north are the long, dune-backed beaches of Northumberland. Rambling across the region is Hadrian's Wall, 73 miles of iconic Roman history, while a modern slant on architectural celebrity is proffered by the Millennium Bridge, BALTIC Centre and Angel of the North. The famously bracing air whets hearty appetites for local Cheviot lamb, Coquetdale cheese or Holy Island oysters. And what could be more redolent of the North East than a breakfast of Craster kippers?

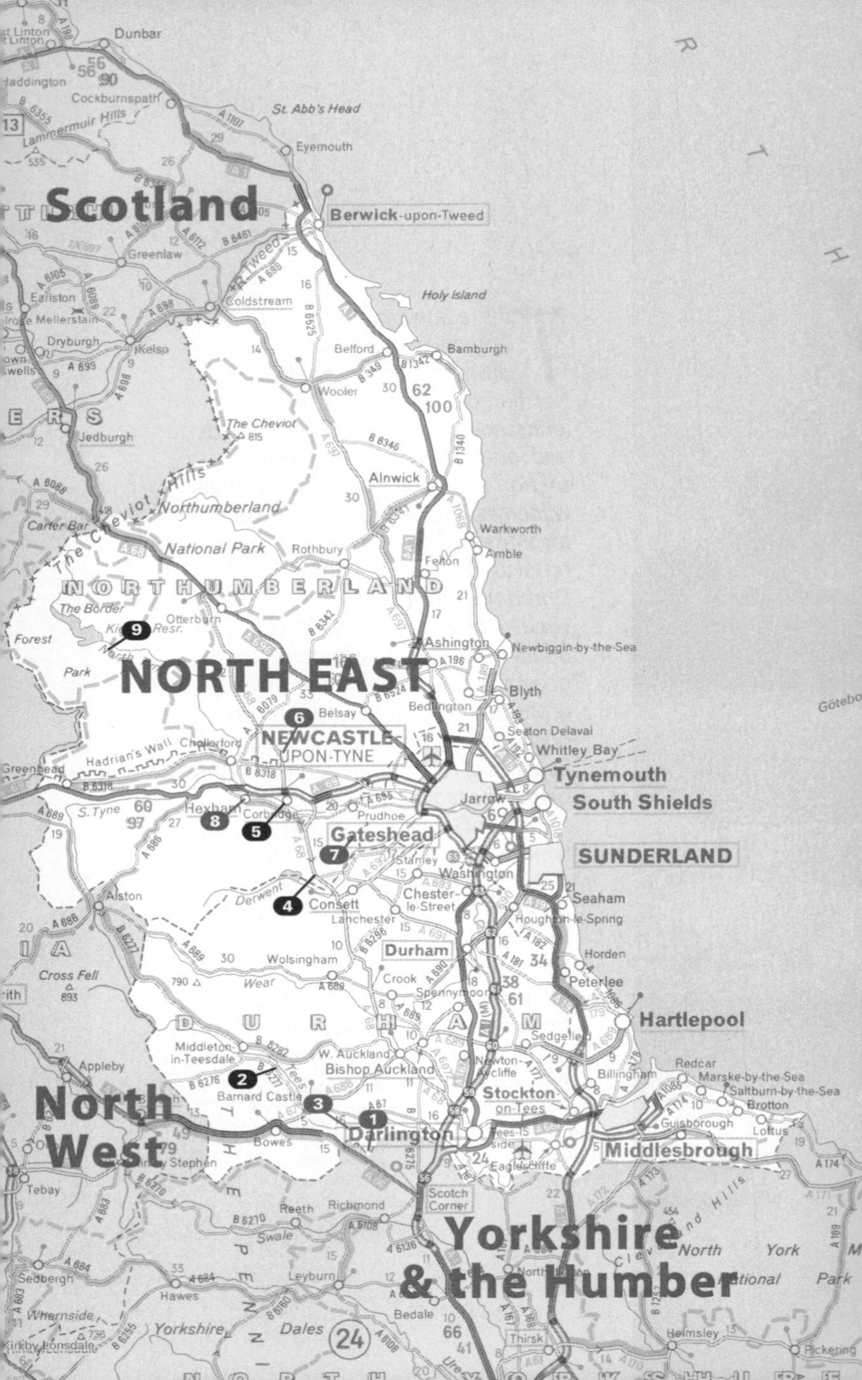

Scotland
NORTH EAST
North West
Yorkshire & the Humber
NORTHUMBERLAND
DURHAM
NEWCASTLE-UPON-TYNE
Berwick-upon-Tweed
Holy Island
Bamburgh
Alnwick
Warkworth
Amble
Ashington
Newbiggin-by-the-Sea
Blyth
Tynemouth
South Shields
SUNDERLAND
Gateshead
Durham
Hartlepool
Middlesbrough
Darlington
Stockton-on-Tees
Hexham
Corbridge
Consett
Barnard Castle
Bishop Auckland
The Cheviot
Northumberland National Park
Kielder Resr.
Hadrian's Wall
Alston
Cross Fell
Dunbar
Eyemouth
St. Abb's Head
Coldstream
Kelso
Jedburgh
Wooler
Rothbury
Otterburn
Belsay
Whitley Bay
Seaham
Peterlee
Redcar
Saltburn-by-the-Sea
Guisborough
Richmond
Scotch Corner
Yorkshire Dales
North York Moors National Park

1 The Oak Tree Inn

Hutton Magna DL11 7HH

Tel.: (01833)627371

Website: www.elevation-it.co.uk/oaktree

Black Sheep Best, Timothy Taylor Landlord, Charles Wells Bombardier

If you are privy to the fact that owner/ chef Alastair spent many years perfecting his craft at various upmarket London establishments, you'll be expecting a lot from a meal at this part-18C whitewashed inn and, the good news is, you won't be disappointed. This unpretentious dining pub serves good value, modern pub dishes made with locally sourced, seasonal ingredients, and wife Claire supplies a friendly welcome and polite service. Rural life in this small, unspoilt village is about as far from the frenetic pace of the city as it is possible to get, so relax and sip an aperitif by the fire, flick through the eclectic collection of reading matter provided or simply admire the beams and stone walls of the simply-furnished, old-fashioned, homely bar. Once ready to eat, move through to the dining area with its plain décor, heavy wood tables, leather chairs and food-themed prints.

Food serving times

Tuesday-Sunday:
6.30pm-8.30pm

Closed 24-26 and 31 December, 1-2 January

Dinner only. Booking essential.

Prices

Meals: a la carte £ 26/33

Typical Dishes

Crispy pork belly salad
Roast fillet of turbot
Peanut butter parfait

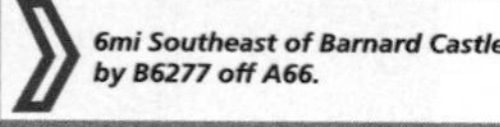

6mi Southeast of Barnard Castle by B6277 off A66.

2 Rose and Crown

Romaldkirk DL12 9EB
Tel.: (01833)650213 – Fax: (01833)650828
e-mail: hotel@rose-and-crown.co.uk
Website: www.rose-and-crown.co.uk

Theakston Bitter, Black Sheep Bitter

With the warmth of the welcome, the service and the décor, plus the heat from the open fires, you'll be feeling positively balmy after a visit to this ivy-clad former coaching inn, a previous pub of the year winner. Built in 1733, the village green it overlooks is still home to antiquated stocks and an aged water pump, and inside, the various dining areas come accompanied with large dollops of rustic charm. The well-stocked, wood-fitted bar is central to proceedings and its rough stone walls are hung with various brasses and etchings. The panelled, linen-laid restaurant is similarly decorated with ornaments, cartoons, wine labels and other such paraphernalia. Good-sized menus offer classically-based meals of a superior quality, local serving staff are polite and efficient, and comfortable, individually-appointed bedrooms further illustrate the owners' commitment to providing those all-important extra touches.

Food serving times

Monday-Sunday:
12pm-1.30pm,
7.30pm-8.45pm

Closed 24-26 December

Set price lunch Sunday only

Prices

Meals: £ 18/30
and a la carte £ 15/28

12 rooms: £ 85/165

Typical Dishes

Pink trout
Wood pigeon & lentils
Honey & whisky pannacotta

3.5mi Southeast of Middleton-in-Teesdale on B6277. On the village green, next to the church. Parking.

3 The Bridge Inn

Whorlton DL12 8XD
Tel.: (01833)627341 – Fax: (01833)627995
e-mail: info@thebridgeinnrestaurant.co.uk
Website: www.thebridgerestaurant.co.uk

 **Two guests ales such as Greene King IPA, Theakston Black Bull**

Situated in a pleasant Durham village, this stone-built pub takes its name from the nearby Whorlton suspension bridge that crosses the River Tees. Its styling has changed several times and is hard to define; to one side you'll find a traditional bar but to the other is a vast restaurant decorated all in white, with bistro style chairs and a vast plasma TV showing live kitchen footage. The chef aims to use his past experiences to inform the present, by taking city sophistication and combining it with fresh country ingredients. He has created a modern, restaurant style menu, with good flavours, well-executed combinations and precise presentation. Starters may include smoked salmon terrine with caviar cream cheese or roast rabbit, bacon and mushroom pie, to follow, maybe fillet of lamb with basil mousse or roast pigeon with black truffle pasta, and to finish, rhubarb jelly with rhubarb chantilly and madeleines.

Food serving times

Wednesday-Saturday: 12pm-3pm, 6pm-11pm

Sunday: 12pm-3pm

Closed 25-26 December, 1 January

Prices

Meals: £ 14 and a la carte £ 16/40

Typical Dishes

Pig's trotter salad
Roast wood pigeon
Hunter House farm cheeses

5mi East of Barnard Castle by A67 and minor road South

4 Manor House Inn

Carterway Heads DH8 9LX
Tel.: (01207)255268
Website: www.manorhouse-a68.co.uk

  AE

Theakston Best Bitter, Courage Directors, Charles Wells Bombardier and regularly changing guest ale

A personally owned and run pub with a growing reputation for good, honest homecooked food: a separate dining room overlooking the countryside allows you to forget the inn's on a busy road, but you'll find more of a local atmosphere in the trim little wood-fitted bar – good for a pint and a game of darts with the locals if you're feeling confident; a characterful lounge with comfy banquettes and views over the fields has the best of both worlds. Amiable staff serve a mix of popular pub dishes and robust British classics. Pleasant, conveniently appointed bedrooms make a handy stopover if you're heading on north of the border, while a deli shop at one end of the restaurant sells local farm produce and home-made goodies. A short drive west takes you to Derwent Reservoir, with lakeside walks through rolling moorland and pine forest.

Food serving times
Monday-Saturday:
12pm-2.30pm, 7pm-9.30pm
Sunday:
12pm-2.30pm, 7pm-9pm
Closed dinner 25 December

Prices
Meals: a la carte £ 18/20
4 rooms: £ 46/75

Typical Dishes
Manor House chicken liver paté
Braised lamb shank
Sticky toffee pudding

3mi West of Consett at junction of B6278 and A68. Parking.

5 The Angel of Corbridge

Main St,
Corbridge NE45 5LA
Tel.: (01434)632119 – Fax: (01434)633796

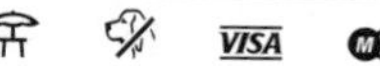

Timothy Taylor Landlord, Black Wheep, Nels Best, Tyneside Blonde, Magus

This 18C coaching inn took on a new lease of life when it was refurbished in the not-too-distant past. It's now the focal point of a pretty, riverside village and quite rightly so. At the entrance, the warm, wood-panelled lounge is furnished with leather Chesterfield and comfy chairs and would be a nice place to settle into, if it weren't for counter claims in other parts of the establishment. A rather charming bar has coil flooring, whitewashed walls, beams and open fires - in other words, a winning mix of rustic and contemporary - while a modern, split-level restaurant sources elaborate weekend meals. During the week, like the bar, it proffers good-sized menus, classical in style with modern twists, on which Northumbrian produce is proudly served at good value prices. Stay overnight in rooms whose taste harmonises with the age of the inn; those at the front boast Tyne Valley views.

Food serving times
Monday-Sunday:
12pm-9pm

Prices
Meals: a la carte £ 15/25
15 rooms: £ 65/120

Typical Dishes
Cheese & chive soufflé
Grilled seabass fillets
Raspberry pannacotta

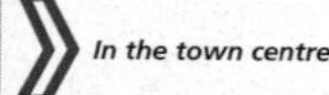

In the town centre.

England • North East • Northumberland

6 Queens Head Inn

Great Whittington NE19 2HP
Tel.: (01434)672267 – Fax: (01434)672267
Website: www.the-queens-head-inn.co.uk

Take one charmingly sleepy, rural village near Hadrian's Wall, only half an hour's drive from Newcastle city centre. Add a traditional stone built 17C coaching inn with long-standing owner, an accomplished chef and a pinch of classic, regionally-influenced cooking with dishes involving black pudding, local lamb, fresh fish and reassuring hotpots and casseroles. Blend with delicious desserts, good sized menus and a warm welcome. Combine a small characterful timbered bar and seating area with a large dining area with cloth-laid tables. Mix with open fires and stone walls and furnish with wooden chairs and pews. Sprinkle with ornaments, pictures, and assorted knick-knacks. Garnish with polite, friendly, aproned staff, add a dash of relaxed, informal atmosphere, marinate in beautiful, rolling wooded countryside for several years and serve. The perfect recipe to protect against the stressful pace of modern life.

Food serving times

Monday-Thursday:
12pm-3pm, 6pm-9pm

Friday-Saturday:
12pm-9.30pm

Sunday: 12pm-6pm

Closed 25 December for food, January-March dinner and Monday

Prices

Meals: a la carte £ 20/35

Typical Dishes

Gilled mushroom stack
Seared fillet of salmon
Toffee apple meringue

6mi North of Corbridge by A68 off B6318.

7 The Feathers Inn

Hedley on the Hill NE43 7SW

Tel.: (01661)843607

e-mail: info@thefeathers.net **Website:** www.thefeathers.net

Mordue Workie Ticket, Jarrow Westoe IPA, Hadrian and Border Gladiator, Consett Red Dust, Wylam Northern Kite

Scale the steep hill that leads up to this attractive stone pub and you'll not only work up your appetite but will be rewarded with great views over Newcastle and Gateshead. Far removed from a modern gastro-pub, this traditional inn is warm, welcoming and friendly and, in true community style, there's always something going on. Quizzes, festivals and theme nights take place throughout the year and they even stage an annual beer barrel race; perhaps their strangest claim to fame, however, is as host to the county's longest standing "Leek Club". As you might hope, the cooking is straightforward and British: tasty combinations of hearty, wholesome fare and good clear flavours. Ingredients are carefully sourced and suppliers are listed on the menu alongside a map. Lunch is lighter than dinner but don't expect bar snacks – you'll find battered North Sea fish, a generous Ploughman's featuring regional cheeses or local sausage and mash.

Food serving times

Monday: 6pm-11pm

Tuesday-Saturday: 12pm-11pm

Sunday: 12pm-10.30pm

Prices

Meals: a la carte £ 15/20

Typical Dishes

Black pudding

Braised Longhorn beef

Burnt Northumbrian cream

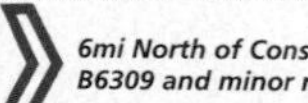

6mi North of Consett by A694, B6309 and minor road

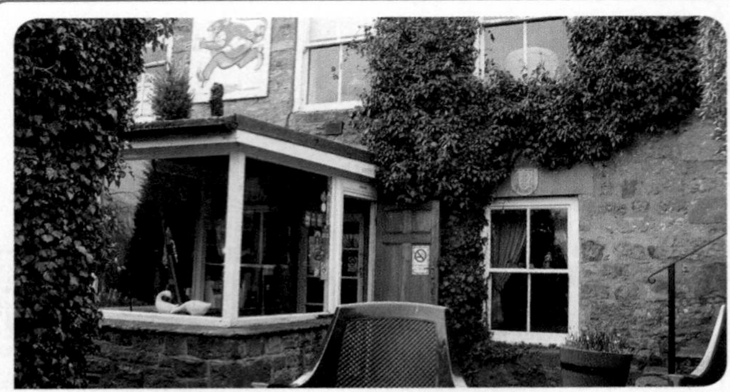

8 The Rat Inn

Anick, Hexham
NE46 4LN
Tel.: (01434)602814
e-mail: info@theratinn.com **Website:** www.theratinn.com

Bass Draught, Deuchars IPA and 3 other ales from local micro breweries

A, B or C, all vote now: A) Rat catchers used to use this as a meeting place, B) This was once home to a large rat, C) A local snitch lived here during the Jacobite rebellion. Unfortunately nobody knows the answer as to how the pub got its name, so just be grateful for the pleasant garden views across the Tyne valley and the tasty, wholesome cooking instead. Situated in a small hamlet on a hillside, this 18C former drovers inn is the perfect place to escape from the rat race of the city. A multi-levelled garden boasts arbours and picnic sets, whilst the traditional interior displays wooden beams and an open range. The daily blackboard menu is concise but covers a good range of dishes, from pastas and risottos, to pub classics such as cottage pie, and more ambitious dishes such as rib of beef or rack of lamb for two. Produce is always fresh, good quality and locally sourced; and there's no need to worry, rodent isn't on the menu.

Food serving times

Tuesday-Saturday:
12pm-2pm, 6pm-9pm

Sunday: 12pm-3pm

Prices

Meals: a la carte £ 15/30

Typical Dishes

Ham hock terrine

Roast Northumbrian rib of beef

Sticky toffee pudding

1mi North of Hexham off A69

9 The Pheasant Inn

Falstone,
Stannersburn NE48 1DD
Tel.: (01434)240382 – Fax: (01434)240382
e-mail: enquiries@thepheasantinn.com **Website:** www.thepheasantinn.com

 **Timothy Taylor Landlord, Wylam, Rocket, Northern Kite, Spring Thing, Turbinia**

If you've been admiring any of the modern visual art and architecture dotted about the Kielder landscape, you'll find it contrasts sharply with the traditional setting of The Pheasant Inn. Here, framed prints, photos and cartoons of the local community in times gone by hang on the stone walls alongside old farm implements, brass jugs and pans. Take a seat next to the log fire in the low-beamed bar of this old, ivy-clad 17C farmhouse, and you'll find yourself transported back to a time when life went by at a slower pace. Family run for over twenty years, service is friendly and polite and the changing blackboard menu offers hearty homemade pub classics made with local ingredients. Stay in one of the comfy, cottage-style rooms set around a pretty courtyard; a great base from which to take advantage of the cycling, fishing and riding to be enjoyed in the beautiful surroundings of the Northumberland National Park.

Food serving times

Monday-Sunday:
12pm-2.30pm, 7pm-9pm

Closed 25-27 December and November-March Monday-Tuesday

Bar lunch Monday-Saturday

Prices

Meals: a la carte £ 17/25

8 rooms: £ 50/90

Typical Dishes
Chicken liver parfait
Grilled seabass
Treacle & orange tart

0.5mi Northeast crossing North Tyne river. Parking at front and rear.

3

Energised by Liverpool's swagger as 2008's European City of Culture, the north west feels like a region reborn. Dovetailed by the confident sophistication of a reinvigorated Manchester, the country's oldest industrial heartland boasts an impressive cultural profile. And yet arty urban centres are a million miles away from the rural grandeur of the region: trails and paths crisscross the area all the way from Solway Firth to Cheshire. Cumbria is a walker's paradise: from Hadrian's Wall to the glories of the Lake District, and along the vast shoreline of Morecambe Bay with its rich gathering of waders and wildfowl, there's a vivid contrast in scenery. The architectural landscape of the region covers the ages, too. Lancaster Castle reverberates to the footsteps of ancient soldiers, while Chester's walled city of medieval buildings is a true gem. Blackpool is now Europe's biggest seaside resort while the flavour of the north west is hot pot, black pudding and Morecambe Bay shrimps.

Scotland
North East
NORTH
Yorkshire & the Humber
CUMBRIA
Lake District
Cumbrian Mountains
ISLE OF MAN
Dumfries
Carlisle
Workington
Whitehaven
Barrow-in-Furness
Morecambe
Lancaster
NEWCASTLE UPON TYNE
Douglas
Lockerbie
Langholm
Canonbie
Longtown
Gretna
Annan
Bowness-on-Solway
Brampton
Greenhead
Hadrian's Wall
Chollerford
Hexham
Corbridge
Alston
Penrith
Appleby
Brough
Kirkby Stephen
Tebay
Orton
Sedbergh
Kendal
Windermere
Ambleside
Grasmere
Coniston
Bowness
Patterdale
Ullswater
Keswick
Derwent water
Skiddaw
Cockermouth
Maryport
Aspatria
Wigton
Thursby
Silloth
Abbey Town
Bothel
Frizington
Buttermere
Rosthwaite
Egremont
Gosforth
Scafell Pikes
St. Bees Head
Broughton-in-Furness
Millom
Ulverston
Dalton
Greenodd
Grange-Over-Sands
Carnforth
Ingleton
Kirkby Lonsdale
Whernside
Hawes
Leyburn
Reeth
Settle
Threshfield
Bowes
Barnard Castle
Middleton-in-Teesdale
Wolsingham
Consett
Cross Fell
Solway Firth
Wigtown Bay
Luce Bay
Mull of Galloway
Burrow Head
Isle of Whithorn
Whithorn
Port William
Drummore
Glenluce
Cairnryan
Stranraer
Newton Stewart
Wigtown
New Galloway
Gatehouse of Fleet
Castle Douglas
Ringford
Kirkcudbright
Auchencairn
Dalbeattie
New Abbey
Forest Park
Point of Ayre
Ramsey
Ballaugh
Peel
Snaefell
Port Erin
Port St. Mary
Castletown
Ronaldsway
Belfast

IRISH SEA
BLACKPOOL
Fleetwood
Cleveleys
Lytham St. Anne's
Southport
Ainsdale
Formby
LIVERPOOL
Liverpool Bay
Bootle
Wallasey
Hoylake
Birkenhead
Bebington
Ellesmere Port
Runcorn
Widnes
St. Helens
Warrington
Wigan
Bolton
Bury
Rochdale
Oldham
MANCHESTER
Stockport
Altrincham
Leigh
Preston
Kirkham
Leyland
Darwen
Blackburn
Accrington
Burnley
Nelson
Colne
Padiham
Clitheroe
Gisburn
Long Preston
Skipton
Keighley
Bingley
BRADFORD
Halifax
Todmorden
Brighouse
Rawtenstall
Huddersfield
Holmfirth
Ashton-under-Lyne
Hyde
Ormskirk
Skelmersdale
LANCASHIRE
WEST
East Midlands
Buxton
Bakewell
Peak District
Whaley Bridge
Wilmslow
Knutsford
Macclesfield
Congleton
Northwich
Winsford
Frodsham
CHESHIRE
Tarporley
Middlewich
Sandbach
Crewe
Nantwich
Chester
Kidsgrove
Little Moreton Hall
Leek
Newcastle-under-Lyme
STOKE-ON-TRENT
Audlem
Whitchurch
Uttoxeter
Stone
West Midlands
Wrexham
Wrecsam
Ruabon
Ellesmere
Oswestry
Llangollen
Corwen
Bala
Berwyn
Queensferry
Flint/Fflint
Mold/Yr Wyddgrug
Holywell
Mostyn
Prestatyn
Rhyl
Colwyn Bay/Bae Colwyn
Abergele
St. Asaph
Denbigh/Dinbych
Llandudno
Great Ormes Head
Conwy
Penmaenmawr
Llanfairfechan
Bangor
Beaumaris
Menai Bridge
Llangefni
Llanerchymedd
Amlwch
ANGLESEY
Holyhead/Caergybi
Holy Island
Isle of Anglesey
Rhosneigr
Newborough
Caernarfon
Caernarfon Bay
Bethesda
Carnedd Llewelyn
Llanberis
Snowdon
Snowdonia
Capel Curig
Llanrwst
Betws-y-coed
Wales
Cerrigydrudion
Blaenau Ffestiniog
Ffestiniog
Beddgelert
Porthmadog
Penrhyndeudraeth
Criccieth
Pwllheli
Abersoch
Nefyn
Lleyn Peninsula
Aberdaron
Harlech
GWYNEDD
Snowdonia National Park
Belfast
Dublin
Larne
Mostyn

Alderley Edge

1 The Wizard

Macclesfield Rd, Alderley Edge SK10 4UB
Tel.: (01625)584000 – Fax: (01625)585105
e-mail: wizardrestaurant@googlemail.com
Website: www.wizardrestaurant.googlepages.com

    AE

Tanglefoot, 1st Gold, Golden Glory, Champion, Jennings Cumberland

The National Trust has a good presence in these parts in the shape of Hare Hill and the local watermill. The Wizard – named after a children's book called "Wizard of Alderley Edge" – has proved an institution worth preserving in its own right. It's a 200 year-old pub which, these days, has restaurant sensibilities. Standing on the edge of a woodland park with superb walks clsoeby, it earns a tick in the box on most rustic counts: beamed, flagged and wood floors, with heavy wooden tables and chairs located everywhere. The menu - good value lunches and evening à la carte - is wide ranging and eclectic; the cooking's interesting and precise. Try grilled black pudding on mash with poached egg and mustard cream, cod with buttered spinach and salsa verde, or sea bass with red chard, avocado salad, lemongrass and coriander.

Food serving times

Tuesday-Saturday:
12pm-2pm, 7pm-9.30pm

Sunday: 12pm-2pm

Closed Christmas-New Year

Prices

Meals: a la carte £ 20/40

Typical Dishes

Seared king scallops
Thai green chicken curry
Glazed lemon tart

1.25mi Southeast on B5087.

2 The Grosvenor Arms

Chester Rd, Aldford CH3 6HJ
Tel.: (01244)620228 – Fax: (01224)620247
e-mail: grosvenor-arms@brunningandprice.co.uk
Website: www.grosvenorarms-aldford.co.uk

 **Thwaites, Weetwood, Deuchars IPA, Moorhouses, Archers**

Designed by local Victorian architect John Douglas, this 19C red brick property started life as the Talbot Inn and later became the Grosvenor Arms Hotel, before finding itself closed and in a state of disrepair. By a good turn of fortune, it fell into the right hands and now, once again, is a grand looking building. A hit with the locals, it has a convivial atmosphere and the friendly staff are welcoming to one and all. There's no shortage of choices when it comes to places to sit: the smart terrace, neatly-kept garden, plant-filled conservatory or one of several characterful rooms – which might feature attractive wood or tile flooring, half-panelled walls or unusually leaded windows. The daily changing menu also provides plenty of choice, with tasty, generous dishes ranging from pub favourites to more sophisticated options; this may include anything from chicken pie or shoulder of lamb through to crab pannacotta or aubergine moussaka.

Food serving times

Monday-Saturday:
12pm-10pm

Sunday and Bank Holidays:
12pm-9pm

Closed 25-26 December dinner and 1 January dinner

Prices

Meals: a la carte £ 18/30

Typical Dishes

Corned beef hashcake
Blade of pork cassoulet
Sticky toffee pudding

3.5mi South of Chester by B5130. On the main village road. Parking.

3 Dysart Arms

Bowes Gate Rd,
Bunbury CW6 9PH

Tel.: (01829)260183 – Fax: (01829)261286

e-mail: dysart-arms@brunningandprice.co.uk **Website:** www.dysartarms-bunbury.co.uk

   AE

Thwaites Original, Flowers Original, Brains Reverend James, Deuchars IPA

Sitting comfortably next to the parish church, this red brick pub is named after the local landowners of yesteryear – the Earls of Dysart – and their coat of arms hangs above the door. Originally a farm belonging to the Estate, this building took on a new role in the late 1800s, operating simultaneously as the local pub, farm and abattoir; later, the outbuildings were converted into kitchens, and a conservatory was added alongside the existing cosy oak-filled rooms. Today, open fires, heaving bookcases and mismatching furniture create a relaxed, informal feel, while French windows provide plenty of light – as well as access to the terrace and garden. Menus change daily and feature fresh, tasty British and Mediterranean dishes. These include light bites such as sandwiches and salads, as well as more substantial dishes such as lamp rump, swordfish or belly pork. Orders are sent to the kitchen via an old department store style tube.

Food serving times

Monday-Saturday: 12pm-9.30pm

Sunday: 12pm-9pm

Closed 25 and 31 December

Prices

Meals: a la carte £ 18/28

Typical Dishes

Ham hock terrine
Braised lamb shoulder
Sticky toffee pudding

3.25mi South by A49 then take Bunbury Mill Road.

4 The Combermere Arms

Burleydam SY13 4AT

Tel.: (01948)871223 – Fax: (01948)661371

e-mail: combermere.arms@brunningandprice.co.uk

Website: www.combermerearms-burleydam.co.uk

  VISA MC AE

Weetwood Cheshire Cat, Thwaites Original and Mild, Sharps Doombar, Whippet Gold Cup

A clever merging of styles allows the old and the new to link stylistic arms here. There are old beams on view as you step inside, but beyond them the adjoining rooms have been opened up around the central bar, and skylights added, so that everything's open and airy, although you can still find a snug spot if that's what you're after. Walls are covered in pictures of every style and hue. There's an informal menu, and you can eat anywhere you like: lots of choice right across the board means a good selection from sandwiches to more substantial dishes; the wine list is worthy of note, too. This is the ideal dining spot for bigger parties, as some truly cavernous tables are up for grabs. Service is efficient from staff who are used to being busy.

Food serving times

Sunday-Thursday:
12pm-9.30pm

Friday-Saturday:
12pm-10pm

Prices

Meals: a la carte £ 18/29

Typical Dishes

Smoked duck breast
Braised lamb shoulder
Rhubarb crumble

4.25mi East of Whitchurch on A525. Parking.

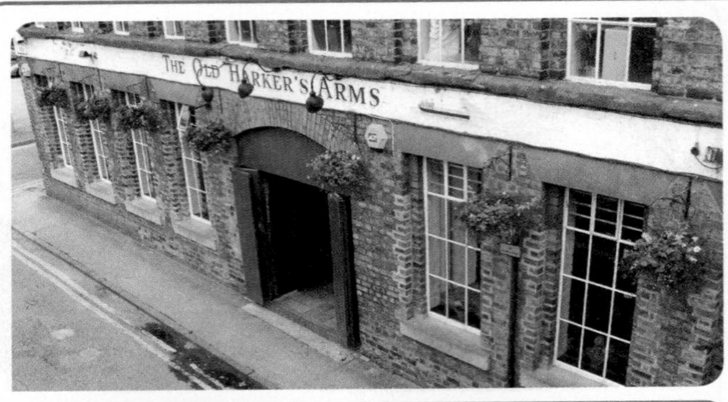

5 The Old Harkers Arms

1 Russell St,
Chester CH3 5AL
Tel.: (01244)344525 – Fax: (01244)344814
e-mail: harkers.arms@brunningandprice.co.uk **Website:** www.brunningandprice.co.uk

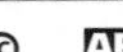

Weetwood Cheshire Cat, Wadworth 6X, Thwaites Original and daily guest beers

If you like water with your whisky this is definitely the pub for you. A few minutes walk from the station, this converted Victorian warehouse is situated in an idyllic canalside location and comes complete with a well stocked bar – housing no less than 100 different whiskies. Previously Mr. Harker's canal boat chandlery, the spacious interior boasts wooden floors, exposed brickwork, a ceiling lined with wine box ends and a large bar that spans two sides of the room, while an eclectic mix of pictures adorns the walls. This is a characterful, good old-fashioned drinking pub, but one that serves good food too. Cooking is rustic, unfussy and generous, and the daily-changing menu displays plenty of tasty pub favourites – which might include fish and chips, sausage and mash, rump steak or lamb chops. For snackers there's an interesting selection of light bites and for all, there's a good selection of wines and local ales.

Food serving times

Monday-Sunday:
12pm-9.30pm

Closed 25 December

Prices

Meals: a la carte £ 20/30

Typical Dishes

Farmhouse terrine
Chicken breast
Selection of cheeses

Between A51 and the canal.

6 The Pheasant Inn

Higher Burwardsley CH3 9PF
Tel.: (01829)770434 – Fax: (01829)771097
e-mail: info@thepheasantinn.co.uk **Website:** www.thepheasantinn.co.uk

 **Weetwood, Phoenix, Slaters, Spitting Feathers**

Located right at the top of a large sandstone outcrop – an unusual sight in the middle of the flat Cheshire Plains – this pub, neighbour to Peckforton Castle, enjoys great views over the surrounding countryside. A lovely garden and terrace attracts walkers of the Sandstone trail, keen to be at one with nature, while inside, diners vie for seats next to the over-sized windows. The open plan interior features stone columns and reclaimed timber beams throughout, while squashy sofas in the bar provide a more relaxed feel than the formal dining room. The daily changing menu features local and, wherever possible, free range produce. You can choose between afternoon tea; cheese, fish or charcuterie deli boards; and some good old pub favourites, including maybe sausage and mash or fish pie – followed by crumble or bread and butter pudding. In the adjacent stone barn, bedrooms are compact, stylish and comfortable, and most afford good views.

Food serving times

Monday:
12pm-3pm, 6pm-9.30pm

Tuesday-Thursday:
12pm-9.30pm

Friday-Saturday:
12pm-10pm

Sunday: 12pm-8.30pm

Prices

Meals: a la carte £ 17/30

12 rooms: £ 65/130

Typical Dishes
Pea & mint risotto
Slow-roast belly pork
Lemon possett

2.5mi Southeast of Tattenhall.
Parking.

7 Duke of Portland

Penny's Lane,
Lach Dennis CW9 7SY
Tel.: (01606)46264 – Fax: (01606)41724
e-mail: info@dukeofportland.com **Website:** www.dukeofportland.com

   MC AE

Marston Pedigree, Deuchar, Thwaites Bomber, Bishop's Tipple

The Belle Epoque in Knutsford is not an oxymoron: it's a restaurant that's been a renowned local stalwart for 30 years, and its long-standing owners have built up a solid reputation. Good reason, then, for a visit to the rurally set Duke of Portland, seven miles away, now overseen by those same owners, the Mooney family. There's a nice rustic feeling of space inside, accentuated by two airy lounges where low-level sofas are a good place to peruse the menus. Adjacent dining areas feature natty wooden balustrades; in summer months, visitors often prefer to tuck in on the smart outdoor terrace or in the garden. Frequently changing menus offer a very well priced and eclectic mix of modern and traditional dishes: local favourites are the delicious homemade burgers or hotpot. Drinkers are well catered for with an impressive range of real ales and wines by the glass. (871c)

Food serving times
Monday-Sunday:
12pm-2.30pm, 5.30pm-10pm

Prices
Meals: a la carte £ 20/40

Typical Dishes
Black pudding terrine
Sirloin steak
Crème brûlée

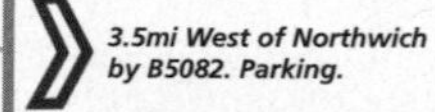
3.5mi West of Northwich by B5082. Parking.

8 Chetwode Arms

Street Lane,
Lower Whitley WA4 4EN
Tel.: (01925)730203 – Fax: (01925)730203
e-mail: claudia.d@btinternet.com **Website:** www.chetwodearms.com

 **Adnams Broadside, Jennings Cumberland, Black Sheep and one changing guest beer**

Starting life over 400 years ago as a farmhouse, this building was converted into a roadside inn before taking up its position in the last century as a good old-fashioned pub. It's had its fair share of history, with rumours of a resident ghost and talk of a tunnel leading to the church but it's now better known for its large bowling green, pleasant terrace and great food. Having previously been run by the same family for 300 years, it's currently under the control of a local and his Austrian wife, who, along with the cosy rooms and narrow wood-panelled corridors, create a warm, welcoming feel. The wide-ranging à la carte features British and Austrian dishes, as well as a selection of medleys that are cooked on super heated rocks – these include many South African meats, such as ostrich, kudu, crocodile, springbok and even zebra. At lunch and before 6.30pm a good value set menu offers three courses for £10, or two with a glass of wine.

Food serving times

Monday-Saturday:
12pm-2.30pm, 6pm-9pm

Sunday: 12pm-7pm

Closed 25 December and 1 January

Prices

Meals: £ 10 (lunch)
and a la carte £ 20/38

Typical Dishes
Chilli crab cakes
Game pie
Apple strudel

6.5mi Northwest of Northwich by A533 off A49.

9 The Frozen Mop

Faulkeners Lane, Mobberley
WA16 7AL
Tel.: (01565)873234
Website: www.thefrozenmop.co.uk

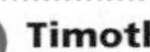 **Timothy Taylor Landlord, Marston Pedigree**

You don't have to be a "WAG" or "lady who lunches" to feel right at home amongst the smart clientele of this intriguingly named pub; nobody knows quite where the name came from but it makes an interesting talking point. Set on a fairly busy country lane, this cream brick-built pub dates back to the late 19C, although you wouldn't guess it from the inside; in the usual stylish gastropub vein it's spacious and open-plan, with contemporary furnishings, low beamed ceilings, chunky pillars and wooden floors aplenty. One side of the long bar houses leather sofas and comfy tub seats, while at the other end high-backed chairs are arranged around chunky oak tables; despite this set-up you can eat anywhere, including the pleasant rear terrace in the warmer months. The narrow A3 menu is modern and wide-ranging, so it's easy to find something for everyone; there are sharing platters, salads, pastas, pizzas, grills and a variety of other dishes.

Food serving times
Monday-Sunday:
12pm-3pm, 6pm-10pm

Prices
Meals: a la carte £ 18/23

Typical Dishes
Potted salmon & prawns
Spit roast duck
Apple & rhubarb crumble

2 mi east by B5085

10 Drunken Duck Inn

Barngates,
Ambleside LA22 0NG

Tel.: (01539)436347 – Fax: (01539)436781

e-mail: info@drunkenduckinn.co.uk **Website:** www.drunkenduckinn.co.uk

 **Barngates Brewery : Catnap, Chesters Strong & Ugly, Red Bull Terrier**

A handsome inn that takes its name from a story involving a 19C landlady, a leaky barrel and a gaggle of unsteady ducks, this trusty Lakeland landmark still marks the old crossroads, in the midst of stunning fell and high peak scenery. Its bar with open fire is a haven for walkers, particularly those who like real ale, as The Duck has an on-site micro-brewery producing four beers on handpump. Beers can be enjoyed in one of the cosy, beamed rooms which radiate from the bar, but this is a dining destination at heart, with meals served in two pleasant dining rooms: lunch offers dishes such as cold poached asparagus or scallops, while the modern style evening à la carte has an ambitious edge with dishes such as Westmorland gold brined Anjou pigeon and salt and peppered foie gras. Bedrooms are of fine quality; they all boast the excellent view and cream tea greets you on arrival. Booking is essential, as this place can get very busy.

Food serving times

Monday-Sunday:
12pm-2.30pm, 6pm-9.30pm

Prices

Meals: a la carte £ 35/50

17 rooms: £ 95/250

Typical Dishes

Peppered beef fillet
Roast halibut
Praline soufflé

3mi Southwest of Ambleside by A593 and B5286 on Tarn Hows road. By the crossroads at the top of Duck Hill. Parking.

England • North West • Cumbria

11 The Wheatsheaf

Brigsteer LA8 8AN
Tel.: (015395)68254 – Fax: (015395)68948
e-mail: wheatsheaf@brigsteer.gb.com **Website:** www.brigsteer.gb.com

VISA AE

Hesket Newmarket, Tirril, Dent, Hawkshead Cumbrian Legend, Derwent, Coniston

No longer hidden deep underneath Artex and thick carpets, The Wheatsheaf's inner beauty has once again been allowed to shine through. Total refurbishment means that the 18C pub is now light and airy, with tiled and wooden floors, and contemporary furnishings in each of its three rooms.
The menu is proudly seasonal, Cumbrian and traceable, so you know that your smoked salmon came from Cartmel Valley and the shrimps were netted in Morecombe Bay, while wild garlic, flat mushrooms and damsons are sourced from even closer to home; the bank just outside the inn. Dishes on the à la carte might include carved loin of organic roe deer, roast crown of wild mallard, rabbit and leek stew or grilled whole local trout – all fairly priced and prepared with the greatest of care by a young, ambitious and disciplined team. Word is spreading fast, so it's a good idea to book. Three classically styled bedrooms come with pine furniture.

Food serving times

Monday-Sunday:
12pm-2pm, 5.45pm-9pm

Booking essential Monday in winter

Prices

Meals: £ 17 and a la carte £ 15/25

3 rooms: £ 70/85

Typical Dishes
Smoked haddock
Stuffed lamb shank
Baked egg custard

3 3/4mi South West of Kendal by All Hallows Lane. Parking.

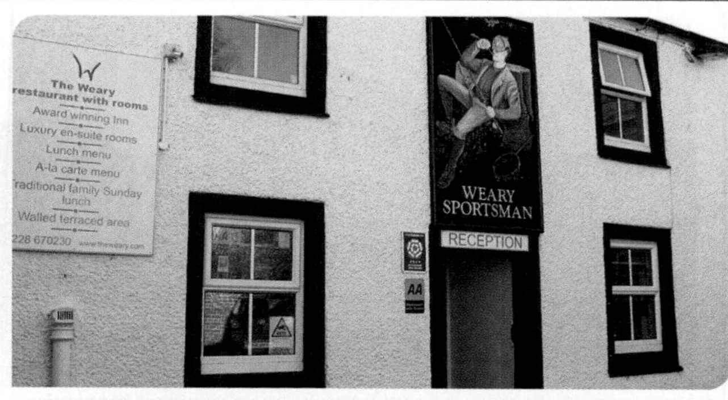

12 The Weary at Castle Carrock

Castle Carrock CA8 9LU
Tel.: (01228)670230 – Fax: (01228)670089
e-mail: relax@theweary.com **Website:** www.theweary.com

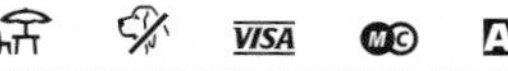

Brampton Geltsdale Brewery - Tarnmonath, Kings Forest - Black Dub

Formerly known as the Weary Sportsman, the original sign still hangs above the door of this pub, but it's the newer sign alongside which hints at its modern interior. The candlelit bar area with its comfy seating and relaxed ambience is the most popular area in which to eat, but there is also an outside terrace, a conservatory and a room known as "The Square." Whilst the bar menu serves traditional dishes such as chunky fish pie and lasagne, the à la carte also incorporates more international flavours, with Thai dishes a particular bent. Steak nights on Tuesdays are popular, and the servers' friendliness and good cheer compensate for any slippages in service during busy periods. Superior, strikingly contemporary bedrooms are equipped with the latest technology, including televisions in the bathroom tiles so you watch while you wash. Stay overnight and you will conclude that it must be really rarely that the weary leave The Weary weary.

Food serving times

Tuesday-Sunday:
12pm-2pm, 6pm-9pm

Closed 25-26 December, 1 January

Monday residents only

Prices

Meals: a la carte £ 14/32

5 rooms: £ 79/125

Typical Dishes
Cumbrian roast lamb fillet
Pan-fried Eden salmon fillet
Sticky toffee pudding

4mi south of Brampton on B6413. Parking.

13 The Punch Bowl Inn

Crosthwaite LA8 8HR
Tel.: (01539)568237 – Fax: (01539)568875
e-mail: info@the-punchbowl.co.uk
Website: www.the-punchbowl.co.uk

   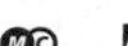

AE

 **Tag Lag, Westmorland Gold, 1077, Cracker, Bluebird**

Our 2009 Pub of the Year is surrounded by delightfully unspoilt countryside, and its stylish, richly furnished bar and restaurant have an appealingly informal feel. Both offer the same menu, with tasty, classically created dishes such as chicken liver parfait, Cumbrian cheddar cheese soufflé or roast loin and braised shoulder of lamb making good use of local, seasonal ingredients; and lighter dishes also offered at lunchtimes. Luxurious bedrooms are another highlight; individually styled, with designer décor and excellent attention to detail. Shown to your room, you are greeted by the melodious strains of Classic FM emitting from a Roberts radio. There are flat screen TVs, homemade biscuits on which to nibble, underfloor heated limestone bathrooms and extra large bath towels. Noble, with its twin roll top baths, covers the whole of the third floor and Danson boasts particularly glorious valley views. Breakfast is not to be missed.

Food serving times
Monday-Sunday:
12pm-3pm, 6pm-9.30pm

Prices
Meals: a la carte £ 25/35
9 rooms: £ 83/310

Typical Dishes
Grilled scallops
Roast lamb
Dark chocolate fondant

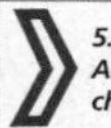

5.25m west of Kendal by All Hallows Lane. Next to the church. Parking

14 The Highwayman

Nether Burrow LA6 2RJ
Tel.: (01524)826888
e-mail: enquiries@highwaymaninn.co.uk **Website:** www.highwaymaninn.co.uk

   AE

 **Lancaster Bomber, Thwaites Original, Wainwrights**

(With apologies to Alfred Noyes) The meat's from the Forest of Bowland among the gusty trees, / The fish it comes from Fleetwood, tossed upon cloudy seas, / The asparagus comes from Formby, over the purple moor, / The suppliers are on the menu – menu - menu, / and the customers they come riding, up to the old inn door. Having undergone a million pound refurbishment, and with owners passionate about local, traceable food, The Highwayman is certainly delivering the goods - from all over Lancashire, Cumbria and Yorkshire - and so serious are they here about sourcing their ingredients locally, they even have framed pictures of their suppliers decorating the walls. Friendly and efficient service from the smartly attired staff oils the wheels of the dining experience, and the spacious inn with its numerous open fires, banquette seating and pleasant stone terrace makes an agreeable environment in which to enjoy the flavoursome food.

Food serving times
Monday-Friday:
12pm-2pm, 6pm-9pm
Saturday:
12pm-2pm, 5.30pm-9pm
Sunday: 12pm-8.30pm
Closed 25 December

Prices
Meals: a la carte £ 17/28

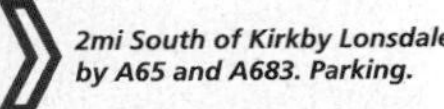

15 The Strickland Arms

Sizergh LA8 8DZ
Tel.: (01539)561010 – Fax: (01539)561067
e-mail: thestricklandarms@yahoo.co.uk

 **Coniston Bluebird, Hawkshead Gold, Dent Ales, Thwaites Ales, Black Sheep**

Like next door Sizergh Castle, this imposing grey building is owned by the National Trust and, having been cleverly restored to its former glory, attracts locals and tourists, walkers, dogs and children in large numbers. Huge portions of hearty homecooked dishes like game casserole and lamb hotpot obviously have the hiker in mind and ensure that no one leaves this historic hostelry hungry; there's a good selection of real ales and wines by the glass and the extremely friendly Antipodean service is a bonus. Simply and stylishly decorated with period furniture, the stone and wood floors and candlelit, dark wood dining tables give it a rustic feel. There is plenty of space over two floors but if the kids still need somewhere to burn off any extra energy, there is also a large garden with pretty apple trees along one side of the pub. Popular events here include fish nights, jazz sessions, quiz nights and a real ale lovers festival.

Food serving times

Monday-Friday:
12pm-2pm, 6pm-9pm

Saturday:
12pm-2.30pm, 6pm-9pm

Sunday:12pm-8.30pm

Closed 25 December for food

Prices

Meals: a la carte £ 20/30

Typical Dishes

Potted Morcambe Bay shrimps

Beer battered fish & chips

Cumberland rum Nicky tart

3mi South West of Kendal by A391. Parking.

16 The Queen's Head

Troutbeck LA23 1PW

Tel.: (01539)432174 – Fax: (01539)431398

e-mail: feast@queensheadhotel.com **Website:** www.queensheadhotel.com

  MC

 **XB, Unicon, Doublehop Cumbrian Way**

If it's inspiring Lakeland scenery you're after, then a visit to this black and white inn, tucked away in Troutbeck Valley, is a must. Its atmospheric bar features deep flag floors and carved Elizabethan detail, while the beams crammed with coins hark back to a time when people would wedge their change in the wood, ready to pay for the drinks on a future visit. These days, it's as much about the food here as the beer; traditional, wholesome cooking, on offer all day, is served in big white bowls; the wide-ranging menu including dishes such as homemade black pudding, braised brisket of locally sourced beef or roast chump of Lakeland lamb, as well as a delicious assortment of homemade bread. Grab a seat by the window in the bar or take a pew in either of the two equally informal restaurant areas. Bedrooms are bright and modern, yet retain their coaching inn character. Rooms 10 and 11 have great fell views, and breakfast is quite a feast.

Food serving times

Monday-Sunday: 12.30pm-2pm, 6pm-9pm

Closed 25 December

Prices

Meals: £ 19 and a la carte £ 19/36

14 rooms: £ 76/120

Typical Dishes

Lentil and bacon soup

Brainsed lamb shank

Homemade bread and butter pudding

4mi North to Windermere by A592. Parking

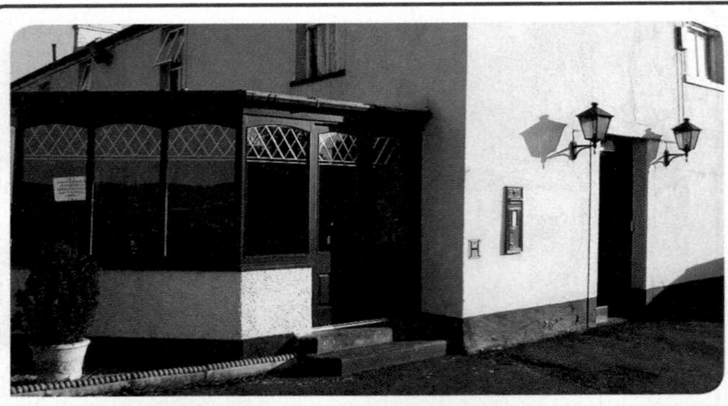

17 The Bay Horse

Canal Foot,
Ulverston LA12 9EL

Tel.: (01229)583972 – Fax: (01229)580502

e-mail: reservations@thebayhorsehotel.co.uk **Website:** www.thebayhorsehotel.co.uk

  AE

Cocker Hoop, Cumberland, Ringwood Seventy Eight

Commanding views of the Lancashire and Cumbria Fells are just one reason to recommend this well-established little inn by Ulverston Sands. The bar area, well known for its capacious horse's head of stone, has a smart ambience, afforded by plush built-in wall banquettes, stylish wooden armchairs, beams and open fire. An adjacent conservatory houses a more formal linen-clad restaurant, which boasts fine views over Morecambe Bay. Tasty, effectively prepared cooking finds favour with appreciative diners, who have long admired the flavourful, seasonal menus, typified by roast fillet of halibut, or Cumberland sausage with date chutney, cranberry and apple sauce. Bedrooms - snug and with a host of extras - have the enviable coastal view.

Food serving times

Monday: 7.30pm for 8pm

Tuesday-Sunday:
12pm-2pm, 7.30pm for 8pm

Closed Monday lunch

One sitting for dinner
7.30pm for 8pm

Prices

Meals: a la carte £ 22/45

9 rooms: £ 80/120

Typical Dishes

Rich liver terrine
Monkfish and scallops
Poached rhubarb

2.25mi East of Ulverston by A5087, turning left at Morecambe Tavern B&B and beyond industrial area, on the coast. Parking.

18 Brown Horse Inn

Winster LA23 3NR

Tel.: (01539)443443

e-mail: steve@thebrownhorseinn.co.uk **Website:** www.thebrownhorseinn.co.uk

 **Hawkshead Bitter, Coniston Bitter**

Nestled in the countryside of the Winster valley, not too far from Lake Windermere, sits this traditional 1850s coaching inn. Previously an Italian restaurant, the new owners said arrivederci to pizza and welcomed back the locals with the lure of log fires and a dartboard, plus seasonal, flavoursome food made with locally sourced ingredients. Brown horse paintings and dried hops decorate the green walls, and diners sit at candlelit tables. The lunch menu offers soup, sandwiches, salads and jacket potatoes, plus favourites such as sausage and mash and fish and chips. Blackboard specials add to the choice, with local lamb always a feature. The dinner menu offers robust, tasty food, classically prepared with prime produce, with dishes such as steak and chunky chips or deep fried squid salad – but book ahead at weekends, as this place is making a name for itself. Bedrooms are light and modern, simply decorated yet comfortable.

Food serving times

Monday-Sunday:
12pm-2pm, 6pm-9.30pm

Prices

Meals: a la carte £ 18/25

9 rooms: £ 50/90

Typical Dishes

Quail eggs
Roast rack of lamb
Trio of chocolate

4mi South of Windermere by A5074. Parking.

19 The Yanwath Gate Inn

Yanwath, Penrith CA10 2LF
Tel.: (01768)862386
e-mail: enquiries@yanwathgate.com **Website:** www.yanwathgate.com

VISA  

Doris' 90th Birthday Ale, Dickie Doodle, Tirril Old Faithful, Keswick Brewing Co Thirst Run

The sign above the door reads: "This gate hangs well and hinders none, refresh and pay and travel on"; a reference to the pub's original function as a toll gate. Nowadays the Yat, as it is affectionately known, functions somewhat as a destination pub for special occasions; its carefully balanced cooking displaying finesse without being too showy. Dishes on offer might include anything from shrimps or fish and chips at lunchtime to black pudding and haggis, lemon sole or glazed pork belly in the evening. The careful sourcing of local produce is of paramount importance here and the list of suppliers on the menu is extensive. The real ale on tap is also proudly Cumbrian and everything, including bread and desserts, is made on the premises. Church candles cast their flickering light in the cosy bar – a seat by the fire is particularly atmospheric - while through the back you will find the oak panelled restaurant.

Food serving times
Monday-Sunday:
12pm-2.30pm, 6pm-9pm

Closed 25 December

Prices
Meals: a la carte £ 24/37

Typical Dishes
King scallops
Braised wild rabbit
Bread & butter pudding

2mi South West of Penrith by A6 on B5320. Parking.

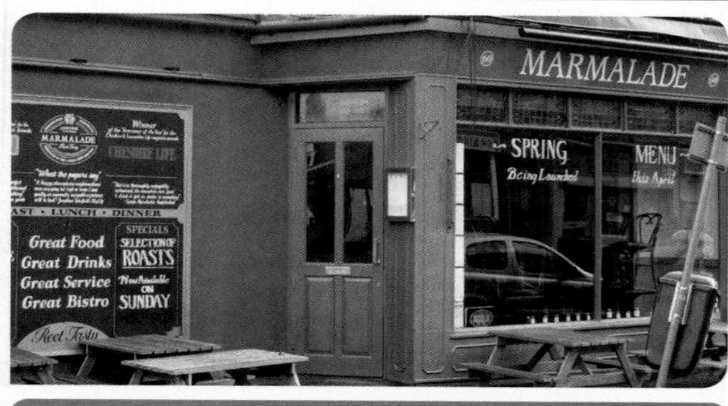

20 Marmalade

60 Beech Road,
Chorlton-cum-Hardy M21 9EG
Tel.: (0161)8629665 – Fax: (0161)8617788
e-mail: jqmarmalade@tiscali.co.uk **Website:** www.mymarmalade.co.uk

Abbot Ale, Old Speckled Hen, Adnams Explorer

Don't get the impression that this neighbourhood hostelry deals only in charming knickknacks. Yes, there are things like silver three-tier cake stands, wall-hung antique suitcases and framed replicas of Manchester buses. You can even buy a jar of the eponymous sticky stuff which gives the pub its name. All of which could sidetrack you from the fact that, most of all, John the owner and Phil the chef want you to enjoy the serious food served here. Seasonally changing menus have a strong British accent, from the cracking Lancashire hotpot to mouth-watering mussels and lobster from Wales. Mature ribs of local beef are hung for 42 days and served with home-made chips; everything is freshly cooked on the premises, and the result is well-executed, tasty fare, eaten at simple wooden tables.

Food serving times
Monday-Sunday:
12pm-3pm, 5.30pm-late

Prices
Meals: £ 12/14
and a la carte £ 22/27

Typical Dishes
Poor man's paté
Roast beef
Pemberton Ash cheese

3mi South of Manchester by A5103 and minor road west. Parking in the road.

21 The Ox

71 Liverpool Rd,
Castlefield, Manchester M3 4NQ
Tel.: (0161)8397740/60
e-mail: gmtheox@baabar.co.uk **Website:** www.theox.co.uk

Timothy Taylor Landlord and guest ales

The pub's proximity to Castlefield Heritage Park, the Science Museum and the local Granada studios provides a steady flow of drinkers and diners to The Ox, as well as incognito appearances by a few television celebrities. Apart from the massive, block-bold "OX" monogram, stamped like a cattle-brand between the eaves and glowering in at the windows, it's an understated corner pub, more pleasant and homely than the logo suggests. An open though still intimate-feeling bar room leads on to a traditionally styled dining area, and this is where The Ox sets itself apart from its neighbours: the menu has an unmistakeably eclectic touch, with a number of lightly fusion-influenced dishes in among the more familiar favourites. Fresh and popular food served unpretentiously.

Food serving times

Monday-Saturday: 12pm-10pm

Sunday: 12pm-6pm

Closed 25 December, 1 January

Prices

Meals: £ 14 (weekdays 3 course Sunday lunch) and a la carte £ 18/27

Typical Dishes

Mussels with white wine
Steak
Manchester tart

City centre. Pay and display in neighbouring streets.

22 The White Hart Inn

51 Stockport Rd,
Lydgate, Oldham OL4 4JJ
Tel.: (01457)872566 – Fax: (01457)875190
e-mail: bookings@thewhitehart.co.uk **Website:** www.thewhitehart.co.uk

AE

Manchester Ale, J W Lees, Timothy Taylor

Rurally set, overlooking Saddleworth Moor, The White Hart Inn presents you with several choices. Firstly, where to eat: will you dine near the open log fire in the cosy, beamed brasserie or more formally, in the modern, linen-clad restaurant? The library is the choice for more private dining, while the smart Oak Room is also available for functions. Once you are settled, more choice comes in the form of the seasonally changing menus. Dishes range from soups, sandwiches and smoked sardines through to roast rabbit leg or rib eyed steak. The sumptuous selection of homemade Saddleworth sausages and differently flavoured mashed potatoes are particularly popular, while a fish menu is also available on Tuesdays. Staying the night? Twelve comfortable bedrooms, named after local dignitaries, are housed in the original building, built in 1788.

Food serving times

Monday-Sunday:
12pm-2.30pm, 6.30pm-9pm

Closed 26 December

Booking essential

Prices

Meals: a la carte £ 20/33

12 rooms: £ 85/130

Typical Dishes

Deep-fried prawns
Pork & apple sausages
Sticky toffee pudding

3mi East of Oldham by A669 on A6050. Parking.

23 The Red Pump Inn

Clitheroe Road, Bashall Eaves
BB7 3DA
Tel.: (01254)826227 – Fax: (01254)826750
e-mail: info@theredpumpinn.co.uk **Website:** www.theredpumpinn.co.uk

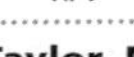 **Timothy Taylor, Moorhouses, Bowland, Grindleton**

Reputedly one of the oldest inns in the Ribble Valley, this former farm is situated on a quiet country lane, with great views of the surrounding hillside. After a notorious murder in the 1930s, on which no one could – or would – shed any light, the hamlet was dubbed "The Silent Village", and, like its name, the area remains peaceful for most of the year. In the game season, however, the local fells ring with the sound of gunshots, and pheasant, venison, mallard, grouse, partridge and rabbit can often be found on the daily specials. The traditional menu is hearty and generous, featuring regional cheeses, fish, preserves and chutneys, as well as herbs from the pub garden. This friendly pub also hosts special seasonal events such as Lamb and Game "Fests", and homemade breads, cakes and pâtés are available for sale in the deli during summer. Bedrooms are spacious and modern with attractive handmade furniture, oversized beds and great views.

3mi North West of Clitheroe by B6243 and minor road North West

Food serving times

Tuesday-Sunday:
12pm-2pm, 6pm-9pm

Closed 1 week mid February

Prices

Meals: a la carte £ 15/30

3 rooms: £ 45/90

Typical Dishes

Potted Pendle beef
Lancashire game pie
Blackcurrant sponge & compote

24 Eagle & Child

Bispham Green L40 3SG

Tel.: (01257)462297 – Fax: (01257)464718

e-mail: eagle@ainscoughs.co.uk **Website:** www.ainscoughs.co.uk

 **Thwaites Original, Moorhouses Phoenix**

If you fancy a trip back to the good old days then this 200 year old pub is the place to come, with its wooden beams, flag floors, busy walls and seasoned group of locals propping up the bar, dogs dozing at their feet. For the best spot pass by them into the snug, where a blazing fire means it's always warm and cosy. Cooking is hearty and tasty, with the bar menu continuing the traditional theme by offering simple British classics, such as sausage and mash, cod and chips or steak and ale pie. For those who fancy something a little more adventurous, head for the daily-changing specials where you'll find maybe braised oxtail, roast suckling pig, pan-fried black bream or trio of pheasant, wigeon and partridge. It's not just the food that matters here and with as many as 12 real ales available at any one time you're spoilt for choice – even without the renowned beer festival that's held here every first May bank holiday.

Food serving times

Monday-Thursday:
12pm-2pm, 6pm-8.30pm

Friday-Saturday:
12pm-2pm, 6pm-9pm

Sunday: 12pm-8.30pm

Prices

Meals: a la carte £ 17/26

Typical Dishes

Grilled sardines

Loin of wild boar

Fresh fruit salad

Between Rufford and Parbold East of B5246

Fence Gate Inn

25 Fence Gate Inn

Wheatley Lane Road,
Fence BB12 9EE

Tel.: (01282)618101 – Fax: (01282)615432
e-mail: info@fencegate.co.uk **Website:** www.fencegate.co.uk

 **Theakston, Deuchars and 2 weekly changing guest ales**

Owner Kevin Berkins has been at The Fence Gate Inn for over a quarter of a century. A former master butcher, he is committed to serving locally sourced food, so your lamb might come from Pendle, your beef from Bowland, and your pork from Samlesbury. If bangers and mash is your thing, then you're in for a treat, as he produces a fine selection of speciality sausages on the premises. Perched high on the moor land, this huge 17C pub offers a wide selection of dishes, with the traditional bar serving simpler offerings like cod and chips, burgers and pies, whilst the more contemporary Topiary brasserie serves more elaborate creations, ranging from classical dishes like Lancashire tart through to dishes with an international influence, such as crispy duck and pancakes. Eight daily specials on top means that it could take you a while to order, but when you do finally decide, you'll find the local staff friendly, with a good sense of humour.

Food serving times
Monday-Sunday:
12pm-2.30pm,
6.30pm-9.30pm

Prices
Meals: a la carte £ 25/35

Typical Dishes
Lancashire tart
Braised Bowland lamb shank
Lancashire cheese slate

2mi South West of Junction 13 on M65 by A6068. Parking.

26 The Bay Horse Inn

Bay Horse Lane,
Forton LA2 0HR

Tel.: (01524)791204 – Fax: (01524)791204
e-mail: bayhorseinfo@aol.com **Website:** www.bayhorseinn.com

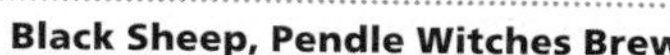
Black Sheep, Pendle Witches Brew

The photos hanging among the quirky bibelots in the bar of the Bay Horse Inn display the local Lancashire landscape with an almost tangible sense of pride; and it is this Lancastrian pride that is also palpable in the provenance of the produce on the menu. Shrimps are fresh from Morecambe Bay, duckling and chicken have travelled only as far as Swainson Farm, venison is from Grizedale and beef from Bowland. Tasty choices conjured up by self-taught chef Craig might include classics such as Lancashire hot pot or fish pie as well as more modern dishes such as smoked duck Caesar salad. The welcome here is a warm one and the inn is a delightful spot for a meal – choose between the dining room and the rustic bar with its open fire. Two new bedrooms, located in a converted corn mill opposite the pub, are beautifully appointed with bespoke bathrooms – but book well in advance as they are proving very popular.

Food serving times

Tuesday-Saturday and Bank Holiday Monday:
12pm-1.45pm, 7pm-9.15pm

Sunday: 12pm-1.45pm

Closed 25-26 December, Tuesday after Bank Holiday Monday

Prices

Meals: £ 20 (lunch)
and a la carte £ 17/30

3 rooms: £ 79/89

Typical Dishes

Potted crab
Slow-cooked duckling
Rhubarb trifle

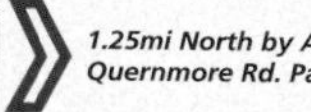
1.25mi North by A6 on Quernmore Rd. Parking

27 The Borough

3 Dalton Sq, Lancaster
LA1 1PP
Tel.: (01524)64170
e-mail: info@theboroughlancaster.co.uk **Website:** www.theboroughlancaster.co.uk

VISA 

Thwaites Original and Wainwrights, Black Sheep, Hen Harrier and guest ales such as Barngates, Bank Top

This Victorian-fronted Georgian building has been jack of all trades, housing the Mayor and then a Working Men's Club, before finally finding its calling as a modern dining pub. Built in 1824, it retains many original features, including leaded windows and Victorian floor tiles. Leather armchairs and sofas occupy the bar area, whilst to the rear the spacious dining room features bench seats and booths, leading out onto a pleasant terrace. Cooking is straightforward, tasty and Northern through and through, featuring regional produce and dishes such as hotpot, black pudding or Fleetwood fish, the latter being served in the "Borough News". For something a bit different try an Ostrich burger, or the pay-per-item Deli Boards, where you can choose from a selection of fish, meat, cheese or salad to create either a light snack, main course or sharing platter. Portions are generous and the food is good, so make sure you book for weekends.

Food serving times

Monday-Saturday:
12pm-2.30pm,
5.30pm-9.30pm

Sunday: 12pm-9pm

Closed 25 December and 1 January

Prices

Meals: a la carte £ 16/35

Typical Dishes
Black pudding
Lancashire hotpot
Local cheeseboard

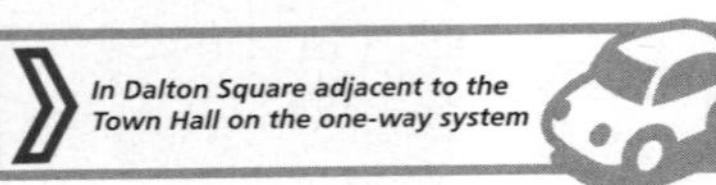

28 The Three Fishes

Mitton Road,
Mitton BB7 9PQ
Tel.: (01254)826888 – Fax: (01254)826026
e-mail: enquiries@thethreefishes.com **Website:** www.thethreefishes.com

Hen Harrier, Bowland, Bomber, Wainwrights, Golden Trough

Pies and hotpots, platters of tongue and brisket, black pudding and potted Morecambe shrimps – a look at the Three Fishes menu is the stuff of northern dreams. It's rare to find cuisine so thoroughly rooted in a region, but the richly savoury and heartening Lancastrian recipes are given pride of place here, prepared in a kitchen which is stocked by a host of hand-picked local suppliers, and served in a very spacious, modern pub. There is a special menu for children but the dairy specials are for all. Find a table then order at the bar – this is such beer-friendly food that it's worth trying a north-western cask ale to go with it. This updated and professionally run pub has come a long way since it served passengers from the river Ribble ferry, but its change of tack has been a definite success, so be warned: it gets very busy.

Food serving times
Monday-Friday:
12pm-2pm, 6pm-9pm
Saturday:
12pm-2pm, 5.30pm-9pm
Sunday: 12pm-8.30pm
Closed 25 December

Prices
Meals: a la carte £ 17/29

Typical Dishes
Morecambe Bay shrimps
Three Fishes Pie
Rice pudding

2.5mi Northwest of Whalley on B6246. Parking.

29 The White Bull

Church Street,
Ribchester PR3 3XP
Tel.: (01254)878303
e-mail: enquiries@whitebullribchester.co.uk **Website:** www.whitebullrib.co.uk

Inspectors' favourites

Bowland Brewery Sorceress, Copper Dragon Best Bitter, Shepherd Neame Spitfire

The chef may have an international C.V., but there's nothing fancy or pretentious about the food served at The White Bull in Ribchester. This is unfussy, British cooking at its best, with proper hearty pub dishes such as fish pie, bangers and mash and pork chops. All are homemade using the best produce available, and the pub is assured of the finest cuts of local meats as well as awfully good offal, since one of the owners also happens to be the local butcher. Traceability and seasonality are of paramount importance and the menus and specials change often. Proper pub food needs a proper village pub, and The White Bull fits the bill very nicely. With a 1707 birth date, pillars which some say have their roots in Roman times, and the remains of the Roman bath visible from the beer garden, the pub has a suitably ancient history; the open fire in the bar creates a warm, welcoming feel, and three charming bedrooms complete the picture.

Food serving times

Tuesday-Saturday:
12pm-2.30pm, 6pm-9.30pm

Sunday:
12pm-8pm, 6pm-9.30pm

Closed 2 January

Prices

Meals: £ 17 and a la carte £ 17/24

3 rooms: £ 55/70

Typical Dishes

Ham hock terrine
Garstang suckling pig
Chocolate sauce pudding

7mi North of Blackburn by A666 and B6245. Parking.

30 The Lunesdale Arms

Tunstall LA6 2QN
Tel.: (01524)274203 – Fax: (01524)274229
e-mail: info@thelunesdale.co.uk **Website:** www.thelunesdale.co.uk

 **Black Sheep, Dent Brewery Aviator, Skipton Brewery Copper Dragon**

This mellow stone pub with its weather-worn sign may not look all that much from the outside, but its owner – herself a villager and a key member of the enthusiastic, friendly team here – once went to great lengths to save it from the developers' clutches. Several years on and this tenaciousness has more than paid off, with people coming from all over to enjoy the pub's relaxed atmosphere and tasty, honest cooking. The spacious interior, brightened by local art and the bar manager's photographs, boasts comfy sofas and a log burner, a separate room for private dining and a games room with pool and table football. Cooking is traditional, unpretentious and frill-free; the blackboard menu offering staples such as sausage and mash, Guinness and mushroom pie or sirloin steak, as well as a range of other choices depending on what the best local suppliers have available. Make sure to save room for one of the delicious homemade puddings.

Food serving times

Monday-Friday:
12pm-2pm, 6pm-9pm

Saturday-Sunday:
12pm-2.30pm, 6pm-9pm

Closed 25-26 December, 1 January

Prices

Meals: a la carte £ 20/25

Typical Dishes

Smoked fish
Roast shoulder of lamb
Rhubarb & ginger pannacotta

4mi South of Kirkby Lonsdale on A683. Parking.

31 The Inn at Whitewell

Forest of Bowland,
Whitewell BB7 3AT

Tel.: (01200)448222 – Fax: (01200)448298

e-mail: reception@innatwhitewell.com **Website:** www.innatwhitewell.com

Timothy Taylor Landlord, Skipton Brewery Copper Dragon and Moorhouses, Bowland Brewery

A delightful location in a river valley in the Forest of Bowland means that a visit is always going to be special. The pub itself is an extended 14C cottage which once served as a coaching inn; nowadays it's very personally run with a endearing eccentricity which surfaces at the unlikeliest moments! It has considerable charm downstairs with a lovely faded bar full of eyecatching curios, a reception-cum-shop and an intimate restaurant overlooking the River Hodder and Trough of Bowland. Dishes have a traditional base and make good use of sound Lancastrian produce: just pull up a chair in the bar for a hearty meal or ask for a table in the restaurant for a more formal occasion. The large, comfortable bedrooms, whether traditional or modern, boast plenty of style, with good views and, in some cases, real peat fires. All have CD players and fittings that touch on the highest inn standards.

Food serving times

Monday-Sunday:
12pm-2pm, 7.30pm-9.30pm

Prices

Meals: a la carte £ 18/40

23 rooms: £ 70/98

Typical Dishes

Seared king scallops

Roast loin of Bowland lamb

Cheese board

6mi Northwest of Clitheroe by B6243. Parking.

32 The Mulberry Tree

9 Wood Lane,
Wrightington Bar WN6 9SE
Tel.: (01257)451400 – Fax: (01257)451400
e-mail: info@themulberrytree.info **Website:** www.themulberrytree.info

Inspectors' favourites

No real ales offered

Located on a busy through road, not far from the M6, this immense 19C pub has reputedly functioned previously as a wheelwright's, a blacksmith's and a brewery. You can eat in either the airy open bar or at linen-laid tables in the more formal dining area; the bar menu offers dishes such as fish and chips, sausage and mash, ploughman's, salads and speciality sandwiches, while the dining room menu delights with more ambitious dishes such as steamed scallops and baby lobster, roast fillets of red snapper, or slow roast confit of belly pork. Produce has not had to travel far to your plate, so black pudding comes from Bury, cod comes from Fleetwood and you might find twice baked Lancashire cheese soufflé alongside roast rack of Cumbrian lamb. The only problem with so many menu options is that, rather than make choosing your meal easier, it actually has the opposite effect, with a tendency to leave your head spinning somewhat.

Food serving times
Monday-Sunday:
12pm-2.30pm, 6pm-10pm
Bar snacks available all day Saturday-Sunday

Prices
Meals: £ 17/20
and a la carte £ 25/40

Typical Dishes
Lancashire cheese soufflé
Roast Goosnargh duck breast
Chocolate melting pudding

3.5mi Northwest of Standish by A5209 on B5250. Parking

The south east abounds in handsome historic houses once lived in by the likes of Disraeli and the Rothschilds, and it's no surprise that during the Plague it was to leafy Chalfont St Giles that John Milton fled. It is characterised by rolling hills such as the Chilterns with its ancient beechwoods, and the lilting North and South Downs, which cut a rural swathe across busy commuter belts. The film and television worlds sit easily here: Hambleden and Turville, in the Chilterns, are as used to the sound of the autocue as to the crunch of ramblers' boots. Meanwhile, James Bond's Aston Martin glistens in Beaulieu's Motor Museum, in the heart of the New Forest. Spinnaker Tower rivals HMS Victory for dominance of the Portsmouth skyline, while in Winchester, the Great Hall, home for 600 years to the Arthurian round table, nods acquaintance with the eleventh century Cathedral. Good food and drink is integral to the region, from Whitstable oysters and Dover sole to established vineyards.

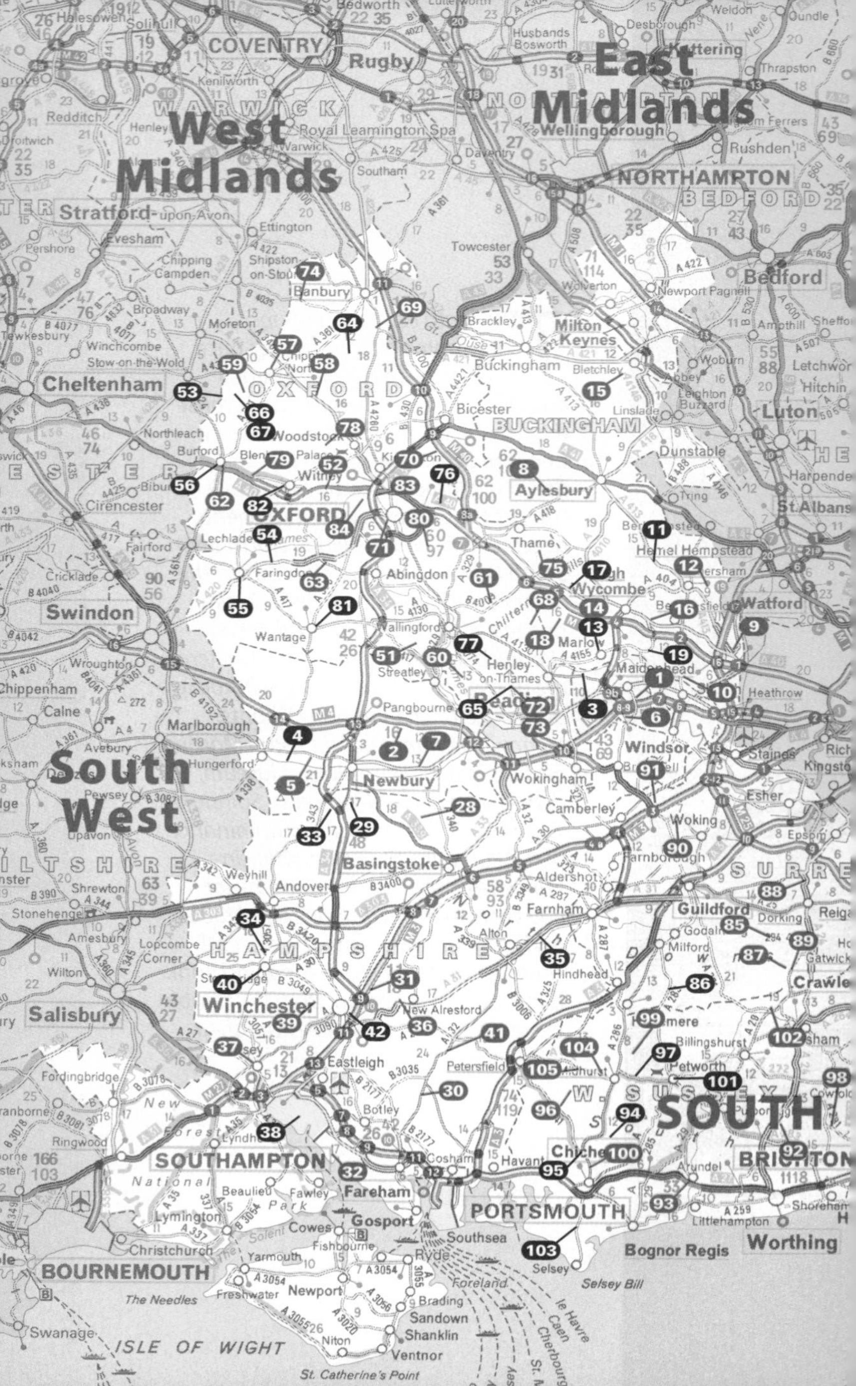
West Midlands
East Midlands
South West
SOUTH
COVENTRY
Rugby
Kettering
Wellingborough
NORTHAMPTON
BEDFORD
Bedford
Stratford-upon-Avon
Royal Leamington Spa
Warwick
Banbury
Cheltenham
OXFORD
Oxford
Milton Keynes
Buckingham
BUCKINGHAM
Aylesbury
Luton
Watford
Swindon
Reading
Newbury
Windsor
Marlborough
Basingstoke
Andover
Guildford
Winchester
Salisbury
Southampton
SOUTHAMPTON
Fareham
Gosport
PORTSMOUTH
BOURNEMOUTH
Bognor Regis
Worthing
BRIGHTON
Newport
ISLE OF WIGHT
The Needles
Selsey Bill
St. Catherine's Point
Le Havre
Caen
Cherbourg
HAMPSHIRE
SURREY
WILTSHIRE

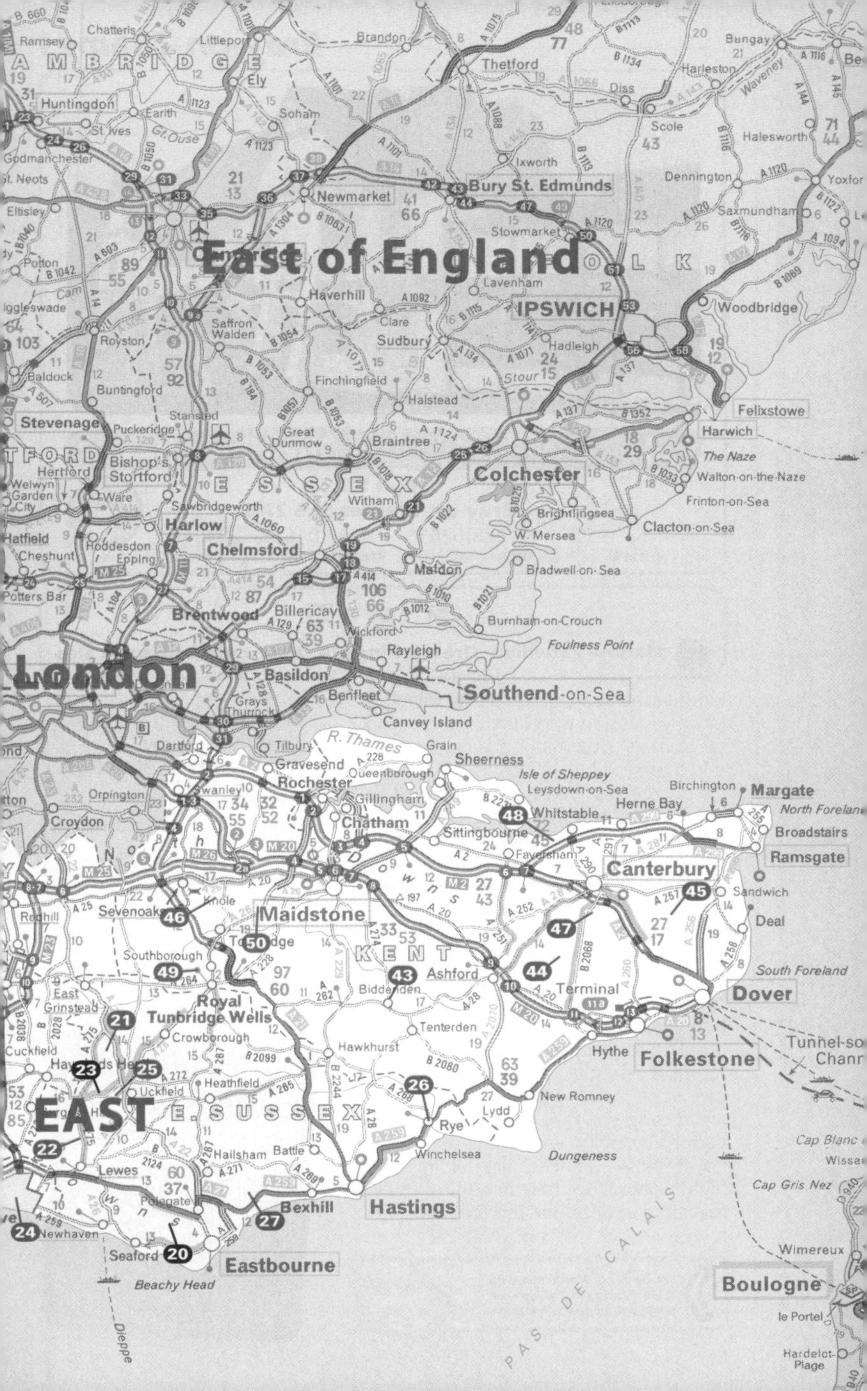

East of England
London
EAST SUSSEX
KENT
Huntingdon
St. Ives
Godmanchester
St. Neots
Ramsey
Chatteris
Littleport
Ely
Soham
Earth
Brandon
Thetford
Diss
Harleston
Bungay
Scole
Halesworth
Dennington
Yoxford
Saxmundham
Ixworth
Bury St. Edmunds
Newmarket
Stowmarket
Lavenham
IPSWICH
Woodbridge
Hadleigh
Felixstowe
Harwich
The Naze
Walton-on-the-Naze
Frinton-on-Sea
Clacton-on-Sea
Brightlingsea
W. Mersea
Colchester
Sudbury
Clare
Haverhill
Saffron Walden
Royston
Baldock
Buntingford
Stevenage
Puckeridge
Stansted
Bishop's Stortford
Hertford
Ware
Welwyn Garden City
Sawbridgeworth
Harlow
Hatfield
Hoddesdon
Cheshunt
Epping
Potters Bar
Chelmsford
Brentwood
Billericay
Wickford
Rayleigh
Basildon
Benfleet
Canvey Island
Southend-on-Sea
Maldon
Bradwell-on-Sea
Burnham-on-Crouch
Foulness Point
Witham
Braintree
Great Dunmow
Finchingfield
Halstead
Grays Thurrock
Tilbury
Dartford
Gravesend
Rochester
Chatham
Gillingham
Queenborough
R. Thames
Grain
Sheerness
Isle of Sheppey
Leysdown-on-Sea
Whitstable
Herne Bay
Birchington
Margate
North Foreland
Broadstairs
Ramsgate
Sandwich
Deal
South Foreland
Dover
Canterbury
Faversham
Sittingbourne
Maidstone
Sevenoaks
Knole
Swanley
Orpington
Croydon
Redhill
Tonbridge
Southborough
Royal Tunbridge Wells
Ashford
Biddenden
Tenterden
Hawkhurst
Terminal
Folkestone
Hythe
New Romney
Lydd
Dungeness
Rye
Winchelsea
Hastings
Bexhill
Battle
Hailsham
Heathfield
Uckfield
Crowborough
East Grinstead
Cuckfield
Lewes
Polegate
Eastbourne
Seaford
Newhaven
Beachy Head
Dieppe
PAS DE CALAIS
Tunnel-sous-Manche
Cap Blanc
Wissant
Cap Gris Nez
Wimereux
Boulogne
le Portel
Hardelot-Plage

1 The Hinds Head

High St,
Bray-on-Thames SL6 2AB
Tel.: (01628)626151 – Fax: (01628)623394
e-mail: info@hindsheadhotel.co.uk **Website:** www.hindsheadhotel.co.uk

Inspectors' favourites

VISA MC AE

Marlow Rebellion, Greene King IPA, Abbot Ale and guest ales

Right in the heart of the pretty village of Bray – beside the church and not too far from its alma mater, the Fat Duck – sits this charming pub, much as it has done for hundreds of years; its dark panelling, log fires and flag floors creating a characterful, almost medieval feel. With Heston Blumenthal at the helm, you'd be right to expect passionately prepared cooking, but we're not talking molecular gastronomy here: dishes are fiercely British, and some date back to Tudor times. Try a dandelion salad to start, perhaps, followed by a heart-warming oxtail and kidney pudding, and an aptly named quaking pudding for dessert. Booking for the dining rooms is essential, although reservations cannot be made in the bar, so if you arrive early, you may be in luck. With past patrons including various members of the Royal Family – Prince Philip held his stag night celebrations here in 1947 – you'll be following in distinguished footsteps.

Food serving times

Monday-Saturday:
12pm-2.30pm, 6.30pm-9pm

Sundays: 12pm-4pm

Closed 25-26 December

Prices

Meals: a la carte £ 18/32

Typical Dishes
Pea & ham soup
Oxtail & kidney pudding
Treacle tart

1mi South of Maidenhead by A308. Parking in 2 village car parks and opposite the pub.

2 The Pot Kiln

Frilsham RG18 0XX
Tel.: (01635)201366
e-mail: info@potkiln.org **Website:** www.potkiln.org

Brick Kiln, Mr Chubbs, Maggs Mild and weekly changing guest ales

Set in a picturesque rural location and surrounded by fields and distant woodland, this 350 year old red brick pub is the very essence of local country pub. The owners' dogs greet you at the entrance and there's a small but pleasant wood-filled bar. To say that the food is fresh and local doesn't cover it. Bread and pasta are homemade, veg, salad and herbs come from the kitchen garden, meat is from local farms or estates and fish is delivered from the Brixham day boats. On top of that, 90% of the game and all the river fish are caught by the owner himself. The menu reads more like a newsletter with this information, as well as events and of course, the wide-ranging list of food. There's the choice of sandwiches, brunch and old pub favourites with a local/modern twist, or some more restaurant style dishes served only in the dining area. At lunch there's a good value set menu and to wash it all down, there's beer from just down the road.

Food serving times

Monday-Sunday:
12pm-2pm, 7pm-9pm

Closed 25 December

Bar meals only Sunday evening

Prices

Meals: £ 15 (lunch)
and a la carte £ 27/34

Typical Dishes

Wood pigeon salad
Pavé of venison
Treacle tart

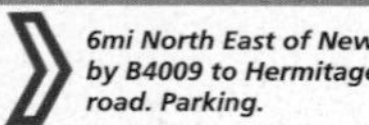

6mi North East of Newbury by B4009 to Hermitage and minor road. Parking.

3 Black Boys Inn

Henley Rd,
Hurley SL6 5NQ
Tel.: (01628)824212
e-mail: info@blackboysinn.co.uk **Website:** www.blackboysinn.co.uk

Inspectors' favourites

 **Brakspear Organic**

Behind the traditional façade of this 16C brick pub, on the busy main road between Hurley and Henley, lies a stylish modernised interior. A wood burning stove separates the comfy lounge from the beamed, wood floored dining area; there's a smaller room for those after a more intimate experience, and a terrace at the rear for those occasions when only al fresco dining will do. The overall impression that Black Boys tends more towards restaurant than inn in all but name is confirmed on perusing the menu, where you'll find dishes involving rillette of duck, Salcombe crab, sautéed calf's sweetbread and foie gras with prune and Armagnac chutney. Cooking is well-crafted and flavoursome and the friendly, knowledgeable service adds its own zesty tang. Individually-styled bedrooms come with excellent fitted bathrooms; but don't be surprised if the water supply splutters somewhat, since it has had to work its way up from the inn's very own well.

Food serving times

Tuesday-Saturday:
12pm-2pm, 7pm-9pm

Sunday: 12pm-2pm

Closed 2 weeks at Christmas, 2 weeks in August

Prices

Meals: a la carte £ 24/37

8 rooms: £ 75/120

Typical Dishes

Salcombe crab

Squab pigeon à la ficelle

Chocolate sablé

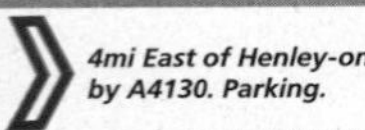

4mi East of Henley-on-Thames by A4130. Parking.

4 The Dundas Arms

Station Rd,
Kintbury RG17 9UT
Tel.: (01488)658263
e-mail: info@dundasarms.co.uk **Website:** www.dundasarms.co.uk

 **Adnams Bitter, Ramsbury Gold, West Berkshire Good Old Boy**

After supplying Kintbury with sustaining dinners and its daily pint for over three decades, the long-standing landlord knows he's among friends in the bar. Never ones to pass up a good thing, the locals arrive on the dot for filling dishes like steak and chips or roast duck breast and a friendly, familiar atmosphere prevails. If it gets a bit busy for your taste, the trick is to ask if they're opening the rear restaurant, usually reserved for more formal dinners; enjoy dishes such as pan-fried pigeon breasts or rump of lamb here, with views over the canal. On a summer afternoon, there's only one place to be, however. A lovely double terrace borders the edge of the Kennet and the canal: watch the narrowboats passing the lock as the stopping trains roll away to Bedwyn and the Wessex Downs. Five neat, light bedrooms face the river.

Food serving times

Monday-Saturday:
12pm-2pm, 7pm-9pm

Closed 25 December,
31 December dinner

Prices

Meals: a la carte £ 22/27

5 rooms: £ 80/95

Typical Dishes

Beef fillet salad
Steak & kidney pie
Raspberry brûlée

3.5mi East of Hungerford by A4.
Parking.

Marsh Benham

5 The Red House

Marsh Benham RG20 8LY
Tel.: (01635)582017 – Fax: (01635)581621
e-mail: enquiries@redhousemarshbenham.co.uk
Website: www.redhousemarshbenham.co.uk

 **Ruddles County, Hoppit**

Quintessentially English in both its style and its ambience, and boasting a beautiful thatched roof, this 18C red brick inn is situated in a quiet rural hamlet, two miles west of Newbury, and close to the Kennet and Avon canal. The front door leads into the wood-floored bar, with its warm red walls, hunting prints, attractive carved wood bar and relaxed, inviting atmosphere; go down the steps to the light, spacious restaurant for comfortable dining with countryside views by day and a more intimate feel by night. If the weather's looking on the bright side, then the terrace makes for a pleasant al fresco experience, and they also have a dining room set aside for private parties. There's a Mediterranean feel to the à la carte menu, with dishes such as woodland pigeon and foie gras terrine or veal saltimbocca, while the set menu is simpler, with good value English classics like shepherd's pie or pan-fried calves liver.

Food serving times

Monday-Sunday:
12pm-2.15pm, 6pm-9.30pm

Closed 26-27 December, 1 January

Prices

Meals: £ 17 a la carte
£ 29/38

Typical Dishes
Irish smoked salmon
Roast rack of lamb
Rhubarb & apple crumble

Off the A4 between Newbury and Hungerford. Parking

6 The Royal Oak

Paley Street SL6 3JN

Tel.: (01628)620541

e-mail: royaloakmail@aol.com

Website: www.theroyaloakpaleystreet.com

   VISA MC

 **Fuller's London Pride**

Being the offspring of a famous parent can be a struggle, what with the pressure to move out of their shadow and succeed in your own arena. Two such successes are to be found at this innocuous-looking roadside pub, in a small village close to the M4. Slickly run by Nick Parkinson, son of Michael, it offers a warm welcome to its eclectic clientele; knowledgeable staff take time to chat, and the atmosphere is friendly and relaxed. Head chef Dominic Chapman - son of Kit, a grandee of the hotel industry - creates good value, flavourful and fiercely British dishes of the home cooked, classic comfort food variety. Try the calf's sweetbreads, fricassee of duck hearts with bacon and onions or salt beef stovey; perhaps followed by bread and butter pudding or apple and rhubarb crumble. Grab a pint and a snack in the beamed bar with its comfy leather sofas, go al fresco on the spacious terrace, or dine like a royal in the rustic main dining area.

Food serving times

Monday-Saturday:
12pm-2.30pm, 6pm-10pm

Sunday: 12pm-2.30pm

Closed 26 December

Prices

Meals: a la carte £ 24/35

Typical Dishes

Jerusalem artichoke soup

Peppered haunch of venison

Bread and butter pudding

3.5 mi Southwest of Bray-on-Thames by A308,A330 on B3024. Parking

7 The Angel

Bath Rd,
Woolhampton RG7 5RT

Tel.: (0118)9713301

e-mail: mail@thea4angel.com **Website:** www.thea4angel.com

 **Fuller's London Pride**

Conveniently situated for motorists, on the A4 between Newbury and Reading, the ivy-clad Angel sits in the heart of the village, providing passers-by and locals alike with a friendly welcom and tasty, satisfying food. Its design is distinctive; wine bottles line the ceiling, dried foliage and hops hang from the beams, and all available surfaces seem to be covered with jars and bottles filled with pastas, fruits and berries. Sit on a cushioned banquette in the bar or take a seat in the restaurant; if the weather's half decent, then you might prefer ti head outside and dine al fresco. You can still pop in for a pint, but food is where the main emplhasis now lies – as illustrated by the self-applied `gastro´ tag – and while the lunchtime menu offers sandwiches, the a la carte is more varied, with dishes ranging from a soup or steak and chips to mussels in white wine, slow roast belly of pork or tiger prawns with linguini.

Food serving times
Monday-Sunday:
12pm-3pm, 6pm-11pm

Prices
Meals: a la carte £ 19/30

Typical Dishes
Parma ham
Honey-roast duck breast
Warm chocolate fondant

 *On A4 between Reading and Newbury. Parking* 

8 The Crown

Aylesbury Rd,
Cuddington HP18 0BB
Tel.: (01844)292222
e-mail: david@thecrowncuddington.co.uk **Website:** www.thecrowncuddington.co.uk

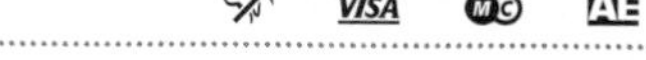
Adnams, Fuller's London Pride and one guest ale

There are many attractive thatched properties in pretty Cuddington, but, even so, this 16C pub still seems to stand out. From the outside, it looks appealingly like a traditional village pub - and what you see is exactly what you get. No gastropub modernisation here, thank you very much. It's got the carpets, the low beamed ceilings, the quarry tiled floors and the burgundy walls. Bric-a-brac and horse brasses abound and the gents has a surprisingly large collection of Victorian nudes. Two huge inglenook fireplaces featuring beehive chimneys add to the sense of history, although neither of them is actually used. Still very much a drinkers pub, there's plenty of room at the bar, but the food also attracts many a hungry punter. Enjoy tasty, modern dishes made with an eclectic range of ingredients; dishes might include fillet of red mullet with Spanish rice and saffron sauce or warm duck and bacon salad with raspberry vinaigrette.

Food serving times
Monday-Sunday:
12pm-2pm, 6.45pm-9.15pm
Closed Sunday dinner

Prices
Meals: £ 13/24
and a la carte £ 23/29

Typical Dishes
Battered black pudding
Confit rump of lamb
Raspberry & chocolate cheesecake

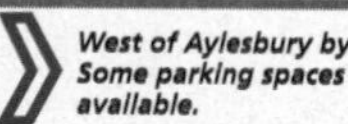
West of Aylesbury by A418. Some parking spaces are available.

9 The Swan Inn

Village Rd,
Denham UB9 5BH

Tel.: (01895)832085 – Fax: (01895)835516
e-mail: info@swaninndenham.co.uk **Website:** www.swaninndenham.co.uk

 **Courage Best, Wadworth 6X, Marlow Rebellion IPA**

You can hear the muted rumble of the M25 and the A40 in the distance - or maybe it's your empty stomach complaining - but this unspoiled village is nevertheless an attractive spot for this wisteria clad pub. The open plan bar has a relaxed feel to it, happily harbouring both drinkers and diners, as does the large garden and terrace, whilst "The room behind the bar" is used for private parties of up to ten. The contemporary à la carte menu evolves with the seasons and, along with the specials board, offers ample choice. Among the "small plates," you might try the baked thyme-studded brie, which comes with sticky red cabbage and melba toast, or the twice-baked crab soufflé, accompanied by saffron and grain mustard syrup. The interesting flavours continue with the mains, so wasabi tempura seabass might come on Asian salad with hoi sin dressing, and a confit duck leg on sage gnocchi with fig and sherry cream sauce. Booking is recommended.

Food serving times

Monday-Friday:
12pm-2.30pm, 7pm-10pm

Saturday:
12pm-3pm, 7pm-10pm

Sunday:
12pm-4pm, 7pm-10pm

Closed 25-26 December

Booking essential

Prices

Meals: a la carte £ 20/30

Typical Dishes

Crayfish & crab vol-au-vent

Roast shoulder of lamb

Spiced pear tarte Tatin

6mi Northeast of Slough by A412;in the centre of the village. Small car park.

10 The King of Prussia

Blackpond Lane,
Farnham Royal SL2 3EG
Tel.: (01753)643006
e-mail: gm@tkop.co.uk **Website:** www.thekingofprussia.com

 **Fuller's London Pride, Amstel**

At 100 years of age, The King of Prussia is relatively youthful as pubs go, and its stylishly refurbished bar with polished wooden floorboards, leather bucket chairs and low wood tables seems to suit its modern day abbreviation to TKOP. The décor may be modern, but the cooking is more classical in its style, and the experienced kitchen treats its quality seasonal ingredients simply to create traditional British dishes like fish and chips, sausage and mash or potted Aylesbury duck. Everything, including the bread, is homemade, with pies a speciality and therefore always a wise choice for the particularly hungry. It's unusually located on a housing estate, but the rear garden has decking and a children's play area, making it a pleasant spot for al fresco dining, while inside, the spacious dark wood conservatory and restored barn with its heavy wood beams make for a much more formal experience. Slick service completes the picture.

Food serving times

Monday-Saturday:
12pm-2.30pm, 6pm-9.30pm

Sunday: 12pm-2.30pm

Closed 25 December and 1 January

Prices

Meals: a la carte £ 20/35

Typical Dishes

Chicken livers
Fillet steak
Chocolate mousse

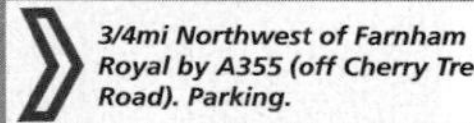

3/4mi Northwest of Farnham Royal by A355 (off Cherry Tree Road). Parking.

11 The Nags Head

London Road,
Great Missenden HP16 0DG

Tel.: (01494)862200 – Fax: (01494)862945
e-mail: goodfood@nagsheadbucks.com **Website:** www.nagsheadbucks.com

VISA MC AE

 **Black Sheep, Fuller's London Pride, Timothy Taylor Landlord**

This traditional 15C inn set in the Chiltern Hills is a far cry from Del Boy and Rodney's ageing local in the streets of Peckham. Situated in a peaceful town on the original coaching trail to London, the ancient clatter of carriage wheels and echo of horseshoes has been replaced by the gentle pat of tennis balls and comforting thwack of leather on willow from the clubs nearby. Inside chunky brick walls divide the characterful main room in two, while a large inglenook fireplace and local scenic prints add to the rustic charm. Mimicking its sister pub ten miles away, the cooking features a strong Gallic base, with classical Burgundy dishes such as oeufs en meurette or foie gras playing a starring role and some good British classics alongside; home-smoked meats feature strongly too. The individually styled bedrooms are bright, modern and comfortable and you are greeted by a good continental breakfast in the morning. "Lovely Jubbly".

Food serving times

Monday-Saturday:
12pm-2.30pm,
6.30pm-9.30pm

Sunday: 12pm-2.30pm

Closed 25 December

French Mediterranean

Prices

Meals: a la carte £ 25/38

6 rooms: £ 90/110

Typical Dishes

Crab & home-smoked salmon
Chicken breast
Stuffed crêpe

Between Wendover and Amersham on A413

The Sugar Loaf Inn

12 The Sugar Loaf Inn

Station Road,
Little Chalfont HP7 9PN
Tel.: (01494)765579
e-mail: info@thesugarloafinn.com **Website:** www.thesugarloafinn.com

 **Timothy Taylor Landlord, Adnams Bitter, Adnams Broadside**

This inn was originally a motel, built by the local railway company in the 1930s to serve travellers arriving at the nearby station. Typical of its period, its exterior is not exactly prepossessing, but venture inside and you'll be impressed by the restored oak panelling and wooden floors. Simple, contemporary décor is enhanced by the Jack Vettriano prints for sale on the walls. The central bar serves two areas; one with sofas and tables for drinkers, and the other exclusively for diners. There is also a pleasant conservatory and a rather modest rear garden and decked terrace. Lunch and dinner menus offer value-for-money pub classics, as well as more modern dishes with a European flavour. No one seems to know the origins of the pub's sweet-sounding name but suggestions range from the shape in which refined sugar used to be exported, to a type of pineapple, via a breed of horse and a 1970s pop band. Answers on a postcard, please.

Food serving times

Monday-Sunday:
12pm-2.30pm, 5.30pm-10pm

Closed 25-26 December
and 1 January

Prices

Meals: £ 10 (lunch)
and a la carte £ 20/26

Typical Dishes

Smoked duck salad
Roast cod
Dark chocolate tart

2mi East of Amersham by A404.
Parking.

13 The Hand and Flowers

126 West St,
Marlow SL7 2BP

Tel.: (01628)482277 – Fax: (01628)401913

e-mail: theoffice@thehandandflowers.co.uk **Website:** www.thehandandflowers.co.uk

Inspectors' favourites

    AE

 **Abbot Ale, Greene King IPA**

There aren't many pubs that offer diners the opportunity of spending a whole day shadowing one of the chefs but then The Hand and Flowers is rightly proud of its food and its smart, new kitchen. Owner Tom Kerridge has developed a menu to enthuse, rather than frighten off the natives and his impressive command of assorted cooking techniques is evident, from braising to poaching, curing to roasting; dishes have depth and clarity and a lot of work goes into making them so easy on the eye. But most importantly, he never forgets that this is a pub - the beer pumps are the first thing you see, you have to duck to avoid the beams and service is never po-faced. Moreover, there are simpler dishes available at lunch and you'll even find the odd piece of culinary post-modernism: check out the salt cod Scotch egg or the whitebait served as an amuse bouche. There are four pretty bedrooms in two neighbouring cottages; "Angus" has an outdoor Jacuzzi.

From town centre follow Henley signs West on A4155. Pub on right after 350metres. Parking.

Food serving times

Monday-Saturday:
12pm-2.30pm, 7pm-9.30pm

Sunday: 12pm-3.30pm

Closed 24-26 December

Prices

Meals: a la carte £ 28/36

4 rooms: £ 140/190

Typical Dishes

Home cured anchovies
Squab pigeon
Banana soufflé

14 The Royal Oak

Frieth Rd,
Bovingdon Green, Marlow SL7 2JF
Tel.: (01628)488611 – Fax: (01628)478680
e-mail: info@royaloakmarlow.co.uk **Website:** www.royaloakmarlow.co.uk

Fuller's London Pride, Brakspear, Marlow Rebellion IPA

Travel to the outskirts of historic Marlow and, on a busy country lane just past the woods, you will light upon The Royal Oak. Its name splashed boldly across its front, this pub is contemporary in style; open plan, with a large bar and a light and airy conservatory. Parts of the pub date from 17C – so for a taste of its rustic character, head for the cosy beamed area on the left behind the bar, with its mismatch of furniture, wood burning stove and flagged floors. Out front you are greeted by the scent of rosemary, and the pub's sizeable lawned garden – complete with petanque piste - makes for a very pleasant spot to dine on a summer's evening. Well-run by an enthusiastic team, service is friendly and a relaxed atmosphere prevails throughout. The modern menu is supplemented with blackboard specials, and dishes on offer might range from creamy Italian bean cassoulet to steak and fat chips, with plenty of fresh fish and local game.

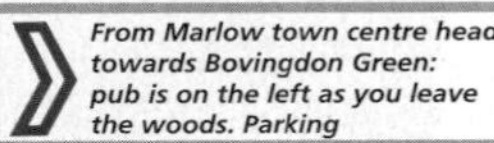
From Marlow town centre head towards Bovingdon Green: pub is on the left as you leave the woods. Parking

Food serving times
Monday-Friday:
12pm-2.30pm, 7pm-10pm
Saturday:
12pm-3pm, 7pm-10pm
Sunday:
12pm-4pm, 7pm-10pm
Closed 25-26 December

Prices
Meals: a la carte £ 20/29

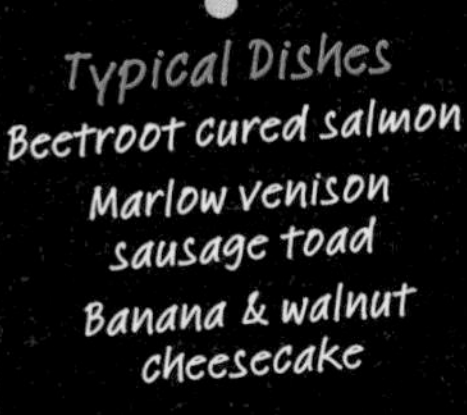

Newton Longville

15 The Crooked Billet

2 Westbrook End,
Newton Longville MK17 0DF
Tel.: (01908)373936
e-mail: john@thebillet.co.uk **Website:** www.thebillet.co.uk

Inspectors' favourites

IPA, Abbot, Hobgoblin, Old Speckled Hen, Old Peculier, 6X., Ruddles Orchard, Tring Breweries

You can't help feeling that this attractive, 17C thatched pub would be better suited to life in a picturesque little countryside village than on the outskirts of MK, but everything else about it feels exactly right, thanks to the formidable team that is John and Emma Gilchrist. As illustrated by the way the suppliers are credited on the menu, the couple are serious about food - even the people of the village get a mention for growing the vegetables and herbs – and Emma cooks well-balanced, modern dishes. Menus range from sandwiches, wraps and pasta at lunchtime through to a six course gourmet menu, and there is a rather interesting cheeseboard too. John's former life as a sommelier is evident in the remarkable wine list, with over 300 bins to choose from - and the vast majority of them available by the glass. Locals still gather solely for a drink, and the pub's low ceilinged, firelit bar makes this an atmospheric place for a pint.

Food serving times

Monday: 7pm-10pm

Tuesday-Saturday:
12pm-2pm, 7pm-10pm

Sunday: 12pm-4pm

Closed 25 December

Prices

Meals: a la carte £ 20/28

Typical Dishes
Pan-fried scallops
Cassoulet
Orange & chocolate mousse

6mi Southwest of Milton Keynes by A421. Parking.

The Old Queens Head

16 The Old Queens Head

Hammersley Lane,
Penn HP10 8EY
Tel.: (01494)813371 – Fax: (01494)816145
e-mail: info@oldqueensheadpenn.co.uk **Website:** www.oldqueensheadpenn.co.uk

Greene King IPA, Ruddles County

In the same year that the Great Fire of London was destroying large parts of the capital city, not too far away, in a tile-making village in leafy Buckinghamshire, the original part of the Old Queens Head was being constructed. Nowadays, it's an attractive, modern dining pub but it still retains charmingly rustic reminders of its ancient vintage, like its flagged floors now decorated with rugs, low ceiling rafters and beams, brick fireplaces and roughly plastered walls. There are a number of adjoining rooms but the oldest and most characterful is the more formal dining room, built over two levels and containing a hotchpotch of old wooden furniture. A small rear garden with picnic tables extends the pub's relaxed atmosphere outside. The menu offers an eclectic mix of traditional and more modern dishes, seasonally changing and served in generous portions, while specials are chalked up on a blackboard.

Food serving times
Monday-Friday:
12pm-2.30pm, 7pm-10pm
Saturday:
12pm-3pm, 7pm-10pm
Sunday:
12pm-4pm, 7pm-10pm
Closed 25-26 December

Prices
Meals: a la carte £ 20/29

Typical Dishes
Gurnard goujons
Coq au vin
Spiced pears

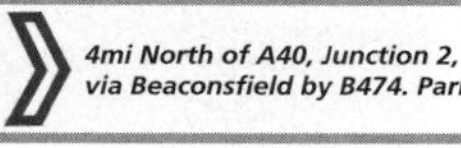
4mi North of A40, Junction 2, via Beaconsfield by B474. Parking.

England • South East • Buckinghamshire

17 The Three Horseshoes Inn

Bennett End,
Radnage HP14 4EB
Tel.: (01494)483273
e-mail: threehorseshoe@btconnect.com **Website:** www.thethreehorseshoes.net

 **Rebellion beers, IPA, Intruder, Blonde**

In the heart of the Buckinghamshire countryside stands the Three Horseshoes Inn; an attractive red brick pub dating from 1745. Its tiny front bar with its unusual inglenook fireplace, flagged floor and settles gets busy with locals at the weekends and although you can eat here, most people tend to dine at the linen-laid tables in the rear restaurant area. In the laid-back summer months you can eat tapas on the terrace while enjoying views out over fields and the garden – including the duck pond with its strangely submerged red telephone box. Numerous plates by the bar detail the owner / chef's fine pedigree, and the good value, modern British cooking he serves up here has a noteworthy precision and quality. Meals are well-presented, and ingredients are carefully sourced - locally wherever possible. Modern, comfortable bedrooms are individually decorated - Molières is the nicest - with character beds and modern bathrooms.

Food serving times

Monday: 7pm-9.30pm

Tuesday-Saturday:
12pm-2pm, 7pm-9.30pm

Sunday: 12pm-2pm

Closed Sunday dinner and Monday

Closed Tuesday following Bank Holiday Monday

Prices

Meals: a la carte £ 24/30

6 rooms: £ 85/145

Typical Dishes

Seared scallop salad

Pot-roasted Guinea fowl

Hot chocolate fondant

5mi West of High Wycombe by A40 and minor road North. Parking.

18 The Bull & Butcher

Turville RG9 6QU
Tel.: (01491)638283 – Fax: (01491)638836
e-mail: info@thebullandbutcher.com **Website:** www.thebullandbutcher.com

 **Brakspear's Bitter, Hooky Dark, Oxford Gold**

This whitewashed, 16C, Grade II listed pub is situated in the middle of the charming village of Turville; a location which may well give you a sense of déja vu, having been immortalised in various television programmes and films including The Vicar of Dibley and Goodnight Mr. Tom. Seek out a seat at the well table, built around a well in the middle of one of the rooms or sit in the garden facing north, and you'll see a beautiful white windmill on the hill, which was part of the set from Chitty Chitty Bang Bang. The atmosphere here is one of cosy comfort; local photos line the walls and there are wood beams, quarry tiles, log fires and scrubbed pine tables. The Bull room – a small converted barn - is used for private parties. Tried and tested pub favourites are to be found on the menu here, - steak and Dibley pudding, anyone? - but for more modern, Truly Scrumptious dishes, plump for one of the specials chalked up on the blackboard.

Food serving times

Monday-Friday:
12pm-2.30pm, 6pm-9.30pm

Saturday:
12pm-4pm, 6pm-9.30pm

Sunday & Bank Holidays:
12pm-4pm, 7pm-9pm

Prices

Meals: a la carte £ 20/27

Typical Dishes

Smoked salmon & avocado paté
Grilled seabass fillet
Selection of local cheeses

5mi North of Henley-on-Thames by A4130 off B480. Parking

19 Chequers Inn

Kiln Lane,
Wooburn Common HP10 0JQ
Tel.: (01628)529575 – Fax: (01628)850124
e-mail: info@chequers-inn.com **Website:** www.chequers-inn.com

Greene King IPA, Abbot Ale, Old Speckled Hen, Marlow Brewery Smuggler

Run by the same family for more than thirty years, this attractive red brick 17C inn has had time to build itself a reputation and, although seemingly situated on a country lane in the middle of nowhere, it does get surprisingly busy. The beamed bar with its open fire is as charming as it is small and makes a cosy place for a meal from the blackboard bar menu with its choice of old favourites, whereas the spacious, stylish lounge with its comfy sofas and coffee tables is more popular with the ladies who lunch. The à la carte menu is served in the formal restaurant housed in the extension, and might include pork or pigeon, beef or bream, and a table d'hôte and a two course 45 minute menu are also available for those counting either the pennies or the clock. Good-sized modern bedrooms also housed in the extension have views over the surrounding fields; room 17 has a four poster and is the most comfortable.

Food serving times

Monday-Sunday:
12pm-2.30pm, 6pm-9.30pm

Closed dinner 25 December and 1 January

Prices

Meals: £ 19 (weekdays)/28 and a la carte £ 27/30

17 rooms: £ 88/108

Typical Dishes

Smoked salmon platter
Chicken supreme
Whisky & apricot bread & butter pudding

3.5mi Southwest of Beaconsfield by A40. Parking.

20 The George Inn

High St,
Alfriston BN26 5SY
Tel.: (01323)870319
e-mail: info@thegeorge-alfriston.com **Website:** www.thegeorge-alfriston.com

 **Greene King IPA, Abbot Ale and guest ale - Old Speckled Hen**

A delightful South Downs village complete with bell ringers, cricket club and village green is the setting for this equally charming stone and timber building, the epitome of the traditional English inn. Some parts of it date back to the 13C and a network of smugglers' tunnels purportedly lead from its cellars. It's still very much a locals' pub, with a warm, homely feel; dried hops hang from the eaves, three rooms all boast inglenook fireplaces for cosy winter drinking and dining, while the summer swell is accommodated by the large rear gardens. They offer a good selection of dishes, and while those who prefer their culinary influences to be closer to home will be happy to see slow roast belly of pork or roasted rack of lamb on the menu; those who like food of a more international provenance will like the sound of dishes involving Thai style chicken balls, veal saltimbocca or bouillabaisse. Characterful bedrooms feature oak beams.

Food serving times

Sunday-Thursday:
12pm-2.30pm, 7pm-9pm

Friday-Saturday:
12pm-2.30pm, 7pm-10pm

Closed 25-26 December

Prices

Meals: a la carte £ 21/28

6 rooms: £ 60/130

Typical Dishes
Grilled stuffed mushrooms
Roast rack of lamb
Poached peaches

Two public car parks 150 metres and street parking.

21 Coach & Horses

School Lane,
Danehill RH17 7JF

Tel.: (01825)740369 – Fax: (01825)740369

e-mail: coachandhorses@danehill.biz **Website:** www.coachandhorses.danehill.biz

 **Harveys Best, Hammerot Meteor and others**

Some pubs tend to forget those living on their doorstep, but not this characterful stone inn. It has a formally laid area for dining, converted from the original stables, but at its hub is its charming bar, seemingly unchanged since its creation in 1847, where locals enjoy a pint and a chat; dog optional. The bar can't take all the credit for the relaxed, unpretentious atmosphere here though - the friendly, informal service also plays its part, and on sunny days the pretty garden positively encourages somnolence. Traditional menus offer a good mix of meat and fish dishes at very reasonable prices; ingredients are locally sourced wherever possible and, since beasts are bought whole and butchered in the kitchen, the blackboard specials menu often includes more unusual offerings such as venison liver or braised heart. Snacks and sandwiches are available at lunchtimes and you can purchase the ever popular Ladypots preserves at the bar.

Food serving times

Monday-Friday:
12pm-2pm, 7pm-9pm

Saturday-Sunday:
12pm-2.30pm, 7pm-9.30pm

Closed 25 December dinner, 26 December, 1 January dinner

Prices

Meals: a la carte £ 21/27

Typical Dishes

Grilled local sardines
Slow roasted pork belly
Treacle tart

0.75mi Northeast on Chelwood Common Rd. Parking

22 The Jolly Sportsman

Chapel Lane,
East Chiltington BN7 3BA
Tel.: (01273)890400 – Fax: (01273)890400
e-mail: info@thejollysportsman.com **Website:** www.thejollysportsman.com

 **Dark Star Hophead and one guest beer**

Meandering through the winding lanes of Sussex, even the journey to this pub feels like a jolly japer; staff are jolly and they serve jolly good food too. With a raised rear garden and a paved terrace area, this creeper-clad pub is very popular during the summer months, but a seat by the fire in the cosy bar, or in the airy dining room is just as pleasant any month of the year and the owner's hands-on approach helps it to run like the proverbial clockwork. The confident kitchen's simply presented cooking delivers the promise of the menu, letting the quality of the ingredients shine through. There is a subtle Mediterranean influence with fish a particular strength; dishes might include fresh truffle pappardelle or teal breast, fallow deer loin or grilled Pollock, and all display a vitality that comes from knowing which flavours go well together. The exceptional wine list includes a lengthy selection of claret and burgundy.

Food serving times

Tuesday-Thursday:
12.30pm-2.30pm,
7pm-9.30pm

Friday-Saturday:
12.30pm-2.30pm,
7pm-10pm

Sunday: 12.30pm-3pm

Closed 25-27 December

Prices

Meals: £ 16 (3 course lunch) and a la carte £ 23/30

Typical Dishes
Braised pig's cheek
Rump of Ditchling lamb
Orange three ways

5.5mi Northwest of Lewes by A275 and B2116 off Novington Lane. Parking

23 The Griffin Inn

Fletching TN22 3SS

Tel.: (01825)722890 – Fax: (01825)722810

e-mail: info@thegriffininn.co.uk **Website:** www.thegriffininn.co.uk

   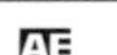 

 **Harveys Best Bitter, Kings of Horsham, Hepworth Iron Horse**

This red and white brick 16C coaching inn is the kind of pub everyone would like to have in their village. Well-established and owned by the same family for thirty years, it's got the cosy beamed bar packed with locals, the open fires and a linen-laid candlelit dining area. It also has its own cricket team, a terrace and a large garden - the ideal spot for summer Sunday barbeques, watching the sun set over the Downs. The buzzing atmosphere more than makes up for any slippage in service and the food here is fresh and homemade, using local produce, including Rye Bay seafood. The daily-changing menu offers modern British cooking with some Italian influences; dishes such as shellfish stew, saltimbocca of monkfish or rump of Romney Marsh lamb. A choice of individually decorated rooms is available; each comfortable, and some with four posters and roll top baths; those in the adjacent Griffin House are the best.

Food serving times

Monday-Sunday:
12pm-2.30pm, 7pm-9.30pm

Closed 25 December,
1 January dinner

Restaurant closed dinner Sunday

Prices

Meals: £ 30 (Sunday lunch) and a la carte £ 21/35

13 rooms: £ 70/145

Typical Dishes

Grilled baby squid
Roast rump of lamb
Hot chocolate fondant

Between Uckfield and Haywards Heath off A272. Parking.

24 The Ginger Pig

3 Hove Street,
Hove BN3 2TR
Tel.: (01273)736123
Website: www.gingermanrestaurants.com

   AE

 **Harveys Best and monthly changing local Sussex guest beers**

Located just off the seafront in up and coming Hove actually, The Ginger Pig is the third of the Gingerman group's ventures in the Brighton area and is proving just as popular as its siblings. Entry into this striking, part-gabled building – a former smugglers' haunt - is through equally striking revolving doors. Once inside, chill out with a drink on low sofas in the contemporary bar or venture up the steps to the spacious, open plan dining area with its mix of leather banquettes and dark wood chairs and tables, beyond which lies the sun-trap of a terrace. Like the décor and the bold art hanging on the walls, the cooking here is modern and fresh, and the concise European menu offers tasty, refined dishes, all homemade using local produce, and served in filling portions. Specials are chalked up on a blackboard menu and keen, young servers form a well-drilled team – but bookings are not accepted, so those in the know arrive early.

Food serving times

Monday-Friday:
12pm-2pm, 6.30pm-10pm

Saturday-Sunday:
12.30pm-4pm, 6.30pm-10pm

Closed 25 December

Bookings not accepted

Prices

Meals: a la carte £ 21/31

Typical Dishes

Braised Puy lentil salad
Guinea fowl breast
Rhubarb fool

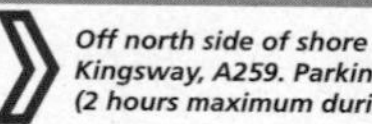

Off north side of shore road, Kingsway, A259. Parking meters (2 hours maximum during day).

25 The Peacock Inn

Shortbridge,
Piltdown TN22 3XA
Tel.: (01825)762463
e-mail: matthewarnold@aol.com **Website:** www.peacock-inn.co.uk

 **Harveys Best, Fuller's London Pride, Bombardier**

Early records show that this pub – previously named The Star – started life as an 18C alehouse, selling home-brewed beers to passers-by. It still sells a good selection of beers but now there is also a focus on quality pub grub, with plenty of steaks and grills on the menu and a specials board that often features fresh fish. Dishes are straightforward with no frills and might include pan-fried sea bass, roasted lamb rump or fisherman's pie. Summer is particularly appealing here, when colourful shrubs and hanging baskets welcome you and the brick BBQ in the rear garden is often doing a roaring trade. Inside is equally appealing, with the unique light oak parquet floor providing an elegant contrast with the heavy dark-wood furnishings. They are not unused to the odd celebrity appearance here; Thora Hird used to be a regular and Dame Vera Lynn sometimes drops by.

Food serving times
Monday-Sunday:
12pm-3pm, 6pm-10pm

Closed 25-26 December

Booking advisable
at weekends

Prices
Meals: a la carte £ 20/30

Typical Dishes
Smoked salmon & crayfish salad
Fillet steak Monroe
Bailey's cheesecake

8mi East of Haywards Heath by A272 and Shortbridge Lane. Parking.

26 Globe Inn

10 Military Rd,
Rye TN31 7NX
Tel.: (01797)227918
e-mail: info@theglobe-inn.com **Website:** www.theglobe-inn.com

 AE

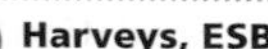
Harveys, ESB

There are modern dining tables, a contemporary bar counter with hand pumps for real ales, trendy leather sofas, coffee tables, and a large outside terrace. Take a closer look at around you, however, and you'll notice an underlying quirkiness inspired by Janette's passion for all things '40's. Vera Lynn plays on the sound system, there are cabinets containing old china and collections of vintage newspapers and magazines - plus the lady herself even dresses in a wartime style, with her hair tied up and strappy high heels on. Thankfully, the '40's feel does not extend to the food and a generously-sized à la carte offers seasonal, locally-sourced produce translated into dishes such as chicken liver parfait, braised beef shin or loin of monkfish. There's freshly baked bread, a short snack menu at lunchtimes and a choice of homely puddings. Drinks are served with parsnip crisps and there are plenty of homemade goodies for sale at the bar.

Food serving times

Tuesday (July-September):
12pm-2.30pm, 7pm-9pm

Wednesday-Saturday:
12pm-2.30pm, 7pm-9pm

Sunday: 12pm-2.30pm

Prices

Meals: £ 16 (lunch)
and a la carte £ 26/37

Typical Dishes
Lobster risotto
Braised local monkfish
Bread & butter pudding

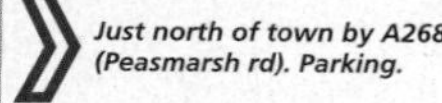
Just north of town by A268 (Peasmarsh rd). Parking.

27 The Lamb Inn

Wartling Rd,
Wartling BN27 1RY

Tel.: (01323)832116 – Fax: (01323)832637
e-mail: alison.farncombe@virgin.net **Website:** www.lambinnwartling.co.uk

  AE

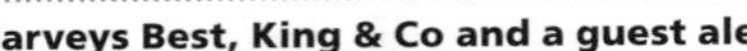
Harveys Best, King & Co and a guest ale

With its traditional whitewashed appearance and attractive rear courtyard, it is perhaps easy to see that this elevated roadside inn began life as a pair of cottages, and its characterful interior, with its flag floors and beamed ceilings further vouches for its early 16C origins. Quality and traceability are the bywords here when it comes to food; they bake their own bread, whilst seafood comes from Hastings and Newhaven and most of the meat hails from neighbouring Chilley Farm, who specialise in traditionally-farmed stock with no additives, and slow-reared rare breeds such as Gloucester Old Spot pork and extra mature Sussex beef. Homemade dishes might include anything from robust pies to cassoulet of duck, and mutton, enjoying something of a renaissance, also appears. Eat in the bar or in the more formal restaurant; the welcome is friendly and this place is clearly a hit with the locals, with themed evenings particularly popular.

Food serving times

Monday-Saturday:
11.45am-2.15pm,
6.45pm-9pm

Sunday: 11.45am-2.15pm

Closed Sunday dinner

Prices

Meals: a la carte £ 18/30

Typical Dishes

Grilled king scallops
Confit of duck leg
Chocolate espresso tartlet

3.75mi Southeast of Herstmonceaux by A271 and Wartling Rd. Parking

The Wellington Arms

28 The Wellington Arms

Baughurst Rd,
Baughurst RG26 5LP
Tel.: (0118)9820110
e-mail: info@thewellingtonarms.com **Website:** www.thewellingtonarms.com

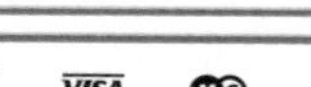

 **Wadworth 6X**

A country dining pub with a warm, friendly atmosphere, this former hunting lodge of the Duke of Wellington is characterful and cosy, its traditional tile floors and wooden beams blending well with more modern touches like the pretty floral blinds. They are passionate about food here: local produce is sourced with the utmost care, they grow their own vegetables and herbs and keep chickens and bees in the garden - with eggs and honey for sale at the bar alongside homemade preserves and teas, salt and soap imported from Australia. Flavoursome, modern British cooking takes centre stage on the blackboard menu, and dishes might include roast rack of English lamb, local venison potpie braised with real ale or seared turbot fillet, with good value lunch menus also featuring pub favourites such as cottage pie or fish and chips. Service is polite and chatty - but with only eight tables set for dining, you should be sure to book ahead.

Food serving times

Tuesday: 6.30pm-9.30pm

Wednesday-Saturday:
12pm-2.30pm, 6.30-9.30pm

Sunday: 12pm-2.30pm

Closed Sunday dinner, Monday (all day), Tuesday lunch

Prices

Meals: £ 18 (lunch)
and a la carte £ 18/32

Typical Dishes
Country terrine
Roast turbot
Rhubarb & elderflower jelly

8mi North of Basingstoke by A339 and minor road through Ramsdell and Pound Green; South on the Kingsclere / Newbury road. Parking.

29 Carnarvon Arms

Winchester Rd,
Whitway, Burghclere RG20 9LE
Tel.: (01635)278222 – Fax: (01635)278444
e-mail: info@carnarvonarms.com **Website:** www.carnarvonarms.com

   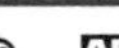

 **Spitfire, Fuller's London Pride, Grteene King IPA and various guest ales**

You might well wonder why the walls of the vaulted dining room in the barn conversion of this smart 19C inn are decorated with hieroglyphics - but it begins to make sense when you know that the pub is named after the 5th Earl of Carnarvon, who lived at nearby Highclere House and was one of the men who discovered Tutankhamen's tomb. The pub is situated on a busy country lane which runs alongside the A34, the welcome is a friendly one and you can choose to dine on leather sofas in the spacious main bar and lounge, or in one of the open plan rooms which surround it. There's plenty of choice on the modern British menu, too, from sandwiches to more substantial dishes, and all at reasonable prices. Try the pigeon pie, pot roast pork collar or honey roasted Gressingham duck breast; or perhaps the more classic sausage and mash or pan-fried liver with bacon. A myriad of small, up-to-date bedrooms are popular with businessmen during the week.

Food serving times

Monday-Thursday: 12pm-2.30pm, 6.30pm-9pm

Friday: 12pm-2.30pm, 6.30pm-9.30pm

Saturday: 12pm-2.30pm, 6.30pm-10pm

Sunday: 12pm-3pm

Prices

Meals: £ 15 (lunch) and a la carte £ 25/35

23 rooms: £ 70/100

Typical Dishes

Pan-roasted scallops

Sussex Downs lamb

Trio of chocolate desserts

5mi South of Newbury by A34 and minor road East. Parking.

30 The Bakers Arms

High St,
Droxford, Fareham SO32 3PA
Tel.: (01489)877533
e-mail: info@thebakersarmsdroxford.com **Website:** www.thebakersarmsdroxford.com

Inspectors' favourites

 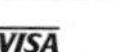 

Bowman Ales - Swift One & Wallops Wood

Situated in a peaceful village which lies on the banks of the river Meon, this traditional whitewashed pub is run by two thoroughly keen owners and their friendly team. With a commitment to providing quality, local food in a traditional pub atmosphere, they make the most of the local produce around them. Cooking is simple and unfussy, featuring classic British combinations with the odd French or Mediterranean touch; Droxford pork or sausages and steak or chicken from Hampshire are often on the menu, with time-honoured desserts such as apple and rhubarb crumble or bread and butter pudding to follow. The pub itself is characterful, featuring a mixture of wood and parquet flooring, pine tables and chairs and leather sofas, whilst a random array of Victorian photographs, historic beer advertisements and stags heads line the walls. Beers and wines are sourced locally, and can be enjoyed over a newspaper or a game of scrabble by the fire.

Food serving times

Tuesday-Saturday:
12pm-2.30pm,
6.30pm-9.30pm

Sunday: 12pm-2.30pm

Closed Bank Holiday Mondays

Prices

Meals: a la carte £ 20/24

Typical Dishes

Goats cheese tart
Droxford pork belly
Hampshire cheese plate

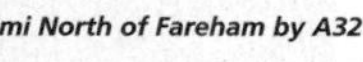
6mi North of Fareham by A32

England • South East • Hampshire

31 The Chestnut Horse

Easton SO21 1EG
Tel.: (01962)779257 – Fax: (01962)779037
e-mail: info@thechestnuthorse.com **Website:** www.thechestnuthorse.com

  VISA MC

 **Sussex, Badger, Hopping Hare, Tanglefoot**

A colourful pub, in more ways than one, despite being not a million miles from Winchester or the M3, the Chestnut Horse is still set in a pleasantly rural village and its pretty rear terrace spills over with vibrant floral blooms. If it's an intimate atmosphere you're after of an evening, take a seat next to the log fire in the romantic red room, where you can gaze lovingly at your partner over candlelight. The green room is the natural choice for lunch, but be aware that reservations are essential at weekends if you want to eat in either room. The building dates from 1564, and the characterful timbered bar, where tankards and jugs hang from the beams, is a monument to old times. Pub favourites rub alongside more modern dishes on the extensive menu, supplemented with an interesting list of daily specials chalked up on the blackboard. Pleasant staff are on hand, and are happy to deal with any special requests.

Food serving times
Monday-Sunday:
12pm-2pm, 6pm-9.30pm
Closed Sunday dinner in winter

Prices
Meals: a la carte £ 16/30

Typical Dishes
Crab & crayfish tian
Roast pork tenderloin
Warm chocolate brownie

4 mi Northeast of Winchester by A3090 off B3047. Parking

32 The Bugle

High St,
Hamble SO31 4HA
Tel.: (023)80453000 – Fax: (023)80453051
e-mail: manager@buglehamble.co.uk **Website:** www.buglehamble.co.uk

Courage Best and 2 guest beers such as Wadworth and a Hampshire Brewery

Sister to the White Star Tavern five miles away, this attractive 12C pub is situated at the end of a narrow, cobbled high street. Adjacent to one of the slipways leading into Southampton Water – yachting's Mecca – it can get very busy in the summer with landlubbers and yachties alike. Restored to retain much of its original character, the inn boasts exposed beams and brickwork, wattle walls, stone and oak floors and a wood burning stove. The 16C ground floor dining room is intimate and cosy and has a proper bar, while above it the private dining room comes complete with its very own wine cellar. The pub is fairly small inside but there is a large terrace to spill out onto in warmer weather. The traditional menu consists of a single sheet, with dishes such as sausage and mash or homemade fishcakes. Daily specials are chalked on the board and appealing bar bites such as pork pies are also available. Booking is essential.

Food serving times

Monday-Thursday:
12pm-2.30pm, 6pm-9.30pm

Friday:
12pm-2.30pm, 6pm-10pm

Saturday: 12pm-10.30pm

Sunday: 12pm-9pm

Closed 25 December and 1 January (reduced hours)

Prices

Meals: a la carte £ 18/27

Typical Dishes

Baked goats cheese
Homemade burger
Baked vanilla cheesecake

7mi South East of Southampton by A3024 or A3025 and B3397. Public car park next to pub.

33 The Yew Tree

Hollington Cross,
Andover Road, Highclere RG20 9SE
Tel.: (01635)253360 – Fax: (01635)255035
e-mail: info@theyewtree.net **Website:** www.theyewtree.net

   AE

 **Adnams Southwold, Black Sheep, Timothy Taylor, Weston's Old Rosie, Young's**

Anyone expecting darts and a bit of spit and sawdust should think again: Marco Pierre White doesn't do casual and, sure enough, every table in his inn comes dressed in crisp linen; even the bar is a wondrous marble topped affair. The dining room may now be slightly larger but, through the magic of lighting, becomes more intimate in the evening. The menu reads like Marco Pierre White's CV, from Box tree apprentice to grandee of the London dining scene and only the terminally indecisive will struggle to make a choice, from a menu that blends French sophistication with British frankness. Dishes that have featured in his Big City restaurants like Parfait of foie gras or Omelette Arnold Bennett jostle for your attention with more pub-like offerings, such as pies of the steak and ale, shepherd or fish variety. There are six bedrooms available for those wishing to make a night of it; ask for the Cartoon Room.

Food serving times
Monday-Sunday:
12.30pm-2.30pm,
6pm-9.30pm

Prices
Meals: £ 19 (lunch)
and a la carte £ 38/55

6 rooms: £ 100

Typical Dishes
Kipper paté
Honey roast belly pork
Raspberry soufflé

5mi South of Newbury by A343.
Parking.

34 The Peat Spade Inn

Village Street,
Longstock SO20 6DR
Tel.: (01264)810612 – Fax: (01264)811078
e-mail: info@peatspadeinn.co.uk **Website:** www.peatspadeinn.co.uk

 **Ringwood Best, Ringwood 49er and guest beers**

Well run by a keen, experienced young couple, the 19C Peat Spade Inn is the ultimate shooting and fishing pub, and therefore often teems with anglers here for the rivers and hunters here for the game. Locals certainly don't lose out though – and even have tables reserved especially for them. The country pursuits theme is reflected in the delightful décor - there are mounted fish, fishing rods and nets on the walls - and the relaxed country-life ambience is further enhanced by fine framed photos and the soft glow of candlelight. The food here is proper, proud locally sourced pub cooking and the menu features classics such as braised faggots, fish and chips and sausage and mash; full of flavour, well presented and great value. Bedrooms are modern and stylish, with everything just so; from the plump beds to the jet showers and fluffy towels. The residents lounge has an honesty bar and is stacked with DVDs.

Food serving times

Monday-Saturday:
12pm-2pm, 7pm-9.30pm

Sunday: 12pm-2pm

Closed 25 December,
1 January

Prices

Meals: a la carte £ 30/35

6 rooms: £ 120

Typical Dishes
Chicken liver parfait
Calves liver
Chocolate mousse

1.5 mi North of Stockbridge on A3507. Parking

35 The Anchor Inn

Lower Froyle GU34 4NA
Tel.: (01420)23261
e-mail: info@anchorinnatlowerfroyle.co.uk
Website: www.anchorinnatlowerfroyle.co.uk

Ringwood Best, Ringwood 49er and guest beers - King Alfred, Swift One, Moondance

Sister to the Peat Spade Inn in Longstock, this pub has its focus just as firmly set on fishing and shooting. It may not look particularly ancient but step inside and its 14C origins become apparent: the traditional bar boasts low cushioned beams, open fires and horse brasses, its deep green walls filled with a captivating selection of bric–à-brac. The more formal drawing room is similarly styled, with candlelight contributing to its cosy, informal ambience. The bar menu offers simple treats like oysters or devilled lambs kidneys, while the à la carte tempts with traditional British dishes like potted rabbit or Barnsley chop; precisely crafted from well sourced English ingredients. Old school puds might include spotted dick or bread and butter pudding, but do watch those side orders as they can push the price up. Heavily beamed bedrooms named after war poets are well equipped and very comfortable, with Rupert Brooke the most luxurious.

Food serving times
Monday-Sunday:
12pm-2.30pm,
6.45pm-9.30pm

Closed 25 December

Prices
Meals: a la carte £ 15/30

5 rooms: £ 130/170

Typical Dishes
Baked egg
Anchor mixed grill
Apple & Guiness fritter

5mi North East of Alton by A31

36 The Bush Inn

Ovington SO24 0RE
Tel.: (01962)732764 – Fax: (01962)735130
e-mail: thebushinn@wadworth.co.uk

   AE

 **Wadworths, 6X, Henrys IPA, Bishops Tipple, Horizon, Old Timer and occasionally guest ales**

Friendly, family-run 18C inn, hidden away in an idyllic spot surrounded by trees and little tributaries of the River Itchen; a picnic table in its garden the ideal setting for a lazy summer luncheon. Worry not if sunny days are but a distant memory, however, as The Bush is equally as appealing in the winter months. Four rooms surround the small central bar, their walls cluttered with pictures, china and taxidermy, and real fires give the inn a warm, cosy feel. Blackboard menus offer a wide selection of wholesome, unfussy dishes ranging from simple sandwiches and ploughman's through to steak or slow roast belly pork. Quality produce, including seafood from Loch Fyne, is carefully sourced, and since Alresford, the centre of the British watercress industry, is just down the road, expect to see the green stuff cropping up somewhere on the menu. Tables are particular sought after here at weekends, so make sure you've booked in advance.

Food serving times

Monday-Saturday:
12pm-2pm, 7pm-9pm

Sunday: 12pm-4pm

Closed 25 December

Prices

Meals: a la carte £ 21/35

Typical Dishes

Black pudding salad
Rib eye steak
Baked fresh figs

5.75 mi East of Winchester by B3404 and A31. Parking.

37 The Three Tuns

58 Middlebridge St,
Romsey SO51 8HL
Tel.: (01794)512639
Website: www.thethreetunsromsey.co.uk

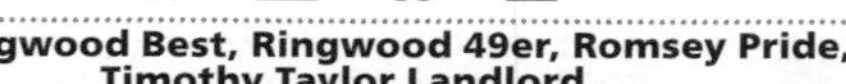

Ringwood Best, Ringwood 49er, Romsey Pride, Timothy Taylor Landlord

Despite a mandatory modicum of modernisation in the form of a slate floor and a few black leather sofas, the thickly beamed, 300-year-old Three Tuns is still very much a proper pub, with a cosy, period feel and real ales being drunk by real locals at the bar. An ex-Navy chef, used to feeding hungry Matelots, David Palmer's culinary skills are now being put to good use feeding hungry civilians. Lunch menus offer a raft of pub favourites such as sausage and mash or homemade honey roast ham, as well as classics like eggs Benedict or smoked salmon; while things move up a notch in the evening, when you can push the boat out with dishes like sautéed calves liver, seared scallops and roast pork belly. Service is friendly and you certainly get the feeling that the staff know the ropes; eat in either the bar or in the equally rustic dining room and afterwards maybe take a post-prandial wander to the gates of Broadlands, home of the Mountbattens.

Food serving times

Tuesday-Sunday:
12pm-10.30pm

Monday, 6.30pm-10pm

Closed 26 December,
also Monday lunch

Prices

Meals: a la carte £ 15/27

Typical Dishes

Arnold Bennett soufflé
Roast duck
Chocolate marquise

Towards the western end of the town, off the by-pass. Parking

38 White Star Tavern, Dining and Rooms

28 Oxford Street,
Southampton SO14 3DJ
Tel.: (023)80821990 – Fax: (023)80904982
e-mail: manager@whitestartavern.co.uk **Website:** www.whitestartavern.co.uk

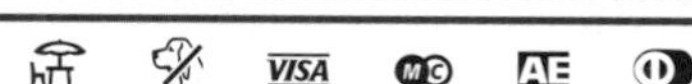

Fuller's London Pride and changing local bitters

Situated on the city's prime dining street, in the historic maritime district, this smart corner pub has provided nourishment and lodgings for seafarers since the late 19C; and with its eye-catching black exterior, large windows and great quality food, it still serves as a beacon to the city's visitors – be they mariners or more land-loving folk. Informal in feel and modern in style, its central bar is surrounded by airy open plan areas, with green Chesterfields and a hotchpotch of tables; while you can eat anywhere at lunchtime, the evening à la carte is only served in the dining room. Foodwise, there's everything you could want here, from sandwiches and pub classics to more sophisticated dishes with a modern European style, such as breast of pheasant or fillet of sea bass. Bedrooms are named after J class yachts and the legendary White Star liners; understated in style, they come with flat screens and modern bathrooms.

Food serving times
Monday-Friday:
7am-9.30am, 12pm-3pm, 6pm-10pm
Saturday-Sunday:
9am-10pm
Closed 25-26 December

Prices
Meals: a la carte £ 20/29
13 rooms: £ 83/155

Typical Dishes
Chicken liver parfait
Steamed fillet of bream
Chocolate & hazelnut delice

Southeast of West Quay shopping centre, off Bernard Street. Parking meters directly outside and public car park 2 mins walk away

39 Plough Inn

Main Road,
Sparsholt SO21 2NW
Tel.: (01962)776353 – Fax: (01962)776400

 **Bishops Tipple, Henry's IPA, Wadworth 6X, Horizon**

Reputedly this pub began life, several hundred years ago, as coach house for Sparsholt Manor, although nobody seems quite sure of its exact vintage. Inside, it's traditionally styled and open plan with a long bar, exposed brickwork and a rustic hotchpotch of tables and chairs. The delightful lawned garden offers a profusion of picnic benches with countryside views, as well as a children's play area to keep the little ones amused for suitably long periods. Two blackboard menus cover a wide range of dishes; one offers traditional favourites with lots of comfort appeal, such as sausage and mash or steak and ale pie, while the other concerns itself with more elaborate dishes, involving maybe lamb shank, sea bass or duck breast. If pigeon is your favourite dish, you are likely to be disappointed; since the large shed in the garden is apparently the local pigeon fanciers' clubhouse, it's the one bird you're unlikely to see on the menu.

Food serving times

Monday-Sunday:
12pm-2pm, 6pm-9pm

Closed 25 December

Booking essential

Prices

Meals: a la carte £ 20/30

Typical Dishes

Sautéed kidneys
Breast of duck
Trio of chocolate mousse

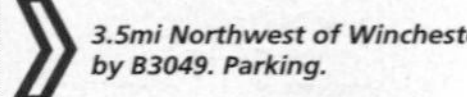

3.5mi Northwest of Winchester by B3049. Parking.

40 The Greyhound

31 High St,
Stockbridge SO20 6EY
Tel.: (01264)810833
e-mail: enquiries@thegreyhound.info **Website:** www.thegreyhound.info

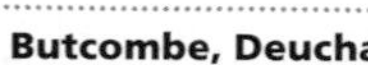
Butcombe, Deuchars

The Greyhound may not quite be the pedigree it once was but it can still impress. The pub comes divided into two areas: the beamed ceiling, subtle lighting and exposed brick of the rather sophisticated main dining area, with its huge – but sadly empty – inglenooks, and the more relaxing bar area, with its sofas and open fire. The kitchen has a commendably classical bent, where ingredient combinations won't scare the horses and while the emphasis may be on offering satisfying, modern pub fare, dishes still come appetisingly presented and precisely executed. Service can occasionally be a tad brusque but the job gets done efficiently enough. The cream coloured bedrooms are modern and stylish, and come with huge showers. The attractive surroundings of the market town of Stockbridge remain a great draw, as does the local stretch of the Test, one of the country's most famous fly-fishing rivers.

Food serving times

Monday-Thursday:
12pm-2pm, 7pm-9pm

Friday-Saturday:
12pm-2.30pm, 7pm-9.30pm

Sunday: 12pm-2.30pm

Closed 25-26 and 31 December, 1 January and 1 week in January

Prices

Meals: £ 24 (3 course lunch) and a la carte £ 30/40

8 rooms: £ 90/120

Typical Dishes

Goats cheese soufle
Loin of pork
Dark chocolate fondant

15mi East of Salisbury by A30.
Parking.

England • South East • Hampshire

41 The Thomas Lord

High Street,
West Meon GU32 1LN
Tel.: (01730)829244
e-mail: enjoy@thethomaslord.co.uk **Website:** www.thethomaslord.co.uk

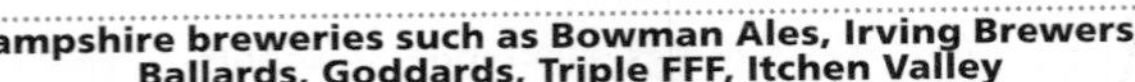

Hampshire breweries such as Bowman Ales, Irving Brewers, Ballards, Goddards, Triple FFF, Itchen Valley

Anyone for cricket? Named after the founder of Lord's cricket ground, this pub is a sanctuary for all kinds of cricketing memorabilia; the highlight of which is a display case above the bar, where a collection of stuffed stoats, ferrets and squirrels play the noble game. Built in 1936, this pub fell into disrepair, but was saved by two locals who bought it and enlisted the help of the village to return it to its former glory. You can eat in the snug, with shelves crammed full of second-hand books for sale (the proceeds of which go towards new community projects), or in the larger, lighter dining room, where the constantly evolving menus change as often as twice a day. The cooking is generous and robust, mainly British, with dishes such as faggots and ham hock, and the odd hint of Mediterranean influence. Produce is passionately regional, and with over 50 suppliers, 95% of ingredients are locally sourced. How's that for a good deal?

Food serving times

Monday-Thursday:
12pm-2pm, 7pm-9pm

Friday-Saturday:
12pm-3pm, 7pm-9.30pm

Sunday: 12pm-3pm

Prices

Meals: a la carte £ 21/29

Typical Dishes

Goats cheese & beetroot toast

Ham hock pie

Isle of Wight cheeseboard

9mi West of Petersfield by A272 and A32 South

42 The Wykeham Arms

75 Kingsgate St, Winchester SO23 9PE
Tel.: (01962)853834 – Fax: (01962)854411
e-mail: wykehamarms@accommodating-inns.co.uk
Website: www.accommodating-inns.co.uk/wykeham

    AE

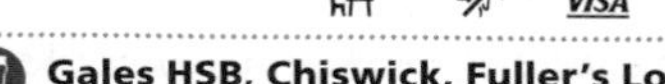

Gales HSB, Chiswick, Fuller's London Pride, Butser Discovery

Although hidden away among the ancient, narrow streets betwixt cathedral and college, this characterful 18C inn is invariably filled with a diverse collection of tourists and locals; including maybe a judge or two and perhaps even a bishop. It's named after William of Wykeham, who founded the college, and the link is obvious everywhere you look: boys hurry past the windows on their way to rugby practice, school vests line the walls of the bar, housemasters pop in for a pint of real ale on their way home from school and punters sit at school desks purloined from the classrooms. Lunch – best eaten in the surprisingly spacious bar - sees traditional dishes such as shepherd's pie and sausage and mash gracing the menu, while dinner is more elaborate, and accompanied by a very good wine list. Bedrooms are split between the inn and the St. George annex opposite; those in the annex are quieter, and come with their own terrace garden.

Food serving times

Monday-Saturday:
12pm-2.30pm, 6.30pm-9pm

Sunday: 12pm-2.30pm

Closed 25 December

Prices

Meals: a la carte £ 20/26

14 rooms: £ 62/150

Typical Dishes

Pigeon breasts

Roast rack of lamb

Passion fruit mille feuille

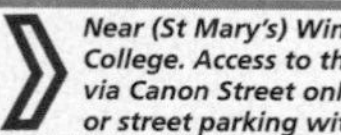

Near (St Mary's) Winchester College. Access to the car park via Canon Street only. Parking or street parking with permit.

43 The Three Chimneys

Hareplain Road,
Biddenden TN27 8LW
Tel.: (01580)291472

 **Adnams Best, Cambridge, Youngs, Harvey's Old, Adnams Broadside**

Legend has it that when French prisoners were held at nearby Sissinghurst Castle during the Seven Years' War, they were permitted to walk along the lanes but forbidden to pass the road junction where the pub lay; the pub's name being a mistranslation into English of the phrase "les trois chemins" (the three roads). It's a hugely characterful, low-ceilinged pub, with cask ales kept on a shelf behind the bar, a restaurant at the rear and a pleasant garden; as well as plans to convert the outbuildings into a farm shop and create a small orangery. The menu is chalked up on blackboards and covers everything from liver and bacon or fillet steak to duck leg confit and pan-fried fillets of Monkfish; with asparagus grown by the farmer opposite and hearty, nursery puddings like Bakewell tart or sticky toffee pudding. Portions are large enough for a starter to constitute a light lunch, and the small wine list includes the local Biddenham wine.

Food serving times

Monday-Saturday:
12pm-2pm, 6pm-9.30pm

Sunday:
12pm-2.30pm, 6pm-9pm

Closed 25 and 31 December

Prices

Meals: a la carte £ 20/33

Typical Dishes

Grilled goats cheese
Breast of Guinea fowl
Sticky toffee pudding

 *1.5mi west by A262. Parking.* 

Froggies at the Timber Batts

44 Froggies at the Timber Batts

School Lane,
Bodsham TN25 5JQ
Tel.: (01223)750237 – Fax: (01223)750176
e-mail: post@thetimberbatts.co.uk **Website:** www.thetimberbatts.co.uk

Fuller's London Pride, Adnams Southwold, Woodforde Wherry

If you suffer from ranidaphobia, it's probably best to avoid this 15C pub, for the little green creatures are everywhere. There are knitted frogs, tin frogs, paper frogs and china frogs; there's even one that croaks at you as you walk in through the front door. The reason for all this frog frivolity is the jolly French owner, who as well as having a well-developed sense of irony, also does a mean line in mouth-watering meals. With the help of his son, the Gallic gastronome produces authentic French dishes like coq au vin, duck confit or rack of lamb; there's plenty of seafood, as well as classic desserts such as crème brûlée, tart au citron or tart Tatin - and lighter choices like sandwiches, Croque Monsieur or omelette can be enjoyed next to the inglenook in the traditional beamed bar. The French know that good food takes time; Rosbifs who appreciate this will find plenty on the wine list to divert them while they wait.

Food serving times

Monday-Sunday:
12pm-2pm, 7pm-9.30pm

Closed one week at Christmas

- French -

Prices

Meals: 26 and a la carte £ 30/38

Typical Dishes

Duo of scallops
Duck leg confit
Tarte Tatin

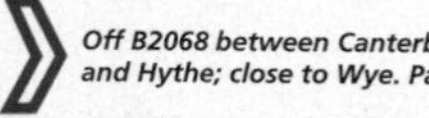

Off B2068 between Canterbury and Hythe; close to Wye. Parking.

England • South East • Kent

45 The Fitzwalter Arms

The Street,
Goodnestone CT3 1PJ
Tel.: (01304)840303

VISA 

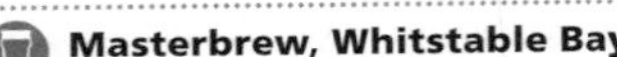

Masterbrew, Whitstable Bay

About as far from your typical-looking boozer as it's possible to get, this striking brick building, with its castellated exterior and mullioned windows may well owe something to the fact that, before it served as a hostelry, it was reputedly the keep for Goodnestone Park, manor house of the Fitzwalter estate - famous for the beautiful country gardens where Jane Austen regularly used to take a turn. With such a history, you might think this place would have since been turned into a fancy dining pub, but thankfully, no – it has very much kept the feel of the village local, with people playing darts or bar billiards, or simply shooting the breeze by the open fire in the characterful, beamed bar. Eat in the small dining area overlooking the headstones in the churchyard, where the daily-changing blackboard menu might offer dishes such as coq au vin, faggots or John Dory. The large beer garden comes into its own in the summer months.

Food serving times

Monday and Wednesday-Saturday: 12pm-2pm, 7pm-9pm

Sunday: 12pm-2.30pm

Closed 25 December and 1 January

Prices

Meals: a la carte £ 21/28

Typical Dishes

Pan-fried scallops
Roast loin of pork
Lemon tart

7mi West of Sandwich by A257, B2046 and minor road.
Parking on road in front of pub.

46 Harrow Inn

Common Rd,
Ightham Common TN15 9EB
Tel.: (01732)885912 – Fax: (01732)885912

 **Greene King IPA, Abbot**

It's located down a little lane and doesn't look much from the outside, but don't be so shallow as to let appearances mislead you; once inside this part-17C stone and brick pub, you'll find a welcoming atmosphere, with a fire flickering in the grate and candles lit on every table. This place has food at its core, with hearty, rustic dishes like game pies and coarse pâtés chalked up on a blackboard in the traditional bar, as well as a printed à la carte in the comfortable, more formal restaurant. If and when the summer sun decides to put in appearance, the small back terrace makes a convenient place to plonk your behind, but wherever you choose to sit, you'll find that the food is tasty and the service is pleasingly low-key and efficient. Handily situated for a spot of lunch or dinner on your way to or from the historic National Trust properties of Knole House, birthplace of Vita Sackville-West, or 14C medieval manor house, Ightham Mote.

Food serving times

Tuesday-Saturday:
12pm-2pm, 6pm-9pm

Sunday: 12pm-2pm

Closed 25-26 December

Prices

Meals: a la carte £ 21/35

Typical Dishes

Hot Kent smokie
Scallops with pancetta
Rhubarb crumble

5mi South East of Sevenoaks by A25 on Common Road. Parking.

47 The Granville

Street End,
Lower Hardres CT4 7AL
Tel.: (01227)700402 – Fax: (01227)700925

 VISA  AE

Masterbrew, Spitfire

Just another common-or-garden pub on an unremarkable main road, you might well be thinking as you drive on by, but do so and you'll be missing a treat. Going into The Granville is like entering into another world; a world where open plan, Scandinavian-style rooms loom large; where you can watch the chefs on show in the kitchen, partake in a game of Scrabble® or sink into a leather sofa with the day's papers. The chalked up menu happily highlights local produce and keeps things brief and simple: find a table, place your order at the bar and you'll soon be tucking into juicy olives and slices of crusty homemade bread while awaiting your pork belly, duck confit or slow-roast chicken breast. Desserts are equally as mouth-watering; try the trio of lemon with sorbet sprinkled with "sparkle dust". With a winning combination of good food and a relaxing setting that clearly appeals to all ages, this is the kind of place you covet for your local.

Food serving times
Tuesday-Saturday:
12pm-2pm, 7pm-9pm
Sunday: 12pm-2.30pm
Closed 25-26 December

Prices
Meals: a la carte £ 23/36

Typical Dishes
Bresaola
Pan-fried ox liver
Lemon Tart

3mi South of Canterbury on B2068. Parking.

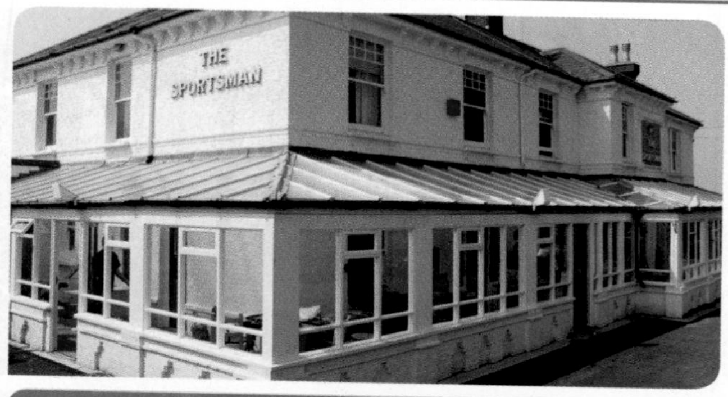

48 The Sportsman

Faversham Rd,
Seasalter CT5 4BP
Tel.: (01227)273370
Website: www.thesportsmanseasalter.co.uk

Bishop's Finger, Goldings, Masterbrew, Porter

Travelling along the coastal road, you spot The Sportsman from far off, sandwiched between sea and marsh. Inside the owners have refrained from going gastro, and instead have their own blend of shabby chic, with open fires, worn wood flooring and scrubbed pine tables - but the décor's irrelevant anyway, since here, it's all about the food. Self-taught chef Stephen is seriously passionate about his job and an advocate of "terroir" – that is, cooking that is rooted in its locality - so his ingredients come from local farms, he makes his own salt from the sea in order to cure his own hams, he makes butter from unpasteurised cream and, where possible, picks his vegetables the very day they are to be served up on the plate. Not surprisingly, his cooking is confident, unfussy and fantastically flavoursome, but this does mean that, despite its isolated position, this place is often deservedly busy, and you'd be advised to book in advance.

Food serving times

Tuesday-Saturday:
12pm-2pm, 7pm-9pm

Sunday: 12pm-2pm

Closed 25-26 December

Prices

Meals: a la carte £ 23/34

Typical Dishes
Salmagundi
Braised turbot
Jasmine tea junket

2mi south-west of Whitstable by B2205 following the coast road. Parking.

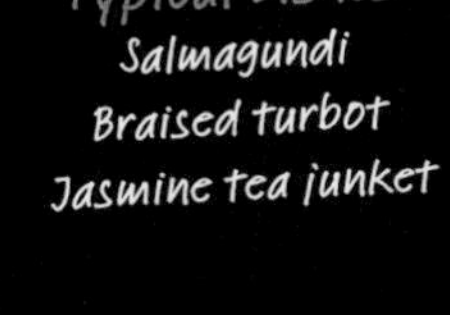

49 George & Dragon

Speldhurst Hill,
Speldhurst TN3 0NN
Tel.: (01892)863125 – Fax: (01892)863216
e-mail: julian@leefe-griffiths.freeserve.co.uk **Website:** www.speldhurst.com

 **Harveys Best, Harvey Pale, Larkins Trad**

This George and Dragon is a pub for all seasons: in summer, the drowsy scent of lavender drifts across the lovely outdoor terrace while on colder days, the snug interior and warm character that one expects from somewhere dating from the 13C won't disappoint. The beams, log fires and inglenooks are all there, along with a good smattering of locals which also includes the majority of the serving team; the atmosphere is never less than warm and welcoming. The same menu is served throughout so that makes the bar the more convivial choice, rather than the separate dining room. The pub also prides itself on its use of Kent's rich seasonal bounty, from its orchards and rivers to its forests and farms. The cooking is suitably rustic and forthright: warm salads, local sausages and platters of cheese and hams that arrive on wooden boards are the high points, along with the decidedly heart-warming puddings.

Food serving times

Monday-Saturday:
12pm-2.45pm, 7pm-10pm

Sunday: 12pm-2.45pm

Closed 25 December,
1 January

Prices

Meals: a la carte £ 20/28

Typical Dishes

Pigeon with Le Puy lentils
Roast belly of pork
Lemon posset

3,5 mi North of Royal Tunbridge Wells by A26. Parking.

50 The Swan on the Green

West Peckham ME18 5JW
Tel.: (01622)812271 – Fax: (0870)0560556
e-mail: info@swan-on-the-green.co.uk **Website:** www.swan-on-the-green.co.uk

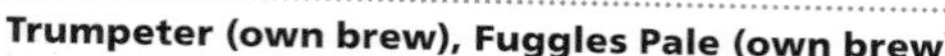

Trumpeter (own brew), Fuggles Pale (own brew)

Pub settings rarely come more attractively old English than this – the Swan's redbrick and ornate gabled exterior sits idyllically by the green, right next to the village's Saxon church. There's no pub garden, but benches perch along the terrace at the front. Inside, a framed history puts the inn's origins at 1526, but it's been given a pleasing modern makeover with pale wood throughout: the dried hops and real fire add a rustic twist. At the back is a micro-brewery, so a selection of unique ales are chalked up on the board behind the bar. There's a loyal local following and menus, featuring an interesting eclectic à la carte, change weekly. Try to visit in summer, when the owners provide blankets for you to eat on the green.

Food serving times

Sunday-Monday:
12pm-2pm

Tuesday-Saturday:
12pm-2pm, 7pm-9pm

Closed 25 December

Prices

Meals: a la carte £ 22/27

Typical Dishes

Wok-fried squid
Pan-fried skate wing
Lemon & ginger cheesecake

7.75mi Southwest of Maidstone by A26 and B2016. Follow sign to church and green. Parking.

51 The Sweet Olive at The Chequers Inn

Baker St,
Aston Tirrold OX11 9DD
Tel.: (01235)851272
Website: www.sweet-olive.com

 VISA MC AE

Brakspear, Fuller's London Pride

Down narrow winding lanes in a country village, with a loyal band of locals inside, this red-brick Victorian inn couldn't appear more British. Step inside, however, and you are greeted with a "bonjour" from the French owner behind the bar; his compatriot behind the scenes in the kitchen. Bringing a touch of their own culture, the wine list features a selection from their homeland, Alsace, whilst panels of old French boxes deck the bar. The blackboard menus and verbally explained specials provide some interest, with French dishes such as fish soup, onglet of beef or crème brûlée, alongside others of a more international flavour, such as Moroccan lamb. In honour of the pub's name you are provided with a dish of exceptionally succulent olives to start your meal and in recognition of their new home, there is even the odd British number, such as treacle sponge with custard and ice cream. All that's left to say is "bon appétit".

Food serving times

Monday-Tuesday:
12pm-2pm, 7pm-9pm

Thursday-Saturday:
12pm-2pm, 7pm-9pm

Sunday: 12pm-2pm

Closed February and 1 week in July

Prices

Meals: a la carte £ 23/30

Typical Dishes

Tempura tiger prawns
Escalope of venison
Treacle sponge

4mi South West of Wallingford by minor road through South Moreton. Parking.

52 The Boot Inn

Barnard Gate OX29 6XE
Tel.: (01865)881231
e-mail: info@theboot-inn.com **Website:** www.theboot-inn.com

 **Youngs Best Bitter, Wells Eagle IPA, Hook Norton Best Bitter, Courage Best, Fuller's London Pride**

Foot fetishists take note: a fascinating collection of celebrity footwear is displayed on the walls at The Boot Inn, ranging from the Bee Gees shoes to a flipper from Michael Heseltine and a football boot from George Best, along with signed photos and letters; all obtained by the pub's owners in exchange for a donation to each celebrity's favourite charity. Aside from its bootylicious collection, this is very much a traditional inn; with flagged floors, beamed ceilings, a central bar and an open fire. A perfect stopping off point for anyone who happens to be pootling along the A40, light lunches on offer might include salmon, steak, salads and sandwiches, while more substantial dinner dishes could include beef fillet, roast duck breast or monkfish brochettes – with daily specials expanding your choice further. Jazz nights in winter are just the thing to get your fingers clicking and your boots tapping.

Food serving times
Monday-Sunday:
12pm-2.30pm, 7pm-9.30pm
Booking essential

Prices
Meals: a la carte £ 20/35

Typical Dishes
Italian antipasta
Grilled seabass fillets
Pecan fudge tart

3.25mi East of Witney by B4022 off A40 Parking.

53 The Kings Head Inn

The Green,
Bledington OX7 6XQ

Tel.: (01608)658365 – Fax: (01608)658902
e-mail: kingshead@orr-ewing.com **Website:** www.kingsheadinn.net

Inspectors' favourites

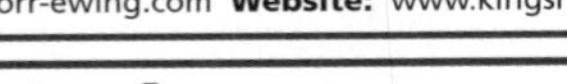

Hook Norton, Butts Bitter, Pigbrook, Doombar, Donningtons BB

Set on the pretty village green with a stream running alongside, this warmly welcoming 15C inn underwent a full refurbishment in 2007 due to knee deep flood damage. Thankfully, the pub lost none of its charm in the process and a seat in its low ceilinged, beamed bar, in the glow of the open fire, is as popular as ever. If the bar becomes too busy, as is its wont, the dining room is just as comfortable, if perhaps not quite as atmospheric, while the paved terrace is great for al fresco dining in the sun. The same menu is served in all areas and you'll find traditional dishes such as pan-fried lamb cutlets or homemade steak, ale and root vegetable pie, with the odd international influence thrown in. Cooking is robust and rustic in style, with local ingredients well used. Bedrooms are smart, with good facilities and some antique furniture; those in the pub itself are older and more characterful, while the others have a more stylish feel.

Food serving times

Monday-Sunday:
12pm-2pm, 7pm-9pm

Closed 25-26 December

Prices

Meals: a la carte £ 20/28

12 rooms: £ 50/125

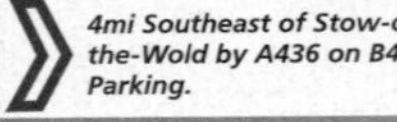

54 The Lamb at Buckland

Lamb Lane, Buckland SN7 8QN
Tel.: (01367)870484 – Fax: (01367)870675
e-mail: enquiries@thelambatbuckland.co.uk
Website: www.thelambatbuckland.co.uk

   VISA

Oxfordshire Ales, Marsh Mallow, Oxford Gold, Tribute, Hooky

Thankfully The Lamb is well signposted, for you'd never find it otherwise. Once inside, there's no doubting you're in the right pub though, thanks to the veritable flock of ovine-inspired items to be found here – in the form of cuddly toys, paintings, curios, life-sized models and even lamb motif carpets. This 17C stone-built building has a bar in which you can eat, a linen-laid restaurant in the heavily beamed oldest part of the building, plus a rear garden with a little sunken terrace for al fresco dining in the summer. Tasty, traditional British food is chalked on the large blackboard menu above the open fireplace, and the same food is served throughout. In quiet months, they also offer a good value fixed price menu. Family owned for a number of years, the atmosphere is one of cosy familiarity, so even if you're not a local, there's no need to feel sheepish. Altogether now; "Four legs good, two legs baaad..."

Food serving times

Tuesday-Saturday:
12pm-2.30pm, 7pm-9.30pm

Sunday: 12pm-2.30pm

Closed from 24 December for 2 weeks

Prices

Meals: a la carte £ 16/35

1 room: £ 95/145

Typical Dishes

Warm scallop salad
Seared fillet of seabass
Raspberry brûlée

Between Faringdon and Kingston Bagpuize off A420. Parking.

55 The Trout at Tadpole Bridge

Buckland Marsh SN7 8RF

Tel.: (01367)870382 – Fax: (01367)870912

e-mail: info@troutinn.co.uk **Website:** www.troutinn.co.uk

Ramsbury Estate Bitter, Youngs PA Bitter, Burford Best Bitter, Archers Golden, Barbus Barbus

Its location by the River Thames makes this pretty stone-built pub, and more specifically its garden, the place to be in summer months, and since it has its own moorings, it's particularly popular with boat users. Its experienced owners have breathed new life into the old Trout, and it offers quality cooking made with fresh, local produce at sensible prices. The open plan bar, where locals gather for their evening pint, has space for dining on either side; log burners glow enticingly and the large table by the dartboard is a sought-after spot for anyone after a little privacy. For those who prefer to sit away from the bar, a light, modern room is available at the rear – but if you're here for an evening meal or Sunday lunch, wherever you sit, booking is essential. Superior bedrooms – six in the main house, three in a ground floor extension – are comfortable and well-furnished in light, pastel shades.

Food serving times

Monday-Saturday:
12pm-2pm, 7pm-9pm

Sunday: 12pm-2pm

Closed 25-26 December

Prices

Meals: a la carte £ 23/30

6 rooms: £ 75/110

Typical Dishes

Tian of Brixham crab

Calves Liver

Lemon posset

4.5mi Northeast of Faringdon by A417, A420 on Brampton road. Parking.

56 The Lamb Inn

Sheep St,
Burford OX18 4LR
Tel.: (01993)823155 – Fax: (01993)822228
e-mail: info@lambinn-burford.co.uk **Website:** www.cotswold-inns-hotel.co.uk

Inspectors' favourites

VISA MC AE

 **Hook Norton, Brakspear**

This attractive Cotswold stone inn lies in a quiet spot on Sheep Street; not a coincidence, but a reminder that this town was historically the site of sheep fairs and famous for its wool. Upon entering, the delicious smell of wood smoke wafts by your nostrils, but watch out for the uneven flag floors, for this inn has all the charming features you would expect from one with its origins in the 14C. Open fires blaze in front of deep sofas in the lounges, and you can eat from the bar menu here or at one of the simple wood tables in the characterful bar. For a much more formal dining experience, the restaurant, with its glass skylight, burgundy walls and dressed tables has a separate, fixed price menu, offering dishes such as roasted squab pigeon, roast mallard or confit pork belly. Bedrooms named after flowers have a cosy, warm feel. Choose "Rosie," which has its own private garden, or "Allium;" the most luxurious.

Food serving times
Monday-Sunday:
12pm-2.30pm, 7pm-9.30pm

Prices
Meals: £ 33 (3 course dinner) and a la carte £ 20/33

17 rooms: £ 145/255

Typical Dishes
Pavé of Salmon
Trio of Pork
Chocolate Battenberg

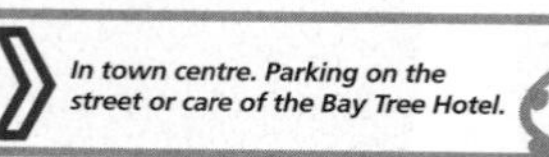

57 The Masons Arms

Banbury Rd,
Swerford, Chipping Norton OX7 4AP
Tel.: (01608)683212 – Fax: (01608)683105
e-mail: themasonschef@hotmail.com **Website:** www.masons-arms.com

Inspectors' favourites

 **Hook Norton Best, Brakspears Special**

This rurally-set roadside inn – a former Masonic lodge - has retained a touch of rustic character in the form of the odd wooden beam and an inglenook fireplace, but is for the most part a modernised dining pub, with a light and airy style and a relaxed, friendly atmosphere. With westerly views over the surrounding countryside, the new extension is the best place to sit – alternatively, head for the picnic benches in the neat garden. The chef-owner has previously worked with some notable names and confidently produces precise, well-presented and flavoursome dishes which are easy on the pocket as well as on the eye. With various set menus and an à la carte, there's plenty of choice – from simple sandwiches, salads or ploughman's through to classic British dishes with a modern slant, such as mushroom and leek shepherd's pie, farmhouse lamb and mint sausages, grilled pigeon breast with hazelnut mash and even the odd chicken Korma.

Food serving times

Monday-Saturday:
12pm-2pm, 7pm-9pm

Sunday: 12pm-2pm

Closed 25-26 December

Prices

Meals: £ 15/20
and a la carte £ 24/29

Typical Dishes
Timbale of crab
Shoulder of pork
Raspberry crème brûlée

5mi Northeast of Chipping Norton by A361. Parking.

58 The Crown Inn

Mill Lane,
Church Enstone OX7 4NN
Tel.: (01608)677262 – Fax: (01608)677394
Website: www.crowninnenstone.co.uk

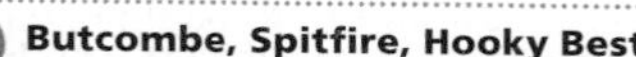

Butcombe, Spitfire, Hooky Best

A pretty inn built with Cotswold stone, situated in a picturesque village, The Crown Inn has the feel of a true dining pub, where drinkers and diners gladly mix. Well-kept and well-run, with a homely feel, regulars sit on stools at the bar, close to the open fire, while the light and airy conservatory overlooking the picnic tables outside makes a particularly pleasant place to eat. In the entrance hall, you'll find a large display of locally handcrafted walking sticks for sale and the many accolades displayed on the wall of the pub testify to the success of the owner chef's signature dish, steak pie. Food here is unfussy, honest and well-prepared, with ingredients sourced from local farms and a nod to the chef's Northern roots. The large menu is chalked up on blackboards and might offer a simple steak and Hooky pie or crispy duck salad at lunch, and maybe sea bass, steak and chips or breast of pheasant in the evening.

Food serving times

Monday-Saturday:
12pm-2pm, 7pm-9pm

Sunday: 12pm-2pm

Closed 26 December,
1 January

Prices

Meals: £ 18 (lunch)
and a la carte £ 18/27

Typical Dishes

Scallop & bacon salad
Steak and Hooky pie
Warm chocolate pudding

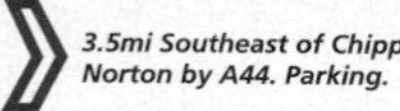

3.5mi Southeast of Chipping Norton by A44. Parking.

59 The Chequers

Church Rd,
Churchill OX7 6NJ
Tel.: (01608)659393

Timothy Taylor, Abbot Ale, Hobgoblin, Hook Norton Banbury 400 and Best Bitter, Bass, Flowers, London Pride, Pedigree

If popularity with the locals is the test of a good pub, then The Chequers passes with flying colours, its big bar providing ample space for all the regulars to assemble on their stools. The rest of the pub is open plan, and has charm aplenty in the form of its flagstone floors, exposed Cotswold stone walls and inglenook fireplace.
If you are eating here during the week then the best seats are in the large high-ceilinged extension at the rear, but at weekends – when it can get very busy and is a good idea to book ahead - the rooms on the mezzanine above the bar are your best bet for a little peace and quiet. Even during hectic periods, the experienced owners run a tight ship, and the overall ambience is warm and welcoming. Set menus are available at both lunch and dinner, while the à la carte offers quite traditional dishes, such as rack of lamb, sea bass, guinea fowl or fisherman's pie - and Thursday nights are roasted half duck night.

Food serving times
Monday-Saturday:
12pm-2pm, 7pm-9.30pm
Sunday: 12pm-3pm
Closed 25 December for food

Prices
Meals: a la carte £ 20/29

Typical Dishes
Ham hock terrine
Braised lamb shank
Lemon & ginger cheesecake

Southwest of Chipping Norton by B4450. Parking.

60 The White Lion

Goring Rd, Goring Heath, Cray's Pond RG8 7SH
Tel.: (01491)680471 – Fax: (01491)684254
e-mail: reservations@thewhitelioncrayspond.com
Website: www.thewhitelioncrayspond.com

 **Abbot Ale, IPA**

The walls are filled with menus from renowned restaurants around Great Britain; a sign perhaps of the dizzy heights to which the team at The White Lion aspire. Their dinner menus - a small à la carte plus a set menu – certainly contain their own culinary contenders, such as breast of partridge or sword fish steak, while their lunch menus contain good old pub favourites like steak or sausage and mash – all well-presented and served in ample portions. Local drinkers gather near the open fire in the characterful bar, while diners have a choice between wooden tables and paper napkins in the dining area or tablecloths and a garden view in the conservatory. The atmosphere throughout is warm and friendly, but take heed; the pub was built in 1756 and has the low beams to prove it – and while helpful signs warn you to "duck or grouse," some thoughtfully-placed cushions make any bumps that are incurred that little bit less traumatic.

Food serving times

Tuesday-Friday:
12pm-2pm, 6pm-9pm

Saturday-Sunday:
12pm-9pm

Closed 25-26 December, Sunday dinner and Monday

Prices

Meals: a la carte £ 20/30

Typical Dishes

Marinated salmon
John Dory & seabass
Warm chocolate gooey

 ***2mi East of Goring on B4526. Parking.*** 

61 The Half Moon

Cuxham, Watlington 0X49 5NF
Tel.: (01491)614151
e-mail: info@thehalf-moon.com **Website:** www.thehalf-moon.com

 **Brakspears**

With original red and black floor tiling and exposed wooden beams proudly on display, you'd never guess that this 17C whitewashed pub had been all but destroyed by fire back in 2002. A sympathetic renovation salvaged what it could of the original building and characterful rustic features, while a complete interior refurbishment added a modern edge via some contemporary furnishings. The atmosphere is laid back and relaxed and there's always a warm welcome, especially from Harry the Springer Spaniel. With vegetables from the kitchen garden and meat from animals that have been taken on the hoof and properly butchered, the twice-daily blackboard menu features a good selection of local, ethical ingredients. Nothing is left to waste, so there's always plenty of offal to be found; there may be ox tongue or duck's hearts on toast, alongside less unusual offerings such as potted crab, roast hake, confit belly pork or seared beef fillet.

Food serving times

Monday-Saturday:
12pm-2pm, 6pm-9pm

Sunday:
12pm-3pm, 6pm-9pm

Prices

Meals: a la carte £ 19/30

Typical Dishes

Dry cured ham
Pork belly
Sticky toffee pudding

 *In village centre on B480* 

62 The Carpenter's Arms

Fulbrook Hill, Fulbrook OX18 4BH
Tel.: (01993)823275 – Fax: (01993)823275
e-mail: info@thecarpentersarmsfulbrook.co.uk
Website: www.thecarpentersarmsfulbrook.co.uk

 **IPA, Old Hooky**

Just outside the charming town of Burford, known as the southern gateway to the Cotswolds, sits this long, narrow and rather unprepossessing pub. Do not be fooled by its commonplace appearance, however, for inside you will find character and charm galore in the form of flagged floors, beamed ceilings and chunky mismatched furniture, as well as a stylish sprinkling of modern touches, like a pair of matching wood burners, a selection of contemporary art, and a conservatory, which leads out into the rear garden. Simple, carefully-presented cooking casts its net surprisingly wide, with choices such as gravadlax, coq au vin, bonito sashimi or osso buco risotto Milanese featuring on the menus alongside plenty of fresh fish landed at Looe, Newlyn or Brixham. Desserts might include rhubarb crumble or a choice of ice creams, and bright, friendly service is the other key ingredient in a pleasant, unhurried lunch or evening out.

Food serving times

Tuesday-Saturday:
12pm-3pm, 6.30pm-9.30pm

Sunday: 12pm-3pm

Closed Sunday dinner, Monday

Prices

Meals: a la carte £ 22/36

Typical Dishes

Baked king scallops
Calves liver
Bramley apple crumble tart

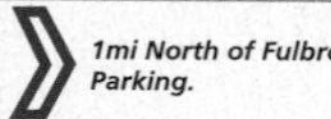

1mi North of Fulbrook by A361. Parking.

63 The White Hart

Main Road,
Fyfield OX13 5LW
Tel.: (01865)390585
e-mail: info@whitehart-fyfield.com **Website:** www.whitehart-fyfield.com

Inspectors' favourites

 **Hooky Bitter, Hullabaloo, Village Idiot, Ironside, Azzaparrot, Gem**

Hurtling along the A420, on your way up to Oxford or down to Swindon? Take the turning for Fyfield, head for The White Hart and allow yourself to get into another gear entirely. Found it yet? Its white exterior is appealing enough, but gives no hint of the character that lies within, or the fascinating history that lies behind, and it's only once you're inside that you can truly appreciate the historic structure of this 15C former chantry house, complete with huge timbered arch, minstrels' gallery and cellar room. The set lunch menu is a prudent option, but you might well find yourself drawn to the large choice available on the globally influenced à la carte, whose sharing boards – antipasti, mezze or fish – are great to go halves on as a starter. Local sources are listed and food is fresh and flavoursome. The uplit terrace and large garden are popular in the summer; your meal oiled by smooth service from a polite, friendly young crew.

Food serving times

Tuesday-Saturday:
12pm-2.30pm, 7pm-9.30pm

Sunday: 12pm-4pm

Closed Sunday dinner

Prices

Meals: £ 17 (3 course lunch) and a la carte £ 24/32

Typical Dishes
Seared scallops
Roast rack of lamb
Hot chocolate fondant

10mi South West of Oxford by A420. Parking.

64 Falkland Arms

Great Tew OX7 4DB
Tel.: (01608)683653 – Fax: (01608)683656
e-mail: sjcourage@btconnect.com **Website:** www.falklandarms.org.uk

    AE

 **Choice of 7 from Wadworth, Hook Norton, Cains, Jennings, Highgate**

Charming village full of chocolate box cottages? Check. Fire flickering gently in the grate? Check. Locals gathered at the bar? Check. If it's a traditional country inn you're looking for, look no further, for this is the real deal, to the extent that as you enter The Falkland Arms, you get a sense that time seems to have stood still. Real ales are still dispensed from antique pot hand pumps, hundreds of jugs and cups hang from the low beams and the walls are crowded with adverts from years gone by. Folk groups play here on Sunday evenings and five comfortable, traditionally furnished bedrooms – two with four poster beds - are located up a steep spiral staircase. Lunch here can be a simple affair, with baguettes, jacket potatoes and casseroles, while the short, seasonally-changing à la carte dinner menu offers traditional dishes like lamb shank and poached haddock. No bookings are taken at lunch, but booking for dinner is imperative.

Food serving times

Monday-Saturday:
12pm-2pm, 7pm-8pm

Sunday: 12pm-2pm

Booking essential for dinner - not accepted for lunch

Prices

Meals: a la carte £ 15/30

5 rooms: £ 110/115

Typical Dishes

Black pudding salad
Pan-fried seabass
Sticky toffee pudding

6.5mi East of Chipping Norton by A361 and B4022. Parking in village car park.

65 The New Inn

Chalkhouse Green Rd,
Kidmore End RG4 9AU

Tel.: (0118)9723115 – Fax: (0118)9724733

e-mail: thenewinn@uve.co.uk **Website:** www.thenewinnrestaurant.co.uk

 **Brakspear Original**

The hustle and bustle of Reading is only five miles away but you wouldn't realise it from the sleepy charms of this Oxfordshire hamlet and the comfy enticements of its focal point, The New Inn, which, though smartened up outside, still proudly bears its 16C hallmarks within. The cosy, atmospheric bar's rough floorboards, beams and open fires are all you'd expect from a proper pub of the era, and this is a fine spot to lay your hat and sup a pint. Most diners, meanwhile, head to the snazzy restaurant, where a few original beams merge tastefully with the smart wood tables and crisp white walls. Here, there's a nicely balanced menu ranging from pub favourites to more adventurous fare; you can also eat in the bar or delightful canopied terrace. A treat awaits overnighters: six bedrooms, some with balconies, which are stylish, modern, very comfy and well equipped.

Food serving times

Monday: 6.30pm-9.30pm

Tuesday-Saturday: 12pm-2.30pm, 6.30pm-9.30pm

Sunday: 12pm-2.30pm

Prices

Meals: a la carte £ 18/29

6 rooms: £ 65/220

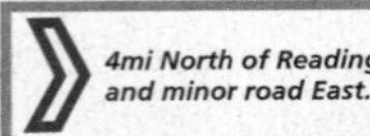

66 The Kingham Plough

The Green, Kingham
OX7 6YD

Tel.: (01608)658327 – Fax: (01608)658327
e-mail: book@thekinghamplough.co.uk **Website:** www.thekinghamplough.co.uk

Hook Norton Bitter, St Austell Tribute and one guest ale such as Fuller's London Pride

Chef-owner Emily Watkins was formerly sous-chef at The Fat Duck under Heston Blumenthal but that doesn't mean that she is now serving up snail porridge here in the depths of the Cotswolds. Far from it: a few touches – like the intensely flavoured steak cooked "sous vide" or the trademark "triple-cooked" chips may hint at her Fat Duck past, but this is a quintessentially British pub offering gutsy pub food, so expect to find hand-raised pork pies, potted duck, game pie or crisp lamb sweetbreads on the daily-changing menu, as well as a cracking collection of cheeses. The food is firmly rooted in the region and local suppliers range from former Blur bass player Alex James, to "Roy the rabbit," a local lady who talks to her cauliflowers and a 12 year old boy who provides the quails' eggs. There's real ale on tap, pigs' ears for your dog, and stylish, comfortable bedrooms boasting pocket sprung beds and crisp Egyptian linen.

Food serving times

Monday-Sunday:
12pm-2pm, 7pm-9pm

Closed 25 December

Prices

Meals: a la carte £ 20/35

7 rooms: £ 70/110

Typical Dishes

Chilled tomato soup
Pigeon Wellington
Granny Smith & toffee doughnut

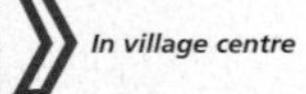

In village centre

The Tollgate Inn

67 The Tollgate Inn

Church St,
Kingham OX7 6YA
Tel.: (01608)658389
e-mail: info@thetollgate.com **Website:** www.thetollgate.com

 **Hook Norton Bitter, Cotswold Lager**

Built in 1720, this attractive Grade II listed pub started life as a Georgian farmhouse. With its bold colours and contemporary feel it bears little resemblance to its past, although a sympathetic refurbishment has left many original features in place alongside the more modern décor. Centred around huge inglenook fireplaces the bar and lounge boast wooden floors and exposed stone walls, juxtaposed with striking orange paintwork and brown leather tub chairs; they are warm, welcoming and there's a relaxed, informal atmosphere. If you're after a more formal experience, head for the lighter, brighter dining rooms, where you'll find chunky pine tables and high backed leather chairs. Snacks, blackboard specials and an à la carte menu are served throughout, the latter displaying dishes of a more ambitious nature; these might include wild mushroom and chicken gateau or pan-fried turbot with slow-roasted veg. Bedrooms are simple, light and airy.

Food serving times
Tuesday-Saturday:
12pm-2pm, 7pm-9pm
Sunday: 12pm-3pm

Prices
Meals: a la carte £ 20/30
9 rooms: £ 60/100

Typical Dishes
Smoked salmon terrine
Turbot fillet
Chocolate & chilli tart

3mi South West of Chipping Norton by B4450 to Churchill and minor road West. Parking.

68 The Five Horseshoes

Maidensgrove RG9 6EX
Tel.: (01491)641282 – Fax: (01491)641086
e-mail: admin@thefivehorseshoes.co.uk **Website:** www.thefivehorseshoes.co.uk

  MC AE

 **Brakspear Bitter, Oxford Gold**

Line up your muddy boots outside, sit in one of the snug, beamed, burgundy bars, or enjoy the fine southerly views over the Chilterns from the suntrap conservatory. The food served here includes homely lunchtime classics such as pork pie or bangers and mash plus mains like grilled sea trout or rump of Chiltern lamb. Dare you attempt to devour a "Doorstep of the Day"; so bulky it comes with its own breadboard? Still very much a locals' pub, bar games like bagatelle and dominoes are positively encouraged here, and the value for money Friday "Pie and a pint" evenings and first Sunday of the month hog roasts attract many takers. It is in the summer months when this pub really comes to life though, with busy weekend barbeques in the gardens, and Pimms and Mojitos the drinks du jour. If you ask for a glass of Chablis in a loud voice, be aware that the owner's dog might well come running. Classier than a daughter called Chardonnay, anyday.

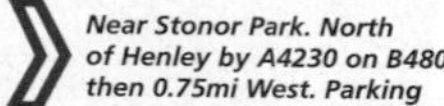

Near Stonor Park. North of Henley by A4230 on B480, then 0.75mi West. Parking

Food serving times

Monday-Friday:
12pm-2.30pm,
6.30pm-9.30pm,

Saturday:
12pm-3pm, 6.30pm-9.30pm

Sunday: 12pm-4pm

Closed Sunday dinner

Prices

Meals: a la carte £ 20/32

Typical Dishes

Pigs Trotter
Roast haunch of venison
Apple beignet

69 The Black Boy Inn

Milton OX15 4HH
Tel.: (01295)722111
e-mail: info@blackboyinn.com **Website:** www.blackboyinn.com

 **Greene King IPA, Adnams Best, Giant, Village Idiot, Hooky Gold**

This 16C inn could have been named after its previous incarnation as a tobacconist – which were then known as "Black Boys" - or might equally have been named after swarthy Charles II; but even to its owners, its history is a bit of a mystery. There's no mystery when it comes to its popularity as a dining destination, however; traceability is all important, the enthusiastic, confident kitchen sources ingredients from local farms, and its modern menu, although it has a French edge, does not overlook the pub classics. Service is old fashioned in the nicest sense of the word – the keen, experienced staff are caring without being overbearing and make guests' enjoyment the priority; candles and fresh flowers decorate the tables, and diners haven't been allowed to usurp the drinkers, so the locals can still be found enjoying a tipple or two in the bar. The conservatory is a pleasant spot for dining – but booking is essential at weekends.

Food serving times

Monday-Saturday:
12pm-2.30pm, 6.30-late

Sunday: 12pm-2.30pm

Prices

Meals: £ 15 and a la carte £ 20/30

Typical Dishes

Smoked haddock fishcake

Marinated Guinea fowl

Trio of chocolate

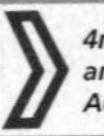

4mi South of Banbury by A4260 and a minor road West via Adderbury. Parking.

70 The Nut Tree

Main Street,
Murcott OX5 2RE
Tel.: (01865)331253

  ⓂⒸ

 **Hook Norton, Toptotty, 6X, Black Beauty Porter, Marshmellow, Kents Best, Odyssey and others**

This pub may look like your traditional thatched variety but the sight of pigs being reared in a pen is a clue to its great strength. You enter into one of those comfy bars with mind-your-head-beams and a gaggle of locals. If you're after more than just a snack head for either the dining room or the small conservatory extension; tables are smartly dressed and service is friendly yet attentive. One look at the owner-chef's appealing and nicely balanced menu and you'll start to realise that this is somewhere a little special. Its main thrust is "proper" pub food such as fishcakes or chicken liver pâté but still executed with real care and understanding. There are also more restaurant style dishes like roasted foie gras, soufflés and others involving those pigs. By using the best ingredients it ensures that flavours are fresh, clear and eminently satisfying. The Nut Tree proves that tradition and good food can happily go together.

Food serving times

Monday-Saturday:
12pm-2.30pm, 7pm-9pm

Sunday:
12pm-2.30pm, (summer only) 7pm-9pm

Prices

Meals: £ 18 (weekdays 3 course lunch & dinner) and a la carte £ 27/40

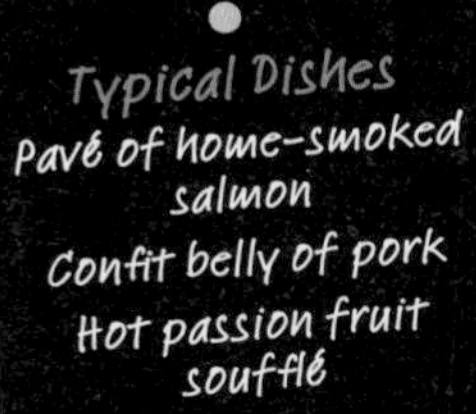

5mi from Bicester by A41 East and a minor road South via Lower and Upper Arncott; at T-junction beyond the motorway turn right. Parking.

71 The Fishes

North Hinksey Village,
North Hinksey OX2 0NA
Tel.: (01865)249796
e-mail: fishes@peachpubs.com **Website:** www.fishesoxford.co.uk

 **Greene King IPA and 1 guest beer - Golden Glow**

First impressions of this red brick pub, with its wood flooring, low leather seating and lively atmosphere might be of a modern wine bar - but there's much more to it than that. The pretty gardens are an idyllic spot for riverside picnics in the summer; order at the bar, before picking your spread up from the kitchen hatch, complete with cutlery, crockery and even a blanket on which to sit. Inside, colourful abstract artwork mixes with traditional features like stuffed fish in display cases; the best place to sit being the conservatory-style extension. In keeping with the company's ethos, local suppliers and producers are well-used, and the resulting robust dishes get the thumbs up from all comers. Tapas-style deli boards made for sharing are a popular feature, and the wine list is small but well-chosen, with a decent selection by the glass. Servers in T-shirts are friendly, polite, well-organised and obviously used to being busy.

Food serving times

Monday-Friday:
12pm-2.30pm,
6.30pm-9.45pm

Saturday:
12pm-3pm, 6.30pm-9.45pm

Sunday:
12pm-4pm, 6.30pm-9.30pm

Closed 25 December

Prices

Meals: a la carte £ 18/32

Typical Dishes

Cornish sardines
Aberdeenshire rump steak
Lemon meringue parfait

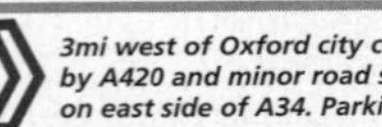

3mi west of Oxford city centre by A420 and minor road south on east side of A34. Parking.

72 The Greyhound

Gallowstree Rd,
Rotherfield Peppard RG9 5HT
Tel.: (01189)722227 – Fax: (01189)242975
e-mail: greyhound@awtrestaurants.com **Website:** www.awtrestaurants.com

 **Fuller's London Pride, IPA Rebellion, London Hoppit**

This attractive, timbered 17C pub is situated on the edge of a picturesque village. There is a small bar for regular drinkers and several more formal areas for dining, including a clapperboard-clad barn extension with exposed timbers and banquette seating, where boar and deer heads stare down at you from the walls. The sizeable front garden has a Petanque pitch for anyone who fancies their chances at the Gallic game, plenty of seating and a classic Italian car won by Antony Worrall Thompson in a celebrity rally a few years ago. There's plenty of choice here, with a light lunch menu, two or three course set menus, salads, side orders and specialities. Dishes from the recent past such as prawn cocktail and beef Stroganoff make a cheery comeback, but the menu is dominated by meat. "Well bred, well fed, well hung" is Worrall Thompson's motto, and the aged Aberdeen Angus steak and Middle White suckling pig are pretty good too.

Food serving times
Monday-Thursday:
12pm-2.30pm, 6pm-9.30pm
Friday:
12pm-2.30pm, 6pm-10pm
Saturday:
12pm-3.30pm, 6pm-10.30pm
Sunday: 12pm-9.30pm
Closed dinner
25-26 December and
1 January
Booking essential

Prices
Meals: a la carte £ 35/55

Typical Dishes
Chilli-salt squid
Fillet steak
Triple chocolate

4mi South of Nettlebed by B481 and minor road ~West towards Gallowstree Common. Parking.

73 The Lamb

Satwell RG9 4QZ
Tel.: (01491)628482 – Fax: (01491)628257
e-mail: thelamb@awtrestaurants.com **Website:** www.awtonline.co.uk

 **Loddon Hoppit, Fuller's London Pride, Marlow Rebellion IPA**

If you've previously avoided The Lamb, suspicious that a celebrity chef at the helm might equal fiddly, overpriced food, then take heart; this unpretentious pub serves simple, heart warming classics, representing good value for money. The menu is split into distinctive sections, including "Fodder for a fiver" and "World in a stew;" with generous portions making side orders seem somewhat surplus to requirements. "Soup and a couple of hunks" might sound particularly tempting…but, regrettably, Antony Worrall Thompson's not in everyday. The interior of this tiny 17C pub is full of cosy character, with its low beamed ceilings, quarry tiled floors and inglenook fire. Old photos hang on the walls and candlelight casts spectral shadows on the walls; or is it just George, the resident ghost, making an appearance? Bookings are not accepted here and it can get very busy, tending to quieten down somewhat later in the evenings.

Food serving times

Monday-Friday:
12pm-2.30pm, 6pm-10pm

Saturday:
12pm-4pm, 6pm-10.30pm

Sunday: 12pm-9.30pm

Closed dinner
25-26 December

Bookings not accepted

Prices

Meals: a la carte £ 17/26

Typical Dishes

Fishy platter
Irish stew
Sticky toffee pudding

3mi South of Nettlebed by B481. Parking.

74 The Wykham Arms

Temple Mill Road,
Sibford Gower OX15 5RX
Tel.: (01295)788808 – Fax: (01295)788806
e-mail: info@wykhamarms.co.uk **Website:** www.wykhamarms.co.uk

Purity Ubu, St Austell Tribute, Wizard Ales, Hook Norton Bitter

The thatched 17C Wykham Arms is one of the highlights of this picturesque, narrow-laned village situated on the county border; another being the Manor house opposite, whose blue plaque tells us was once home to Frank Lascelles (1875-1934) pageant master, writer, painter and sculptor. Pageants involving hundreds or thousands of people were the fashion of the day and the grandiose Lascelles made his name directing them. Although the interior of the pub has been modernised, history is writ large within its rural character, typified by the exposed beams and flag floor, and also evident in the glass-covered well in the floor. The bar menu offers classic dishes such as beef pie and spaghetti, while the sensibly-priced evening à la carte, though small, provides a more varied selection, including dishes such as sautéed chicken livers, trout or sea bass. All dishes are freshly prepared and local suppliers are listed on the blackboard.

Food serving times

Tuesday-Saturday:
12pm-2.45pm, 7pm-9.30pm

Sunday: 12pm-2.45pm

Closed 1 January

Prices

Meals: £ 20 (lunch)
and a la carte £ 19/30

Typical Dishes
Sautéed scallops
Brixham cod
Brioche and butter pudding

8mi West of Banbury by B4035.
Parking.

75 Sir Charles Napier

Sprigg's Alley OX39 4BX
Tel.: (01494)483011 – Fax: (01494)485311
e-mail: info@sircharlesnapier.co.uk **Website:** www.sircharlesnapier.co.uk

 **Wadworth IPA, Wadworth 6X**

Reputedly the first gastropub in the UK, the Sir Charles Napier has been run by the same family since 1975 and the mother and daughter team are as serious about food now as they ever were. The modern British menus are heavily seasoned with French flavourings, so dishes are as likely to include roast partridge with bubble and squeak or omelette "Arnold Bennett", as they are bouillabaisse or French onion soup. Hardly your typical pub grub – and with an international wine list to match, it's no wonder the Sir Charles Napier is so well-regarded. Situated in a small hillside hamlet, this early 18C inn seems to charm all who eat in her. Sofas occupy the quarry-tiled bar area and a hotchpotch of wooden tables provides rustic appeal in the two beamed dining rooms, while the beautiful rear gardens and vine-covered terrace come alive in the warmer months. Sculptures inside and out are by Michael Cooper, a family friend – and all are for sale.

Food serving times

Tuesday-Saturday:
12pm-2.30pm, 6pm-10pm

Sunday: 12pm-3.30pm

Closed 3 days at Christmas

Prices

Meals: a la carte £ 32/45

Typical Dishes

Seared scallops
Roast partridge
Amaretto soufflé

2.5mi Southeast of Chinnor by Bledlow Ridge rd. Parking.

76 The Talkhouse

Wheatley Rd,
Stanton St John OX33 1EX

Tel.: (01865)351648 – Fax: (01865)351085
e-mail: talkhouse@fullers.co.uk **Website:** www.talkhouse@foyers.co.uk

 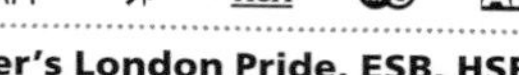

Fuller's London Pride, ESB, HSB and Discovery

The meaning of the carved stone flag in the bar room reading, "Home of the Wind and Bottom Club," at first seems sure to be scatological, but actually stems from an alliterative tale involving buxom barmaid Betty Bottom, her absent husband and his rival suitor, Lord Wind, whose ghost is now rumoured to haunt this pub. Situated on the outskirts of Oxford, the partly thatched building dates from the 1660s and has been sympathetically modernised in order to keep its charming character. The walls are lined with artwork, flag floors gleam, open fires crackle, and heavy beams hang over the open plan interior. Refurbished bedrooms look onto the summer terrace; a suntrap perfect for lazy summer lunches. The modern pub menu features classics, which come in generous portions, including pies of the shepherd and fish variety as well as more adventurous dishes involving oysters or lobster, foie gras or maybe duck.

Food serving times
Monday-Sunday:
12pm-3pm, 6pm-9pm

Prices
Meals: £ 10 and a la carte £ 15/30
4 rooms: £ 55/75

Typical Dishes
Parfait foie gras
Crispy belly of pork
Chocolate orange fondant

5mi East of Oxford via Headington and minor road North East from roundabout on A40 bypass. Parking.

77 The Cherry Tree Inn

Stoke Row RG9 5QA
Tel.: (01491)680430
e-mail: info@thecherrytreeinn.com **Website:** www.thecherrytreeinn.com

 **Brakspear, Hobgoblin, Oxford Gold**

An attractive 400 year old, Grade II listed building, this pub is set right in the heart of Stoke Row, a village famous for the Maharajah's well and the making of tent pegs during World War II. Contemporary in style and decor, it still retains its rustic charm in the shape of bare scrubbed floorboards, flagged stone floors and low beamed ceilings. Originally made up of four cottages, there are now numerous rooms in which to dine. Food is an interesting mix of good value, modern European dishes, such as moules marinière, roast guinea fowl or belly of pork with mash. Drinkers are still welcomed too and recommended beers are printed next to individual dishes on the menu. Should conversation dry up after dinner, there's a cupboard of board games thoughtfully provided. Bedrooms in a converted barn annex are modern and spacious and, like the pub itself, are named after fruit-bearing trees.

Food serving times
Monday-Sunday:
12pm-3pm, 7pm-10pm
Closed 25-26 December

Prices
Meals: a la carte £ 25/40
4 rooms: £ 95

Typical Dishes
Crispy duck salad
Roast rack of Chiltern lamb
Treacle tart

 *Between Henley-on-Thames and Goring off B481. Parking.* 

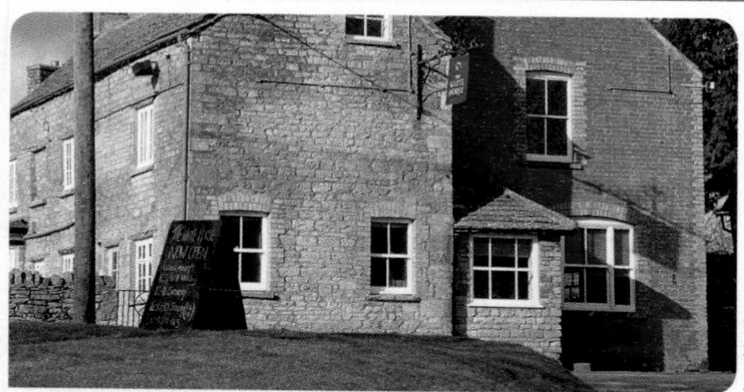

The White Horse

78 The White Horse

The Ridings,
Stonesfield OX29 8EA
Tel.: (01993)891063
e-mail: info@thewhitehorse.uk.com **Website:** www.thewhitehorse.uk.com

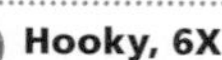

It's the only pub in the village, but doesn't really look like one, save for the small red and white sign swaying in the breeze. So far, so unremarkable. Venture inside, however, and you'll see that this pub is actually more of a dark horse than a white horse, and having lain derelict for four years, has undergone a vast transformation into a modern dining pub. Admire the abstract landscapes on the walls whilst eating in the smart, oak-floored dining room, or lounge in a leather sofa or comfy chair next to the open fire. Locals make the most of the real ales on offer, whilst people travel to taste the snacks and salads on the lunch menu, as well as the more modern dishes on the evening à la carte. Choices range from the simple - cassoulet, steak, salmon, soup - to the more ambitious, including some curious combinations, such as wood pigeon and chocolate pithivier or slow roasted belly pork with sage and onion ice cream.

Food serving times

Tuesday-Saturday:
12pm-2.30pm, 6pm-10.30pm

Sunday: 12pm-4pm

Closed 25 December

Prices

Meals: a la carte £ 17/25

8mi South of Chipping Norton by B4026, B4437 and minor road South. Parking.

79 The Swan Inn

Swinbrook OX18 4DY
Tel.: (01993)823339
e-mail: swanninnswinbrook@btconnect.com
Website: www.theswannswinbrook.co.uk

Hook Norton, 6X, Wye Valley, North Cotswold, Purity

Situated on a country lane next to the River Windrush, with Wisteria climbing up the walls, The Swan Inn is a proper English country pub. Owned by the Dowager Duchess of Devonshire, last of the Mitford sisters, its walls are adorned with black and white photo-canvasses of her friends and family – part of her own private collection. Having been refurbished, the interior is very light and open, especially in the attractive green oak conservatory, which boasts a huge glass wall. Using local, seasonal produce as their base, menus are balanced between traditional and modern British; game and smoked meats are provided by the neighbouring Barrington Estate, while Aberdeen Angus beef comes from the leasee's uncle in the next village. Typical dishes might include braised oxtail, pan-fried sweetbreads or potted shrimps, followed by roast smoked duck breast, sautéed calves liver or pan-fried sea bass; puddings feature all the old favourites.

Food serving times

Monday-Saturday:
12pm-2pm, 7pm-9.30pm

Sunday: 12pm-2pm

Closed 25 December

Closed Monday dinner in winter

Prices

Meals: a la carte £ 20/30

Typical Dishes

Carpaccio of venison
Cornish lemon sole
Pear tart Tatin

3mi North East of Burford by A40 and minor road North. Parking.

80 The Mole Inn

Toot Baldon OX44 9NG
Tel.: (01865)340001 – Fax: (01865)343011
e-mail: info@themoleinn.com
Website: www.themoleinn.com

 **Hook Norton, Pedigree**

You can see from this pub's neat, well-kept exterior that it's something out of the ordinary and on stepping inside, first impressions are thoroughly confirmed. It's an old building but has clearly had the full treatment, with no stone, brick or beam left unturned; the ceilings are timber-filled, floors are wooden or tiled and brick work exposed. There are plenty of places to sit to match your mood; maybe on a sofa in the lounge, at a chunky wooden table in the Victorian-style conservatory or out on the charming landscaped terrace. There lunch menus offers traditional pub dishes, but your best bet is to choose from the more modern à la carte or daily specials, where dishes like sautéd baby squid with hot peanut sauce and chop of Old Spot pork reside. Cooking is tasty and assured and well-priced portions are princely enough to render side orders redundant. Friendly staff add to an all round delightful dining experience.

Food serving times
Monday-Sunday:
12pm-2.30pm, 7pm-9.30pm
Closed 25 December

Prices
Meals: a la carte £ 20/30

Typical Dishes
Seared scallops
Loin of venison
Pain perdu

6mi Southeast of Oxford; between B480 and A4074. Parking.

81 The Boar's Head

Church St, Ardington,
Wantage OX12 8QA
Tel.: (01235)833254
e-mail: info@boarsheadardington.co.uk **Website:** www.boarsheadardington.co.uk

 **Best Mates Brewery, Vicar's Daughter Butts, Barbus Barbus**

This pretty, part-timbered pub is the 18C centrepiece of unspoiled Ardington, a Victorian model village built by local benefactor Lord Wantage in the Vale of the White Horse. A teetotaller, he decided that the pub profits would be best put to use paying for the lighting in the village. The pub has three rooms which surround the bar, with beams and bunches of dried hops providing a sense of the building's rustic past. Family run, by real foodies, the few snacks and sandwiches chalked up above the bar are the only pub grub in sight here. The regularly-changing à la carte menu offers a small selection of competently cooked modern British dishes, with fish a speciality, and presentation is exacting. If you're after a quick meal at lunchtime, the "Menu Rapide" will promptly deliver. Three large, stylish, modern bedrooms provide more than you would expect from a pub. Room number 3 is your best bet - and perfect for a family.

Food serving times
Monday-Sunday:
12pm-2pm, 7pm-9.30pm

Prices
Meals: £ 24 (lunch)
and a la carte £ 23/40

3 rooms: £ 80/150

Typical Dishes
Razor clams
Poached fillet of venison
Toffee banana crumble

2.25mi East of Wantage by A417.
Next to the church. Parking.

82 The Fleece

11 Church Green,
Witney OX28 4AZ
Tel.: (01993)892270
e-mail: fleece@peachpubs.com **Website:** www.fleecewitney.co.uk

 **Greene King IPA, Moreland Original, Old Speckled Hen**

One of the things that makes The Fleece special is its staff; polite and bubbly, they take pride in recognising their regulars and provide keen yet informal service, efficient even when busy – and with its all-age appeal and ability to attract a wide range of people, The Fleece does often get busy. Its modernised interior consists of a front room with polished wood tables, leather suites and newspapers, and an open plan rear restaurant decorated in warm shades of brown, cream and burgundy, where mirrors create a feeling of space and black and white photos hang on the walls. The British-based menu uses freshly prepared, seasonal ingredients and local produce to create flavourful dishes; daily specials, written on the mirrors, include sausage and risotto of the week, and the deli boards make for a very social way to eat. Ten comfortable bedrooms boast individual, eye-catching décor – the ones at the front overlook the village green.

Food serving times
Monday-Sunday:
8am-11.30am, 12pm-6.30pm, 6.30pm-9.45pm

Closed 25 December;

Prices
Meals: a la carte £ 18/32

10 rooms: £ 80/120

Typical Dishes
Shell baked scallops
Roast cod
Rhubarb compote

11mi West of Oxford by A40. Parking.

83 Trout Inn

195 Godstow Rd,
Wolvercote OX2 8PN
Tel.: (01865)302071
Website: www.thetroutoxford.co.uk

  VISA MC AE

Adnams, Timothy Taylors

One of the chief attractions of this modernised Cotswold stone inn, only a few miles out of Oxford, is its idyllic riverside location and in the summer, it's not unusual to see people packed onto its fabulous terrace like sardines. Originally built in the 12C as a hospice for the nearby Godstow nunnery, the inn itself dates back to the 17C, and with numerous little nooks and crannies, roaring fires and an interesting literary history, which includes visits from the fictional character of Inspector Morse, it is also a popular destination come wintertime. The menu may not win any prizes for originality, but there's plenty of choice, with sections offering starters, pastas and salads, pizzas, grills, stove and sharing plates, while the specials board allows the kitchen to show a little more creativity. Since there are no trout in the river, the pub's name is actually a bit of a misnomer, but the greedy chub that gather like to be handfed.

Food serving times

Monday-Thursday:
12pm-10pm,

Friday-Saturday:
12pm-10.30pm,

Sunday 12pm-9.30pm

Prices

Meals: a la carte £ 20/40

Typical Dishes

Potted Salmon and Prawns
Fillet steak
Apple and rhubarb crumble

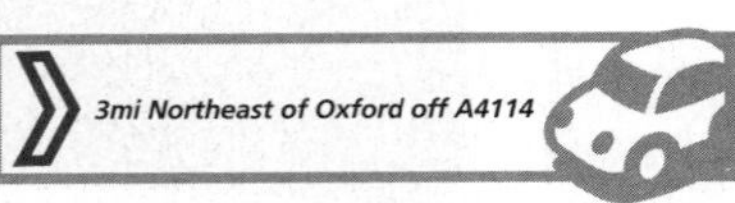

3mi Northeast of Oxford off A4114

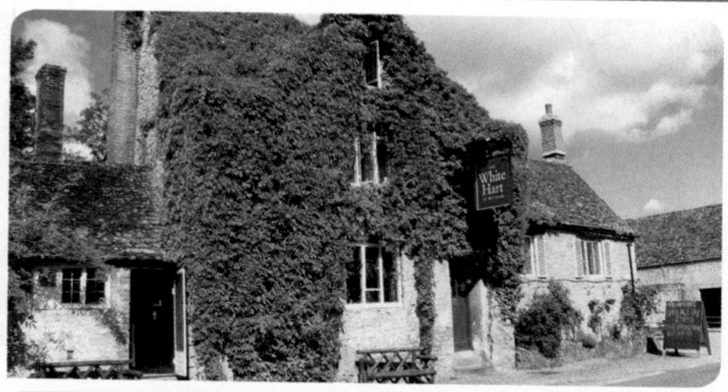

84 The White Hart

Wytham OX2 8QA
Tel.: (01865)244372 – Fax: (01865)248595
e-mail: enquiries@thewhitehartoxford.co.uk
Website: www.thewhitehartoxford.co.uk

  MC

 **Hook Norton, Timothy Taylor**

Located in a charming village, just out of earshot of the A34, this pretty, ivy-clad, stone building is just as characterful on the inside as it is on the out. Four distinct rooms are designed to give a different dining experience; choose from the romantic Red Room, with its mellow lighting and elm floorboards, the French-style Parlour with its scrubbed pine tables, the comfy Vine Room with its wood burner, or the cosy bar with open fire and flagstone floor. On sunny summer days, the courtyard terrace is an added delight. Erring towards being a restaurant rather than a pub, people now come to this popular place primarily to eat. The food is modern gastrofare, with a seasonal European menu which mixes the classic with the contemporary. Supplemented by daily specials, the menu should also please any vegetarians in your group. The service manages to be at once laid back and efficient and the atmosphere is warm and welcoming.

Food serving times

Monday-Friday:
12pm-3pm, 6.30pm-10pm

Saturday:
12pm-4pm, 6.30pm-10pm

Sunday: 12pm-9pm

Closed dinner 25 December

Prices

Meals: a la carte £ 24/37

Typical Dishes

Ham hock terrine
Rump of lamb
Chocolate & hazelnut fondant

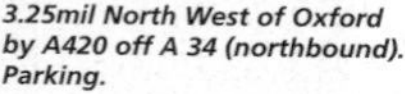
3.25mil North West of Oxford by A420 off A 34 (northbound). Parking.

85 Stephan Langton Inn

Friday St,
Abinger Common RH5 6JR
Tel.: (01306)730775
e-mail: chris@stephan-langton.co.uk **Website:** www.stephan-langton.co.uk

Hogs Back TEA, Ranmore Ale, Fuller's London Pride

In the heart of the privately owned Wooton estate, in the tiny hamlet of Friday Street - down a long windy lane and past the pond - this pub, named after one of the signatories of the Magna Carta, can be well and truly described as off the beaten track. Modestly furnished in earthy tones, with wood floors, open fires, a bar, restaurant and popular summer terrace, it is a good illustration of how keeping things simple can often be the most successful course of action; a philosophy which is also reflected in the food. The concise seasonal menu changes daily, with the emphasis firmly on quality; game comes from the estate, bread is home baked, and you can enjoy delicious homemade fudge with your after-dinner coffee. At lunchtime, you'll find traditional homemade pies, parfaits and pickles on offer, while the evening menu involves more substantial dishes such as lamb shank, breast of Gressingham duck or pan-fried fillet of sea bass.

Food serving times

Wednesday-Saturday:
12.30pm-2.30pm, 7pm-9pm

Sunday & Tuesday:
12.30pm-2.30pm

Prices

Meals: a la carte £ 18/28

Typical Dishes
Soup of the day
Pork pie
Buttermilk pudding

5mi South West of Dorking by A25 and minor road South

86 The Swan Inn

Petworth Rd,
Chiddingfold GU8 4TY
Tel.: (01428)682073 – Fax: (01428)683259
e-mail: enquiries@theswaninn.biz **Website:** www.theswaninn.biz

 VISA MC AE

TEA, Fuller's London Pride

During the reign of Elizabeth I, Chiddingfold became famous for its glass-making, and some of the finest buildings in the country – including St Stephen's Chapel in Westminster – boasted its glass. At only 200 years old, this pub is too young to display such craftsmanship but with a "Swan Inn" having stood on this site since the 14C, its predecessor may well have. Having been gutted by fire in 2003, it comes as no surprise that this majestic building hides a modern, stylish interior. There's a large bar, a small linen-laid dining room and a very popular terrace with an awning, so there's plenty of choice whatever the weather. Food is simple, unfussy and classical; dishes might include smoked haddock, rump of lamb or medallions of pork, while specials change twice a day in line with the latest seasonal produce. Service is courteous but can sometimes lack warmth. Bedrooms are contemporary, with good bathrooms and the latest mod cons.

Food serving times
Monday-Sunday:
12pm-2.30pm, 6.30pm-10pm

Prices
Meals: a la carte £ 26/35
11 rooms: £ 75/150

On East side of the A283. Parking opposite.

Typical Dishes
Salad of smoked salmon
Lamb rump
Vanilla pannacotta

Parrot Inn

87 Parrot Inn

Forest Green RH5 5RZ

Tel.: (01306)621339

e-mail: drinks@the parrot.co.uk **Website:** www.the parrot.co.uk

  MC

 **Ringwood Best, Youngs Ordinary, Adnams Broadside, Ringwood 49er**

When this attractive 17C pub became available, the owners of a nearby cattle, pig and sheep farm took the chance to exchange their bustling London pubs for the slower pace of the country. Overlooking a vast village green, it exudes plenty of character, boasting slate floors, low beams, wood burning ranges and cosy little booths. As you might expect, there's plenty of home-reared meat on the menu and a strong emphasis on quality, local ingredients. The same generous cooking and daily specials are served throughout, with dishes including maybe pork rib eye or slow braised Aberdeen Angus beef, with the burgers in particular proving extremely popular. Sandwiched between the bar and restaurant a farm shop sells homemade bread (fresh from the oven if you arrive in the morning), cheese, chutney, jam, their own meat and a selection of pies – Nose to Tail (consisting of cheeks, tongue, loin and rump) being the speciality. Booking is advisable.

Food serving times

Monday-Saturday:
12pm-3pm, 6pm-10pm

Sunday: 12pm-5pm

Closed 25 December for food

Prices

Meals: a la carte £ 20/28

Typical Dishes

Wild mushrooms on brioche

Pork rib eye

Treacle & pistachio tart

8mi South of Dorking by A24, A29 and B2126 West. Parking.

88 The King William IV

Byttom Hill,
Mickleham RH5 6EL
Tel.: (01372)372590
e-mail: iduke@another.com **Website:** www.king-williamiv.com

Shere Drop, Adnams Best, TEA, Sharps Doombar

Many a rambler has sunk gratefully into a chair in the bar of the King William IV, having exhausted themselves climbing Box Hill, and even those customers who weren't planning on partaking in any exercise may have found themselves having to huff and puff their way up Byttom Hill after parking at its base. Any exertion will seem worth it when your food arrives, however, for this is robust, hearty cooking in the shape of traditional homemade pies, beef Wellington or calves liver, with heaps of simply-cooked fresh vegetables; old school desserts like homemade treacle tart, plus a daily specials board - and local handpumped ales with which to wash it all down. Every available space in the long, narrow room seems to have a table, but even so, it's worth booking ahead since you can bet you won't be the only walker wanting to refuel. In summer, a table in the terraced garden is a treat, with views of the surrounding countryside.

Food serving times

Monday-Saturday:
12pm-2pm, 7pm-9.30pm

Sunday: 12pm-2pm

Closed Sunday dinner

Prices

Meals: a la carte £ 19/28

Typical Dishes

Scallops on crayfish towers
Beef Wellington
Treacle tart

0.5mi North of Mickleham by A24. Difficult off-road parking nearby. Public car park at the bottom of Byttom Hill

89 Bryce's

Old School House,
Stane St, Ockley RH5 5TH
Tel.: (01306)627430 – Fax: (01306)628274
e-mail: bryces.fish@virgin.net **Website:** www.bryces.co.uk

VISA 

Sussex Bitter, Fuller's London Pride

The eponymous owner opened Bryce's back in '92 and such has been its success that he's now cooking up a sea storm over at its newer sister restaurant in Worthing. This place has been left in more than capable hands, however, and the basic tenet has remained the same: to serve market-fresh seafood at market-fresh prices; simply cooked and full of flavour. The Old School House underwent a total refurbishment in 2007 and both the bar and restaurant are now contemporary in style, with an attractive copper-topped bar counter and high backed leather chairs. A lighter menu is available in the bar, with some salads, open sandwiches and steaks alongside cullen skink and fishcakes, while restaurant offerings may have more exotic origins, with dishes such as Cajun salmon or spring rolls featuring, as well as the freshest fish available, plus a tasty selection of breads. A friendly young team provide attentive service for Bryce's faithful regulars.

Food serving times

Monday-Sunday:
12pm-2.30pm, 7pm-9.30pm

Closed 25-26 December and 1 January; also dinner Sunday November, January and February

- Seafood -

Prices

Meals: £ 25/31
and a la carte £ 22/28

Typical Dishes

Prawn and crab cocktail
Red mullet risotto
Orange & ginger pudding

8mi South of Dorking by A24 and A29. Parking.

90 The Inn @ West End

42 Guildford Road,
West End GU24 9PW
Tel.: (01276)858652
e-mail: greatfood@the-inn.co.uk **Website:** www.the-inn.co.uk

VISA  AE

 **Youngs Bitter, Fuller's London Pride and occasional guest beers : Spitfire, Timothy Taylor Landlord**

With beautiful hanging baskets, prettily laid tables, a friendly service team, delicious desserts and the choice between a light, airy sun lounge or a lovely garden and terrace, you could easily be mistaken for thinking that you are in a tea shop. The food also belies that of a pub: it is hearty yet wholesome – quality ingredients cooked simply and well – and extremely fresh, with an on-site plucking machine for preparing game and a chiller van for collecting the latest catch. Dishes arrive in front of you exactly as described on the menu: pan-fried field mushrooms on toast is just that, thick slices of mushroom on chunky granary bread. The owner also runs a small wine business, so the choice is good, and there are frequent wine tasting sessions. For a bit of variety they hold regular, imaginative theme nights, such as "School Dinners Night" or the "60s Retro Dinner", where the locals dress accordingly.

Food serving times

Monday-Saturday:
12pm-2.30pm, 6pm-9.30pm

Sunday:
12pm-3pm, 6pm-9pm

Prices

Meals: £ 24 (Sunday lunch) and a la carte £ 25/75

Typical Dishes

Welsh rarebit on mushroom
Saddleback pork loin
Dark chocolate tart

2.5mi South East of Junction 3 on M3 by A322. Parking (40 spaces).

91 The Brickmakers

Chertsey Rd,
Windlesham GU20 6HT
Tel.: (01276)472267 – Fax: (01276)451014
e-mail: thebrickmakers@4cinns.co.uk **Website:** www.4cinns.co.uk

  AE

Fuller's London Pride, Courage Best

This red-brick pub appears rather small in the shadows of the many grand houses that surround it but once inside you'll find it's a lot bigger than it first seemed. There's a bar area with tables, comfy sofas and an open fire and a linen-laid restaurant that extends out into a conservatory – probably the best place to eat. In the summer this pub really comes into its own, with the sizeable garden playing host to a good many tables, as well as a BBQ area. The bar menu features fairly straightforward dishes, such as pâté and toast or the particularly tasty Welsh Rarebit, which comes with a bottle of Lea and Perrins so you can splash away to your heart's desire. The more substantial à la carte menu displays flavoursome, well-cooked dishes that might include crayfish and crab cocktail or goat's cheese and apple salad, followed by half shoulder of lamb or stuffed chicken breast; desserts are chalked on the board alongside the specials.

Food serving times

Monday-Sunday:
12pm-2.30pm, 6.30pm-10pm

Prices

Meals: £ 24 and a la carte £ 22/30

Typical Dishes

Avocado with crabmeat
Roast stuffed pork fillet
Home-made ices

East 1mi on B386. Parking.

92 The Fountain Inn

Ashurst BN44 3AP
Tel.: (01403)710219

  VISA MC

 **Harveys, Fuller's London Pride, HSB**

Writer Hilaire Belloc wrote about it in his book "The Four Men" in 1902, Laurence Olivier was a regular visitor and favoured the large seat next to the inglenook in the front bar, and it was even the setting for Paul McCartney's video for "Wonderful Christmastime" back in 1979. It will come as no surprise, therefore that the 16C Fountain Inn is overflowing with character and charm, boasting beamed ceilings, thick brick walls, flagstone floors and open fires. There's a garden and a pond, plus a skittle alley for a spot of retro entertainment; the pub hosts a classic car get together every summer, and as in all the best pubs, the locals in the bar are more than willing to chat. Cooking is down-to-earth, fresh and full of flavour; choices might include steak, mushroom and ale pie or Sussex Smokie as well as salads and steaks, plus a large selection of daily specials – and puds like ginger treacle tart and hot chocolate fudge cake.

Food serving times

Monday-Saturday:
11.30am-2.30pm,
6pm-9.30pm

Sunday: 12pm-3pm

Prices

Meals: a la carte £ 16/32

Typical Dishes
Goats cheese salad
Hot Thai curry
Sticky toffee pudding

3.5mi North of Steyning on B2135. Parking.

93 George and Dragon

Main St,
Burpham BN18 9RR
Tel.: (01903)883131 – Fax: (01903)883341
e-mail: sara.cheney@btinternet.com **Website:** www.georgeanddragonburpham.com

Arundel Brewery and guest beer Betty Stoggs

Once home to the late Mervyn Peake, artist and creator of the Gormenghast trilogy – (he is now buried in the local churchyard) – and with stunning views over the rolling English countryside, the picturesque village of Burpham seems a thoroughly fitting setting for a pub with such a typically English name. Cooking continues the English theme, with seasonal offerings from local suppliers including game from the adjacent Duke of Norfolk's Estate, and suckling pig an occasional treat for Sunday lunch - although themed evenings – think Country and Western or Burns Night - also give more far-flung flavours a look in from time to time. The menu is chalked up on blackboards and served both at scrubbed wooden tables in the bar and at more formally laid tables in the dining area. Service is attentive and the wine list short but lively. Feel a sense of timelessness as you enjoy a post-prandial riverside stroll, with views to Arundel Castle.

Food serving times

Monday-Friday:
12pm-2pm, 6.30pm-9pm

Saturday:
12pm-3pm, 6.30pm-9pm

Sunday: 12pm-3pm

Closed 25 December and Sunday dinner

Prices

Meals: £ 16 and a la carte £ 16/28

Typical Dishes

Seared pigeon salad
Baked whole black bream
Strawberry cheesecake

3mi Northeast of Arundel by A27. Parking.

94 The Fox Goes Free

Charlton PO18 0HU

Tel.: (01243)811461 – Fax: (01243)811712

e-mail: thefoxgoesfree-always@virgin.net **Website:** www.thefoxgoesfree.com

Ballards Best Bitter, Fox Bitter, Harveys Bitter

Over recent years, more and more pubs have had the interior designers in and been "gastroed"; the result being a glut of homogenous identipubs. Not so The Fox Goes Free; with its exposed stone walls, tile floors and large inglenook, this early 17C flint building retains its individual character and remains cheerfully free from over-modernisation. Interesting moments in the pub's history are recorded for posterity on the walls: a plaque contends that the first ever meeting of the Women's Institute was held here in 1915, while a more recent photograph reveals that part of a Dr. Who episode was filmed here in the days of K9 and Tom Baker. Menus are short and seasonal, with a strong reliance on local produce, including game from local shoots; you can eat in one of several dining areas, in the bar or in the rear garden overlooking the South Downs - and if you're making a weekend of it, you'll find the bedrooms comfortable and well-equipped.

Food serving times

Monday-Friday:
12pm-2.30pm, 6.30pm-10pm

Saturday-Sunday:
12pm-10pm, 6.30pm-10pm

Closed 25 December

Prices

Meals: a la carte £ 20/30

5 rooms: £ 60/140

Typical Dishes

Caramelised onion tart
Ribeye steak
Homemade cheesecake

6,75 mi North of Chichester by A286. Parking.

95 The Royal Oak Inn

Pook Lane,
East Lavant PO18 0AX
Tel.: (01243)527434
e-mail: info@royaloakeastlavant.co.uk **Website:** www.royaloakeastlavant.co.uk

Inspectors' favourites

    AE

 **Sharps Doombar, Betty Stoggs, Arundel Gold**

The contemporary combines with the more traditional in this 18C inn to provide a warm, rural atmosphere in which to wine and dine. Locals patronise the place – always a good sign – but you may have to fight them if you've got your eye on table number four; a popular corner banquette next to the fireplace. Seasonal cooking has a modern base, and you might find fish and chips and shepherd's pie on offer, alongside fillet steak, pork loin, breast of wood pigeon or calves liver. Game, supplied by the nearby Goodwood Estate, is very popular in the winter months, while weekly trips to the London markets provide the fish and vegetables. Wine is clearly the preferred tipple of Chichesterians, with bottles cleverly displayed on racks and shelves around the room, but there is also a choice of real ales on tap for those of a more beery persuasion. Bedrooms – some above the bar, others in cottages and a barn – are furnished to a high standard.

Off A286 after the hump-back bridge. Parking.

Food serving times

Monday-Sunday:
12pm-3pm, 6pm-10pm

Closed 25-26 December

Prices

Meals: a la carte £ 25/35

8 rooms: £ 75/180

Typical Dishes
Tempura vegetables
English lamb cutlets
Red berry fool

96 Three Horseshoes

Elsted GU29 0JY
Tel.: (01730)825746

 **Bowmans Swift One, Flowerpots Bitter, Timothy Taylor Landlord, Fuller's London Pride**

The Three Horseshoes is what you would call a no frills pub - and all the better for it. Its ancient beamed interior is simple yet cosy, with flowers on each table giving the place a cheerful, homely touch. The furthest of the three rooms is the most comfy and, since it overlooks the garden, also lets in the most light. You must order at the bar and there's no special treatment for celebrities or dignitaries, as both Madonna and Prince Andrew found out when they stopped off here. As with the décor, so too with the food: a simple blackboard menu offers tasty, traditional dishes like ploughman's, casseroles and pies; this is wholesome, hearty cooking which comes served in such enormous portions that it takes a concerted effort to leave trouser space for dessert. Service is pleasantly informal, staff and locals are chatty and the large garden, with its agreeable aspect over the South Downs, makes a great spot for al fresco dining.

Food serving times
Monday-Saturday:
12pm-2pm, 6.30pm-9pm
Sunday:
12pm-2pm, 7pm-8.30pm

Prices
Meals: a la carte £ 20/30

Typical Dishes
Potted shrimps
Venison fillet
Treacle tart

Halfway Bridge

97 The Halfway Bridge Inn

Halfway Bridge GU28 9BP
Tel.: (01798)861281
e-mail: enquiries@halfwaybridge.co.uk **Website:** www.halfwaybridge.co.uk

Betty Stogs Bitter, Ringwood Bitter, Ballards

Years ago you would have approached from the front but now, due to the vagaries of modern road planning, you enter via the back. Once inside you are greeted by a series of cosy rooms featuring exposed brickwork and log fires, carefully designed to retain the 17C character while also providing a more comfortable, contemporary edge. The menu displays good, honest British cooking that comes in hearty, flavoursome portions, featuring dishes such as calves liver, sea bass or lamb shank. In addition, the daily-changing specials board lists even more pub classics and for those with a sweet tooth, plenty of old-fashioned sticky puddings. Across the 250 year old stable yard, bedrooms take on the same styling, blending rustic features with modern facilities and coming complete with everything from an umbrella to a Playstation. This pub is popular, especially in the polo season, so it pays to plan ahead, as empty tables are rarities.

Food serving times
Monday-Sunday:
12pm-2.30pm,
6.30pm-9.15pm
Closed 25 December

Prices
Meals: a la carte £ 23/30
6 rooms: £ 75/140

Typical Dishes
Spinach & Stilton tart
Rost stuffed sea bass
Treacle tart

Halfway between Midhurst and Petworth on the A272. Parking.

98 The Ginger Fox

Albourne,
Henfield BN6 9EA
Tel.: (01273)857888
e-mail: info@gingermanrestaurants.com **Website:** www.gingermanrestaurants.com

 **Harvey's Sussex Bitter, Flowers IPA, Abbot Ale**

It's not in Albourne village and your sat nav may well lead you somewhere else entirely, so don't take the postal address too literally. Nestling behind a large hedge, the first thing that you will see from the road is a fox chasing a pheasant along the newly thatched roof. As with their three other Gingerman establishments, the owners' main focus here rests on the food, with locality and seasonality playing an important role. The à la carte menu and blackboard specials change slightly every day and the descriptions are pleasantly straightforward, leaving the rich, deep flavours to speak for themselves; you might find braised veal cheeks, spiced lamb neck kebabs or smoked haddock, mussel and leek pie, whilst in summer a rare breed hog roast is on offer at weekends. Book in advance if you can, as only a handful of tables are set aside for walk-ins; they can be close together so opt for one by the window if it's available.

Food serving times
Monday-Friday:
12pm-2pm, 6pm-10pm
Saturday-Sunday:
12.30pm-4pm, 6.30pm-10pm
Closed 25 December

Prices
Meals: a la carte £ 21/26

Typical Dishes
Squid tempura
Madeira braised rabbit
Bitter chocolate tart

8mi North of Shoreham by A283 and A2037

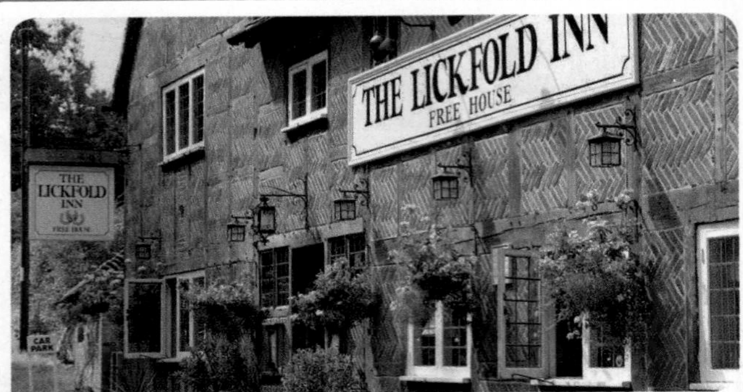

99 The Lickfold Inn

Lickfold GU28 9EY
Tel.: (01798)861285
e-mail: lickfold@live-once-inns.co.uk **Website:** www.live-once-inns.co.uk

 **IPA, Old Speckled Hen, TEA**

Dating back to the 1400s, this characterful red-brick pub sits at the end of a narrow, winding lane in the picturesque Sussex countryside. In contrast with its colourful DJ owner – Chris Evans – it displays a relaxed, traditional charm, boasting wooden beams, stone floors and inglenook fireplaces. More importantly, there are no signs of flashy patronage, just friendly, unassuming service as you would expect to find in any country inn. Cooking is fairly ambitious, taking a step away from traditional country pub fare and towards a more restaurant style (although a few sandwiches are available at lunch). The fish pie contains lobster and monkfish, the salad Niçoise comes with tuna cooked to your taste, and offering a dozen or so choices the cheese selection is an occasion in itself, coming complete with a descriptive menu of its very own. The dishes on offer at lunch and dinner are similar but a few more are added in the evening.

Food serving times

Monday-Saturday:
12pm-3pm, 6pm-10pm

Sunday: 12pm-3pm

Closed 25 December

Prices

Meals: a la carte £ 22/33

Typical Dishes

Scottish smoked salmon
Braised lamb shank
Knickerbocker glory

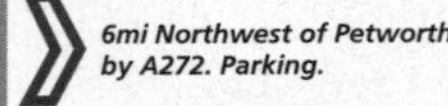

6mi Northwest of Petworth by A272. Parking.

100 The Earl of March

Mid Lavant,
Chichester PO18 OBQ
Tel.: (01243)533993 – Fax: (01243)783991
e-mail: gt@theearlofmarch.com **Website:** www.theearlofmarch.com

 **Fuller's London Pride, Ringood Best Bitter, Hopback Summer Lightning**

Situated on the edge of the Goodwood Estate, this pub has pleasant pastoral views across to the racecourse's main stand in the distance. The pub's owner has built up a good relationship with the Estate's latest resident, The Earl of March, who has given permission for the pub to use his family crest on its signage. A modern makeover has seen the bar and restaurant areas becoming clearly defined, the first being fitted out with comfy sofas and a blazing log fire. The à la carte menu is supplemented in the evening by daily-changing blackboard specials; in the winter, game from the local estates and in the summer fresh fish. Cooking is flavoursome and hearty, featuring simple British dishes such as stew, sea bass or steak. While eating you'll often see a Rolls Royce drive by from the nearby test centre and there's a great collection of motoring photographs from the Festival of Speed on the walls.

Food serving times

Monday-Saturday:
12pm-2.30pm, 6pm-9.30pm

Sunday: 12pm-2.30pm

Prices

Meals: a la carte £ 21/29

Typical Dishes

Pan-fried scallops
Pan-seared fillet of venison
Vanilla pannacotta

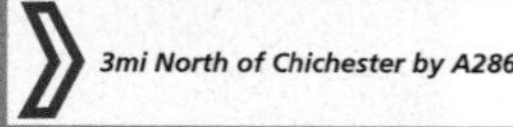

3mi North of Chichester by A286

101 Badgers

Coultershaw Bridge,
Petworth GU28 0JF
Tel.: (01798)342651

 **Badgers First Gold, King & Barnes Sussex & seasonal guest ales**

With its sash windows and River Rother location (it's just past the bridge), this smart white-painted former railway tavern is an ideal destination in pretty Petworth.
Its eye-catching garden boasts weeping willows, and next door is the unique, Michelin Red Guide recommended Old Railway Station guesthouse. Badgers' interior is most pleasant: a beautiful oak-panelled bar has carvings with a "badger and honey" theme, and lots of old photos depict its former Railway Inn-carnation. Jack Vettriano fans will find two of his sexy pictures, The Assessment and Game On, in a single-table alcove that gives a new twist to the word "intimate". Menus offer plenty of choice, a robust and wholesome mix of classic British dishes with global influences. There are fresh fish specials and homemade puddings too. South Downs ramblers staying on have the choice of three comfy, spacious rooms a cut above normal pub accommodation.

Food serving times

Monday-Sunday:
12pm-2pm, 7pm-9pm

Closed 25 December

Closed dinner Sunday October-April

Prices

Meals: a la carte £ 22/35

3 rooms: £ 55/80

Typical Dishes

Chicken & cashew nut pastry
Spanish fish casserole
Crème brûlée

2mi South of Petworth by A285 at Coultershaw Bridge. Parking.

102 The Chequers Inn

Rowhook RH12 3PY

Tel.: (01403)790480

e-mail: thechequers1@aol.com **Website:** nealsrestaurants.biz

VISA 

 **Harveys, Fuller's London Pride, Hepworth Prospect**

Duck is not only the name of a bird on the menu at The Chequers Inn, but also the word your friends will shout at you as you go through the doorways. Annoying maybe, but along with its log fires, uneven floors and relaxed atmosphere, the low beamed ceilings are part of this delightful 18C inn's charm and character. Travel up a few stairs and you'll enter another rustic seating area, where farming implements hang on the walls alongside pictures of local legends. On the other side is what at first glance appears to be a corrugated metal shed but is actually Neal's restaurant, the more formally laid part of the establishment; but since the same menu is served throughout, the bar would have to be your choice for a seat every time. The menu offers aspirational cooking which showcases local produce, including game from local estates, with dishes such as belly pork, venison bresaola and pan-fried halibut, as well as fresh homemade puddings.

Food serving times

Monday-Saturday:
12pm-2pm, 7pm-9pm

Sunday: 12pm-2pm

Closed 25 December

Prices

Meals: a la carte £ 23/30

Typical Dishes

Sautéed Scottish scallops

Trio of Sussex lamb

Ginger pannacotta

3mi West of Horsham by A281. Parking.

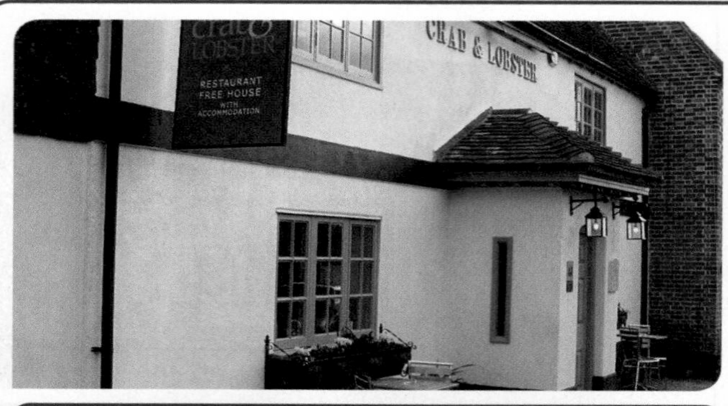

103 Crab & Lobster

Mill Lane,
Sidlesham PO20 7NB
Tel.: (01243)641233
e-mail: enquiries@crab-lobster.co.uk **Website:** www.thesussexpub.co.uk

Inspectors' favourites

   AE

 **Harvey Sussex Best Bitter, Flowers IPA**

350 years ago this was a busy crossing point for ships travelling to France; now it is a harbour nature reserve occupied by the diverse flora and fauna of the local marshlands. The desolate roads that skirt the bay do not prepare you for the bustling atmosphere inside this pub, where slate floors and large fireplaces sit amongst more contemporary features such as counters studded with pebbles from the nearby beach. It is comfortable, appealing and despite the bar, feels more like a place to eat than to drink. The British/Mediterranean menu displays simply constructed, cleanly presented dishes, with plenty of fish, maybe calamari, scallops or lobster to start, with pesto-crusted cod, spiced crab gratin or seafood risotto to follow; make sure you finish with a coffee, as it comes with a shot glass of smarties. Rooms are spacious and contemporary, with sea or rural views - or both in the attic room. Self-contained Crab Cottage is nearby.

Food serving times
Monday-Sunday:
12pm-2.30pm, 6pm-9.45pm

Prices
Meals: a la carte £ 24/36
4 rooms: £ 75/140

South of Chichester : 1 m. by B 2145, then turn right onto Rookery Lane

104 Nava Thai at The Hamilton Arms

School Lane,
Stedham GU29 0NZ
Tel.: (01730)812555 – Fax: (01730)817459
e-mail: hamiltonarms@hotmail.com **Website:** www.thehamiltonarms.co.uk

VISA MC AE

 **Fuller's London Pride, Fuller's HSB, Ballards Best**

Deep in the heart of the Sussex countryside you will find this traditional village inn. At least, so it appears from the outside. Yes, it has the picnic tables and the hanging baskets. Yes, it has the lounge with roaring fire, the bar snacks and the real ale. And yet this pub is so much more: think authentic oriental artefacts, carved wooden panels, and burning incense, in a restaurant where for nigh on two decades Thai staff in traditional uniforms have been serving up tasty Thai dishes. The monosodium glutamate-free menu is extensive, and they also provide a takeaway service, should you prefer to phone in your order. In your patronage, not only will you enjoy delicious Thai cuisine, but through the Mudita Trust, you will also be helping abused and underprivileged Thai children. May sees a Thai festival held on the green when everyone dresses in National costume and all funds raised go to the same worthy cause.

Food serving times
Tuesday-Saturday:
12pm-2.30pm, 6pm-10.30pm
Sunday:
12pm-2.30pm, 7pm-9.30pm
Closed 1-3 January
- Thai -

Prices
Meals: £ 20
(3 course lunch/dinner)
and a la carte £ 15/25

Typical Dishes
Chicken satay
Tiger prawns
Thai egg custard

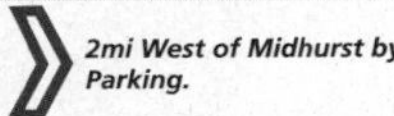
2mi West of Midhurst by A272.
Parking.

105 The Keepers Arms

Trotton GU31 5ER
Tel.: (01730)813724 – Fax: (01730)810780
e-mail: info@keepersarms.co.uk
Website: www.keepersarms.co.uk

 **Dark Star Hophead, Ballards Best, Ringwood Best**

Following its refurbishment in 2007, the focus of this characterful village pub is now firmly on the food. Good value dishes offer a modern take on British classics and the short à la carte is supplemented with daily changing blackboard specials. You might start with a terrine of duck confit or a homemade fishcake, followed by roasted partridge, sausage and mash or sea bass, with rice pudding or perhaps some locally made ice cream for dessert. Cooking is flavoursome and the wine list offers some decent accompaniments. The pub is perched on a hillside and set back from the main road, and while its gastro-makeover means it's been stripped back to basics with whitewashed walls and wooden floors, the slightly raised "Captain's table" and the four poster style "Kazzbar" with its own blinds provide seating arrangements a little out of the ordinary, while the cosy bar offers the warmth of an open fire and the comfort of a Chesterfield sofa.

Food serving times

Monday-Sunday:
12pm-2pm, 7pm-9.30pm

Closed 25 December dinner, 26 December

Prices

Meals: a la carte £ 21/28

Typical Dishes

Wild rabbit ballotine
Roast turbot
Mango mousse

4mi West of Midhurst by A272

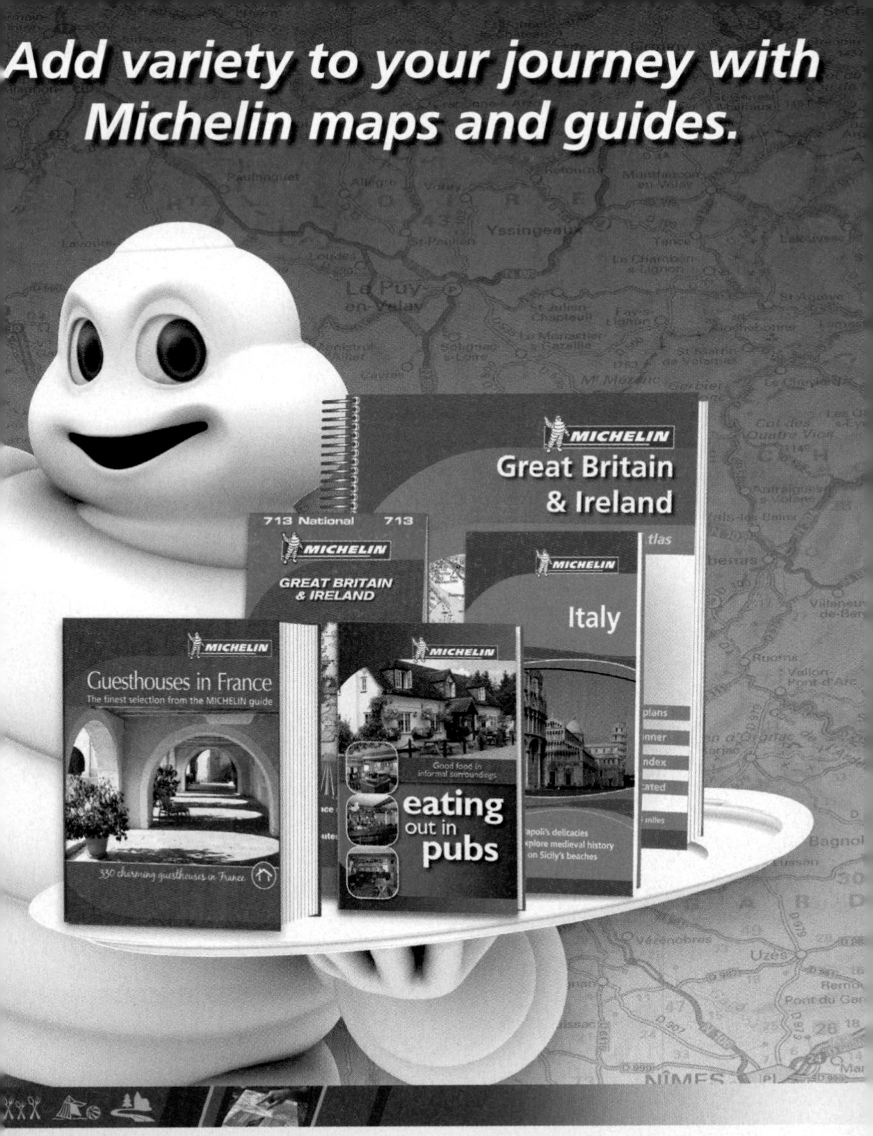

Six hundred miles of relentlessly breathtaking coastline pound the majestic South West, assuring it of a dramatic backdrop whatever the season. Its prestige is bolstered by four UNESCO World Heritage sites: one of them is Dorset's spectacular Jurassic Coast, which includes the 180 billion pebbles of Chesil Beach. Further north, Dartmoor and Exmoor embody the region's untamed beauty. The built environment may be of a more recent time line, but examples are still impressive, ranging from thirteenth century Lacock, home of many a filmed costume drama, to Elizabethan Longleat with its Capabilty Brown designed parkland, and late Victorian Lanhydrock, "the great house of Cornwall". The same county boasts its very own "theatre under the stars", The Minack, where the drama of nature collides with the drama of the written word. Days out in this unforgettable region come complete with pasties and a pint of local ale, or freshly caught lobster, scallops or mussels enjoyed along the quay.

CHANNEL ISLANDS
France
Cherbourg-Octeville
Nez de Jobourg
Beaumont-Hague
les Pieux
Bricquebec
Barneville-Carteret
Carteret
Portbail
la Haye-du-Puits
Lessay
Alderney
Guernsey
St. Peter Port
Sark
Jersey
St-Helier
Gorey
Weymouth
Poole
Lampeter
Llandysul
CARMARTHENSHIRE
Llandeilo
Cross Hands
Ammanford
Kidwelly
Pontarddulais
Llanelli
Swansea
Abertawe
The Mumbles
Port Talbot
Cork
Lundy
Ilfracombe
Combe Martin
Lynton
Croyde
Braunton
Barnstaple
Northam
Hartland Point
Clovelly
Bideford
Great Torrington
Kilkhampton
SOUTH
Stratton
Bude
Holsworthy
Hatherleigh
Winkleigh
Okehampton
DEVON
Tamar
Tintagel
Launceston
High Willhays
Moretonhampstead
Dartmoor
National Park
Camelford
Padstow
Wadebridge
Tavistock
Princetown
Ashburton
CORNWALL
Bodmin
Callington
Newquay
Liskeard
Saltash
Fraddon
Lostwithiel
Plympton
Totnes
Fowey
Torpoint
Looe
Polperro
Modbury
Truro
St. Austell
Tregony
Mevagissey
PLYMOUTH
Plymstock
Newton Ferrers
Ives
Hayle
Redruth
Camborne
Penryn
St. Mawes
Falmouth
Penzance
St. Just
Sennen
Helston
Mount's Bay
St. Keverne
Lizard
Lizard Point
Salcombe
Kingsbridge
Dartmouth
Santander
Roscoff
Tresco
St. Martin's
Isles of Scilly
St. Mary's

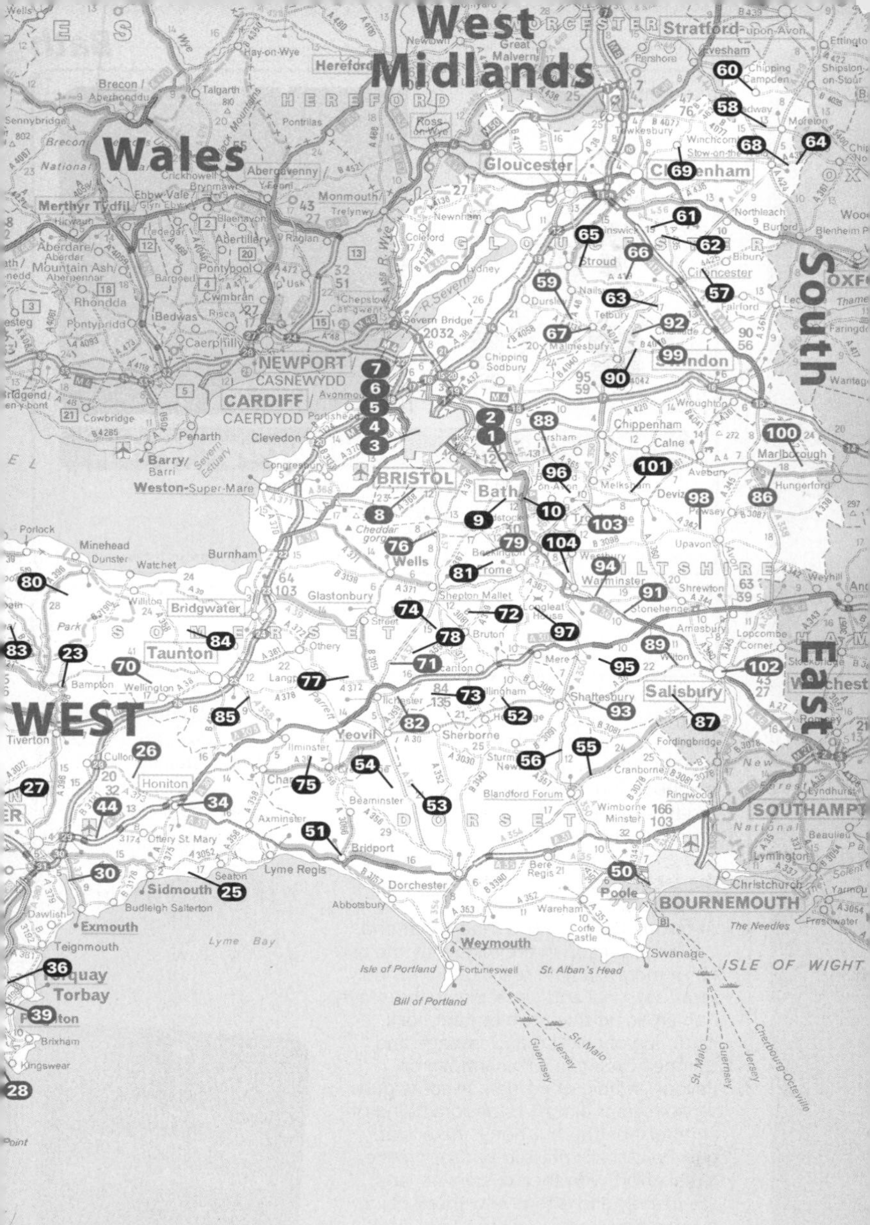

West Midlands
Wales
WEST
South East
Stratford-upon-Avon
Evesham
Chipping Campden
Shipston-on-Stour
Hereford
Hay-on-Wye
Brecon / Aberhonddu
Talgarth
Great Malvern
Pershore
Tewkesbury
Winchcombe
Stow-on-the-Wold
Moreton
Ross-on-Wye
Gloucester
Cheltenham
Abergavenny
Crickhowell
Ebbw Vale
Merthyr Tydfil
Monmouth
Trelynwy
Coleford
Newnham
Lydney
Northleach
Burford
Blenheim
Stroud
Nailsworth
Cirencester
Bibury
Fairford
Aberdare/ Aberdar
Mountain Ash/ Aberpennar
Rhondda
Pontypridd
Pontypool
Cwmbran
Caerphilly
Bedwas
Risca
Usk
Chepstow
Severn Bridge
Dursley
Tetbury
Malmesbury
Swindon
NEWPORT / CASNEWYDD
CARDIFF / CAERDYDD
Cowbridge
Penarth
Barry/ Barri
Clevedon
Portishead
Avonmouth
Chipping Sodbury
Chippenham
Wroughton
Marlborough
Hungerford
Calne
Melksham
Corsham
Avebury
Devizes
Pewsey
Upavon
Weston-Super-Mare
Congresbury
BRISTOL
Bath
Cheddar gorge
Wells
Radstock
Trowbridge
Westbury
Beckington
Frome
Warminster
Shrewton
Stonehenge
Amesbury
Porlock
Minehead
Dunster
Watchet
Burnham
Glastonbury
Shepton Mallet
Longleat House
Bridgwater
Street
Othery
Bruton
Mere
Wilton
Salisbury
Taunton
Wellington
Bampton
Langport
Ilchester
Wincanton
Gillingham
Shaftesbury
Fordingbridge
Tiverton
Yeovil
Sherborne
Ilminster
Chard
Cullompton
Honiton
Beaminster
Sturminster Newton
Blandford Forum
Cranborne
Ringwood
Wimborne Minster
SOUTHAMPTON
Lyndhurst
Beaulieu
Lymington
Ottery St. Mary
Axminster
Bridport
Lyme Regis
Dorchester
Bere Regis
Poole
BOURNEMOUTH
Christchurch
Sidmouth
Seaton
Budleigh Salterton
Exmouth
Dawlish
Teignmouth
Abbotsbury
Weymouth
Wareham
Corfe Castle
Swanage
The Needles
Lyme Bay
Isle of Portland
Fortuneswell
Bill of Portland
St. Alban's Head
ISLE OF WIGHT
Torquay
Torbay
Paignton
Brixham
Kingswear
Guernsey
Jersey
St. Malo
Cherbourg-Octeville

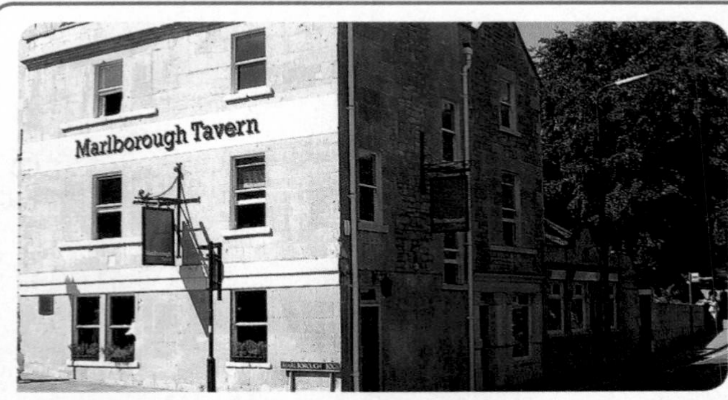

1 Marlborough Tavern

35 Marlborough Buildings,
Bath BA1 2LY

Tel.: (01225)423731

e-mail: info@marlborough-tavern.com **Website:** www.marlborough-tavern.com

Wadworth 6X, Butcombe Bitter

Marlborough Buildings, a prime location right by the Royal Victoria Park and the terrace in which this pub sits, was originally built as a windbreak for the famous neighbouring Royal Crescent. Spacious and modern, with a sage green colour scheme, it features flock wallpaper, exotic lighting and a mishmash of furniture; flowers on the tables and local artists' work for sale on the walls bringing further splashes of colour. Light streams in at either end, while the section in the middle by the bar has a more intimate feel. Food is proudly local, seasonal and traceable, with unfussy, homemade dishes such as ham hock, confit leg of chicken and sausage and split pea casserole which are big on flavour and big of portion. In some pubs, service seems almost to be something of an afterthought, but not so here; staff may be casually dressed but they make a real effort with their customers, and are friendly and attentive without being overbearing.

Food serving times

Monday-Saturday:
12.30pm-2.30pm,
6pm-9.30pm

Sunday: 12pm-4pm

Closed 25 December

Prices

Meals: a la carte £ 22/32

Typical Dishes

Red mullet

Loin of local pork

Rhubarb crème brûlée

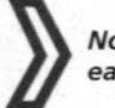

North West of city centre on east side of Royal Victoria Park

2 White Hart

Widcombe Hill,
Bath BA2 6AA

Tel.: (01225)338053 – Fax: (01225)338053

e-mail: enquiries@whitehartbath.co.uk **Website:** www.whitehartbath.co.uk

 **Butcombe Traditional, Butcombe Gold, Butty Bach**

This pub has a good reputation in the local community and as you pass by the small groups of drinkers sharing tapas at the bar, you understand why you had to book to secure a place. Worn wooden tables are adorned with candles and flowers, whilst outside, large umbrellas cover wooden furniture on the attractive patio area; and it's not just the welcoming atmosphere that people come for. This pub is well-known for "getting it right" where the food is concerned, with a concise but hearty selection of dishes that capture the essence of what pub food should be. It is unfussy modern British fare, with the odd hint of Mediterranean influence and an emphasis on simplicity. Ingredients are sourced locally and come together to create dishes such as chicken breast marinated in lime and ginger or rib-eye steak with green peppercorn butter. Desserts are definitely a highlight here, ranging from mouth-watering crumble to rich chocolate truffle cake.

Food serving times

Monday-Saturday:
12pm-2pm, 6pm-10pm

Sunday: 12pm-2pm

Closed 25-26 December,
1 January and Bank Holidays

Prices

Meals: a la carte £ 25/31

Typical Dishes

Seared tuna
Roast rump of lamb
Caramelised rhubarb

 *South East of city centre off A3062* 

3 Albion Public House and Dining Rooms

Boyces Avenue,
Clifton Village, Bristol BS8 4AA
Tel.: (0117)9733522 – Fax: (0117)9739768
e-mail: info@thealbionclifton.co.uk **Website:** www.thealbionclifton.co.uk

 VISA MC AE

Wye Valley, Butcombe, Sharps Doombar, Barnstormer, Otter Ale

Charming Clifton is not all showy attractions like the bridge and the boutique shops; some treats take a little bit of finding, and to say The Albion was hidden away would be an understatement. Armed with a local map, search out this Grade II listed 17C inn hiding in a mews in the heart of the village. At the front is a terrace fronting a seemingly cosy little hostelry. Inside, though, things are more spacious than you'd expect. There's an open plan kitchen, reclaimed wood floors, flagstones, and plenty of space to relax in front of the fires, stand at the big bar or eat at one of the numerous chunky wood tables. Settles and benches line the walls, but if they're all taken, then try upstairs. Menus are concise but read well. They're firmly British, with plenty of locally sourced ingredients and good, down-to-earth West Country dishes.

Food serving times

Tuesday-Saturday:
12pm-3pm, 7pm-9.30pm

Sunday: 12pm-3pm

Closed 25-26 December,
1 January

Booking essential.
Sunday evening barbecue in summer.

Prices

Meals: a la carte £ 20/38

Typical Dishes

Three ways with pig
Roast piece of brill
Bitter chocolate fondant

In Clifton Village. Parking in Victoria Square or surrounding roads.

4 The Kensington Arms

35-37 Stanley Rd,
Bristol B56 6NP
Tel.: (0117)9446444 – Fax: (0117)9248095
e-mail: info@thekensingtonarms.co.uk **Website:** www.thekensingtonarms.co.uk

  VISA MC AE

 **Morelands Original, Greene King IPA, Ruddles Best**

What once languished, neglected, as a studenty "pork-pie-and-a-pint, please" sort of a place has recently made a pain-free and highly successful metamorphosis into a trendy paragon of gastropubbism, dedicated to dining. With its high ceiling, arty design and walls filled with framed photos, mirrors and old adverts, the interior has a quirky feel. The chefs are on show at work behind you, service is eager, and the more formal upstairs dining room is used at weekends. The Kenny's kitchen takes a modern, commendably no-nonsense approach to food and dishes come served exactly as their descriptions suggest, with no unnecessary frills. Recreated pub classics like faggots and peas and sausage and mash clamour for your attention on the mainly British menu, while traditional puds such as toffee apple crumble and sticky toffee pudding provide a tempting finale. Keep an eye out for Molly the dog as she skates around the floor catching ice cubes.

Food serving times
Monday-Sunday:
12pm-3pm, 6pm-10pm
Closed 25 December,
1 January

Prices
Meals: a la carte £ 23/40

Typical Dishes
Ham hock terrine
Nose-to-tail suet pudding
Trifle

In city centre.

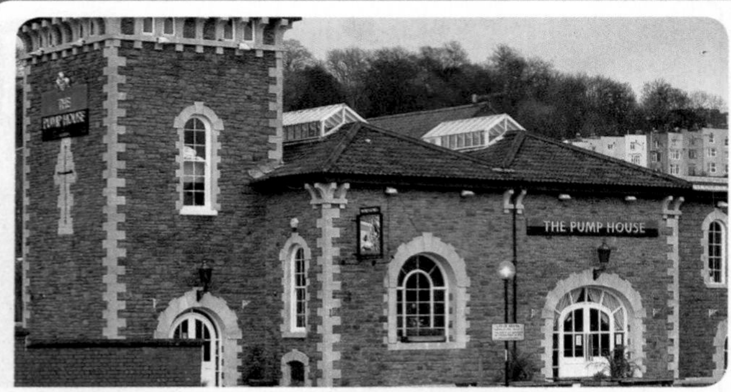

5 The Pump House

Merchants Rd,
Bristol B58 4PZ
Tel.: (0117)9272229 – Fax: (0117)2279557
e-mail: info@the-pumphouse.com **Website:** www.the-pumphouse.com

 **Theakstons Old Peculier, Greene King IPA, Courage Directors**

In the days of steam this impressive converted Victorian pumping station provided power for the bridges and machines in the docks. Its role is somewhat different today, but it still provides power of a sort - for the people of Bristol in the form of the duel fuel of food and drink. It's a vast place, but don't let that put you off – having undergone extensive refurbishment in 2007, it's now stylish and modern, with exposed stone, trendy lighting, a mezzanine restaurant and a cool outside terrace overlooking the water. Besides, it's not the décor but the cooking that's the main attraction here: modern French/British menus offer fashionable yet substantial dishes like langoustine and vanilla risotto, or roast guinea fowl with spiced red cabbage and truffle mash, and even the most traditional-sounding dish comes imaginatively served, with a splash of panache. Friendly, efficient staff will take orders either at the bar or at your table.

Food serving times

Monday-Saturday:
12pm-3pm, 7pm-9.30pm

Sunday:
12pm-3pm, 6pm-9.30pm

Closed 25 December, 1 January

Prices

Meals: £ 19 (lunch) and a la carte £ 18/30

Typical Dishes

Seared Bath chap

Saddle of Wincanton rabbit

Apple tarte Tatin

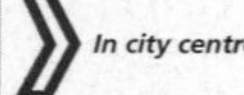

In city centre.

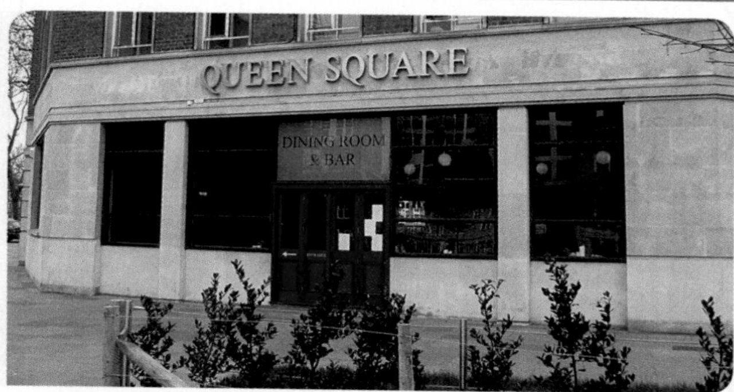

6 Queen Square Dining Room and Bar

63 Queen Square,
Bristol BS1 4JZ
Tel.: (0117)9290700
e-mail: info@queen-square.com **Website:** www.queen-square.com

    AE

 **Butcombe, Fuller's London Pride**

It's easy to while away a few hours people-watching as you dine outside this former post-office, set just off the corner of the redeveloped Georgian square. Inside, the vibe's a contemporary one; bright abstract art decorates the open plan space, while the noise from the open kitchen mingles with modern music and the gentle hum of contented customers to create a lively atmosphere. Drinkers tend to gather on the soft leather sofas near the entrance but you can also eat from the bar menu here, with its choice of sandwiches and classic meals like sausage and mash or fish and chips. With its linen-laid tables, the restaurant area at the back gives off a distinctly more formal air. Choose here from the popular set menu or the daily-changing à la carte, which offer precisely cooked, modern dishes such as honey roast breast of duck, pumpkin tart, oxtail cottage pie or loin of Gloucester Old Spot. Young, local staff provide polite service.

Food serving times

Sunday-Monday:
12pm-2.30pm

Tuesday-Friday:
12pm-2.30pm, 6pm-9.30pm

Saturday: 6pm-9.30pm

Closed 25-30 December

Prices

Meals: a la carte £ 19/30

Typical Dishes

Smoked haddock fishcake

Rump of lamb

Banana pannacotta

In city centre in the bend of the Floating Harbour, North side. Parking meters in Queen Square.

7 Robin Hood's Retreat

197 Gloucester Rd,
Bristol BS7 8BG
Tel.: (0845)2025091
Website: www.robinhoodsretreat.co.uk

 VISA MC AE

Timothy Taylor, Otter Ales

A metropolitan retreat from the bustling streets maybe, but for Robin Hood it's a long way from Sherwood Forest. A red-brick Victorian pub nestling between shops, previously a bikers' haven, it has been tastefully smartened up without losing sight of the fact that it is still a pub. Drinkers are welcome, with eight constantly rotating ales on tap – but dining is now very much a focus. Considering the quality of the ingredients, all local and seasonal, and the wide choice available, the prices are very reasonable. The original and interesting menu offers a daily-changing mix of re-created British classics, using techniques that owe more than a nod to France; dishes are satisfying, comforting and flavoursome. Period décor, wonky tables and mismatched chairs add character but it's the food that is the main attraction here. The small but dedicated team have got their priorities right, focusing on fine food in traditional surroundings.

Food serving times
Monday-Saturday:
12pm-3pm, 6pm-9.30pm
Sunday: 12pm-3pm
Closed 25 December

Prices
Meals: a la carte £ 21/40

Typical Dishes
Devilled kidneys on toast
Braised shoulder of lamb
Treacle tart & custard

In city centre.

8 Bear & Swan

13 South Parade,
Chew Magna BS40 8SL
Tel.: (01275)331100 – Fax: (01275)331204
e-mail: enquiries@bearandswan.co.uk **Website:** www.bearandswan.co.uk

 VISA MC

Butcombe, Courage Best, Cheddar Potholer

Thanks to a winning combination of good food, real ales, friendly staff and a warm, genuine ambience, this well-established village pub enjoys a bustling trade and a loyal local following. The bar boasts rustic stone walls and reclaimed wooden floors; take a seat by the fireside and order one of the old favourites from the "Bear Basics" bar menu – maybe sausage and mash or a ploughman's - and if you ask nicely, they'll even pull down the big screen so you can watch the rugby while you munch. With its flickering church candles and view of the chefs hard at work, the restaurant affords a different dining experience. Although there is a smattering of international flavours, dishes are, for the most part, proudly British and ingredients locally sourced where possible, with meat from the village butcher and fish from Devon. Events like moules and frites night or seafood week create quite a buzz. Bedrooms are too modest for us to recommend.

Food serving times
Monday-Saturday:
12pm-2pm, 7pm-9.30pm
Sunday: 12pm-2pm
Closed 25 December

Prices
Meals: a la carte £ 25/30

Typical Dishes
Asparagus & poached egg
Marinated rump of lamb
Home-made summer pudding

8.25mi South of Bristol via A37 on B3130. Parking.

9 The Wheatsheaf

Combe Hay BA2 7EG
Tel.: (01225)833504 – Fax: (01225)836123
e-mail: info@wheatsheafcombehay.com
Website: www.wheatsheafcombehay.com

 **Butcombe Bitter, Butcombe Blonde, Cheddar Valley Cider, Ashton Press Cider**

Just a stone's throw away from hectic city life, this picture perfect pub sits peacefully in a secluded wooded valley, with shrubs framing the doorway and artistically arranged flowers hanging from the walls. The hands-on owners, villagers themselves, have turned this pub around, creating a chic, stylish interior and a friendly, relaxed atmosphere – for the ultimate in comfort seek out the squashy sofas by the fire. The chef has an impressive background in country house hotels, so the food is not your usual pub fare: it may be seasonal and flavoursome, but it comes with a refined and delicate touch. The concise contemporary menu combines British and French influences, featuring dishes such as home-smoked trout with beetroot jelly, followed by Mendip beef with potato and foie gras gallette. Sharing the same designer styling as the pub, the bedrooms boast luxury showers and king size beds, while breakfast times are pleasantly flexible.

Food serving times

Tuesday-Saturday:
12pm-2.30pm, 6.30pm-9pm

Sunday: 12pm-2.30pm

Closed 25 December and first 2 weeks in January

Prices

Meals: £ 22 (lunch)
and a la carte £ 22/55

3 rooms: £ 95/140

Typical Dishes

Seared foie gras
Somerset lamb
White chocolate parfait

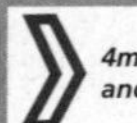

4mi South of Bath by A367 and minor road South. Parking.

10 Wheelwrights Arms

Church Lane,
Monkton Combe BA2 7HB
Tel.: (01225)722287 – Fax: (01225)722259
e-mail: bookings@wheelwrightsarms.co.uk **Website:** www.wheelwrightsarms.co.uk

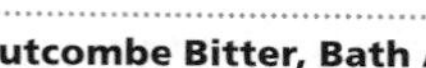

Butcombe Bitter, Bath Ales Gem

The picturesque village in which this 18C pub is set seems an auspicious sign, and as you click open the latch on the front door and are encompassed by a warm, rosy glow, you know for sure that you've made an excellent choice. It's charming and intimate, with a cosy front snug perfect for a party of six and a log fire so regularly stoked it will have you peeling off layer after layer. On first glance, the menu may seem a little concise, but in fact there's plenty of choice, and the honest, hearty cooking comes in portions large enough to revive even the most exhausted of walkers. Bedrooms in the converted wheelwright's workshop are luxurious, with dark wood floors, comfy beds and fresh flowers, while bathrooms come with jet powered showers, fast-filling baths and fine French toiletries. Rugby fans are sure to want to take up the offer of two tickets to a game at Bath, and breakfast fans will be delighted with delicious bacon sandwiches.

Food serving times
Monday-Sunday:
12pm-3pm, 6pm-10pm

Prices
Meals: a la carte £ 19/26
7 rooms: £ 95/145

Typical Dishes
Smoked haddock & cheese fishcakes
Indian spiced lamb
Passion fruit pannacotta

2mi South East of Bath city centre by A3062

England • South West • Avon

11 Fleur du Jardin

Castel,
Kings Mills (Guernsey) GY5 7JT
Tel.: (01481)257996 – Fax: (01481)256834
e-mail: info@fleurdujardin.com **Website:** www.fleurdujardin.com

 **Fuller's London Pride, Timothy Taylor**

This attractive stone built inn stands in its elevated position as it has done for centuries, surrounded by neat lawned gardens and looking out over countryside and sea. With its hanging baskets and colourful borders, it's aptly named, and the heated terrace adds a stylish touch to the exterior. One of the bar areas has recently been refurbished, waving goodbye to cottage-style chintz and saying hello to a new, cosmopolitan look befitting the 21C; three adjoining dining areas await a similar makeover. Extensive à la carte menus offer big portions, from rump of lamb or steak to Thai curry; supplemented by seafood specials and making use of local produce in the form of Guernsey crab, scallops and veal sausages. Service is charming and the Fleur's reputation among both locals and tourists ensures it's often busy. Four contemporary new bedrooms offer superior comfort, while plans to refurbish the remainder are in the pipeline.

Food serving times
Monday-Sunday:
12pm-2pm, 6pm-9pm

Prices
Meals: £ 13 (lunch
3 course lunch)
and a la carte £ 15/25

15 rooms: £ 50/128

Typical Dishes
Roquaine mussels
Pork & veal sausages
Local cheeses

3mi West of St Peter Port. Parking.

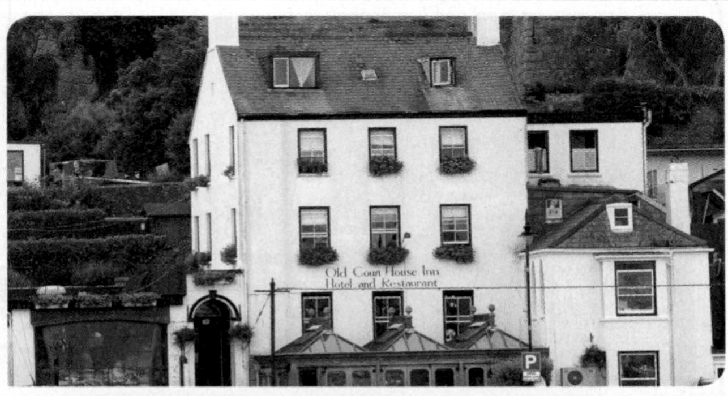

12 Old Court House Inn

St Aubin's Harbour,
Saint Aubin (Jersey) JE3 8AB
Tel.: (01534)746433 – Fax: (01534)745103
e-mail: info@oldcourthousejersey.com **Website:** www.oldcourthousejersey.com

 **Marston Pedigree, Bass**

The owners of this whitewashed quayside inn have long been on the right tack, hence its favourable local reputation. Dating from 1450, it has been witness over the years to judicial comings and goings, as well as being a onetime storehouse for seafarers' illegal booty. There's something for everyone on the extensive menus, including daily seafood specials chosen from the wettest and freshest on offer that day. Thus, local lobster and crab sit alongside more traditional dishes like steak and lasagne, while the dessert menu includes old favourites such as sticky toffee pudding. You'll also be spoilt for choice when it comes to where to sit; the conservatory or the rustic bar are good choices for a lunchtime snack, whilst a seat on the decked terrace affords scenic views across the harbour; and if you feel like pushing the boat out, head for one of the more formal dining rooms, one of which is built in the shape of a galleon.

Food serving times
Monday-Sunday:
12.30pm-2.30pm,
7pm-10pm
Closed 25 December

Prices
Meals: £ 13 (lunch)
and a la carte £ 30/50
9 rooms: £ 40/120

Typical Dishes
Moules marinières
Lamb cutlets
Toffee pudding

4mi West of St Helier.
Public car park opposite and parking in street.

13 The Halzephron Inn

Gunwalloe TR12 7QB
Tel.: (01326)240406 – Fax: (01326)241442
e-mail: halzephroninn@gunwalloe1.fsnet.co.uk
Website: www.halzephron-inn.co.uk

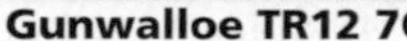

Sharps Doombar, Sharps Own, St Austell Tribute, Organic Halzephron Gold

A visit to this extreme south-westerly corner of Cornwall wouldn't be complete without a visit to the Halzephron, staring out imperturbably across Mount's Bay. It knows its place: it's been here 500 years, and is wonderfully snug and rustic. The low ceiling boasts fine old timbers; gleaming copper and original paintings adorn the walls. Knick-knacks, curios and higgledy-piggledy décor enrich four adjoining dining rooms: food's a serious business here, and wide-ranging menus are fiercely Cornish in produce and style. Portions are of the hearty variety; an impressive selection of local real ales is an ideal way to wash down lunch or dinner, followed by a walk on the nearby South West Coast Path. Two neat, cosy bedrooms await.

Food serving times

Monday-Sunday:
12pm-2pm,
6.30pm (7pm winter)-9pm

Closed 25 December

Prices

Meals: a la carte £ 19/35

2 rooms: £ 50/94

Typical Dishes

Crab and prawn risotto
Roast pork tenderloin
Bread & butter pudding

3.5mi South of Helston by A3083. Parking.

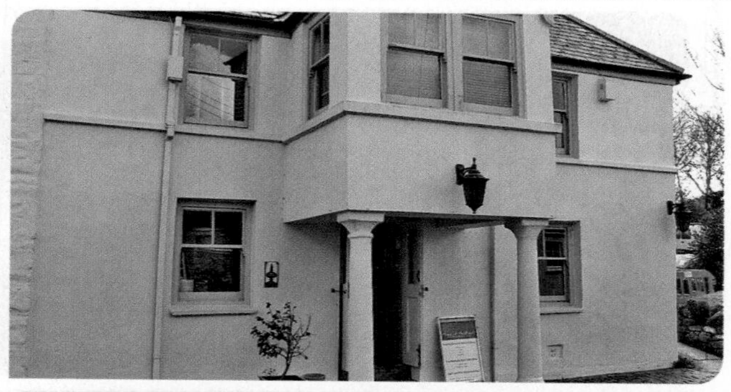

14 The Plume of Feathers

Mitchell TR8 5AX
Tel.: (01872)510387 – Fax: (01872)511124
e-mail: enquiries@theplume.info **Website:** www.theplume.info

 **Sharps Doombar, Fuller's London Pride, Skinners Cornish Blond, Eden Ale**

As good a break as you'll find from the drone of the A30, this smartly refurbished part 16C dining pub, away from the visitors' hotspots, comes into its own as an escape from the tourist influx of a Cornish summer, but you'll find a reassuringly good turnout - families and couples, groups of friends - on most days of the year. Set aside from an airy, sympathetically restored bar, several connecting lounges serve as the restaurant, although service is just as alert and organised at the bar. The cooking itself is steady as she goes - there is a sound, classic menu with blackboard specials - but the real draw is the relaxed, everyday atmosphere of the place: they have plenty of regulars, but are always happy to take on a few more. Large, bright bedrooms in the restored barns and stable. A well provides ample pure drinking water and water for the baths and showers.

Food serving times
Monday-Sunday:
9am-11am, 12pm-6pm, 6pm-10pm

Prices
Meals: a la carte £ 18/26
8 rooms: £ 46/70

Typical Dishes
Homemade fishcake
Homemade Angus burger
Chocolate brownie

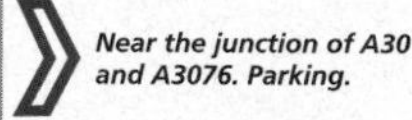

Near the junction of A30 and A3076. Parking.

15 Pandora Inn

Restronguet Creek,
Mylor Bridge TR11 5ST
Tel.: (01326)372678 – Fax: (01326)378958
e-mail: pandorainn@yahoo.co.uk **Website:** www.pandorainn.co.uk

VISA MC AE

Tinners, Tribute, Hicks Special Draught (HSD), Bass

Sail up Mylor Creek, moor at the pontoon, and you'll have taken the scenic route to this stunningly located pub, which dates back to the 13C. Its charming interior comes courtesy of timbered ceilings for the vertically challenged, shiny stone floors, cosy corners, open fire and seaside pot pourri. Food can be eaten at the bar or at the slightly more formal Andrew Miller restaurant upstairs: hearty pub menus take in a wide range of favourites, but are quite rightly dominated by fresh seafood off the blackboard, so be patient with service. Crab bucket and bait are available at the bar or work off your meal with a relaxed walk along the creekside paths.

Food serving times

Sunday-Thursday:
12pm-3pm, 7pm-9pm

Friday-Saturday:
12pm-3pm, 7pm-9.30pm

Prices

Meals: a la carte £ 21/28

Typical Dishes

Black pudding salad
Peppered sirloin steak
Homemade Bakewell tart

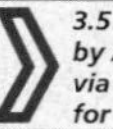

3.5 mi north of Falmouth by A39 and B3292; fork left via Restronguet and Weir rd for 1mi. Parking.

16 Victoria Inn

Perranuthnoe TR20 9NP
Tel.: (01736)710309 – Fax: (01736)719284
e-mail: enquiries@victoriainn-penzance.co.uk
Website: www.victoriainn-penzane.co.uk

 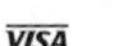 

 **Sharps Doom Bar, St Austell Tribute**

Two minutes walk from the beach and the beautiful views of St. Michael's Mount, the village of Perranuthnoe plays host to what is allegedly the oldest inn in Cornwall. Run by a husband and wife team, you will not be able to miss this pub, just think pink and follow the locals. Inside it is characteristically Cornish; rustic and relaxed, with photos from yesteryear hanging on exposed stone walls and a welcoming wood burning fire. The food is great whether you eat in the more formal dining room or stay in the atmospheric surroundings of the bar. The carefully thought out, classical menu is crafted from local, seasonal produce; the emphasis being on quality ingredients and cooking techniques that allow the natural flavours to stand out. The fish in particular is extremely fresh and, depending on the catch, you may find salmon, crab, prawns, haddock or scallops. Rooms are simple, with a strong nautical design theme.

Food serving times

Monday-Saturday, 12pm-2.30pm, 6.30pm-9pm

Sunday: 12pm-2.30pm

Closed 1 week January, Monday out of season

Prices

Meals: a la carte £ 19/30

2 rooms: £ 45/65

Typical Dishes

Cornish crab
Crispy belly of pork
Vanilla yoghurt pannacotta

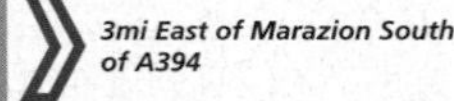

17 Viners

Carvynick,
Summercourt TR8 5AF
Tel.: (01872)510544 – Fax: (01872)510468
e-mail: info@vinersrestaurant.co.uk **Website:** www.vinersrestaurant.co.uk

   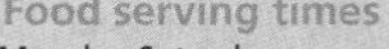

Sharps Doombar, Skinners Betty Stoggs and Cornish Knocker, Atlantic Brewery Organic Ale

Keep a look out for the signs to this charming stone-built pub; it's well-concealed in the Cornish countryside, situated just past an upmarket caravan site and golf club. Rustic in parts, it tends towards the more sophisticated, restaurant-style end of pub dining, but this is of no real consequence, for the enthusiastic young staff proffer a warm welcome and the atmosphere is informal and relaxed. Chef-owner Kevin Viner is something of a culinary godfather in these parts, guiding younger talent with his more than capable hands. He holds regular cookery demonstrations and his awards and memorabilia adorn the walls. Menus are a combination of old favourites (which the locals won't allow him to remove) and more ambitious offerings; so dishes might range from sautéed mushrooms on toast or moules marinière, to chicken and foie gras terrine, lobster or slow roasted pork belly, with plenty of local meats, fish and cheese from which to choose.

Food serving times

Monday-Saturday:
6.30pm-9.30pm

Sunday: 12.30pm-3pm

Closed January and Monday in winter

Prices

Meals: £ 19 (3 course Sunday lunch) and a la carte £ 33/40

Typical Dishes

Pressed country terrine
Grilled fillet of beef
Baked chocolate tart

At Carvybick Golf and Country Club, 1.5mi Northwest of the junction of A30 and A3058. Parking.

18 Springer Spaniel

Treburley PL15 9NS
Tel.: (01579)370424
e-mail: enquiries@thespringerspaniel.org.uk
Website: www.thespringerspaniel.org.uk

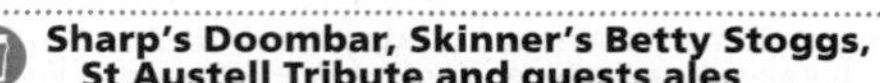

Sharp's Doombar, Skinner's Betty Stoggs, St Austell Tribute and guests ales

Like its namesake, this former 18C coaching inn is popular and friendly, with a reassuringly familiar warmth. The wide ranging, seasonally inspired menus have something for everyone and use only local, traceable produce: vegetables and game from local farms, seafood from Cornish waters and organic meat from the owners' cattle and sheep farm in the neighbouring village. Dinner menus include traditional dishes such as venison and game casserole or confit of duck, whilst daytime menus have lighter offerings such as ploughman's lunches. For children there is a Little Jack Russell menu and if it's not too busy you may get the chance to meet Nutmeg, who inspired it. The dogs are not the only link here to hunting: shooting magazines are scattered about and prints depicting a chase adorn the walls, with the inevitable picture of a springer spaniel amongst them. Like this friendly, family-loving dog, the pub itself is a good all-rounder.

Food serving times

Monday-Sunday:
12pm-1.45pm,
6.30pm-8.45pm

Prices

Meals: a la carte £ 20/36

Typical Dishes

Seared pigeon breasts
Medallions of beef
Poached pear

5mi South of Launceston by A388 in village centre.

19 New Inn

Tresco (Scilly Isles) TR24 0QQ
Tel.: (01720)423006 – Fax: (01720)423200
e-mail: newinn@tresco.co.uk **Website:** www.tresco.co.uk

   MC

Ales of Scilly Firebrand, Scuppered; St Austell Tribute, Skinners Tresco Tipple; beer festivals in May and September

An hospitable stopping off point on your way, perhaps, to the Old Blockhouse or Tresco Abbey Gardens, this stone built former inn may prove difficult to leave. It has a charming terrace garden - with plenty of seating - and views that extend across the beautiful island. In keeping with its surroundings, the traditional bar is packed with nautical memorabilia; other lounges have a friendly, bustling ambience – it's where the locals congregate. Back outside, a large semi-decked sun lounge is a good place to tuck into an extensive "snacky" menu or indulge in blackboard seafood specials. The dining room (remember to book first) is a striking bistro-style restaurant serving traditional favourites. If, indeed, you haven't moved on, bedrooms are simple, well-kept and comfortable.

Food serving times

Monday-Sunday:
12pm-2.15pm, 6pm-9pm

Booking essential for non-residents

Prices

Meals: a la carte £ 18/30

16 rooms: £ 70/230

Typical Dishes

Goats cheese salad
Scillonian monkfish
Saffron poached pear

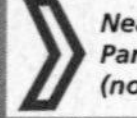

Near Tresco Stores. Parking at Penzance heliport (no cars on Tresco).

20 The Gurnard's Head

Treen,
Zennor TR26 3DE
Tel.: (01736)796928
e-mail: enquiries@gurnardshead.co.uk **Website:** www.gurnardshead.co.uk

VISA 

Skinners Betty Stoggs, Skinners Ginger Tosser, St Austell Tribute

If you're arriving by helicopter you'll have no problem locating this pub, thanks to the large sign boldly painted on its roof. Perfectly situated for St. Ives, Penzance and St. Just, The Gurnard's Head overlooks the rocky headland after which it is named, with its ancient hill fort, abandoned tin mines and hidden coves. Eat in either the main bar or the restaurant, surrounded by paperbacks, stacks of newspapers and colourful art. The menu offers confident cooking, with clever, carefully balanced combinations and an innovative edge, and the wine list is pleasingly unpretentious. Service is laid back, and at Sunday lunch you may be asked to share a large table with other guests. If you've stayed overnight in one of the comfortable rooms, breakfast is a treat with big pots of homemade jam, freshly squeezed orange juice and toast just like it should be. A walk along the coastal path will blow away any remaining cobwebs.

Food serving times

Monday-Sunday:
12.30pm-2.30pm,
6.30pm-9.30pm

Closed 24-25 December

Prices

Meals: a la carte £ 16/25

7 rooms: £ 60/140

Typical Dishes

Salt whiting brandade
Braised shin of beef
Chocolate torte

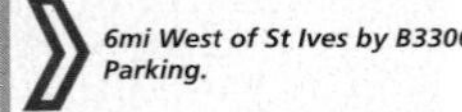

6mi West of St Ives by B3306.
Parking.

21 The Avon Inn

Avonwick TQ10 9NB
Tel.: (01364)73475
e-mail: rosec@beeb.net **Website:** www.eatoutdevon.co.uk

Sharps Doombar, Teignworthy Neap Tide

If you're in this area of South Devon, there's a good chance you've been wandering on Dartmoor, in which case, thoughts turning to sustenance, the Avon Inn is a sure-fire bet. There's nothing too fancy about the pub itself: hanging floral baskets and a small side garden without, a few exposed beams and hop bines within. It's the food that takes centre stage here. The pleasant owners make everyone feel at home, and they take a great pride in the menus on offer. These are wide-ranging with a classical Gallic base (husband Dominique is French). A daily changing blackboard menu incorporates everything from light lunches to full-on dishes featuring plenty of local seafood and fish. The mats are local too, made of the local slate.

Food serving times
Monday: 6pm-9pm
Tuesday-Saturday: 12pm-2pm, 6pm-9pm
Sunday: 12pm-2pm
Closed lunch Monday and dinner Sunday

Prices
Meals: a la carte £ 15/28

Typical Dishes
Scallops & tiger prawns
Steak & mushroom pudding
Chocolate tart

1.5mi South of South Brent by minor road. Parking.

22 The Turtley Corn Mill

Avonwick TQ10 9ES
Tel.: (01364)646100 – Fax: (01364)646101
e-mail: mill@avonwick.net **Website:** www.avonwick.net

 **Tamar, Jail Ale, Butcombe Blond, St Austell Tribute**

Driving down to Cornwall? You could do a lot worse than take a minute's detour off the A38 to locate this refurbished 18C establishment named after one of its former owners. Smart oak and slate floors, local prints and slender bookcases, thoughtfully allied to beams and pillars from the original structure, give the place a clean, light and airy style, spacious enough to seat about 120. It's in an enviable setting, with a duck pond (including info on different breeds) and six acres of grounds bordered by the river Glazebrook. The wheel's been renovated too, though if you think you see it turning you've had too much to drink. There's a good selection of local ales, and the menu offers an ample selection for tired drivers, everything from pub classics to more up-to-date concoctions.

Food serving times
Monday-Sunday:
12pm-9.30pm

Closed 25 December

Prices
Meals: a la carte £ 20/31

Typical Dishes
Fresh asparagus
Pork sausages
Key lime pie

1.5mi South of South Brent by minor road. Parking.

23 The Quarrymans Rest

Bruton St,
Bampton EX16 9LN
Tel.: (01398)331480
e-mail: info@thequarrymansrest.co.uk **Website:** www.thequarrymansrest.co.uk

Inspectors' favourites

 **Butcombe, Bombardier, Exmoor Gold, Yellowhammer, Sams Real Devon Cider**

Despite several name changes – the most recent being inspired by the local stone and slate mine – this 17C inn has not relinquished its rustic roots and has managed to stay an honest village pub. The large bar with its traditional décor and welcoming open fire gives way to a slightly more formal dining room with high-backed leather chairs. The appealing menu has strong seasonal and regional influences and the cooking is careful and knowledgeable, as you would expect from an experienced chef. He prides himself on sourcing local produce: meat and West Country cheese from a traditional butcher, cream and beef from a nearby farm, fish from the Brixham day boats and bread from the local baker. For starters you may find potted salt beef or tempura tiger prawns; to follow, braised knuckle of Devon lamb or fillet of sea bass, and to finish, homemade cheesecake or orange and treacle tart. Like the food, the bedrooms offer good value for money.

Food serving times

Monday-Saturday:
12pm-2pm, 6pm-9.30pm

Sunday: 12pm-4pm

Prices

Meals: a la carte £ 16/23

3 rooms: £ 40/80

Typical Dishes

Potted salt beef
Wild bass
Pannacotta & blueberries

6mi North of Tiverton by A396 and B3190

24 The Normandy Arms

Chapel St,
Blackawton TQ9 7BN

Tel.: (01803)712884 – Fax: (01830)712374

e-mail: peter.alcroft@btconnect.com **Website:** www.thenormandyarms.co.uk

 **Dartmoor Bitter**

It's always a good sign when the owners of a pub take time to chat with their customers, and at this immaculately whitewashed inn, you'll find this hospitality extended to regulars and visitors alike. The pub was closed for a couple years before Sharon and Peter arrived and gave the place a facelift, and you get the feeling that the villagers missed it and are now making up for lost time. There's a comfy lounge area by the entrance and two rooms set for dining; with locals tending to drink in the more atmospheric bar room, where a grandfather clock keeps time. Unfussy cooking is proudly homemade using local produce and the blackboard bar menu offers pub favourites like sausage and mash, while the printed à la carte showcases more elaborate, restaurant-style dishes. A great place to be on the May Day bank holiday, when people descend on Blackawton from far and wide for annual worm charming competition.

Food serving times

Tuesday-Thursday:
7pm-9pm

Friday-Sunday:
12pm-1.45pm, 7pm-9pm

Closed 25 December and 1 week in October

Prices

Meals: a la carte £ 19/30

Typical Dishes

Crab fritter
Fillet of beef
Chocolate fondant

4mi West of Dartmouth by A3122 and minor road

25 Masons Arms

Branscombe EX12 3DJ
Tel.: (01297)680300 – Fax: (01297)680500
e-mail: reception@masonsarms.co.uk **Website:** www.masonsarms.co.uk

   VISA

 **Branoc and Summa That, Otter Bitter, Otter Head, Beachcomber, St Austell Tribute**

The picturesque village of Branscombe is one of the joys of the East Devon coast, nestling piecemeal in a deep valley right next to the sea. At its heart lies this 14C creeper-clad inn, visible to anyone up in the hills. It has a wonderfully bustling atmosphere, built around the unspoilt bar where hotel guests and locals mingle with a pint. The hearty ambience is enhanced with the surrounding ancient ships' beams, slate floors, and stone walls; a huge central fireplace is regularly used to spit-roast joints of meat at lunchtime and in the evening: modern British menus are highlighted by crab and lobster landed on Branscombe's beach. Bedrooms - some of them large and luxurious - are divided between inn and cottages opposite.

Food serving times
Monday-Sunday:
12pm-2pm, 7pm-9pm
Bar lunch

Prices
Meals: £ 28 (3 course dinner) and a la carte £ 19/27
21 rooms: £ 80/165

Typical Dishes
Carpaccio of beef fillet
Grilled fillets of seabass
Saffron & honey crème brûlée

Between Seaton and Sidmouth; South of A3052; in the village centre. Parking.

26 The Drewe Arms

Broadhembury EX14 3NF
Tel.: (01404)841267
e-mail: drewe.arms@btconnect.com

Otter Bitter, Otter Ale, Exmoor Gold

Situated next to the church in the heart of a historic and picturesque cob and thatch village, this pub should be the first port of call in East Devon for any confirmed lover of fish. No typical pub grub here; instead you'll find prime local fish, simply prepared with quality ingredients to produce flavourful dishes. Open sandwiches are available, there's the occasional meat dish and you might also see a few Swedish classics on the menu thanks to the owner's heritage. Family run for years and seen by the residents of the village as their local, this popular pub also attracts outsiders so you'd be advised to book in advance. The slightly casual, if pleasant, service seems to become slicker during busy periods. The snug bar area is strictly for drinkers so grab a seat by the log fire in one of the rustically characterful dining areas, soak up the relaxed atmosphere and marvel at the unusual décor with its marine theme.

Food serving times

Monday-Saturday:
12pm-2pm, 7pm-9.30pm

Sunday: 12pm-2pm

Closed 25 December

Booking essential

- Seafood -

Prices

Meals: a la carte £ 15/30

Typical Dishes

Crab Thermidor

Pollack, mustard and cream

Lemon posset

5mi Northwest of Honiton by A373. Parking.

England • South West • Devon

27 Lamb Inn

Sandford,
Crediton EX17 4LW
Tel.: (01363)773676
e-mail: thelambinn@gmail.com **Website:** www.lambinnsandford.co.uk

Exmoor Ales, Topsham & Exminster, O'Hanlons, Palmers, Cotleigh, Sharps, Warrior Brewery, Skinners, Teignworthy

This sleepy 16C period coaching inn is as picturesque a village pub as you can find. The delightfully attractive exterior is matched by a charming, characterful interior and pleasantly dated décor: low ceilings, chunky mismatched tables and wooden pews, a welcoming open fire, and even an original skittle alley. A variety of events take place throughout the month, including salsa lessons, jazz, casino and cocktail evenings and open mic nights. On the wall, the blackboard displays a frequently changing menu of satisfying and warming dishes that show strong influences from the chef's homeland in France. Presented in a simple, unassuming manner, they might include starters of smoked salmon crostini or butternut squash soup, followed by confit of duck or winter stews. Service is laid back but the excellent cooking makes up for it and there is always a good selection of ales on tap. The recently converted bedrooms are spacious and charming.

Food serving times
Monday-Sunday:
12.30pm-2.15pm,
6.30pm-9.15pm

Prices
Meals: a la carte £ 16/20

Typical Dishes
Goats cheese parfait
Pan-fried black bream
Apple crumble

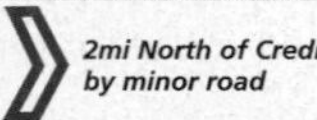

2mi North of Crediton by minor road

28 The Floating Bridge

By Lower Ferry,
Dartmouth TQ6 9PH
Tel.: (01803)832354
e-mail: amf46@btinternet.com **Website:** www.dartmarina.com

Proper Job, St Austell Tribute, Otter Ale

It's not often that you can drop into conversation that you've come by boat, so make the most of the opportunity and take the lower ferry from Kingswear to Dartmouth, whether you're travelling on foot or by car. Unusually situated on the ferry slip road, you may not normally give this pub a second glance but if you need something to tide you over it's well worth a visit, especially in the holiday season. In the large period bar you will find the locals having a chat amongst the seafaring pictures and traditional décor, whilst next door the spacious main dining room provides a more contemporary feel, with blond wood floors, comfy seating and more modern artwork. The menu is traditional and predominantly local, displaying tasty, wholesome fare; out of season the choice is limited to four dishes per course but in summer this expands and is supplemented by a blackboard selection, often in the form of fresh fish specials.

Follow signs to Lower Ferry.

Food serving times

Monday-Sunday:
12pm-2.30pm, 6pm-10pm

Closed November-March
Monday-Tuesday

Prices

Meals: a la carte £ 18/28

Typical Dishes

Tomatoes, mozzarella & pesto
Confit duck leg
Granny Smith brûlée

East Allington

29 Fortescue Arms

East Allington TQ9 7RA
Tel.: (01548)521215
e-mail: info@fortescue-arms.co.uk **Website:** www.fortescue-arms.co.uk

Butcombe Bitter, Dartmoor IPA

Built about 200 years ago as part of the Fallapit estate - then owned by the Fortescue family - this well run, ivy-clad pub has two distinct sides to it: turn left and you're in a small beamed bar, with black flagged floors and an open fire; turn right and you enter a smart dining room with rustic stone walls. Although the Austrian chef-owner is apparently known for sculpting things out of lard, the cooking here is thankfully of a rather more traditional bent. On the bar menu you'll find hearty, flavoursome pub classics - think fish pie, stews and casseroles - alongside warm organic bread and a blackboard menu of daily specials. The constantly evolving dining room menu offers more refined dishes such as roast local lamb loin or local roe deer fillet, as well as the odd dish which pays homage to the chef's roots - maybe Austrian potato goulash or Apfelstrudel. First floor bedrooms are pine furnished, with shower-only ensuites.

Food serving times
Monday: 6pm-9.30pm
Tuesday-Sunday:
12pm-2.30pm, 6pm-9.30pm

Prices
Meals: a la carte £ 25/30
3 rooms: £ 40

Typical Dishes
Goats cheese tartlet
Venison
Apple strudel

4mi North East of Kingsbridge by B3264, A381 and minor road

30 The Puffing Billy

Station Rd,
Exton EX3 0PR
Tel.: (01392)877888
Website: www.eatoutdevon.com

  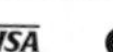 

Otter Bitter and guest beers : Exmoor, Teignworthy, Bays, Cotleigh, Sharps

If only all railway pubs were so inviting. Round the corner form Exton station and along the path beside the water, you come upon this smart, white pub. The open plan interior is decorated with original artwork, wood burner and leather sofas in the bar, banquettes in the dining room or halogen lights and exposed beams in the big, airy extension. Wherever you decide to eat, the menu is a broad one, covering lunchtime sandwiches, traditional pub dishes on the blackboard, fine dining classics and more "informal" dishes, many of which are available in either starter or main course size. If you're interested in seeing how it all happens, a few tables face the open kitchen. Your meal may even be spiced up by gunfire from the Royal Marines' barracks next door.

Food serving times

Monday-Sunday:
12pm-2.15pm,
6.30pm-9.30pm

Closed 8 days from Christmas to New Year

Prices

Meals: a la carte £ 19/32

Typical Dishes

Salmon plate
Free-range duck
Apricot & ginger pudding

Brown tourist sign off A376 to Exmouth, 3mi from junction 30 M5. Parking.

England • South West • Devon

31 The Hart Inn

The Square,
Hartland EX39 6BL
Tel.: (01237)441474
e-mail: bjornmoen@hotmail.com **Website:** www.thehartinn.com

 **Courage Directors, Sharps Doombar, Otter Ale, Bath Gem**

Set on the original coaching route from Bideford to Bude, this spacious inn boasts stonework dating back to the 14 and 16C, making it one of the oldest buildings in Hartland; whilst a rustic interior, exposed stone walls, huge beams, open fires and homely furnishings create a warm and friendly atmosphere. Formerly "The New Inn", it's thought that the name was changed when the draymen delivering the beer kept going to the wrong address; its new title is believed to make reference to the pub being the "heart" of the village, where the local hunt used to meet. The chef is Danish so the regularly changing menu sees some Scandinavian influences, although produce remains local and seasonal; meat and vegetables are supplied by the surrounding farms and fish is delivered from nearby Appledore. Portions are generous and definitely not for the faint-hearted; dishes may include braised shoulder of Lundy lamb, roast spatchcock or baked sea bass.

Food serving times

Monday: 6pm-9pm

Tuesday-Saturday:
12pm-2pm, 6pm-9pm

Sunday: 12pm-2pm

Closed 25 December and first two weeks in February

Prices

Meals: a la carte £ 11/16

Between Bideford and Bude off A39

32 The Rock Inn

Haytor Vale TQ13 9XP
Tel.: (01364)661305 – Fax: (01364)661242
e-mail: cg@rock-inn.co.uk **Website:** www.rock-inn.co.uk

 **Dartmoor Best, Jail Ale**

Having built up an appetite walking on Dartmoor, eat to the sound of birdsong in the quintessentially English garden of this 18C coaching inn, tucked away in amongst a row of cottages in a tiny, very picturesque, rural village. From salads and sandwiches to steak and chips, the simple bar menu is a good choice for lunch; although a more elaborate restaurant menu is also available for dinner. The interior is bursting with rustic character, with several log fires, wood beams, oak furniture and flag floors. The bedrooms, quirkily named after past winners of the Grand National, are set on different levels and the sloping floors simply add to the charm. Once frequented by the quarrymen who transported granite along the railway, this pub is still popular with locals. It has been run by the same family for many years, and the green, white and black flag flying out front is a fitting symbol of the Devonshire pride to be found here.

Food serving times
Monday-Sunday:
12pm-2.15pm, 7pm-9pm
Closed 25-26 December

Prices
Meals: £ 21 (dinner)
and a la carte £ 22/33
9 rooms: £ 67/117

Typical Dishes
Seafood & saffron risotto
Fillet of wild seabass
Toffee pudding

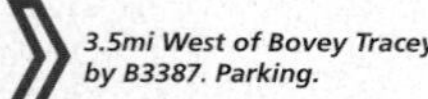

3.5mi West of Bovey Tracey by B3387. Parking.

33 The Dartmoor Union

Fore St,
Holbeton PL8 1NE
Tel.: (01752)830288 – Fax: (01752)830296
e-mail: info@dartmoorunion.co.uk **Website:** www.dartmoorunion.co.uk

  MC

 **Otter Bitter and rotating guest ales such as Sharps Doombar, Tanner Jack, GK IPA, Tanglefoot**

Once a Victorian workhouse and later a cider press-house, the Dartmoor Union seems to have found its true vocation at last - maintaining the tradition of pulling pints brewed in its own microbrewery. For all the activity inside, the pub can be hard to spot, as there's only a discreet brass plaque on its stone façade. Its bar is spacious and smartly furnished, hung with pictures of old Holbeton: gold inscriptions on the walls – including "manners maketh man" – may or may not inspire a more philosophical tone of pub debate. The dining room to one side offers a large, seasonal selection of modern and traditional dishes including a good value set lunch. The flower-filled terrace is lovely in summer, and so are Coastguards beach and its cliff walks, a short drive away.

Food serving times

Monday-Saturday:
12pm-2pm, 6.30pm-9pm

Sunday:
12pm-3pm, 6.30pm-9pm

Prices

Meals: £ 13 (3 course lunch/dinner) and a la carte £ 20/40

Typical Dishes

Thai sirloin of beef
Pan-fried fillet of seabass
Chocolate pots

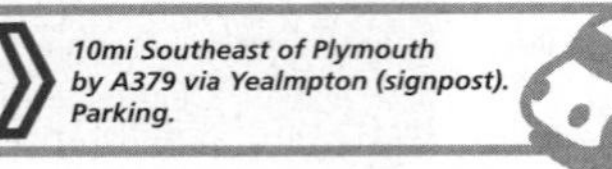

10mi Southeast of Plymouth by A379 via Yealmpton (signpost). Parking.

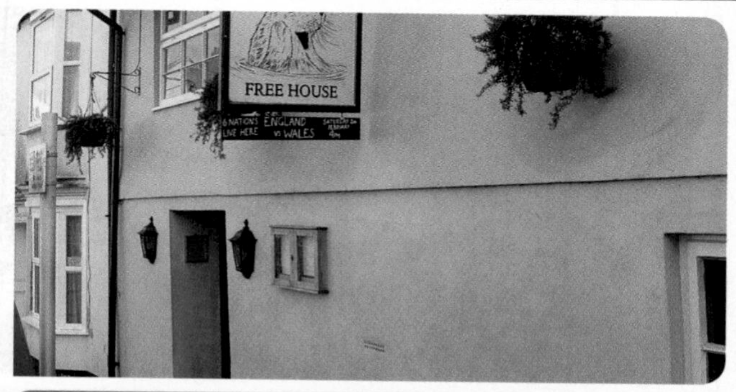

34 The Holt

178 High St,
Honiton EX14 1LA
Tel.: (01404)47707
e-mail: enquiries@theholt-honiton.com **Website:** www.theholt-honiton.com

AE 

Otter Bitter, Otter Ale, Otter Bright, Otter Head

"Holt: the burrowed lair of an animal, especially an otter". Q: So why would you name your pub after this? A: For the good reason that your parents own the nearby Otter Brewery. The McCaig family's mission statement is to provide a "distinctive and sustainable taste of Devon", through both their food and their ales; it really is a family affair, with one brother out front and one behind the scenes, and mum and dad supplying a selection of real ales from down the road. There is a strong drive towards local produce, with a great deal of effort put into sourcing; sustainable methods are also key, so the eco-friendly menus are printed on recycled hops and paper. The interesting menu changes every 6 weeks, with tapas and light dishes on offer at lunch and a more substantial à la carte menu in the evening. Much of the food is homemade, including the tasty sausages, and the smoking of produce also takes place entirely on site.

Food serving times
Tuesday-Saturday:
12pm-2pm, 7pm-10pm
Closed 25-26 December

Prices
Meals: a la carte £ 15/28

Typical Dishes
Home-smoked salmon
Pork belly
Rhubarb fool parfait

On lower end of High Street.

35 The Hoops Inn

Horn's Cross EX39 5DL

Tel.: (01237)451222 – Fax: (01237)451247

e-mail: sales@hoopsinn.co.uk **Website:** www.hoopsinn.co.uk

 VISA MC AE

Hoops Old Ale, Hoops Best, Golden Pig, Doombar, Clouded Yellow

An old wayside inn since the Middle Ages, this sizeable thatched pub still has plenty to offer the passer-by, including those who need a bed for the night – four rooms in the main house are particularly comfortable, but there are a further eight "standard" ones at the back. Its handsome bar preserves its wooden settles, bowed ceiling beams, cups, tankards and porcelains, not to mention traces of the well which once supplied water for home-brewed ales.
A wide-ranging menu covers everything from lunchtime ploughman's and bar favourites, through to tasty modern dishes from the à la carte, eaten in the rustic restaurant. A pretty terrace looks out over the water garden- and don't be surprised if you see a golden eagle merrily perched in the garden – the pub sometimes hold falconry days.

Food serving times

Monday-Sunday:
12pm-3pm, 6pm-9.30pm

Prices

Meals: £ 25 (3 course dinner) and a la carte £ 20/35

13 rooms: £ 65

Typical Dishes

Game & pork terrine

Braised shoulder of lamb

Cheese board

0.5mi West on A39 going to Clovelly. Parking.

36 Bickley Mill

Stoneycombe,
Kingskerswell TQ12 5LN
Tel.: (01803)873201 – Fax: (01803)875129
e-mail: info@bickleymill.co.uk **Website:** www.bickleymill.co.uk

  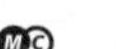 

 **Otter Ale, Teignworthy**

Hidden away in the sleepy village of Stoneycombe lies this converted flour mill dating back to the 13th century. A Free House since 1971, when it was adapted to allow for guest bedrooms, as much thought has been given to the outside of this establishment as the inside. The first thing that strikes you on arrival is the pleasant garden with its large decked terrace; a delightful area in which to soak up the sun on a summer's day. This is a pub for all seasons, however, and there are numerous cosy areas inside ideal in which to dine when dark wintry nights draw in. Although this pub has been modernised and has contemporary art hanging on the walls, it still manages to retain its rustic charm and character with features such as its open fire, stone walls and exposed beams. Pub staples have also been given a makeover here; the mash with your sausages might contain cheddar and chives or your salmon might be cured with beetroot.

Food serving times

Monday-Sunday:
12pm-2pm, 6.30pm-9pm

Closed 27-28 December and 1 January

Prices

Meals: £ 14 (2 course lunch) and a la carte £ 24/35

9 rooms: £ 55

Typical Dishes

Coarse country paté
Gressingham duck breast
Coconut pannacotta

3mi South of Newton Abbot by A380 and minor road east. Parking.

37 The Masons Arms

Knowstone EX36 4RY
Tel.: (01398)341231
e-mail: dodsonmasonsarms@aol.com
Website: www.masonsarmsdevon.co.uk

 **Cotleigh Tawny Bitter**

In the years following his celebrated stint as head chef at The Waterside Inn, country life beckoned for Mark Dodson and his family, and the residents of this secluded Devon village in the foothills of Exmoor have had reason to thank their lucky stars ever since. Dine beneath a beautiful ceiling mural, on food that is clearly both sophisticated and precise. Dishes come attractively presented but never over-wrought and the flavours are pronounced and assured. The excellent quality of the food is further complemented by the charming service. Not surprisingly, booking is essential. Built in the 13th century by the masons who also constructed the village church, the small interior of this pretty, yellow-washed, thatched inn is as full of character as its exterior. There's a tiny beamed bar with inglenook fireplace where the locals gather to drink, a lounge with comfy sofas in which to recline and a rear dining room.

Food serving times

Tuesday-Saturday:
12pm-2pm, 7pm-9pm

Sunday: 12pm-2pm

Closed first two weeks in January

Prices

Meals: a la carte £ 30/37

Typical Dishes

Salad of wood pigeon
Roulade of pork belly
Pineapple & ginger sablé

7mi Southeast of South Molton by A361. Opposite the village church. Parking.

38 The Dartmoor Inn

Moorside,
Lydford EX20 4AY
Tel.: (01822)820221 – Fax: (01822)820494
e-mail: info@dartmoorinn.co.uk **Website:** www.dartmoorinn.com

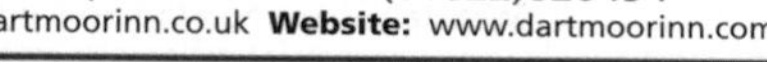

 **Otter Ale, Dartmoor Best, St Austell Tribute**

There's something refreshingly different about a pub which politely asks its customers to turn off the modern menace that is their mobile phone, and although not necessarily the most picturesque of buildings on the outside, this roadside dining pub on the edges of Dartmoor certainly provides an experience above the average when you venture in out of the cold. Gently rustic, with an intimate fireside bar, there are also several dining rooms with linen-laid tables and prints on the walls, and a sheltered terrace to the rear. Keenly run, the seasonal menu serves modern dishes with a Mediterranean influence, whilst a cheaper, more informal "Easy Dining" menu is also served in both of the bars. After eating, browse in the boutique for a memento of your visit. If you are staying over, three large and stylish bedrooms with modern colour schemes and distinctive beds provide a good night's sleep.

Food serving times

Monday: 6.30pm-9pm

Tuesday-Saturday:
12pm-2.15pm, 6.30pm-9pm

Sunday: 12pm-2.15pm

Closed Sunday dinner and Monday

Prices

Meals: £ 18 (weekdays) and a la carte £ 20/35

3 rooms: £ 95/125

Typical Dishes

Home-cured corned beef

Casserole of sea fish

Strawberry fritters

1mi East on A386. Parking.

39 Church House Inn

Village Rd,
Marldon TQ3 1SL
Tel.: (01803)558279 – Fax: (01803)664185
Website: www.churchhousemarldon.com

Dartmoor Best, Bay's Gold Bass, Fuller's London Pride

Hidden away in the sleepy village of Marldon, the Church House Inn started life at the turn of the 13C, when it was built to provide accommodation for the artisans who were constructing the nearby church. It was later turned into a meeting house for the church congregation and finally, became the local inn. Rebuilt in the 18C, the pub still displays some of its original Georgian windows – due largely to the fact that the neighbouring cricket pitch has now had "sixes" outlawed. Inside it's immensely charming, with beamed ceilings, lots of nooks and crannies and even an old bread oven; drinkers and diners mingle together in the bar and spacious first floor dining room, where local artwork adorns the walls. Cooking is traditional and tasty, featuring quality regional produce in generous helpings. You might find asparagus or homemade pâté, followed by Exmoor sirloin steak, local sea bass or honey glazed duck. Service is smooth and assured.

Food serving times

Monday-Sunday:
12pm-2.30pm,
6.30pm-9.30pm

Prices

Meals: a la carte £ 21/30

Typical Dishes

Salmon roulade
Loin of pork
Warm ginger parkin

Off A380 between Torquay and Paignton - well signed. Parking.

40 White Hart

Church St,
Modbury PL21 0QW
Tel.: (01548)831561
e-mail: info@whitehart-inn.co.uk **Website:** www.whitehart-inn.co.uk

6X, Fuller's London Pride

Knowing that the manager of this whitewashed former coaching inn used to dyb dyb dyb and dob dob dob as a local scout troop leader, one would expect it to be well run – and it is (they will do their best). A seasonally-evolving menu offers rustic, honest cooking, with dishes such as tiger prawns, smoked salmon, steak or local haddock served up alongside a choice of local ales. Refurbished to within an inch of its life, the flag-floored bar – serving a tapas-style menu - is modern bordering on stark, with leather suites and low, newspaper-strewn tables, while the cream-coloured dining room has more formally-dressed tables, with humorous, food-related quotations and old photos of the area on the walls. Mind out for the glass-topped "well" – a former inspection hole for the stream that runs under the village. The elegant Assembly Rooms upstairs are used for meetings and parties. Bedrooms are neatly furnished, with modern facilities.

On A379 between Kingsbridge and Yealmpton. Public car park at rear.

Food serving times

Monday-Sunday:
12pm-3pm, 6pm-9pm

Prices

Meals: £ 10/13
and a la carte £ 19/25

5 rooms: £ 58/65

Typical Dishes

Chicken liver parfait
Trio of sausages
Ginger sponge

41 The White Horse Inn

7 George Street, Moretonhampstead TQ13 8PG
Tel.: (01647)440242 – Fax: (01647)440148
e-mail: info@whitehorse-moretonhampstead.co.uk
Website: www.whitehorse-moretonhampstead.co.uk

Otter Ale, Otter Bright, Proper Job and guest beers such as Ebb Tide, Yellowhammer, Jail Ale

Located right in the heart of a busy market village, this 17C stone pub is thought to be home to several ghosts; you might see a man in a top hat, hear the cries of the maids from the former coaching yard, or, more likely, notice nothing at all. The locals aren't put off by the stories at any rate and can be found propping up the slightly shabby front room bar in great numbers. Pass them by and head through to the converted stables and hayloft, where you'll be pleasantly surprised to find two spacious stone-floored dining rooms with rustic charm and character aplenty; and an inner courtyard with large open windows and a light, airy feel. There's a well-balanced menu which features tasty, unfussy dishes, ranging from good British classics such as steak or fish and chips through to more diverse Mediterranean offerings. Despite there being more than a hint of Italian influence, the produce remains local and seasonal wherever possible.

Food serving times

Monday-Sunday:
12.30pm-2.30pm,
6.30pm-9pm

Restaurant closed
25 December

Italian influences

Prices

Meals: a la carte £ 20/35

Typical Dishes

King scallops
House Cassoulet
Ginger crème brûlée

In heart of village.

42 The Ship Inn

Noss Mayo PL8 1EW

Tel.: (01752)872387 – Fax: (01752)873294

e-mail: ship@nossmayo.com **Website:** www.nossmayo.com

 **Jail Ale, Tamar, Dartmoor, Butcombe Blonde, Dune**

Time and tide wait for no man, so get yourself down to The Ship Inn, pronto, but be careful. Arguably one of the most picturesque, peaceful spots in South Devon, those foolhardy souls who park on the beach, or "Noss Hard", of the Yealm estuary at Noss Mayo might later choke on their calamari as they catch sight of their car floating past at high tide. Floating vehicles aside, the upside to this location is, of course, the wonderful waterside views, and the large outside patio and first floor decked terrace are both perfect for idling away the hours boat and people-watching. The oldest part of this beamed pub dates from the 1700s, and the interior is full of character, with wooden floors, open fires and a large collection of local knick-knacks and pictures lining the walls. Friendly staff serve a wide range of dishes including local seafood and fresh fish from a daily-changing menu.

Food serving times

Monday-Sunday:
12pm-9.30pm

Prices

Meals: a la carte £ 20/30

Typical Dishes

Crab & prawn crostini
Roast duck breast
Warm chocolate Brownie

Signed off A379 10.5mi Southeast of Plymouth; turn right into B3186. Restricted parking, paricularly at high tide.

England • South West • Devon

43 The Harris Arms

Portgate EX20 4PZ

Tel.: (01566)783331 – Fax: (01566)783359

e-mail: whiteman@powernet.co.uk **Website:** www.theharrisarms.co.uk

   VISA MC

 **Sharps Doombar, Exe Valley**

Much more than just a stopping off point on the way down to Cornwall, The Harris Arms' reputation attracts "locals" from Okehampton to Tavistock, Launceston to Bodmin. The owners of this traditional 16C pub offer a very friendly welcome and have helped create a warm, relaxed ambience with their hands-on style. Award-winning winemakers previously based in New Zealand and France, it stands to reason that their wine list is excellent, with bottles personally selected and fairly priced. It's not only the wine that impresses here though. The aroma of home cooking and spices fills the air and robust, hearty, confidently flavoured food shows off the chefs' artistic talent. The owners pride themselves on local and seasonal cooking and have a regularly changing specials board, whilst puddings are proudly homemade. Sit in the front bar or in the back extension overlooking the decked terrace, and keep an eye out for Reg the cat.

Food serving times

Monday-Sunday:
12pm-2pm, 6.30pm-9pm

Closed 26 December,
1 January

Prices

Meals: a la carte £ 21/29

Typical Dishes

Grilled goats cheese
Roast chicken
Crêpe Suzette

3mi East of Launceston by A388 and side road. Parking.

44 Jack in the Green Inn

London Rd,
Rockbeare EX5 2EE
Tel.: (01404)822240 – Fax: (01404)823540
e-mail: info@jackinthegreen.uk.com **Website:** www.jackinthegreen.uk.com

 **Otter Ale, Butcombe Bitter**

Food obviously matters to the owners of this efficiently-run pub near to Exeter airport; ingredients are sourced from local suppliers, menus are dictated by the seasons, every dish is well-presented and they even produce monthly recipe cards so that regulars can recreate their favourite dishes at home. Another thing that plainly matters to the owners is service; staff are friendly and efficient and offer a warm welcome. Enjoy an aperitif in the leather-furnished lounge, where colourful photos of food whet your appetite, before heading into one of the characterful, beamed dining rooms. The à la carte offers unfussy dishes like ham hock terrine, steak or grilled fillet of sea bass, with highlighted dishes made solely from Devonshire ingredients. The value-for-money bar menu (which can be eaten anywhere) provides a large choice of pub favourites, with dishes such as ploughman's, pies or sausage and mash.

Food serving times

Monday-Saturday:
12pm-2pm, 6pm-9pm

Sunday: 12pm-9pm

Closed 25 December-
6 January

Prices

Meals: £ 25 and a la carte
£ 30/40

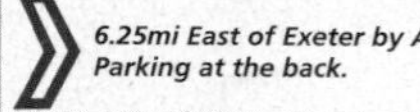
6.25mi East of Exeter by A30.
Parking at the back.

England • South West • Devon

45 The Sandy Park Inn

Sandypark TQ13 8JW
Tel.: (01647)433267
e-mail: enquiries@sandyparkinn.co.uk **Website:** www.sandyparkinn.co.uk

VISA MC AE

Otter Bitter, O'Hanlons, St Austell, Sharps, Princetown

They say that good things come in small packages and could well have been talking about The Sandy Park Inn. Situated on the edge of Dartmoor, five minutes drive from Castle Drogo, this 17C thatched inn is full of character, with flagged floors, open fires and heavy beams. Its three rooms are on the small side, however, and in winter you can expect to be shoulder to shoulder with your fellow pub-goers, keeping one another warm. In summer, the lawned hillside garden is a delight. Modern, sophisticated dishes are made with ingredients sourced from local suppliers and the blackboard menu is displayed above the fireplace. Lighter snacks, sandwiches and soups are also available at lunchtimes. Bedrooms here are small and cosy and you may or may not think they've got their priorities right, depending on your sensibilities; some rooms do not have ensuites, yet they all have flat screen TVs.

Food serving times
Monday-Sunday:
12pm-2.30pm, 6.30pm-9pm

Prices
Meals: a la carte £ 20/28
5 rooms: £ 55

Typical Dishes
Fresh calamari rings
Lingcombe Farm leg of lamb
West Country cheeses

5mi South of A30 from roundabout at Whiddon Down by A382. Parking.

46 The Tower Inn

Church Rd,
Slapton TQ7 2PN
Tel.: (01548)580216
e-mail: towerinn@slapton.org **Website:** www.thetowerinn.com

 **Otter Ale, Otter Bitter, Butcombe Bitter**

Luckily this pub is signposted because, tucked away up a narrow lane in a corner of the quaint little village, you might otherwise miss it. Built in 1347 as cottages for the men who were working on the chantry, much of the tower still overlooks its rear walled garden. The interior is everything you would expect to find in a proper English pub; several cosy adjoining rooms with stone walls, beams, flag floors and, for people of height, dangerously low ceilings. Separate dinner and lunch menus offer wholesome, hearty food including daily specials and an appealing array of traditional puddings. This pub is a great base from which to explore the local area and its history, so stay in one of the simple annex bedrooms and explore the Slapton Ley nature reserve and the misleadingly-named Slapton Sands (they're covered in pebbles), where American troops practised for the D-Day landings in 1944 in the ill-fated Exercise Tiger.

Food serving times

Monday-Saturday:
12pm-3pm, 6pm-9.30pm

Sunday: 12pm-3pm

Closed Sunday dinner

Closed Monday in winter

Prices

Meals: a la carte £ 21/30

3 rooms: £ 40/75

Typical Dishes

Slapton mackerel escabeche

Short rib of beef

Treacle tart with cream

6mi Southwest of Dartmouth by A379; signed between Dartmouth and Kingsbridge. Parking with exceptionally narrow access.

47 The Kings Arms

Dartmouth Rd,
Strete TQ6 0RW
Tel.: (01803)770377
Website: www.kingsarms-dartmouth.co.uk

 **Otter Ales, Adnams**

From being slightly rundown – to put it kindly – The Kings Arms has picked itself up in fine style. A white-painted roadside pub with a distinctive balcony, it's easy to spot as you drive up, but this is not its best side, and anyone who has spent a slow, sunny lunchtime in the garden or the pleasant rear terrace is sure to agree. The bar itself, decorated with old local pictures, is fine but small; it's worth going for the extra comforts of the dining room. Two window tables are the prime spots, but bare beams and seats in nautical blue give the whole place a nice, fresh feel. Lunches are slightly lighter but, even here, fish and chips with mushy peas is the odd one out in a menu of modern classics. Dinners make even more use of local, seasonal ingredients, including Devon seafood, meats and cheeses. Fresh, unfussy flavours.

Food serving times

Monday: 12pm-2pm, (summer only) 6.30pm-9pm

Tuesday-Saturday: 12pm-2pm, 6.30pm-9pm

Sunday: 12pm-2pm, (summer only) 6.30pm-9pm

Closed Sunday dinner and Monday November-Easter

Closed Monday December-February

Seafood

Prices

Meals: a la carte £ 28/36

Typical Dishes

Scallops with Le Puy lentils

Halibut

Hot chocolate fondant

4mi Southwest of Dartmouth by A379. Parking.

48 The Steam Packet Inn

St Peter's Quay,
Totnes TQ9 5EW

Tel.: (01803)863880 – Fax: (01803)862754
e-mail: steampacket@buccaneer.co.uk **Website:** www.steampacketinn.co.uk

Jail Ale, Otter Bright, Courage Best

Named after the postal ships that used to carry the mail, the Steam Packet Inn is situated in a fantastic location on the River Dart, just five minutes walk from the centre of Totnes. With a vast terrace that catches the sun from dawn til dusk and a large conservatory looking out over the water, this is a great spot to relax and watch the coming and goings on the river; but, plenty of other people know this too, so get here early on sunny days. The eclectic, wide-ranging menu has something for everyone, ranging from classic lemon sole and West Country steak to kofta kebabs and even Thai dishes. Fish in particular is a speciality – delivered daily from Looe – and the blackboard displays the day's latest catch. The pleasant service is provided by local, friendly staff, who are pushed to their limit on the busiest days. Should you run out of steam, there are four elegant bedrooms, each cosy and snug but with a contemporary feel.

Food serving times

Monday-Sunday:
12pm-2.30pm, 6pm-9.30pm

Closed 25-26 December dinner, 1 January dinner

Prices

Meals: a la carte £ 17/29

4 rooms: £ 60/80

Typical Dishes

River Exe mussels
Homemade tagliatelli
Homemade blueberry cheesecake

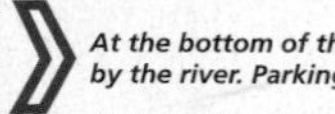

At the bottom of the hill by the river. Parking.

49 Rose & Crown

Market St,
Yealmpton PL8 2EB
Tel.: (01752)880223 – Fax: (01752)881058
e-mail: info@theroseandcrown.co.uk **Website:** www.theroseandcrown.co.uk

Sharps Doom Bar, Otter Ale, Courage, Gales HSB, Abbot Ale, St Austell Tribute

It's easy to whiz through South Hams villages on your way to the delights of Noss Mayo, Newton Ferrers or Burgh Island. But put the brakes on in Yealmpton, and check out this neat, modernised pub on a corner, not least for its attractive rear walled terrace with canopies and water feature. Inside, enclosed by rough stone walls, is a big central bar and a spacious, open plan design that allows for casual seating areas with family-sized leather sofas, and places to eat with large benches and tables or a more formal dining space. Here you can tuck into modern "restaurant" dishes with a Pacific Rim edge, along with a good value fixed priced lunch menu, washed down by Devon ales or something off the accessible wine list. If your taste is for something a bit more fishy, then you can step outside the pub to the Seafood Restaurant where a good range of shellfish is on offer.

Food serving times
Monday-Sunday:
12pm-2.30pm, 6.30pm-9pm

Prices
Meals: £ 13 (3 course lunch) and a la carte £ 20/30

Typical Dishes
Asian pork belly
Fillet of beef
Duo of chocolate

7mi Southeast of Plymouth by A379. Parking.

50 The Cow

58 Station Road,
Ashley Cross, Poole BH14 8UD
Tel.: (01202)749569 – Fax: (01202)307493
e-mail: info@thecowpub.co.uk **Website:** www.thecowpub.co.uk

 **Ringwood Best, Fuller's London Pride, Dorset Steam Ale**

Formerly a run-down hotel, this is now a bright and vibrant suburban pub, which features wood tables, stripped floorboards and a relaxed atmosphere throughout. It is divided into two distinct areas which are very different yet equally appealing: the chilled out bar is furnished with brown leather sofas, cow-themed canvases and a flat screen TV, while the more formal bistro is adorned with wine-themed prints and French posters. At lunch you can eat in either side, choosing from baguettes, pies, or more filling dishes, such as mussels or hearty British classics. The evening welcomes in a substantial à la carte – served only in the bistro – which features appealing starters, such as roast quail with truffled potato, and some equally interesting mains, maybe salmon fillet in porridge oats or ballotine of chicken breast and Parma ham. Whatever you choose you can rest assured that it will be good quality, expertly prepared and well-presented.

Food serving times
Monday-Sunday:
12pm-2.30pm, 7pm-9.30pm

Prices
Meals: a la carte £ 16/36

Typical Dishes
Roast quail
Salmon fillet
Warm poached pear

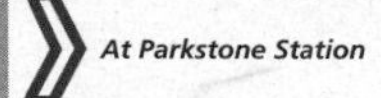
At Parkstone Station

Dave Young 2006

51 The Bull

34 East St,
Bridport DT6 3LF

Tel.: (01308)422878 – Fax: (01308)426872
e-mail: info@thebullhotel.co.uk **Website:** www.thebullhotel.co.uk

   AE

 **Branoc Bitter**

From the moment you set foot inside this Grade II listed building and are greeted by a vast contemporary portrait behind an informal reception desk, you realise it's no ordinary place. This former regency style coaching inn has undergone a massive transformation, which has left an eclectic mix of period features and chic, contemporary décor – a touch of grandeur amongst the bustling streets of this busy market town. The ground floor is surprisingly compact, featuring a small bar room overlooking a courtyard and a simple, fairly informal dining room. The menu here sees a mix of classic English and Mediterranean brasserie dishes, each crafted from local farm meat or fresh fish from nearby Lyme Bay. Upstairs, uniquely styled bedrooms follow a modern designer theme, boasting boldly patterned feature walls, wacky pictures and stylish bathrooms; the residents bar and lounge are particularly alluring and there's even a luxurious ballroom.

Food serving times
Monday-Sunday:
12pm-3pm, 6pm-9.30pm

Prices
Meals: a la carte £ 25/45

14 rooms: £ 60/180

Typical Dishes
Lamb carpaccio
Baked monkfish
Pineapple tart Tatin

In town centre on South side of main street. Parking.

52 The Stapleton Arms

Church Hill,
Buckhorn Weston SP8 5HS

Tel.: (01963)370396 – Fax: (01963)370396
e-mail: relax@thestapletonarms.com **Website:** www.thestapletonarms.com

   AE

 **Butcombe Bitter, Timothy Taylor Landlord, Otter Bitter and 2 regularly changing guest ales**

If you're carrying on down the A303 towards Devon and Cornwall having admired the engineering feat that is Stonehenge, you might do well to stop off for a meal in The Stapleton Arms. It's situated in pretty Buckhorn Weston, a village with its own historical claim to fame: a mention in the Magna Carta. There's nothing ancient about the interior of this pub though - it's up-to-date, smart and stylish with an elegant dining room. This modernity hasn't scared off the locals, and you'll find your muddy boots, dogs and children are all similarly welcome. On a sunny day, sit out the front on the terrace or in the rear garden. With a wide-ranging, daily-changing menu, this pub offers traditional choices like ploughman's or grilled pork chop alongside dishes like salmon fillet and a Thai red curry of mussels and tiger prawns. Spacious, contemporary rooms are available, with underfloor heating a nice touch for cold feet on wintry mornings.

Food serving times
Monday-Sunday:
12pm-3pm, 6pm-10pm

Prices
Meals: a la carte £ 20/25
4 rooms: £ 72/120

Typical Dishes
Salmon gravadlax
Pan-fried fillet of fish
Vanilla pannacotta

7mi West of Shaftesbury by A30 and minor road North. Parking.

53 The Chetnole Inn

Chetnole,
DT9 6NU
Tel.: (01935)872337
e-mail: enquiries@thechetnoleinn.co.uk **Website:** www.thechetnoleinn.co.uk

Sharps Doom Bar, O'Hanlons Yellowhammer, Spitfire

A well run pub set on a T-junction opposite this rural village's church. To the left as you enter is a comfy, sofa-furnished locals' bar with dartboard, jukebox, slot machine and skittle alley. To the right you'll find a cosy beamed room set for dining, with flagged floors, bunches of hops and a warming wood burner. The style here is understated and uncluttered, with decorative herbs in plant pots and simple farmhouse furniture. Like the décor, the cooking's strength lies in its simplicity, and tasty, value-for-money choices might include game terrine, sausage and mash or steak and Guinness pie, with sandwiches also available at lunchtime. The dinner menu adds more spice with dishes such as Thai style salmon fishcake or pan-roasted sea bass fillets, and the specials also compete for your attention. Duck isn't on the menu, but you might well see a few waddle past if you sit in the garden. Pleasant, pine-furnished bedrooms.

Food serving times
Monday-Sunday:
11.30am-2pm, 6.30pm-9pm

Prices
Meals: a la carte £ 20/30
3 rooms: £ 50/85

Typical Dishes
Smoked trout
Thai style salmon fishcake
Passion fruit crème brûlée

7mi South of Yeovil by A37 and minor road East

54 The Acorn Inn

28 Fore St,
Evershot DT2 0JW

Tel.: (01935)83228 – Fax: (01935)83707
e-mail: stay@acorn-inn.co.uk **Website:** www.acorn-inn.co.uk

 **Draymans, Branoc, Melbury Oak**

Situated in a quintessentially English picture postcard village, this characterful coaching inn has its own unique history to tell: it featured in Thomas Hardy's classic "Tess of the d'Urbervilles". Boasting stone walls, oak panelling and flag flooring, no surface is left bare, as pictures aplenty adorn the walls and a vast array of memorabilia is scattered over every worktop. As you might hope, the lunchtime menu displays a selection of British pub classics, with dinner welcoming in some more sophisticated choices. Dishes might include stuffed roasted quail or parmesan, tarragon and truffle oil soufflé, followed by saddle of rabbit or fillet of English beef with seared scallops; for dessert there may be hazelnut crème brûlée or bananas in Malibu caramel. After dinner you can complete your "Hardy" experience by staying in one of the individually designed English country bedrooms, each named after a character or place from his book.

Food serving times

Monday-Sunday:
12pm-2pm, 7pm-9pm

Prices

Meals: a la carte £ 25/30

10 rooms: £ 95/160

Typical Dishes

Boned, stuffed quail
Saddle of rabbit
Roast peaches

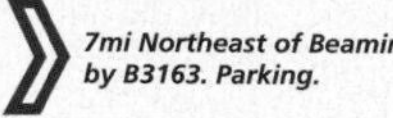

7mi Northeast of Beaminster by B3163. Parking.

55 The Museum Inn

Farnham DT11 8DE
Tel.: (01725)516261 – Fax: (01725)516988
e-mail: enquiries@museuminn.co.uk
Website: www.museuminn.co.uk

Ringwood Best Bitter, Timothy Taylor

Set in the heart of a picture postcard village, this part thatched 17C country inn was built by the founding father of modern archaeology – General August Lane Fox Pitt Rivers – with the purpose of providing refreshment and accommodation for the nearby museum. A sympathetic refurbishment has retained many of the original features, including flag stone floors and an inglenook fireplace, while the walls are adorned with a range of hunting artefacts. There are plenty of place to sit: the bar, two adjoining rooms, a conservatory, and at weekends the "Shed", which despite its corrugated tin exterior, is a smart linen-laid dining room. The menu offers some good British classics such as kidneys or rabbit pie, alongside dishes of a more Mediterranean nature; cooking is seasonal, unfussy and focuses on the quality of the local, traceable ingredients. Spread across the site, bedrooms range from small and cottagey, to spacious with a four-poster.

Food serving times

Monday-Sunday:
12pm-2.30pm, 7pm-9.30pm

Closed 25 December, dinner 31 December and 1 January

Prices

Meals: a la carte £ 25/35

8 rooms: £ 95/120

Typical Dishes
Pan-fried lambs kidneys
Roast rack of lamb
Chocolate fondant

7.5mi Northeast of Blandford Forum by A354. Parking.

56 The Talbot

Iwerne Minster DT11 8QN
Tel.: (01747)811269 – Fax: (01747)811269
e-mail: enquiries@the-talbot.com **Website:** www.the-talbot.com

Hall & Woodhouse - First Gold, Tanglefoot, Hopping Hare

Until the late 19C the Bower family were Lords of the Manor here and the large Talbot hound that guards this mock-Elizabethan building is thought to have originated from their family crest. Unlike many modern gastro-pubs, this inn retains an unfussy, pub-like feel, with a lounge bar and simply-laid dining room to the front and an aptly named "Village Bar" – where the locals will be playing pool or darts – and enclosed terrace to the back. Cooking is hearty and generous – as befits a pub of little pretension – and local produce is a must. Sausages are made by the village butcher, beef and lamb are supplied by the local Estate and even sandwiches or Ploughman's feature local cheese. Menus often change daily and might include starters of Gloucester Old Spot and pistachio terrine, followed by slow-roasted shoulder of lamb or rump steak with pepper sauce. Bedrooms, named after local hills, are comfortable, well-appointed and up-to-date.

Food serving times
Monday-Sunday:
12pm-2.30pm,
6.30pm-9.30pm

Prices
Meals: a la carte £ 18/26
5 rooms: £ 65/95

Typical Dishes
Blue Vinney soufflé
Shoulder of spring lamb
Glazed lemon tart

6mi South of Shaftesbury by A350

57 Village Pub

Barnsley GL7 5EE
Tel.: (01285)740421 – Fax: (01285)740925
e-mail: rec@barnsleyhouse.com **Website:** www.thevillagepub.co.uk

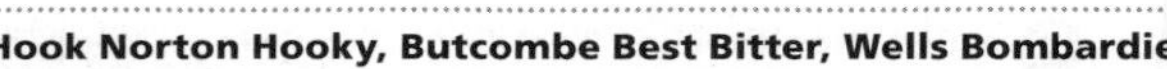

Hook Norton Hooky, Butcombe Best Bitter, Wells Bombardier

Say "Barnsley" and you probably think of football, but this attractive Cotswold stone village in Gloucestershire if a far cry from the energetic fans and bustling streets of the better known Yorkshire industrial town. Even before you arrive on the doorstep, the name "Village Pub" gives you a good idea of what to expect: an inn full of character, from the charming paved terrace, to the cosy open-fired interior – where exposed stone, woodwork and a mix of flag and oak flooring pervade. Characterful bedrooms echo this rustic style, boasting wooden beams, antique furniture and either a four poster or Victorian iron bedstead. Based on the latest local produce available, menus change not only daily but between services too. Dishes vary in style between pub and restaurant, rustic and refined, featuring everything from classic British favourites such as fish and chips, through to more extravagant offerings such as turbot or foie gras parfait.

Food serving times
Monday-Thursday:
12pm-2.30pm, 7pm-9.30pm
Friday:
12pm-2.30pm, 7pm-10pm
Saturday:
12pm-3pm, 7pm-10pm
Sunday:
12pm-3pm, 7pm-9.30pm

Prices
Meals: a la carte £ 20/29
7 rooms: £ 95/220

Typical Dishes
Stuffed squid
Lamb & pumpkin curry
Mixed nut tart

4mi North East of Cirencester, on the B4425. Parking.

58 Horse & Groom

Bourton-on-the-Hill GL56 9AQ
Tel.: (01386)700413 – Fax: (01386)700413
e-mail: greenstocks@horseandgroom.info
Website: www.horseandgroom.info

Purity Pure Gold and guest ales including Goff, Wye Valley, Hook Norton, Battledown, Cotswold

Situated in a remote Cotswold village on the side of a hill it's not surprising that this Georgian yellow-stone pub attracts mainly diners, as, unless you live here, it's a long way to go just for a drink. The relaxed atmosphere makes it popular across the age groups and the friendly, well-paced service stands the test of even the busiest hour. Original beams, pine flooring and exposed stone feature throughout, while an attractive marble-topped counter steals the focus in the bar area. Here two blackboards compete for attention: the first, a growing list of names of those waiting for a table and the second, a much more appealing list of classic British dishes and some more ambitious fare. Local produce features strongly in the hearty, unfussy cooking and despite generous portions most diners manage to find room for all three courses. If the drive back is too much after you've had your fill, then modern, stylish bedrooms await.

Food serving times

Monday: 7pm-9pm

Tuesday-Thursday: 12pm-2pm, 7pm-9pm

Friday-Saturday: 12pm-2pm, 7pm-9.30pm

Sunday: 12pm-2.30pm

Closed 25 and 31 December

Prices

Meals: a la carte £ 19/30

5 rooms: £ 70/125

Typical Dishes

Mozzarella with speck

Grilled salmon & langoustine

Chocolate & peanut torte

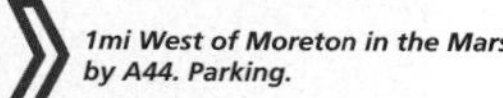

1mi West of Moreton in the Marsh by A44. Parking.

59 The Gumstool Inn

Calcot GL8 8YJ
Tel.: (01666)890391 – Fax: (01666)890394
e-mail: reception@calcotmanor.co.uk
Website: www.calcotmanor.co.uk

 **Sharps Own, Barbary Castle, Butcombe Gold and Butcombe Blonde**

Set in the grounds of the Calcot Manor Hotel, part of a 700 year old Estate, this converted farm out-building is now a highly attractive country pub. With wood-panelled walls, flag flooring, orange and brown chairs and modern artwork, it successfully combines classic country style with contemporary chic. Warm and cosy in the winter, bright and airy in the spring and with a paved terrace ideal for summer, it's welcoming whatever the weather. The wide-ranging monthly menu is seasonal, rustic and hearty, yet also accommodates lighter appetites by offering some scaled down main courses. The extensive daily specials also provide some interesting choices, such as pan-fried skate with avocado or Arbroath smokie cheese soufflé. Service is polite and friendly but make sure you give back what you get, as in the past miscreants were placed on a local gumstool and, as punishment for their offences or profanities, ducked in a pond.

Food serving times

Monday-Sunday:
12pm-2pm, 6pm-9.30pm

Booking essential

Prices

Meals: a la carte £ 25/35

Typical Dishes

Cheddar cheese soufflé
Pork & hop sausages
Calcot bread & butter pudding

3.5mi West of Tetbury on A4135, in grounds of Calcot Manor Hotel. Parking.

60 Eight Bells Inn

Church St,
Chipping Campden GL55 6JG
Tel.: (01386)840371 – Fax: (01386)841669
e-mail: neilhargreaves@bellinn.fsnet.co.uk **Website:** www.eightbellsinn.co.uk

 **IPA, Pigbrook, Hook Norton Best, Old Hooky, Fuller's London Pride**

Situated in the old wool merchants' town of Chipping Campden, with its historic high street, this pub is a great base from which to explore the Cotswolds. Dating from the 14C, when it accommodated the stonemasons building the nearby St. James' church, it gets its name from the fact that it was used to store the bells for the church tower, and even has a "priest hole" rumoured to lead underground to the church. The menu offers an appealing blend of traditional and more contemporary dishes, ranging from fish and chips or toad in the hole to slow-roasted shank of lamb or a Thai-style curry, with specials chalked up on a board. The bustling beamed bar, popular with locals, is the most atmospheric place to sit, but a sandwich and a pint will go down just as well in the terraced garden. If you're staying over, you'll find the bedrooms warmly decorated and well looked after; with its ancient beams, room seven is the most characterful.

Food serving times

Monday-Sunday:
12pm-2.30pm,
6.30pm-9.30pm

Closed 25 December

Prices

Meals: a la carte £ 20/30

7 rooms: £ 55/125

Typical Dishes
Spiced lamb kebabs
Pork & leek sausages
Banoffee pie

In centre of town. Unlimited parking on road.

England • South West • Gloucestershire

61 The Green Dragon Inn

Cockleford GL53 9NW

Tel.: (01242)870271 – Fax: (01242)870171

e-mail: green-dragon@buccaneer.co.uk **Website:** www.green-dragon-inn.co.uk

 **Hook Norton, Directors, Butcombe**

There can't be many pubs in which you can say the mice are part of the furniture - but here they literally are. Many of the seasoned oak furnishings, including tables, the bars and even the lynch gate in the car park, are made by Robert "Mouseman" Thompson, and his distinctive hand carved mouse hallmark scampers merrily along each one. As you watch the burning embers reflecting off beamed ceilings and bare wooden floorboards, you'll agree that the furniture is far from the only characterful thing about this 17C Cotswold stone pub, however. Fancy a game of skittles? Masquerading as a function room, the skittle alley opens out onto the peaceful patio garden, and comfortable, modern bedrooms named after famous racehorses can be found in an annexed block. Alongside British staples come other dishes with more of a colourful Mediterranean pedigree, and lighter meals also available for lunch. Book ahead to avoid disappointment.

Food serving times

Monday-Friday:
12pm-2.30pm, 6pm-10pm

Saturday:
12pm-3pm, 6pm-10pm

Sunday:
12pm-3.30pm, 6pm-9pm

Closed dinner
25-26 December
and 1 January

Prices

Meals: a la carte £ 20/30

9 rooms: £ 65/85

Typical Dishes

Cured salmon

Shoulder of lamb

Sticky toffee & date pudding

5mi South of Cheltenham by A435. Parking.

62 The Colesbourne Inn

Colesbourne GL53 9NP
Tel.: (01242)870376
e-mail: info@thecolesbourneinn.co.uk **Website:** www.thecolesbourneinn.co.uk

 **Wadworth 6X, Wadworth Henrys IPA**

A large pub in spirit and in stature, this early 19C coaching inn sits in the heart of the Cotswolds, halfway between Cirencester and Cheltenham. Three rooms, each with large open fireplace, feature beamed ceilings and flagged floors, with walls covered in photos and dried hops and pewter tankards hanging from the ceiling. Robust, hearty homemade cooking gets the thumbs up from all comers, with produce having travelled as short a distance as possible between field and fork. Unfussy dishes like sausage and mash or steak and ale pie reside on the bar menu alongside sandwiches, soups and salads, while the à la carte features more elaborate offerings like squid, chorizo and basil risotto, poached saddle of lamb, or Chinese style pork. Situated in the former stables and named, somewhat unusually, after local farmers' fields, the bedrooms keep it relatively simple décor-wise, with antique furniture and a few four posters.

Food serving times
Monday-Sunday:
12pm-2pm, 6.30pm-8.45pm

Prices
Meals: a la carte £ 18/32
9 rooms: £ 55/85

Typical Dishes
Thai prawn salad
Confit saddle of lamb
Orange & chocolate pyramids

 *7mi South of Cheltenham by A435* 

63 The Wild Duck Inn

Drake's Island,
Ewen GL7 6BY

Tel.: (01285)770310 – Fax: (01285)770924
e-mail: wduckinn@aol.com **Website:** www.thewildduckinn.co.uk

 **Duckpond, Theakston Best, Theakston OP, Butcombe Bitter, Old Bob, Dorothy Goodbody, Old Speckled Hen**

This characterful stone-built pub has stood in the pretty rural village of Ewen since 1563 and retains not only its original features but plenty of charm too. Secluded gardens and paved terraces lie to the front and back, whilst inside there are exposed stone walls, oak floors, open fires, objets d'art and dried hops aplenty. Originally a barn, the main dining area is made up of various small rooms separated by beams and original wood frames, which creates a great atmosphere. In line with the rustic feel, the cooking takes on a traditional style and menus are filled with pub classics and old British favourites: maybe roast chicken or fish and chips, alongside sirloin or rib-eye steaks. To complete the whole "olde English" experience head for the large, characterful bedrooms in the original building, with their high ceilings, wooden beams and distinct period feel. From start to finish you'll take to this pub like a duck to water.

Food serving times

Monday-Sunday:
12pm-2pm, 6.30pm-10pm

Closed 25 December for food

Prices

Meals: a la carte £ 25/40

12 rooms: £ 80

Typical Dishes

Baked Camembert & Parma ham

Tandoori monkfish

Sticky toffee pudding

3.25mi Southwest of Cirencester by A429. Parking.

64 The Fox Inn

Lower Oddington GL56 0UR
Tel.: (01451)870555 – Fax: (01451)870669
e-mail: info@foxinn.net **Website:** www.foxinn.net

 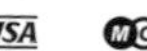

Hook Norton Bitter, Abbot Ale, Wickwar Bitter

Finding yourself in Lower Oddington, you may wish to study the medieval wall painting of the seven deadly sins depicted within scenes of the Last Judgement at the local 11C church of St. Nicholas. And whilst the avaricious are spending their money in Stow-on-the-Wold's many antique shops, gluttons should head to the nearby ivy-clad Fox Inn where they can indulge to their hearts' content in classic, hearty British food. Popular with both locals and visitors, this pub can become busy, so if you're prone to anger, it's best to book ahead. Rustically romantic, with its flag floors, wooden beams and open fires, the red-painted dining room is perfect place for the lustful to enjoy a candlelit meal.Feeling slothful after you've eaten? Stay the night in one of the sumptuously furnished bedrooms. The envy of others who just can't compete, the team at The Fox must feel justifiably proud of their charming village inn.

Food serving times

Monday-Saturday:
12pm-2.30pm, 6.30pm-10pm

Sunday:
12pm-3.30pm, 7pm-9.30pm

Closed 25 December

Prices

Meals: a la carte £ 20/29

3 rooms: £ 95

Typical Dishes

Home-cured gravadlax
Steak & kidney pie
Chocolate St Emillion

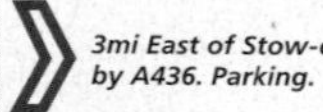

3mi East of Stow-on-the-Wold by A436. Parking.

Minchinhampton

65 The Ragged Cot

Cirencester Rd,
Minchinhampton GL6 8PE
Tel.: (01453)884643 – Fax: (01453)731166
e-mail: info@theraggedcot.co.uk **Website:** www.theraggedcot.co.uk

  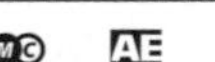 

 **Jennings, Pedigree**

Originally a very small 18C roadside inn that was later sympathetically extended, this pub has recently seen a full refurbishment, opening under new management in April 2008. It boasts a modern bar and three rooms for eating, the largest featuring an A frame roof and floor to ceiling doors which open out onto a wood-furnished terrace, with garden booths and a foliage-draped pergola beyond. Lunch is a list of small and medium sized dishes that can be eaten alone or made into courses, while dinner is more structured, with five or six choices of starter, main course and dessert. Cooking is rustic, robust and uses mainly local ingredients; offal lovers will often find ox tongue and cheek, tripe, deep fried pig's ears, braised pig's head or even mysterious "pork bits" on the menu. Bedrooms are pleasant, with neutral colours and simple, modern facilities: each is named after a Penguin book, with the cover displayed in a frame at the door.

Food serving times
Monday-Sunday:
12pm-3pm, 6.30pm-10pm

Prices
Meals: a la carte £ 20/31
10 rooms: £ 120

Typical Dishes
Braised pigs head salad
Ox tongue "n" cheek
Vanilla cheesecake

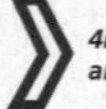

4mi South of Stroud by A419 and minor road South

66 The Bell

Sapperton GL7 6LE
Tel.: (01285)760298 – Fax: (01285)760761
e-mail: thebell@sapperton66.freeserve.co.uk
Website: www.foodatthebell.co.uk

 **Uley Old Spot, Otter Bitter, Bath Ales Gem, Wild Hare**

On a warm summer's day head for this pretty village, where, set above the road, you can relax amongst the neatly-lawned gardens and paved terraces of this charming pub. Inside, exposed stone and wood beams feature throughout, while colourful, contemporary art adorns the walls of the bar and surrounding rooms. From the warm welcome to the smiling departure the service is friendly, efficient and well-paced, even during the daily rush. The wide-ranging monthly menu displays an array of British dishes with the odd Mediterranean touch and some seafood specials. Cooking is refined yet rustic and ranges from classic pies through to more ambitious foie gras; while a quick glance at the back of the menu assures you of the local or regional origins of the produce used. Completing the package is the interesting wine list, which features a number of unusual choices from some lesser-known provinces. All in all, this pub is as sound as a bell.

Food serving times

Monday-Sunday:
12pm-2pm, 7pm-9.30pm

Closed 25 December

Prices

Meals: a la carte £ 23/35

Typical Dishes

Potted salt beef
Calves liver
Fruit mousse

5mi West of Cirencester by A419.
Parking.

67 The Trouble House

Cirencester Rd,
Tetbury GL8 8SG
Tel.: (01666)502206
e-mail: info@thetroublehouse.co.uk **Website:** www.thetroublehouse.co.uk

 VISA  AE

 **Henrys IPA, 6X**

The Trouble House may have changed hands in 2007 but that did not mean that alarm bells needed to be sounded. That was because, like the previous chef-owner, the new man has a considerable pedigree cooking at some stellar Big City establishments but had decided to relocate with his wife to the more pastoral setting of Tetbury for their first solo venture. His cooking shows all the understanding and appreciation of good ingredients that one would expect from an experienced chef and he has clearly discovered some great local producers. But the cooking is also commendably unfussy on the plate, where flavours are kept natural and complementary. The pub itself remains decidedly unremarkable in its façade and location, with cars belting along the road outside, but that just seems to make the warm and characterful interior just that little more welcoming and cosy and proves that it's not just books one shouldn't judge by their covers.

Food serving times

Tuesday-Saturday:
12pm-2pm, 7pm-9.30pm

Sunday: 12pm-2pm

Closed 25 December, first week in January, Bank Holidays

Prices

Meals: £ 20 (dinner tuesday-thursday and lunch) and a la carte £ 24/34

Typical Dishes

Foie gras parfait
Braised ox cheek
Spiced pineapple tart Tatin

2mi Northeast on the A433. Parking.

68 Horse & Groom Village Inn

Upper Oddington GL56 0XH
Tel.: (01451)830584
e-mail: info@horseandgroom.uk.com **Website:** www.horseandgroom.uk.com

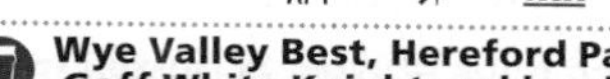

Wye Valley Best, Hereford Pale Ale, Wickwar Bob, Goff White Knight and locally brewed lager

However busy it gets – and it gets very busy – the owners and their team keep on smiling; their enthusiasm was one reason the pub got so busy in the first place so they've only themselves to blame. Another reason is the warm and comfortable surroundings, with its open fireplace, the tidy and well stocked bar, beams and a separate area set for dining. Lunch is particularly popular, especially with those no longer burdened by employment, and the atmosphere is jolly and welcoming. The menu is quite substantial and it's apparent that sourcing is undertaken seriously: the Gloucester Old Spot, Cotswold lamb and Hereford beef have clues in their names; venison comes from the nearby Adlestrop Estate; fish from Brixham and must of the fruit and veg from Oddington itself. It's not just the food that's taken seriously: there are plenty of interesting cask ales and an impressive selection of wines by the glass too.

Food serving times

Monday-Saturday:
12pm-2pm, 6.30pm-9pm

Sunday:
12pm-2pm, 7pm-9pm

Closed 2 weeks January

Prices

Meals: a la carte £ 20/30

8 rooms: £ 85/100

Typical Dishes

Smoke haddock fishcakes

Lamb casserole

Regional cheese

2mi East of Stow-on-the-Wold by A436. Parking (50 spaces).

69 The White Hart Inn

High St,
Winchcombe GL54 5LJ
Tel.: (01242)602359 – Fax: (01242)602703
e-mail: info@wineandsausage.com **Website:** www.wineandsausage.com

 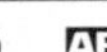 MC AE

 **Goffs Jouster, Hook Norton, St Austell Tribute**

Refurbished and re-launched as Winchcombe Wine and Sausage, this 16C former coaching inn does what it says on the tin, plus a bit more. You want wine? A well-stocked, decently-priced wine shop contains the owner's top 100 wines from around the world – take your pick, pay £5 corkage and enjoy with dinner in the pub; the top 25 each week are also available by the glass. You want sausages? They have their own menu here – choose from flavours such as lamb, mint and apricot or Gloucester old spot. You want somewhere to eat? Try the atmospheric and aptly named Eating Room, complete with picture of comedy pig. And the bit more? Well, they don't just serve wine and sausages. And you don't have to eat in The Eating Room. Real ales, cider, whisky et al; a large selection of hearty homemade dishes, a characterful bar, a rustic dining room and chatty, friendly service; all this plus eight comfortable bedrooms in which to sleep off your excesses.

Food serving times
Monday-Sunday:
12pm-3pm, 6pm-9.30pm

Prices
Meals: £ 18 (lunch)
and a la carte £ 18/35

8 rooms: £ 45/115

Typical Dishes
Breast of wood pigeon
Old Spot belly pork
Cambridge burnt cream

8mi Northeast of Cheltenham by B4632; in town centre. Parking.

70 The Globe Inn

Appley TA21 0HJ
Tel.: (01823)672327
e-mail: globeinnappley@btconnect.com **Website:** www.theglobeinnappley.co.uk

 **Appley Ale, Sharps Doombar, Butcombe Blonde**

Cosy and traditional, even pleasantly old-fashioned in some ways, the inn's welcoming interior shows the influence of a genial man who clearly sees himself as custodian of the Globe, as well as its chef and long-standing landlord. The building itself has origins in the 1400s, but there's nautical history too, in the pictures, prints and photos of the Titanic decorating one wall, and a touch of nostalgia in the display case of die-cast Dinky and Corgi cars and vans. Hard to fault for generosity, the tasty, substantial pub cooking often has a subtle international touch; service is well-organised and invariably polite. If the sun's out, lounge with lunch and beers in the garden before setting off for a walk near the Devon border; if it's not, you could always ask to book the skittle alley.

Food serving times
Tuesday-Saturday:
12pm-2pm, 7pm-9.30pm
Closed 25-26 December

Prices
Meals: a la carte £ 15/25

Typical Dishes
King prawns in garlic butter
Roast pollack
Gooey chocolate pot

 *6mi West of Wellington on A38 (Appley is signed). Parking.* 

71 The Red Lion Inn

Babcary TA11 7ED
Tel.: (01458)223230 – Fax: (01458)224510
Website: www.redlionbabcary.co.uk

 VISA MC AE

 **Teignworthy Reel Ale, O'Hanlon's Yellowhammer, Otter Ale**

Following a brief closure due to fire in early 2008, this attractive thatched pub has re-opened its doors with a tasteful blend of old and new. Brightly coloured paintwork and soft sofas welcome you in, leading you over flagged floors and up to the wooden bar. Big stacks of wood are piled beside the fire – this time of a more welcoming kind – and the blackboard lunch menu presents homemade snacks in the form of pies and casseroles. Bread is baked daily and come Sunday evening there is often freshly made pizza in the oven. Dinner consists of modern, contemporary dishes, made using local ingredients and with a little added flair. Lamb rump or veal cutlets might be offered alongside dishes with a more Asian influence, which come into their own on the regular curry nights. For pudding there may be strawberry crème brûlée or poached nectarines and there is always a selection of homemade ice creams.

Food serving times

Monday-Saturday:
12pm-2.30pm, 7pm-9.30pm

Sunday: 12pm-2.30pm

Closed 25 December

Prices

Meals: a la carte £ 16/22

Typical Dishes
Asparagus
Fillet of wild seabass
Rhubarb compote

4.5mi Northeast of Ilchester by A37. Parking.

72 The Three Horseshoes Inn

Batcombe BA4 6HE
Tel.: (01749)850359 – Fax: (01749)850615
Website: www.thethreehorseshoesinn.co.uk

Butcombe Bitter, Palmers Zoo, Bats in the Belfry (specially brewed)

There's nothing like knowing exactly where your food comes from and, as you enter this pub through its neat little garden, you might spot some of the sprouting seasonal vegetables, or at least get a glance at the wonderfully silky egg-providers as they root around amongst the fish pond and the summer furniture. Inside, the long low-beamed bar with its window seating, inglenook fireplace and wood burning stoves cultivates a cluttered feel; its peach walls covered in old photos of village life, plates, hanging pewter mugs and old beer bottles. The smaller snug off the main bar is the place to head if you're after a more intimate setting, but for a more formal feel, try the restaurant. Local, organic produce features highly on the menu, in the form of dishes such as shoulder of lamb or sausages and mash, but there are other lighter dishes too, and a more extensive choice in the evenings. Bedrooms are neat and simply decorated.

Food serving times

Tuesday-Saturday:
12pm-2pm, 7pm-9pm

Sunday: 12pm-2pm

Closed Sunday dinner and Monday

Prices

Meals: a la carte £ 18/30

3 rooms: £ 50/75

Typical Dishes

Home-cured duck breast

Supreme of chicken cordon bleu

Treacle sponge

Signed off the A359, midway between Castle Carey and Frome. Tucked away behind the church. Parking.

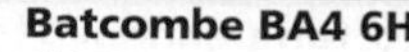

Corton Denham

73 The Queen's Arms

Corton Denham DT9 4LR
Tel.: (01963)220317
e-mail: relax@thequeensarms.com
Website: www.thequeensarms.com

Otter Bitter, Butcombe Bitter, Timothy Taylor Landlord and 2 changing guest beers

Set down twisty turny one track lanes in what seems like the middle of nowhere, this 18C stone pub can be hard to locate – but the ambience here is so informal and relaxed, your blood pressure should swiftly return to normal on arrival. The comfy firelit bar with its motley collection of stools, sofas, settles and benches, is at the pub's hub, but you can't reserve a seat here, so if you want to be sure of a meal, especially at weekends, your best bet is to book ahead for the adjacent dining room. Big on sourcing seasonal, local produce, the team here not only make their own bread but also keep pigs and chickens, with pork pies for sale at the bar. Hearty, flavoursome cooking comes in big bowls and might include lunchtime cock-a-leekie broth or steak and kidney tartlet, with dishes like pan-fried red mullet or three bean and spinach stew on offer in the evening. Bedrooms are modern and stylish with flat screen TVs and smart bathrooms.

Food serving times
Monday-Sunday:
12pm-3pm, 6pm-10pm

Prices
Meals: a la carte £ 19/26
5 rooms: £ 60/120

Typical Dishes
Pearl barley risotto
Braised pork belly
Custard tart

3mi North of Sherborne by B3145 and minor road West. Parking.

74 The Manor House Inn

Ditcheat BA4 6RB
Tel.: (01749)860276
e-mail: info@manorhouseinn.co.uk **Website:** www.manorhouseinn.co.uk

 **Butcombe, Sharps, Exmoor Ales, Otter Ales, Cottage**

Fans of the turf are well catered for – in both senses - at this characterful part 17C ex-coaching inn near Glastonbury. Not only can they tuck into the Manor House's locally renowned rustic fare, they can also sit by the windows of the bar or restaurant and watch a regular procession of horses and jockeys making its way to the local gallops. In the recently opened Sports Bar, framed silks hang proudly: Ditcheat is home to one of racing's top trainers Paul Nichols. Diners can take their pick of places to eat: apart from the flagged bar with hatch and similarly traditional dining room, there's a lawned garden for fine weather. Food covers a pretty eclectic range, from classic British staples to more modern European influenced offerings. There are pleasantly refurbished bedrooms, and an enviable setting next to the village's pretty St.Mary's church.

Food serving times

Monday-Saturday:
12pm-2pm, 7pm-9.30pm

Sunday: 12pm-2pm

Closed 25 December
and Sunday dinner

Prices

Meals: a la carte £ 18/28

3 rooms: £ 50/90

Typical Dishes

Roasted figs & Parma ham

Braised pork tenderloin

White chocolate cheesecake

4mi South of Shepton Mallet by A37 and minor road left. Parking.

Hinton St George

Lord Poulett Arms

75 Lord Poulett Arms

High St, Hinton St George TA17 8SE
Tel.: (01460)73149
e-mail: steveandmichelle@lordpoulettarms.com
Website: www.lordpoulettarms.com

Otter Ale, Branscombe, Branoc, Hopback, Cotleigh

A delightful village, full of thatched period houses, with a delightful village pub at its centre. The 17C Lord Poulett Arms – family motto; Keep the Faith – really does lie at the heart of the community of Hinton-St-George, and you'll find locals, having popped over for a pint before dinner, propping up the bar, while their dogs reacquaint themselves down below. The welcome is warm, as is the atmosphere, and the three main dining rooms are full of character, with open fires, exposed brickwork and solid stone and bare wood floors. The menu offers seasonal cooking made with best local ingredients and dishes might, for example, involve mackerel or scallops from Dorset and pork or lamb from Somerset, with herbs from the pub's own garden. A great selection of real ales and chatty service from local staff complete the picture, unless you are also staying the night, in which case, you'll find the bedrooms are luxurious.

Food serving times

Monday-Sunday:
12pm-2pm, 7pm-9pm

Closed 26 December and 1 January

Prices

Meals: a la carte £ 19/28

4 rooms: £ 59/88

Typical Dishes

Cornish mussels
Glazed pork belly
Molten chocolate tart

1mi North West of Crewkerne by minor road. Parking.

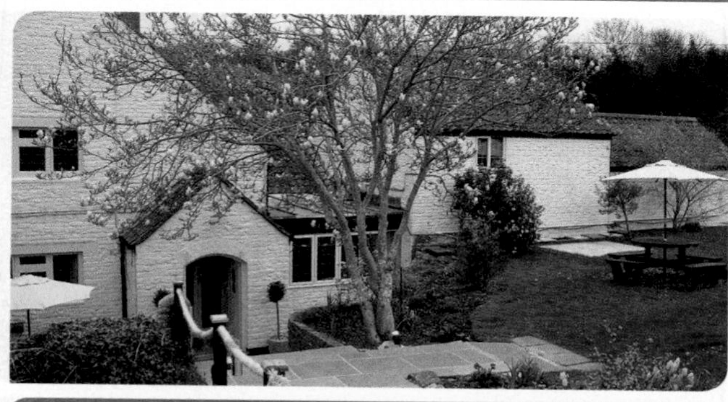

76 The Kings Arms

Litton,
Chewton Mendip BA3 4PW
Tel.: (01761)241301 – Fax: (01761)241301
e-mail: info@thekingsarmslitton.co.uk **Website:** www.thekingsarmslitton.co.uk

 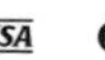  

 **IPA, Morland**

The third venture for a young company, this pub has seen no expense spared, as it sports a refurbished interior of carefully co-ordinated rustic/chic décor good enough to step straight out of any magazine. Backing onto the Chew River, this sizeable property is blessed with plenty of space both indoors and outdoors and there are plenty of tables to choose from; maybe a seat at the piano, in the garden terrace booths or at the extra long Chef's table – although you'll have to book for this privilege. The philosophy here is all about fun; you can have board games brought to your table, while BBQs, tasting menus, wine and music events are all in the pipeline. Cooking ranges from British classics to sharing plates, and is confident, unfussy and generous. If you fancy a challenge try the Kings sandwich and if your meal doesn't already come with it, ask the bright, cheery staff for a slice or two of the freshly baked bread that's on display.

Food serving times

Monday-Saturday:
12pm-3pm, 6pm-10pm

Sunday: 12pm-5pm

Prices

Meals: a la carte £ 20/35

Typical Dishes

Deep fried pigs ears
Braised shoulder of lamb
Rhubarb crumble

North of Chewton Mendip : 1m on B3114

77 The Devonshire Arms

Long Sutton TA10 9LP
Tel.: (01458)241271 – Fax: (01458)241037
e-mail: mail@thedevonshirearms.com **Website:** www.thedevonshirearms.com

 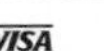 VISA MC

Teignworthy Reel Ale, Exmoor Classic, Cheddar Ales Potholer, Bath Ale Spa

While it appears grand and traditional from the outside, this creeper-clad hunting lodge could not be more contemporary on the inside. Spacious rooms feature mellow lighting, high-backed leather chairs and informally laid light-wood tables, with the striking décor creating a truly modern feel. This extends through to the spacious bedrooms, where rattan furniture sits nicely alongside coir flooring and neutral shades. You can eat in the bar, the restaurant, on the front terrace overlooking the green or in the large back garden, although here it may take a little longer for the serving team to reach you. There's a good value set menu or a light bites selection at lunch, with a concise but more substantial à la carte following in the evening. French and British influences prevail, with the occasional Asian touch creeping in. Signature dishes include crab crème brûlée and fillet of West Country beef, with homemade ice cream to follow.

Food serving times

Monday-Sunday:
12pm-2.30pm, 7pm-9.30pm

Closed 25 December, 1 January

Prices

Meals: a la carte £ 21/35

9 rooms: £ 70/130

Typical Dishes
Crab crème brûlée
Belly pork
Ricotta mousse

4mi East of Langport by A372. Parking.

78 The Pilgrims at Lovington

Lovington BA7 7PT
Tel.: (01963)240597
e-mail: jools@thepilgrimsatlovington.co.uk
Website: www.thepilgrimsatlovington.co.uk

  VISA MC AE

 **Cottage Champflower**

The Pilgrims in the pub's name were, according to legend, those who searched for King Arthur's Tomb; Lovington being the last stop before they entered the hazardous marshlands at Glastonbury Abbey. Modern day wayfarers would also do well to stop here: although unremarkable in outward appearance, this pub's charming interior more than makes up for it. The bar, strewn with cookbooks, gives way to a light, fresh restaurant, and the single sitting policy encourages you to linger over dinner. Their motto "the pub that thinks it's a restaurant," gives a hint of what to expect food wise: a British/Mediterranean menu which uses only regional produce, including meat from local farms, home-grown vegetables and West Country cheese. The old cider barn now houses comfortable, contemporary bedrooms with luxurious walk-in showers and roll-top baths. Substantial breakfasts often include homemade bread, hot specials and a full-English cooked to order.

Food serving times

Tuesday: 7pm-9pm

Wednesday-Saturday: 12pm-2pm, 7pm-9pm

Sunday: 12pm-2pm

Prices

Meals: a la carte £ 17/38

5 rooms: £ 110

Typical Dishes
Smoked eel & bacon
Seabass on pesto mash
6 local cheeses

4mi South West of Castle Cary by B3153. Parking

England • South West • Somerset

79 The Vobster Inn

Lower Vobster BA3 5RJ

Tel.: (01373)812920 – Fax: (01373)812920

e-mail: info@vobsterinn.co.uk **Website:** www.vobsterinn.co.uk

Butcombe Bitter, Butcombe Blonde and 1 guest ale such as Blind Man's Best Cellar

Very much the centre of its tiny Somerset village, the Vobster Inn, run by a husband and wife team, takes its duty seriously and does its best to keep everyone happy, from young families and older couples, out enjoying the sun at the terrace tables, to the unhurried neighbours enjoying a slow pint inside. Adjoining the bar, a long lounge serves as the restaurant, its walls painted with grapes and lined with posters, labels, wine racks and even old wine cases. Sensibly allowing room for market-fresh specials, fish and seafood are always on the menu and there's always a good selection of hand-crafted West Country cheeses on offer.

Food serving times

Monday-Saturday:
12pm-2pm, 6.30pm-9pm

Sunday: 12pm-2pm

Closed 25 December

- Seafood -

Prices

Meals: a la carte £ 18/26

Typical Dishes

Breast of pigeon

Roast fillet of megrim

Limoncello cheesecake

From Frome head northwest to Radstock on the A362. Vobster is signposted approx 5.5mi off the A362. Parking.

80 The Royal Oak Inn of Luxborough

Exmoor National Park, Luxborough TA23 0SH
Tel.: (01984)640319 – Fax: (01984)641561
e-mail: info@theroyaloakinnluxborough.co.uk
Website: www.theroyaloakinnluxborough.co.uk

 **Cotleigh Tawny, Palmers IPA, Exmoor Gold, Exmoor Stag, Butcombe**

Set in a secluded wooded valley between the Brendon and Croyden Hills, the beautiful landscapes of Luxborough are a well kept secret. Passing through this peaceful countryside is the Coleridge Way, a walk that follows the routes that the romantic poet took when drawing inspiration for some of his greatest works. The Exmoor Park authorities are understandably reluctant to put up signs, so it can be tricky finding this red sandstone pub, but it's definitely worth the search; just follow the local hunt. The seasonal menu offers substantial dishes of classically prepared, boldly flavoured foods and despite an international edge to the cooking, focuses on quality, local ingredients: Exmoor meat and Cornish seafood create dishes such as grilled sardines, steamed mussels, slow roasted belly of pork or pan-fried lamb's liver with bacon. Bedrooms are compact but charming and each comes with its own teddy bear. Room 14 has its own terrace.

Food serving times
Monday-Sunday:
12pm-2pm, 7pm-9pm
Closed 25 December

Prices
Meals: a la carte £ 18/28
11 rooms: £ 55/100

Typical Dishes
Filo basket of Brie
Crab and coriander strudel
Deep-fried ice cream

Luxborough is signed off A39 East of Minehead or off B3224 Exford to Taunton road. Parking

England • South West • Somerset

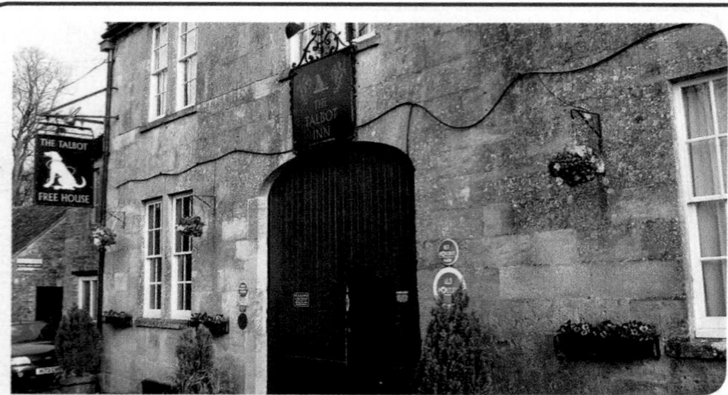

81 The Talbot Inn

Selwood St,
Mells BA11 3PN

Tel.: (01373)812254 – Fax: (01373)813599
e-mail: enquiries@talbotinn.com **Website:** www.talbotinn.com

 **Butcombe Real Ales**

As you would hope when you discover that it's owned by the Earl of Oxford and Asquith, this 15C coaching inn immediately creates an impression. Entering via a large archway you cross a cobbled courtyard and pass a secluded terrace with a vine-covered pergola, before being given the choice of two doors; whichever you choose will lead you to an atmospheric dining room, where candles flicker and low beamed ceilings are hung with hops. In line with the décor, the cooking takes on a true country style: it's reliable and robust, featuring generous portions and well-established flavours. With one menu for meat and another for fish, the chef is rightly proud of the variety offered, especially since everything from rolls to ice creams is homemade. The fact that people without bookings are often turned away, even on a Monday, is a testament to the quality of the cooking. Bedrooms are classical, some a little modest: ask for the Manor Suite.

Food serving times

Monday-Sunday:
12pm-2pm, 7pm-9pm

Closed 25 December

Prices

Meals: £ 13 (lunch)
and a la carte £ 20/30

8 rooms: £ 75/145

Typical Dishes

Grilled scallops

Breast & confit leg of duck

Hot lemon meringue pie

 *4mi West of Frome. Parking.* 

82 The Camelot

Chapel Rd,
South Cadbury BA22 7EX
Tel.: (01963)440448 – Fax: (01963)440301
e-mail: info@thecamelotpub.co.uk **Website:** www.thecamelotpub.co.uk

Yeovil Ales Summerset, Wadworth 6X, Horizon, JCB, Henry's, Otter, Cheddar Ales, Butcombe, Cottage

This creeper-clad village pub is so named because a hill in Cadbury is allegedly the original site of King Arthur's Camelot. It may be true, it may not, but one thing's for sure…good food here is no myth. Okay, so you might not be eating at a round table, and you may not feel any mystical vibes, but there are plenty of hearty dishes to choose from. The bar menu offers traditional British favourites like steak and ale pie, lamb hotpot or cod and chips, while on the à la carte, you can take your pick from dishes such as cassoulet, mussels, salmon, duck or steak; all precisely cooked, using locally sourced produce. There's a light, airy, uncluttered ambience about the place, enhanced by stylish local artwork on the walls, and while modish wood tables are dotted about and laid for eating, there's still plenty of space for locals and walkers who've stopped off en route to enjoy a pint of real ale.

Food serving times
Monday-Sunday:
12pm-2.30pm, 7pm-9.30pm

Prices
Meals: a la carte £ 15/20

Typical Dishes
Crispy aromatic duck salad
Pan-fried pork tenderloin
Camelot cheese plate

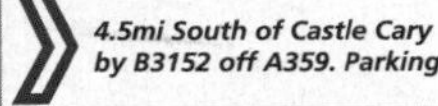

4.5mi South of Castle Cary by B3152 off A359. Parking.

83 Tarr Farm Inn

Tarr Steps TA22 9PY
Tel.: (01643)851507 – Fax: (01643)851111
e-mail: enquiries@tarrfarm.co.uk
Website: www.tarrfarm.co.uk

 **Exmoor Ale, Exmoor Gold**

At 55m in length and with 17 spans, Tarr Steps is one of Britain's finest clapper bridges. It dates back to around 1000 BC and, according to local legend, was built by the devil in order to win a bet. Here, in the idyllic Exmoor countryside, you'll find Tarr Farm Inn, a true destination pub, run by a highly regarded team who can't do enough for you. There's seating for every occasion, so you can have afternoon tea outside, lunch by the bar and dinner in the restaurant. Lunch ranges from sandwiches to a hearty three courses, while the evening menu displays some more ambitious choices. This might include char-grilled Devon sirloin steak, rack of Exmoor lamb with sweetbreads and ratatouille or pan-fried Cornish sea bass with cockles and clams. Bedrooms are elegant and luxurious, providing every conceivable extra and a fine breakfast. Judy is happy to organise a range of outdoor activities and even takes guests walking or riding herself.

Food serving times

Monday-Sunday:
12pm-2.30pm,
6.30pm-9.30pm

Closed 1-13 February

Bar lunch

Prices

Meals: a la carte £ 15/28

9 rooms: £ 75/150

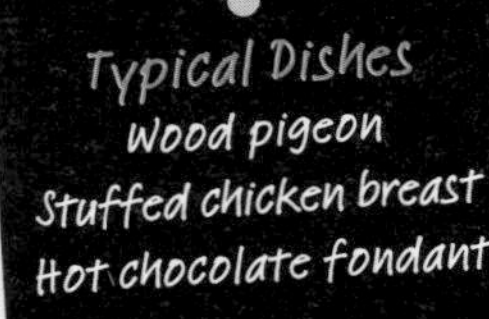

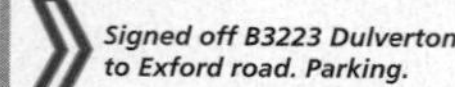

Signed off B3223 Dulverton to Exford road. Parking.

84 The Rising Sun Inn

West Bagborough TA4 3EF
Tel.: (01823)432575
e-mail: jon@therisingsun.info **Website:** www.therisingsun.info

  AE

 **Exmoor and 2 guest ales**

Having previously survived a fire that raged through the surrounding hillside, the future of this inn was once again in the hands of the gods when it went into receivership. Its prospects were secured, however, when white knights appeared in the form of Jon and Christine Brinkman, an ambitious, experienced couple with no fear of hard work and dedication. In a few months they turned the place around and they continue to work towards re-establishing this pub as the hub of the village; even the self-playing piano is a part of the collective experience. If you're feeling peckish then you will be pleased to find a good balance of traditional and modern dishes on the menu, each crafted from local ingredients and presented with an obvious element of care. Around you a seamless mix of wood and slate creates a warm, intimate atmosphere and you rest assured that with this couple at the helm, the Sun will continue to rise more brightly every day.

Food serving times
Monday-Sunday:
12pm-2pm, 6.30pm-9.30pm

Prices
Meals: a la carte £ 14/25
2 rooms: £ 55/85

Typical Dishes
Confit of duckling
Fillet of beef
Warm chocolate brownie

10.5mi North West of Taunton off A358. Parking in the road.

England • South West • Somerset

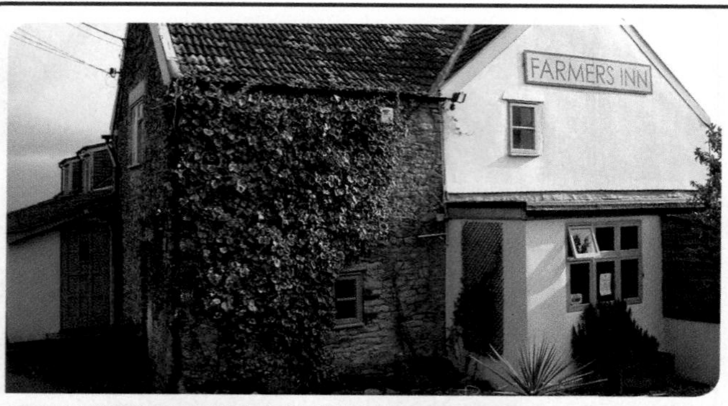

85 The Farmers Inn

Higher West Hatch, Taunton TA3 5RS
Tel.: (01823)480480 – Fax: (01823)481177
e-mail: letsgostay@farmersinnwesthatch.co.uk
Website: www.farmersinnwesthatch.co.uk

  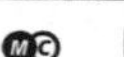

 **Otter Ale, Exmoor Ale, Branscombe Vale, Tawny**

Having been owned in the 1930s by an ex-Met policeman, this soft-stone inn became one of the area's first nightclubs in the 1970s and one wonders what Mr Cridge, the 1906 landlord whose picture takes pride of place in the bar, would have made of it all. Today, you will find the welcoming owners serving local ales and ciders (one home-brewed) behind a timber-framed bar. The traditional snack menu and the monthly-changing lunch and dinner menus are created using local ingredients, including produce from the neighbouring dairy farm. Dishes are modern British and European in their roots; flavoursome but with the occasional tendency towards over-ambition. Five individually designed bedrooms harbour antique furniture, sumptuous fabrics, magnificent bathrooms and luxuries to rival any top hotel. One has its own courtyard, another has French doors into the gardens and most have sitting areas and views across the Somerset levels.

Food serving times

Monday-Friday:
12pm-2pm, 7pm-9pm

Saturday-Sunday:
12pm-2pm, 7pm-9.30pm

Prices

Meals: £ 14 (lunch)
and a la carte £ 20/29

5 rooms: £ 70/140

Typical Dishes

Quail egg salad
Artichoke tartlet
Rich chocolate cake

5mi South East of Taunton by A358

86 The Red Lion Inn

Axford SN8 2HA
Tel.: (01672)520271
e-mail: info@redlionaxford.com **Website:** www.redlionaxford.com

Axford Ale, Good ol' Boy and guest ale

A pleasant drive through the countryside leads you to this Victorian-fronted flint and red-brick pub, with views over the river Kennet to the hills beyond. The convivial owner and his loyal serving team welcome you into a warm and friendly atmosphere, where high attention to detail sees candles and vases of flowers on cloth covered tables. To view the various blackboard menus you have to wander around the room: there's one for starters, another for mains and a third dedicated solely to seafood. The chef, who has worked here since the age of 12, shares the owner's passion for classic recipes and straightforward presentation. Fish and game are his specialties and he's flexible when it comes to special dietary requirements. The overriding ethos of this pub is that dining should be an enjoyable experience, so they provide a single sitting in which you are encouraged to linger over your meal. Special events include a popular pie fortnight.

Food serving times

Monday-Saturday:
12pm-2pm, 7pm-9pm

Sunday: 12pm-2pm

Closed 25 December

Prices

Meals: a la carte £ 20/28

Typical Dishes

Duck breast & livers
Wild venison Wellington
Cheesecake

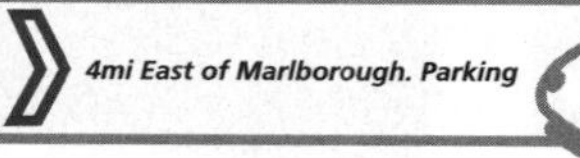

4mi East of Marlborough. Parking

87 The Royal Oak

Cues Lane, Bishopstone SN6 8PP
Tel.: (01793)790481
e-mail: royaloak@helenbrowningorganics.co.uk
Website: www.helenbrowningorganics.co.uk

Moonlight, Arkell 2B, Arkells 3B

Tucked away in a quiet village this pub may not appear to be anything out of the ordinary, but once inside the pleasant country atmosphere and excellent food say otherwise. Taken over in 2006 by organic crusader Helen Browning, it has definitely fallen into the right hands: "local", "organic" and "fair-trade" are the buzz words and a great deal of consideration is given to their carbon footprint. With produce coming from Helen's nearby farm and other small suppliers just down the road, the constantly evolving menu relies on the latest seasonal produce to inform its content, which makes a refreshing change from the usual pub format. Cooking is classic and British but dishes still manage to remain creative, thanks to the chef taking the simplest of recipes and injecting his own techniques: the dying art of curing being one of his particular passions. One thing's for sure, this pub is a real find, a gem in the Wiltshire countryside.

Food serving times
Monday-Sunday:
12pm-2.30pm, 6pm-9pm

Prices
Meals: a la carte £ 18/30
2 rooms: £ 45

Typical Dishes
Devizes pie
Monkfish & chips
Cider jelly trifle

5mi South West of Salisbury by A354 and minor road West

88 The Northey

Bath Road,
Box SN13 8AE
Tel.: (01225)742333
e-mail: office@ohhcompany.co.uk **Website:** www.ohhcompany.co.uk

   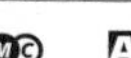

 **Wadworth 6X, Wadworth IPA**

The traditional exterior of this family-run, roadside pub, a few miles from Bath, is in stark contrast to the modern Mediterranean styling to be found on the inside. Large leather sofas and outsized barrel-tables provide lounge space for drinkers, but the majority of the pub is set aside for diners and the oft-changing menu seems to take its inspiration from the décor, offering a blend of Mediterranean and British cooking. Choose from dishes such as Italian platter, Greek salad with calamari or moules marinière; pan-fried calves liver, fillet steak, and haddock and chips. Bread is made on the premises daily and vegetarians will be particularly happy with the recently extended selection of dishes just for them. For those with a musical bent, there's live jazz every other week; a reminder, perhaps, of the days when it was run by Maisie Gay, a music hall artist, and frequented by Noel Coward and friends.

Food serving times
Monday-Sunday:
12pm-2.30pm, 6pm-9.30pm
Closed 25 December

Prices
Meals: a la carte £ 20/35

Typical Dishes
Tempura crab
Tuna fillet & braised fennel
Crème brûlée

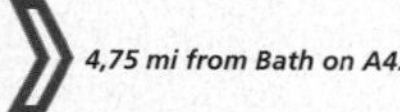
4,75 mi from Bath on A4. Parking.

89 The Ship Inn

Burcombe Lane,
Burcombe SP2 0EJ
Tel.: (01722)743182
e-mail: theshipburcombe@mail.com **Website:** www.theshipburcombe.co.uk

  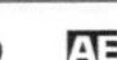

 **Wadworth 6X, Courage Best, Butcombe Bitter**

Watch your footing on the way in, as the steps go straight down from the door. Once safely seated you'll find everything is shipshape, with modern furniture blending nicely with old wooden beams and the sun streaming in through the many windows. The real selling point here has to be the beautiful riverside garden but you may have to compete to get a spot in the summer. When it comes to the food they really push the boat out, with the chef leaving his own mark on every dish, be it at the recipe stage or in the creative presentation. The cooking is a mixture of British and Mediterranean, arriving artistically in large white bowls or on slate tiles, and being generous in size and flavour. At lunch, the light bites menu offers something for everyone, while the seasonal evening menu and twice-daily blackboard specials play host to more substantial dishes; maybe rosemary crusted rack of lamb or Pollock fillet with lemon and parsley.

Food serving times
Monday-Saturday:
12pm-2.30pm, 6pm-9pm
Sunday:
12pm-2.30pm, 6.30pm-9pm
Closed first 2 weeks January

Prices
Meals: a la carte £ 19/30

Typical Dishes
Sautéed chicken livers
Rack of lamb
Vanilla & caramel cheesecake

5,25 mi West of Salisbury by the A36 off A30. Parking.

90 The Horse and Groom

The Street,
Charlton SN16 9DL
Tel.: (01666)823904
e-mail: info@horseandgroominn.com **Website:** www.horseandgroominn.com

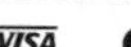

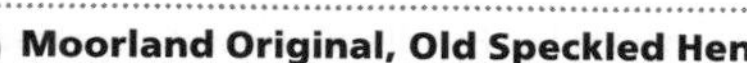

Moorland Original, Old Speckled Hen

It's a lazy summer's day, the birds are singing, there's not a cloud in the sky and you are relaxing in the neatly-kept garden of this 16C Cotswold stone pub; what could be better – an outside bar maybe? Which, coincidently, this pub just happens to have. It's not just in the fine weather that this pub draws the crowds; a sympathetic renovation has provided a smart restaurant and a warm, welcoming bar, where there is always a convivial atmosphere. Featuring local, seasonal ingredients – many from within 40 miles – the menu displays everything from Ploughman's and platters to British pub classics and some more contemporary dishes. Every weekday there's a "Let's do Lunch" set menu and the flexible kitchen staff host special events throughout the week: Tuesday is "Ladies Night", while Fridays are set aside for the locals. Bedrooms are stylish and beautifully appointed, with sumptuous bathrooms, fine toiletries and complimentary wi-fi.

Food serving times
Monday-Saturday:
12pm-2.30pm,
6.30pm-9.30pm
Sunday: 12pm-3pm

Prices
Meals: £ 15 (lunch)
and a la carte £ 17/30
5 rooms: £ 80/90

Typical Dishes
Pan-roast scallop salad
Roast Cotswold chicken breast
Glazed lemon tart

2mi north of Malmesbury by B4040. Parking.

Codford St Mary

91 The George

High St,
Codford Saint Mary BA12 0NG
Tel.: (01985)850270
Website: www.thegeorgecodford.co.uk

Timothy Taylor Landlord, Fuller's London Pride, Stargazer, Hidden Guest, Ringwood Best, Hidden Pint

After an evening of cultural delights at the Woolstone Theatre, cross over the road to this 18C black and white pub. Unspectacular in appearance, it is occupied largely by the locals who have discovered its strength – the food – and chat cheerily at the bar. The chef has a long-established history in the area and together with his protégé they pull out all the stops in the kitchen; classic pub recipes to keep the locals happy and some more ambitious dishes, which go down well with the visitors. For starters you might find caramelised goat's cheese with pineapple and chilli chutney, followed by local pheasant and ale casserole or loin of pork with roast pear and black pudding; then treacle and raspberry jam tart with Earl Grey syrup to finish. Bedrooms do not meet the same high standards as the cooking but whatever the pub may lack in décor and furnishings, it definitely makes up for with talent in the kitchen.

Food serving times

Monday and Wednesday-Saturday:
12pm-2pm, 6.30pm-9pm

Sunday: 12pm-2pm

Prices

Meals: a la carte £ 20/34

Typical Dishes

Rillette of Guinea fowl

Seared loin of local venison

Treacle & raspberry tart

8mi South East of Warminster by A36. Parking.

92 The Potting Shed

The Street,
Crudwell SN16 9EW
Tel.: (01666)577833
Website: www.therectoryhotel.com

Timothy Taylor Landlord, Butcombe Bitter, Bath Gem

Much to the delight of the villagers, the new owners have transformed this previously rough and ready local into a classic country dining pub, with soft candle lighting and a relaxed atmosphere. Situated just across the road from its sister establishment, The Rectory Hotel, its name is an allusion to the large garden beds planted with organic herbs and vegetables at its rear; inside, the gardening theme continues, with features such as trowel door knobs and wheelbarrow lights. The kitchen provides a rustic, seasonal menu which gets to the heart of proper pub cooking; there's nothing fancy here, just well-flavoured, wholesome dishes like sausage and mash or fish and chips, served in generous portions. Puddings display a more adventurous streak - if you've chosen the liquorice ice cream be prepared to leave with a black tongue. Your four-legged friends won't go hungry either, thanks to the thoughtfully provided jar of biscuits on the bar.

Food serving times

Monday-Saturday:
12pm-2.30pm, 7pm-9.30pm

Sunday: 12pm-2.30pm

Prices

Meals: a la carte £ 25/40

Typical Dishes

Baked egg & soldiers

Seabass, confit chicken & fennel

Chocolate brownie

4mi North of Malmesbury by A429

Donhead St Andrew

93 Forester Inn

Lower Street,
Donhead St Andrew SP7 9EE
Tel.: (01747)828038 – Fax: (01747)828038
e-mail: possums1@btinternet.com

   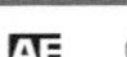 

 **Butcombe, Ringwood Best, Butts**

A thatched, 13C pub set in a charming Wiltshire village, with rustic charm galore in the form of exposed stone walls, wood floors and large inglenook fireplaces. Sup on a pint of real ale alongside the locals in the characterful, beamed bar; then depending on your mood and that of the weather, you can either remain here to eat, dine under the vaulted ceiling in the open plan extension, or go al fresco out on the terrace. Cooking is modern British in style, with influences from the Mediterranean and Asia; fish makes quite an appearance and you can expect to see seafood platters aplenty come summer. The menu changes daily but might include dishes such as tempura prawns and Thai style crab cake or pan-fried foie gras on toasted brioche to start, and roasted Cornish hake, veal Milanese or crisp belly of pork to follow, with locally sourced artisan cheeses a treat with which to finish.

Food serving times

Monday-Saturday:
12pm-3pm, 6.30pm-9.30pm

Sunday: 12pm-3pm

Prices

Meals: £ 17 (lunch)
and a la carte £ 17/30

Typical Dishes

Seared Scottish scallops
Chump of local lamb
Vanilla crème brûlée

5mi East of Shaftesbury by A30.
Parking.

94 The Angel Inn

High St,
Heytesbury BA12 0ED
Tel.: (01985)840330 – Fax: (01985)840931
e-mail: admin@theangelheytesbury.co.uk **Website:** www.theangelheytesbury.co.uk

 **Bath Gem, Greene King IPA, Olde Trip**

A former landlord of the Angel was apparently once heard to say that he caught the sound of Lawrence of Arabia's motorcycle speeding away as he left Heytesbury House en route to his home at Clouds Hill Cottage and his fatal accident. No-one knows the truth but as a stalwart of the village, this pub must have many such stories to tell. Organised around a central bar, the lounge and dining areas display an eclectic mix of wooden beams, exposed brickwork and bright, bold colours, leading into an idyllic courtyard. The menu may be concise but the food is anything but, with sizeable well-hung steaks from the nearby farm or Castle Brae in Scotland, and large sharing boards that might include whole baked sea bass, crispy belly of pork or braised shoulder of lamb. It's enough to challenge any appetite but do not be defeated, a selection of English classics are to follow, maybe apple crumble, sticky toffee or bread and butter pudding.

Food serving times

Tuesday-Thursday:
12pm-2.30pm, 7pm-9.30pm

Friday-Saturday:
12pm-2.30pm, 6pm-10pm

Sunday: 12pm-8pm

Closed 25 December
for food

Prices

Meals: a la carte £ 25/45

Typical Dishes
Dorset crab cakes
Brown trout
Rhubarb & custard

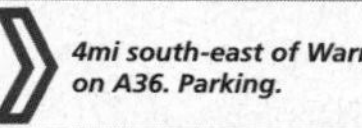

4mi south-east of Warminster on A36. Parking.

95 The Lamb Inn

High St,
Hindon SP3 6DP
Tel.: (01747)820573 – Fax: (01747)820605
e-mail: info@lambathindon.co.uk

 **Charles Wells Bombardier, Young's Bitter, Deuchars IPA**

Country cousin to two London establishments, this pub is part of the Boisdale group, paying tribute to the Outer Hebridean port of the same name. From the outside this is a classic English inn, but inside, the rich red décor, dark wood tables, log fires and tartan carpets are unmistakeably Scottish; walk through the bar you almost expect to find a row of moose heads lining the walls. As you might anticipate, haggis and smoked salmon are always on the menu, with the celebrated Boisdale beef burger, a selection of British classics and some Mediterranean blackboard specials alongside. Produce is predominantly local or, of course, from Scotland. In the centre of the room locals crowd around the bar but they are happy to make a path so that visitors can access the impressive selection of whiskies that it holds. The Scottish theme is continued in the bedrooms, where traditional country-style décor and furnishings abound.

Food serving times
Monday-Sunday:
12pm-2.30pm,
6.30pm-9.30pm

Prices
Meals: a la carte £ 25/30
17 rooms: £ 70

Typical Dishes
South Uist king scallops
Wiltshire sirloin steak
Lemon posset

12mi west of Wilton by A30 on B3089. Parking.

96 The Tollgate Inn

Ham Green,
Holt BA14 6PX
Tel.: (01225)782326 – Fax: (01225)782805
e-mail: alison@tollgateholt.co.uk **Website:** www.tollgateholt.co.uk

  MC

 **Box Brewery, Sharps of Cornwall, Goffs of Gloucester, Hopback, Exmoor**

With beautiful hanging baskets alive with colour, a warm, friendly ambience and cosy décor, it's easy to see why this pub is popular with locals and visitors alike. In the bar area you can settle in beside the fire with a newspaper or feed the affections of Bella the resident cat, before climbing the stairs to the dining room – once a chapel – where the building's original windows are still on display. The traditional British cooking features well-honed recipes and plenty of local produce. At lunch there is a keenly-priced set menu and a selection of tried and tested "light bites", including dishes such as eggs Benedict or smoked kippers. In the evening this moves on to a more substantial à la carte, where there are plenty of good meaty dishes and complimentary sides of vegetables and potatoes – a pleasant rarity in modern times. Bedrooms are cosy and thoughtfully appointed, displaying fresh flowers, fridges and complimentary wi-fi.

Food serving times

Tuesday-Saturday:
12pm-2pm, 7pm-9pm

Sunday: 12pm-2pm

Closed 25 December and 1 January

Prices

Meals: £ 14 (3 course lunch) and a la carte £ 23/30

4 rooms: £ 50/100

Typical Dishes
Confit of duck
Pan-fried skate wing
Tollgate dessert plate

On B3107 midway between Bradford-on-Avon and Melksham. Parking.

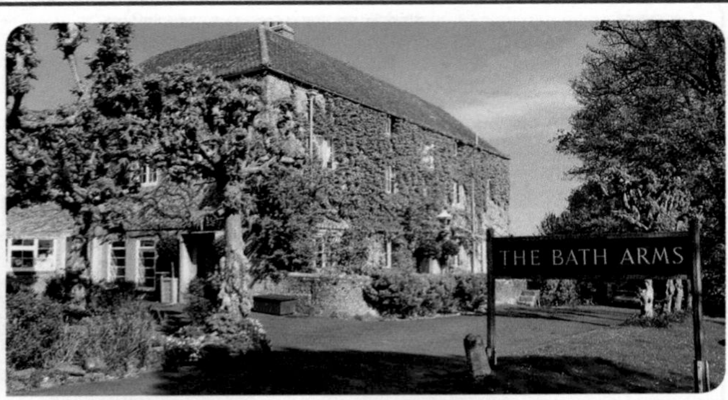

97 The Bath Arms

Longleat,
Horningsham BA12 7LY

Tel.: (01985)844308 – Fax: (01985)845187
e-mail: enquiries@batharms.co.uk **Website:** www.batharms.co.uk

Inspectors' favourites

 **Horningsham Pride, Golden Apostle**

After a day out in the parklands of the Longleat Estate, dine under the watchful eye of Lord Bath in this stylish pub, where specially commissioned paintings of the flamboyant aristocrat adorn the walls. The modern British menu uses seasonal ingredients and features daily-changing dishes presented in an honest, straightforward manner. The chef admirably rises to the challenge of sourcing all produce from within 50 miles: meat from Longleat, Stourhead and Cranborne, fish from Brixham and St. Mawes, and even local organic vodka. Choose from the bar menu, which might include confit of duck leg or pork belly, or the 3 course dinner menu, which may feature grilled brill or braised lamb shank; all meals are accompanied by excellent fresh bread. The uniquely designed bedrooms are colourful and eclectic; try the vibrant, eccentric Flashman room, or the sumptuous Peacock room. The latest addition, a beauty treatment room, is also worth a visit.

Food serving times

Sunday-Thursday:
12pm-2.30pm, 7pm-9pm

Friday-Saturday:
12pm-2.30pm, 7pm-9.30pm

Prices

Meals: £ 16/30
and a la carte £ 14/30

15 rooms: £ 70/145

Typical Dishes

Seared scallops
Rolled saddle of rabbit
Coconut pannacotta

3mi South West of Warminster by A362 and minor road

98 The Millstream

Marden SN10 3RH
Tel.: (01380)848308 – Fax: (01380)848337
e-mail: info@the-millstream.net
Website: www.the-millstream.net

6X, IPA, Horizon Bishop Tipple

A charming pub decorated in a delightfully eye-catching style, with chic country furnishings, antique tables and plenty to keep you entertained between courses; the level of detail a fine reflection of the owners' passion for the place. Lights twinkle, cards and ceramics are for sale, glossy magazines are scattered about and chairs piled high with cookery books, while Oscar Wilde quotations and fine paintings punctuate the wall space. Food here is freshly prepared, using quality local and seasonal ingredients, and the traditional pub dishes come with contemporary influences and a French edge. Champagne is available by the glass, a blackboard informs you of upcoming events - perhaps opera, a hog roast or a picnic - and there are plans in the pipeline for a cookery school and a takeaway menu. The motto at The Millstream is "live a little, drink a little, laugh a lot," and to this might well be added "eat a little or a lot, but eat well."

Food serving times

Tuesday-Saturday:
12pm-3pm, 6.30pm-9.30pm

Closed Monday except Bank Holidays and Sunday

Prices

Meals: £ 16 (lunch)
and a la carte £ 25/36

Typical Dishes

Pigeon salad
Roast loin of pork
Chocolate caramel tart

6.5mi Southeast of Devizes by A342 and minor road North. Parking.

England • South West • Wiltshire

99 The Wheatsheaf at Oaksey

Wheatsheaf Lane,
Oaksey SN16 9TB
Tel.: (01666)577348
e-mail: info@thecompletechef.co.uk **Website:** www.thecompletechef.co.uk

 **Hook Norton, Hooky Bitter, English Rose, Bath Gem, Longbarrow**

Dating back several hundred years, this Cotswold-stone building still shows evidence of its historic roots: above the fire is a lintel reputed to be made from a Roman coffin lid and carved crosses – allegedly to ward off witches – adorn the wooden beams and chimney. The original woodwork and features help the bar retain its traditional character, whilst the crash of skittles and falling dominoes create a homely feel. It is a hit with the locals, who like to linger by the fire with a pint or partake in the pub quiz but there is also a strong emphasis on food, in the bar and the more contemporary rear dining room. The constantly evolving blackboard menu relies on good flavours and simple techniques, offering traditional, heart-warming dishes: mains may include wholesome casseroles or cassoulets, with bread and butter pudding or crumble to follow. Water is presented in old Bombay Sapphire bottles, a unique gesture towards eco friendliness.

Food serving times

Tuesday-Saturday:
12pm-2pm, 6.30pm-9pm

Sunday: 12pm-2pm

Closed Sunday dinner and Monday

Prices

Meals: a la carte £ 20/25

Typical Dishes

Fish pie and salad
Line-caught pollack
Dark chocolate fondant

5.5mi North of Malmesbury; signed from A429. Parking.

100 The Bell

The Square,
Ramsbury SN8 2PE
Tel.: (01672)520230 – Fax: (01672)520832
e-mail: jeremy@thebellramsbury.com **Website:** www.thebellramsbury.com

Ramsbury Brewery : Bell Bitter, Ramsbury Gold, Chalk Stream

Last year saw this Victorian veteran taken over by new owners and a revamp begun; and the locals seem well and truly won over by its new menus and friendly atmosphere. This black and white pub has two distinct sides to it; the bar with its open fire, country scene prints and soft sofas, and the long dining room with its polished wood tables and eye-catching abstract artwork. The bar is the busier side of the establishment, and although you can dine here – or out on the small cobbled terrace - most people choose to eat in the dining room. Lunchtime sandwiches and bar bites are available, whilst the British-themed à la carte provides enough choice to render its side orders all but redundant. Cooking make good use of local produce and while classical dishes might include homemade sausages or fish cakes, other mains could include sea trout, lamb or venison. The young staff are polite - but a little more enthusiasm would not go amiss.

Food serving times

Monday-Saturday:
12pm-2.30pm, 7pm-9.30pm

Sunday: 12pm-2.30pm

Closed 25 December

Prices

Meals: £ 17/22
and a la carte £ 20/35

Typical Dishes

Crayfish
Roast Wiltshire venison
Baked ginger parkin

4mi Northwest of Hungerford by B4192 and minor road West. Parking.

101 The George & Dragon

High Street,
Rowde SN10 2PN
Tel.: (01380)723053
e-mail: thegandd@tiscali.co.uk **Website:** www.thegeorgeanddragonrowde.co.uk

  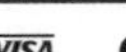

 **Butcombe Bitter, Ringwood 49er, Sharps Doom Bar, Bath Ales, Nicks Bitter, Fuller's London Pride, Wadworths, Kilmington**

When the current owners took over in 2004 they had a hard act to follow, but they admirably rose to the challenge and are now comfortably settled in. Bringing with them London experience and lots of charm, their mission was to inject life and energy into the laid-back countryside, which they seem to have done: their regular village events, including quiz nights, monthly summer BBQs and wine and cheese evenings are extremely popular. Early every morning a fresh catch of fish arrives on the doorstep from St. Mawes and the excellent fish specials are created from whatever is in the box that day. Alongside this, the main menu features a selection of comforting British classics, available in two sizes, which may include devilled lamb's kidneys or rack of lamb: which, in the winter, can be taken by a huge stone-housed fire. If you're feeling weary, the uniquely styled, well-equipped, trendy-meets-old-world bedrooms are not to be missed.

Food serving times
Monday-Friday:
12pm-3pm, 7pm-11pm
Saturday:
12pm-4pm, 6.30pm-11pm
Sunday: 12pm-4pm
Closed 25-26 December
Seafood

Prices
Meals: £ 16 (lunch)
and a la carte £ 24/45
3 rooms: £ 85/105

Typical Dishes
Char-grilled scallops
Roast monkfish
Santiago torte

2mi north-west of Devizes by A361 on A342. Parking.

102 The Gastrobistro at the Pheasant Inn

19 Salt Lane,
Salisbury SP1 1DT
Tel.: (01722)414926
e-mail: gastrobistro@googlemail.com **Website:** www.gastrobistro.co.uk

 **Old Speckled Hen (bottled)**

The enthusiastic owner of this curiously named inn is an anglophilic Frenchmen who has made the Cathedral City his home, so you are just as likely to find steak and chips or sponge pudding on the menu as you are chicken chasseur or ragoût of lamb - all freshly made with local produce and served with a hefty dollop of Gallic charm. The plaque on the wall dates the black and white timbered building back to 1638, but it has the air of one even older, and its rough quarry tiled floors, inglenook fireplaces and ancient beams all add to its distinctive character, as does the cobbled courtyard, the recently installed piano and the rows of empty champagne bottles which pay homage to the owner's home region. Comfy sofas and a super smart happy hour with free nibbles attract their fair share of drinkers, but most people come here to dine, with great value lunch and early evening menus, blackboard fish specials and a popular Sunday lunch.

Food serving times
Monday-Sunday:
12pm-2.30pm, 6pm-9.30pm
Closed 25 December dinner and first 2 weeks January

Prices
Meals: a la carte £ 19/30

Typical Dishes
Smoked tout blinis
Mussels marinières
Tarte Tatin

In city centre North of the cathedral. Salt Lane car park 1 minute's walk.

103 The Lamb on the Strand

99 The Strand,
Semington BA14 6LL
Tel.: (01380)870263 – Fax: (01380)871203
e-mail: philip@cbcc.fsworld.co.uk

 **Ringwood Best, Butcombe and guests beers including Keystone, Titanic, Thwaites, Fullers**

Under the lush coat of ivy lies a smart red-brick inn, with a decked terrace and well-kept garden beyond. Having run the place for over a decade, the family team has managed to build up a steady base of regulars, who, as you might have guessed, head straight for the central bar. For lunch this is probably the best place to eat, with the rooms on either side becoming more popular at dinner time. Worn tables reign over designer styling and along with the cheerful service create a friendly laid-back ambience. The flavoursome cooking displays honest country foundations and produces some great combinations, using local produce wherever possible. New dishes struggle to break through the list of old favourites, especially where the local butcher's sausages, faggots and belly pork are concerned, but, with good homemade choices and puddings that come with the classic choice of custard, cream or ice cream, who's complaining?

Food serving times

Monday-Saturday:
12pm-2pm, 7pm-9pm

Sunday: 12pm-2pm

Closed 25 December and 1 January

Booking essential

Prices

Meals: a la carte £ 19/23

Typical Dishes

Grilled fig, chorizo & Parmesan salad

Medallions of venison

Norwegian cream

Between Trowbridge and Devizes on A361, near Semington village. Parking.

104 The Angel Inn

Upton Scudamore BA12 0AG
Tel.: (01985)213225 – Fax: (01985)218182
e-mail: mail@theangelinn.co.uk **Website:** www.theangelinn.co.uk

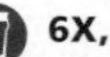 **6X, Butcombe, Tanglefoot and other guest beers**

It's lucky for the locals that this friendly pub is on their doorstep, as there's not much more to this quiet village than a few houses. It has quite a local reputation and deservedly so; service is efficient and comes with a smile, whether you're basking in the sun on the decked terrace or getting cosy beside the fire in the country-cottage interior. Candles and flowers adorn the tables in both the restaurant and the bar, with local artists' paintings decorating the walls. Upon arrival you are greeted with delicious homemade bread, complete with olives and herb oil, whilst at the other end of the meal luscious homemade ice creams and sorbets await. The kitchen has got the balance between pub and restaurant cooking just right, with a menu of hearty main dishes and a blackboard filled with fish specials, courtesy of near-daily arrivals. Rooms are comfortable, modern and spacious; each with pristine, individually co-ordinated furnishings.

Food serving times

Monday-Sunday:
12pm-2pm, 7pm-9.30pm

Closed 25-26 December, 1 January

Prices

Meals: £ 15 (lunch) and a la carte £ 15/25

10 rooms: £ 80/85

Typical Dishes

Sautéed tiger prawns
Roast rump of lamb
Chocolate & Grand Marnier torte

Village signed off A350 to the north of Warminster. Parking.

Garder

The names Gas Street Basin, Custard Factory and Mailbox may not win any awards for exoticism, but these are the cutting edge quarters fuelling the rise of modern day Birmingham, at the heart of a region evolving from its grimy factory gate image. Even the Ironbridge Gorge, the cradle of the Industrial Revolution, is better known these days as a fascinatingly picturesque tourist attraction. The old urban landscapes dot a region of delightful unspoilt countryside with extensive areas of open moorland and hills, where stands Middle Earth, in the shape of Shropshire's iconic Wrekin hill, true inspiration of Tolkien. Shakespeare Country abounds in pretty villages, such as Henley-in-Arden, Shipston-on-Stour and Alcester, where redbrick, half-timbered and Georgian buildings capture the eye. Taste buds are catered for courtesy of a host of local specialities, not least fruits from the Vale of Evesham and mouth-watering meats from the hills near the renowned gastro town of Ludlow.

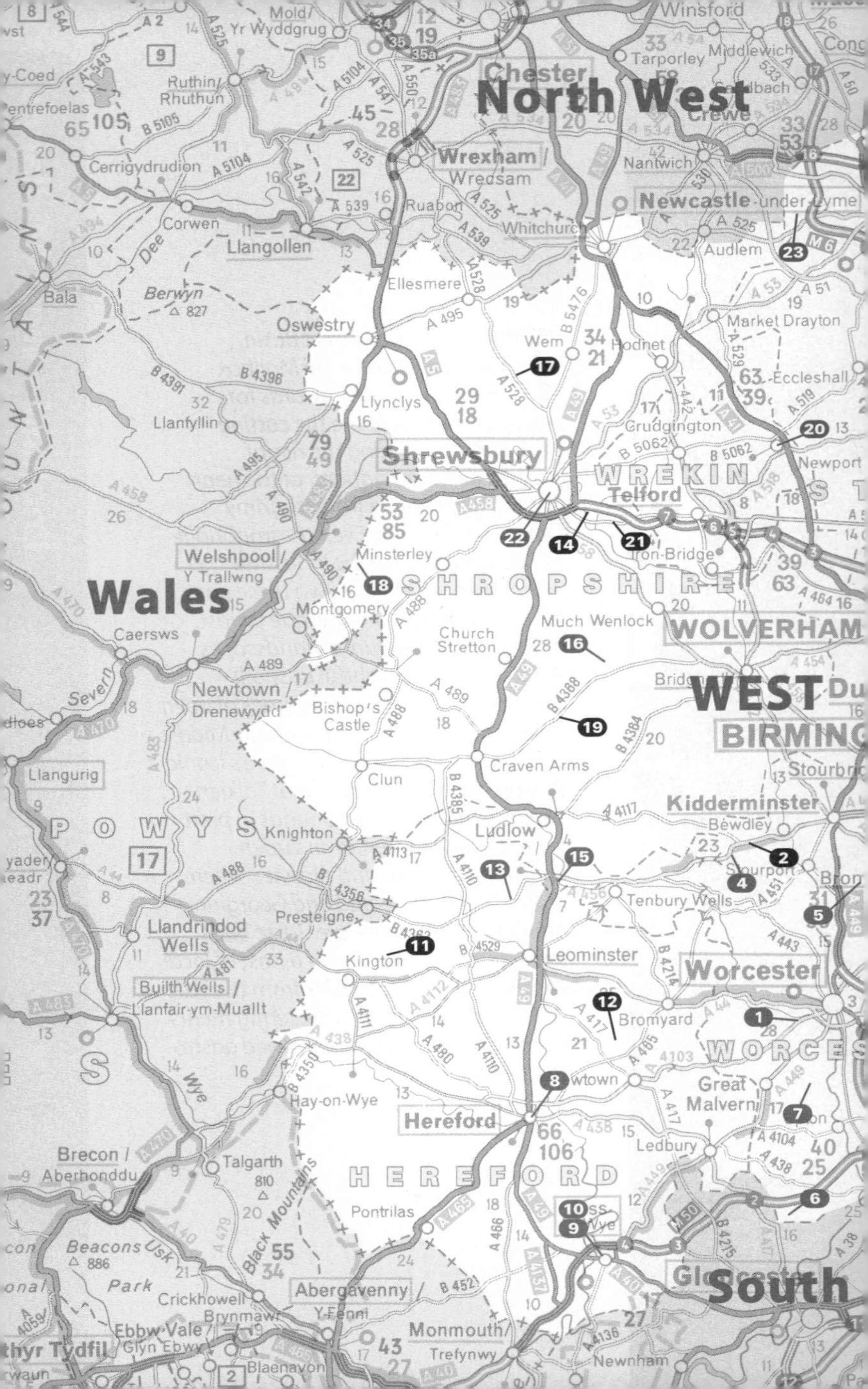

North West
Wales
WEST
South
Chester
Wrexham / Wrecsam
Shrewsbury
Telford
WREKIN
SHROPSHIRE
Oswestry
Welshpool / Y Trallwng
Newtown / Drenewydd
POWYS
Llandrindod Wells
Builth Wells / Llanfair-ym-Muallt
Brecon / Aberhonddu
Hereford
HEREFORD
Abergavenny / Y Fenni
Monmouth / Trefynwy
Leominster
Worcester
Kidderminster
Ludlow
Llangollen
Newcastle-under-Lyme
WOLVERHAM
BIRMING
Ellesmere
Wem
Market Drayton
Much Wenlock
Church Stretton
Bishop's Castle
Craven Arms
Clun
Knighton
Presteigne
Kington
Tenbury Wells
Bromyard
Great Malvern
Ledbury
Hay-on-Wye
Talgarth
Crickhowell
Ebbw Vale / Glyn Ebwy
Blaenavon
Black Mountains
Beacons
Park
Berwyn
Bala
Corwen
Ruthin / Rhuthun
Cerrigydrudion
Mold / Yr Wyddgrug
Winsford
Tarporley
Middlewich
Sandbach
Crewe
Nantwich
Whitchurch
Audlem
Hodnet
Crudgington
Newport
Eccleshall
Iron-Bridge
Minsterley
Montgomery
Caersws
Llangurig
Llanfyllin
Llynclys
Ruabon
Pontrilas
Newnham
Bewdley
Stourport
Stourbri
Bridg
Ross-on-Wye
Glo
Severn
Dee
Wye
Usk

East Midlands
MIDLANDS
West
South East
DERBY
NOTTS
LEICESTER
WARWICK
NORTHAMP
BUCKINGHAM
STOKE-ON-TRENT
NOTTINGHAM
LEICESTER
COVENTRY
Chesterfield
Mansfield
Derby
Matlock
Bakewell
Chatsworth House
Ashbourne
Belper
Alfreton
Ripley
Heanor
Ilkeston
Hucknall
Southwell
Newark-on-Trent
Tuxford
Ollerton
Hardwick Hall
Sutton-in-Ashfield
Clay Cross
Baslow
Leek
Little Moreton Hall
Kidsgrove
Stone
Uttoxeter
Sudbury
Stafford
Abbots Bromley
Rugeley
Cannock
Brownhills
Lichfield
Walsall
Sutton Coldfield
Tamworth
Burton-upon-Trent
Swadlincote
Ashby de la Zouch
Coalville
Loughborough
Long Eaton
West Bridgford
Bingham
Rempstone
Melton
Oadby
Uppingham
Hinckley
Atherstone
Nuneaton
Bedworth
Lutterworth
Market Harborough
Husbands Bosworth
Rugby
Rothwell
Halesowen
Solihull
Kenilworth
Redditch
Droitwich
Henley
Alcester
Warwick
Royal Leamington Spa
Southam
Daventry
Wellingborough
Stratford-upon-Avon
Evesham
Pershore
Ettington
Shipston-on-Stour
Chipping Campden
Broadway
Banbury
Towcester
Brackley
Wolverton
Milton Keynes
Tewkesbury
Winchcombe
Stow-on-the-Wold
Moreton
Chipping Norton
Buckingham
Bletchley
Cheltenham
Bicester
Northleach
Burford
Woodstock
Blenheim Palace
Kidlington
Linslade
Park
R. Trent
Gt. Ouse
Derwent

1 Bear and Ragged Staff

Station Rd,
Bransford WR6 5JH
Tel.: (01886)833399 – Fax: (01886)833106
e-mail: mail@bear.uk.com **Website:** www.bear.uk.com

 **St George's Best Bitter, Fuller's London Pride**

Satisfyingly familiar pub classics and more formal restaurant recipes run side by side on the Bear and Ragged Staff's huge blackboards; add to this the occasional fish specials and there's sure to be something that appeals. What's more, even with such a big choice, it's safe to assume the cooking will be tasty and prepared with sound culinary know-how. In fact, it would be easy to take this country pub for granted: unremarkable on the outside, comfortable and traditional within, it seems almost too pleasant and unassuming for its own good, but fortunately the locals know a good thing when they see it. Service is friendly with no standing on ceremony: though the pub is divided into a classically styled dining room and bar, you can order what you like and eat it where you choose.

Food serving times

Monday-Saturday:
12pm-2pm, 6.30pm-9pm

Sunday:
12pm-2pm, 7pm-8pm

Closed dinner 25 December and 1 January

Prices

Meals: a la carte £ 20/30

Typical Dishes

Stuffed boneless quail
Whole grilled Dover sole
Sticky toffee pudding

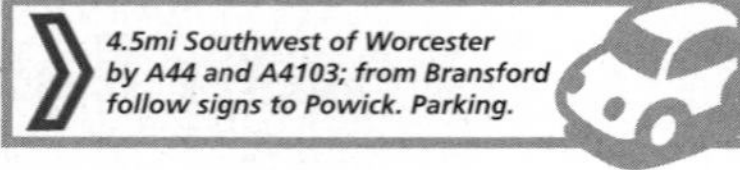

4.5mi Southwest of Worcester by A44 and A4103; from Bransford follow signs to Powick. Parking.

2 The Royal Forester

Callow Hill DY14 9XW
Tel.: (01299)266286
e-mail: contact@royalforesterinn.co.uk **Website:** www.royalforesterinn.co.uk

 **Timothy Taylor Landlord, Hobson Bitter**

Situated right in the heart of the Wyre Forest this pub is aptly named and if it really dates back to 1411 as people believe, is one of the oldest in Worcestershire. A full refurbishment has brought it up-to-date and created a modern feel but it hasn't lost sight of its country origins and retains a relaxed, easy-going atmosphere. The dining room with its chunky wood tables and exposed stone walls is the most rustic in feel, while the bar is lighter and brighter, courtesy of the adjoining terrace. The appealing, down-to-earth menu features a concise, good value set selection or a more wide-ranging à la carte; particularly noteworthy are the local grilled steaks, while other dishes might include scallops with pea purée or linguine with wild mushrooms. The modern, comfortable bedrooms are cleverly designed after colourful foodstuffs; they include purple, green and blue themed rooms – "Aubergine", "Pear" and "Blueberry" respectively.

Food serving times
Monday-Sunday:
12pm-3pm, 6pm-9.30pm

Prices
Meals: £ 13 and
a la carte £ 20/30

7 rooms: £ 55/99

Typical Dishes
Asparagus & poached egg
Grilled turbot
White chocolate cheesecake

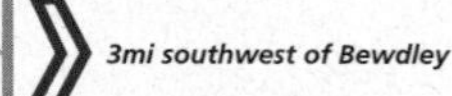

3 Bell & Cross

Holy Cross,
Clent DY9 9QL
Tel.: (01562)730319
Website: www.bellandcrossclent.co.uk

VISA

Enville Ale, Banks Bitter, Wye Valley, Timothy Taylor

Every inch of wall space seems to be filled with framed photos at this friendly little pub – little being the operative word, given the cosy feel in each of its rooms. Traditional-looking both outside and in, with its tiled floors, wheelback chairs and wooden tables; one of its snugs is a great place to settle down in for the evening – while the terrace and pretty garden are the natural choice on sunny days - and the servers are attentive wherever you sit. Cooking is tasty, balanced and well executed and you'll find that classic dishes such as lamb chops and roasted chicken share the menu with more modern and international offerings such as Peking duck rolls or veal Schnitzel Carbonara. Desserts will definitely take you back a few years with old favourites such as knickerbocker glory, rice pudding and trifle on the menu, and who can resist the temptation of treacle tart, when it's listed as being served with Granny's thick custard?

Food serving times
Monday-Saturday:
12pm-2pm, 6.30pm-9.15pm
Sunday: 12pm-7pm
Closed 25 December

Prices
Meals: a la carte £ 20/28

Typical Dishes
BBQ ribs
Calves Liver
Warm treacle sponge

Between Stourbridge and Bromsgrove off northbound A491; the pub is on the left hand side in Holy Cross. Parking.

4 The Colliers Arms

Tenbury Road,
Clows Top DY14 9HA
Tel.: (01299)832242
e-mail: thecolliersarms@aol.com **Website:** www.colliersarms.com

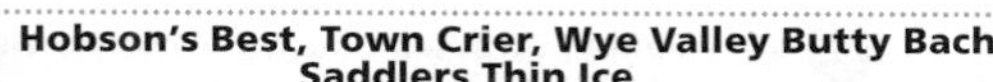

Hobson's Best, Town Crier, Wye Valley Butty Bach, Saddlers Thin Ice

A young new owner may have taken over at the helm of The Colliers Arms but the pub is still very popular with the older generation, who obviously appreciate good quality, homecooked food. Several rooms offer differing atmospheres in which to dine; there's a snug little bar with a traditional feel to it, an open main bar with a log fire, furnished with polished wooden tables and decorated with some decidedly fishy wall paper, plus – the best place to sit - an airy dining room at the rear of the pub, with pleasant views of the garden. There's no danger of finding fashionable fusion dishes here: instead you'll find all the old favourites on the menu; traditional hearty British dishes like steak and chips, sausage and mash and steak and kidney pudding, as well as sandwiches and lighter snacks at lunch. The choice of food on the menu is dictated by the seasons and everything is fresh and homemade.

Food serving times

Monday-Friday12pm-2pm, 6.30pm-9pm

Saturday:12pm-2.30pm, 6.30pm-9.30pm

Sunday: 12pm-4pm

Prices

Meals: a la carte £ 18/25

Typical Dishes

Pan-fried black pudding
Rack of lamb
Calvados rice pudding

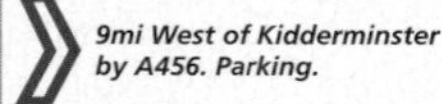

9mi West of Kidderminster by A456. Parking.

5 The Chequers

Kidderminster Rd,
Cutnall Green WR9 0PJ
Tel.: (01299)851292 – Fax: (01299)851744
Website: www.chequerscutnallgreen.co.uk

 **Wye Valley, Ruddles County, Timothy Taylor**

Don't be put off by this roadside pub's unremarkable exterior: it's obviously just a cover to stop the masses thronging here in their droves. Inside it's a different story - extremely characterful, with rustic style aplenty in the form of sandblasted beams, exposed brickwork and wood and tiled floors. There's a lounge bar with sofas and armchairs in which to make yourself comfortable and a restaurant with chunky dark wood tables, whilst the patio and garden area are popular in the spring and summer months. The large à la carte dinner menu offers modern dishes and is supplemented by daily specials. Cooking is flavoursome, with international leanings, so your chicken might come Yuk Sung style, your sea bream might be made into a Goan curry, and your chicken breast might come served with kumara potato and chorizo. The lunchtime menu offers lighter bites; from sandwiches and salads to pasta and panini.

Food serving times

Monday-Saturday:
12pm-2pm, 6.30pm-9.15pm

Sunday: 12pm-2.30pm

Closed 25 December and 1 January

Prices

Meals: a la carte £ 21/27

Typical Dishes
Fish cakes
Calves liver
Treacle tart

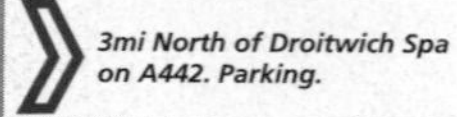
3mi North of Droitwich Spa on A442. Parking.

6 The Butchers Arms

Lime St,
Eldersfield GL19 4NX
Tel.: (01452)840381
Website: www.thebutchersarms.net

 **Wye Valley Butty Bach, RCH Pitchfork, Malvern Hills Black Pear**

Apart from the modern sign swinging outside and the pine picnic benches scattered across the neatly-kept lawn, this pub remains as traditional as ever and wouldn't look out of place on a historic film set. Two small rooms display original beams, part-oak flooring and a wood burning stove, while dried hops hang from the bar and knick-knacks and memorabilia adorn the walls. A few of the small wooden tables – some former sewing tables – are left for the local drinkers, while the rest are set for 20 or so diners, which isn't a bad number for a team of two. With only one person in the kitchen the menu is understandably quite concise but it changes regularly – sometimes even from service to service – and despite the lack of man-power, everything from the bread to the ice cream is homemade. Cooking sees refined pub dishes alongside a few more unusual items such as Bath Chaps (pig's cheeks); while vegetables arrive courtesy of a local villager.

Food serving times

Tuesday: 7pm-8.30pm

Wednesday-Saturday: 12pm-1.30pm, 7pm-8.30pm

Sunday: 12pm-1.30pm

Closed first week in January

Prices

Meals: a la carte £ 25/32

Typical Dishes

Bath chaps & Bramley apple

Rack of lamb

Vanilla & honey cheesecake

South of M50 between Junctions 1 and 2

7 Plough and Harrow

Rhydd Rd,
Guarlford WR13 6NY
Tel.: (01684)310453
e-mail: info@theploughandharrow.co.uk **Website:** www.theploughandharrow.co.uk

 **Wadworth 6X, Henrys IPA**

This modernised country pub is run by a keen, friendly young couple with the help of their team of polite, chatty staff; adept at keeping things well under control, even when there's a rush on. And there might well be a rush on when you visit, since the tasty food on offer here is like all good pub food should be: unfussy in style and cooked with pride and care, using good quality produce; including plenty of fruit, herbs and vegetables from their own kitchen garden. Menus change seasonally, with simpler snacks and sandwiches available at lunchtime alongside dishes like chicken and gammon pie or steak and chips, while dinner dishes have more of a restaurant feel to them; perhaps terrine of ham hock and foie gras or salmon smoked blini to start, followed by breast of Gressingham duck or pan roast scallops. Sit by the open fire in the comfy, beamed bar, or, for a more formal feel, head past the sofa to the bright, split-level dining room.

2mi East of Great Malvern by B4211

Food serving times

Tuesday-Saturday:
12pm-2pm, 6.30pm-9pm

Sunday: 12pm-2pm

Closed first 2 weeks November, 25 December, 1 January

Prices

Meals: a la carte £ 15/30

Typical Dishes

Pressed salmon terrine
Rack of lamb
Raspberry crème brûlée

8 The Wellington

Wellington, Hereford HR4 8AT
Tel.: (01432)830367
e-mail: thewellington@hotmail.com **Website:** www.wellingtonpub.co.uk

 **Hobson's Best, Wye Valley Butty Bach and guest beers**

Everyone wants to live the dream but not many succeed. The owner here is one of the lucky few. Arriving with no experience in either a kitchen or a pub environment, he is now the proud owner of a highly popular, much-loved neighbourhood pub – a real local's local – and has taught himself the culinary skills required. Located in the centre of the village, parking can be challenging but it's definitely worth searching for a spot so you can relax by the fire in the spacious open bar. With smartly laid scrubbed wooden tables and a pleasant conservatory leading out to the gardens, the dining room has a more formal feel, although the service remains laid-back throughout. The chefs use only local, traceable produce and the menu changes daily to reflect their highly seasonal ethos. Dishes feature fairly classical combinations and might include loin of speckle-faced Welsh lamb, pedigree Hereford sirloin steak or rare breed Welsh white pork.

Food serving times

Monday: 7pm-9pm

Tuesday-Sunday:
12pm-2pm, 7pm-9pm

Closed 25 December

Prices

Meals: a la carte £ 23/30

Typical Dishes
King scallops
Fillet of venison
Champagne rhubarb

North 5mi by A49
In village centre.

9 The Lough Pool at Sellack

Sellack,
Ross-on-Wye HR9 6LX
Tel.: (01989)730236 – Fax: (01981)570322
e-mail: david@loughpool.co.uk **Website:** www.loughpoolinn.co.uk

Inspectors' favourites

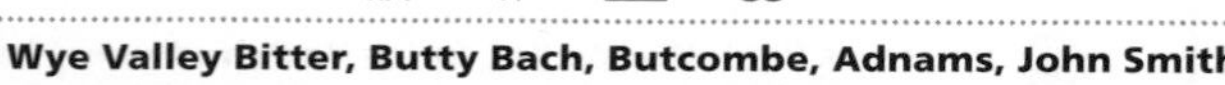

Wye Valley Bitter, Butty Bach, Butcombe, Adnams, John Smith

Situated in a wonderfully rural spot down the country lanes of Hereford, this 16C black and white timbered inn is well off the beaten track. With a name like this you won't be surprised to find that opposite the pub is a pond, complete with ducks and weeping willows, swaying gently in the breeze. Overlooking this beautiful view is the garden, so make time to sit with a real ale or Herefordshire cider and admire the view. With hop bines entwined around wooden beams, flag stone floors and roaring open fires, the atmosphere is truly rustic and, despite the comings and goings of various chefs, the food too has stayed true to its roots. Cooking is traditional and in good pub style, provides great value. With much of the produce being delivered from just down the road, ingredients are well sourced; the latest seasonal availability informing the daily menu – you might find crab salad, followed by loin of lamb, finished off with rhubarb posset.

Food serving times

Monday-Sunday:
12pm-2pm, 7pm-9.30pm

Closed 25 December; also Sunday dinner and Monday in November and from January to March

Prices

Meals: a la carte £ 18/27

Typical Dishes

Mackerel & potato terrine
Loin of Weobley lamb
Iced peanut parfait

3.25mi north-west of Ross-on-Wye; turn right off A49 (Hereford) and follow signs for Hoarwithy. Parking.

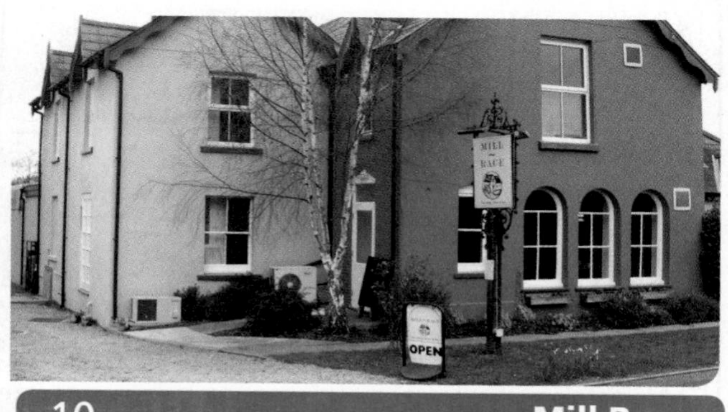

10 Mill Race

Walford,
Ross-on-Wye HR9 5QS
Tel.: (01989)562891
e-mail: enquiries@millrace.info **Website:** www.millrace.info

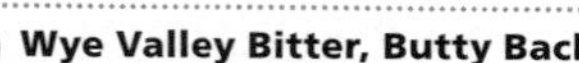

Wye Valley Bitter, Butty Bach

Boasting a spacious interior and a large terrace with countryside views, this bright, modern pub is a relative newcomer to the scene. Built by a local tradesman it plays perfect host to variety of inspired events: the first Monday of each month sees a specials night – maybe French, Game or Creole – which features themed dishes, drinks and cocktails, while during the warmer months regular BBQs and a yearly Food Fayre take place. The constantly evolving menu has a sound seasonal British base and focuses on good quality food cooked simply and well. Dishes are tasty and uncomplicated, and feature carefully sourced, ethical produce – meat from farms that treat their animals humanely and fish from non-depleted stocks or sustainable sources – and on top of that they even convert their used fat into fuel. Reminiscent of the old market days, locals can exchange their home-grown fruit, vegetables or flowers in return for lunch. How satisfying.

Food serving times

Monday-Thursday:
12pm-2pm, 6pm-9pm

Friday:
12pm-2pm, 6pm-9.30pm

Saturday:
12pm-2.30pm, 6pm-9.30pm

Sunday:
12pm-2.30pm, 6pm-9pm

Prices

Meals: a la carte £ 20/40

Typical Dishes

Stilton soufflé
Calves liver & bacon
Rhubarb crème brûlée

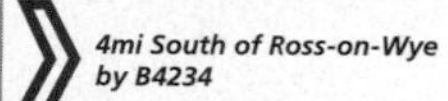

4mi South of Ross-on-Wye by B4234

11 The Stagg Inn

Titley HR5 3RL
Tel.: (01544)230221
e-mail: reservations@thestagg.co.uk
Website: www.thestagg.co.uk

Hobson's Best, Hobson's Town Crier, Brains Revd James, Timothy Taylor Landlord

The busy bar's beams at this characterful country dining pub are almost entirely covered by a collection of porcelain water jugs, and its three dining rooms with their dried hops and polished wood tables are similarly rustic in feel. Local produce is noticeably to the fore on the seasonally-changing menus, and includes the pub's own pigs and chickens as well as fruit and vegetables from the garden. Cooking is classically-based and served without pretence, allowing the flavours of the top quality ingredients to speak for themselves. Weekday bar snacks might include ploughman's and sandwiches, while dishes on the à la carte tend more towards choices like pigeon breast, fillet of Herefordshire beef or saddle of venison. Simply furnished bedrooms have a distinctly rural character, typified by the exposed beams; three are above the pub, the others are situated in the Grade II listed old vicarage a few minutes walk away in the village.

3.5mi Northeast of Kington on B4355. Parking.

Food serving times

Tuesday-Saturday:
12pm-2pm, 6.30pm-9pm

Sunday: 12pm-2pm

Prices

Meals: a la carte £ 21/29

6 rooms: £ 70/120

Typical Dishes

Scallops on parsnip purée
Fillet of beef
Three crèmes brûlées

12 Three Crowns Inn

Bleak Acre,
Ullingswick HR1 3JQ

Tel.: (01432)820279 – Fax: (08700)515338
e-mail: info@threecrownsinn.com **Website:** www.threecrownsinn.com

 **Wye Valley, Butty Bach, Hobsons Best Bitter**

A hallmark of this rural, family-run pub is its unfussy cooking: the chef-owner takes the finest of local ingredients and gives them Three Crowns treatment, producing robust, tasty dishes which are easy on the eye as well as on the pocket. The set blackboard lunchtime menu, located above the fire, offers classic dishes such as moules and frites, while the daily-changing à la carte might tempt you with starters such as roast woodcock with risotto of its liver, followed by confit duck or peppered sirloin of Herefordshire beef. Service is chatty and polite and the atmosphere is relaxed. Hops hang from low beams and there are seats both for drinkers and diners - the most popular being those by the open fire - while the more modern extension is used for dining during busier periods. A bedroom also housed in the extension is smart, with contemporary styling; the owners hope to add more soon.

Food serving times

Monday-Sunday:
12pm-2.30pm, 7pm-9.30pm

Closed 25 December,
1 January

Prices

Meals: £ 15 (lunch)
and a la carte £ 26

1 room: £ 95

Typical Dishes
Cheddar & spinach soufflé
Grilled Cornish Gurnard
Chocolate truffle tart

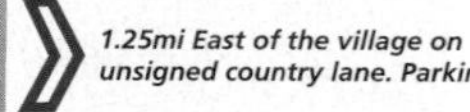

1.25mi East of the village on unsigned country lane. Parking.

England • West Midlands • Hereford and Worcester

13 The Bell Inn

Green Lane,
Yarpole HR6 0BD
Tel.: (01568)780359
Website: www.thebellinnyarpole.co.uk

Wye Valley Pale Ale, Timothy Taylor, Hooky Bitter

Set in the charming village of Yarpole, between Ludlow and Leominster, this black and white timbered inn is mentioned in the Domesday Book, and, as you might hope, has a real sense of identity. Low beams and wonky timberwork are on display throughout the building and the dining room – a converted barn – still houses a cider press and mill wheel; outside picnic tables are strewn across the pleasant, neatly kept garden. Cooking is a mixture of British and French. The bar menu offers traditional classics, with dishes such as prawn cocktail, fish pie, sirloin steak or Hereford snails. The restaurant on the other hand, sees more modern influences, featuring maybe smoked salmon rillettes, Herefordshire rare beef salad or terrine of confit rabbit leg and foie gras; followed by roast fillet of black bream, slow roast leg of Brittany rabbit or Elwy Valley lamb chop with confit lamb breast. Service is skilled and you can guarantee a warm welcome.

Food serving times
Monday-Sunday:
12pm-2.30pm,
6.30pm-9.30pm

Prices
Meals: a la carte £ 19/24

Typical Dishes
Ham hock pressed terrine
Breast of guinea fowl
Lemon posset

4mi North of Leominster by B4361 and minor road West. Parking.

14 The Mytton and Mermaid

Atcham SY5 6QG
Tel.: (01743)761220 – Fax: (01743)761297
e-mail: admin@myttonandmermaid.co.uk
Website: www.myttonandmermaid.co.uk

 **Shropshire Lad, Shropshire Gold, Ludlow Best**

Dating from the 18C, this impressive, ivy-clad Georgian inn is located opposite Attingham Park on the banks of the river Severn and, with its neat lawns and terraces, is a great spot for a summer afternoon meal. It's far from being just a fair weather pub, however; inside you'll find several formal dining areas as well as the rustically modern Mad Jack's Bar with its log fire, strategically placed sofas and interesting history. The bar menu contains traditional dishes such as mussels or steak and chips, alongside more modern treats such as asparagus and goats cheese terrine, or crayfish Caesar salad. The seasonal restaurant menu contains local Shropshire meats as well as dishes such as guinea fowl and foie gras, or Jerusalem artichoke mousse with beetroot crisps. Bedrooms are split between the main house and the stable block annex – those in the former being the more luxurious, although all are well kept and comfortable.

3mi south-east of Shrewsbury on B4380 Ironbridge Rd. Parking.

Food serving times

Monday-Sunday:
12pm-2.30pm, 6.30pm-10pm

Closed 25 December

Prices

Meals: £ 25 and a la carte £ 23/33

18 rooms: £ 80/165

Typical Dishes

Gravadlax & trout salad
Roast rump of lamb
Strawberry brulée

15 The Roebuck Inn

Brimfield SY8 4NE

Tel.: (01584)711230

e-mail: info@theroebuckludlow.co.uk **Website:** www.theroebuckinnludlow.co.uk

  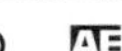 AE

 **Banks Bitter, Pedigree**

The Roebuck Inn has seen several changes in owner in recent years, its fortunes rising up and down accordingly, but with new French chef-owner Olivier Bossut in charge, its star is once again on the up. It comes as no surprise to find dishes such as gateaux of crab in a saffron beurre blanc, terrine of piglet and foie gras, millefeuilles of green asparagus or cassoulet Toulousain on the menu, but French or otherwise, dishes are freshly cooked, seasonal and full of flavour. Meat comes from a butcher in nearby Ludlow, and ingredients are sourced locally. Located right in the middle of the village, and dating back to the 15C, this inn is every inch the classic country pub, with friendly staff and a relaxed, informal feel, and you can eat in either the stylishly furnished dining room or in the bar.
If you want to stay a while and discover the Ludlow area, three bedrooms have a homely feel.

Food serving times

Monday-Saturday:
12pm-2.30pm, 6.30pm-9pm

Sunday: 12pm-2.30pm

Closed 25 December

French

Prices

Meals: a la carte £ 13/34

3 rooms: £ 65/85

Typical Dishes

Lobster ravioli

Steamed squab pigeon

Chocolate fondant

4.5mi South of Ludlow; signed off A49. Parking.

16 The Feathers at Brockton

Brockton TF13 6JR

Tel.: (01746)785202 – Fax: (01746)785202

e-mail: feathersatbrockton@googlemail.com

Website: www.feathersatbrockton.co.uk

 **Hobsons Best, Apley Ale**

Wenlock Edge, in the heart of the Shropshire countryside, is a popular spot for walkers, and word-of-mouth has contributed to this attractive part 16C pub becoming one of their more favoured watering holes. The chef-owner cut his teeth in well-thought-of London establishments and dining is to the fore here, with the constantly changing blackboard menus providing interesting modern English dishes underpinned by local produce, such as Shropshire partridge or beef. Ambience is ideal: the characterful interior boasts a tiled floor, whitewashed stone walls, beams and vast inglenooks with wood-burning stoves. Lots of little areas surround the central bar so a cosy feel snuggles with the rusticity. If anyone feels like splashing out, there are various examples of artwork for sale lining the walls.

Food serving times

Tuesday-Sunday:
12pm-2pm, 6.30pm-9pm

Closed first week in January

Prices

Meals: £ 15 (weekday dinner) and a la carte £ 15/30

Typical Dishes

King prawns

Slow-cooked pork belly

Warm chocolate fondant

5mi south-west of Much Wenlock on B4378. Parking.

17 The Burlton Inn

Burlton SY4 5TB
Tel.: (01939)270284
e-mail: robertlesterrc@yahoo.co.uk **Website:** www.burltoninn.co.uk

 **Robinsons Unicorn, Robinsons Double Hop**

Midway between Shrewsbury and Ellesmere, lies the village of Burlton and its traditional beamed, 18C inn. Inside it's a contemporary look which greets you, and the fire-lit ambience is informal and friendly. Join the regulars for a drink at the bar before choosing a seat, or head outside instead to have your meal on the patio, made pretty with hanging baskets that spill over with flowers. There's no reinventing of the wheel happening on the menu here – cooking focuses on traditional British dishes such as steak, kidney and beer pie, sausage and mash and cod and chips, while more unusual offerings include dishes like a tapas platter of olives, chorizo and crusty bread, goats' cheese, sun-dried tomato, mozzarella and black olive panzotti, or chicken jalfrezi. Six comfortable, modern bedrooms are situated in a separate annex; en suites are well-kept, and breakfast is definitely worth getting up for.

Food serving times

Monday-Friday:
12pm-2pm, 6.30pm-9.30pm

Saturday-Sunday:
12pm-3pm, 6.30pm-9.30pm

Closed dinner Sunday January-February

Prices

Meals: a la carte £ 25/30

6 rooms: £ 50/90

Typical Dishes

Fantail garlic king prawns

Herb crusted rack of lamb

Lemon meringue roulade

8mi North of Shrewsbury on A528. Parking.

18. The Sun Inn

Marton SY21 8JP
Tel.: (01938)561211
e-mail: suninnmarton@googlemail.com **Website:** www.suninn.org.uk

Hobsons Best, Six Bells monthly brew

Set in a quiet village in the Marches on the English-Welsh border, this warm and welcoming stone pub has a real countryside feel. It's very much a family affair, with father and son combo Peter and Dominic cooking up a storm in the kitchen, and wife Jean and daughter-in-law Sally providing smooth, efficient service out front. In the bar area a blackboard displays a list of daily specials, while in the restaurant – with its pastel violet coloured walls – there's a regularly changing modern British/ Mediterranean menu and a fresh fish board alongside. Cooking is straightforward, unfussy and unashamedly classical, using local, seasonal and organic ingredients where possible, including meat from the nearby farms. Dishes may include steak and kidney pudding, roast loin of lamb or wild boar steak, followed by pears in red wine or cappuccino brûlée. It can get busy, especially at weekends, so it's advisable to book in advance.

Food serving times

Tuesday: 7pm-9.30pm

Wednesday-Saturday: 12pm-2pm, 7pm-9.30pm

Sunday: 12pm-2pm

Closed Monday except Bank Holidays

Booking essential

Prices

Meals: a la carte £ 19/33

Typical Dishes

Smoked salmon

Loin of Welsh saltmarsh lamb

Pear & almond tart

8.5mi south-east of Welshpool on B4386. Parking.

19 The Crown Country Inn

Munslow SY7 9ET

Tel.: (01584)841205 – Fax: (01584)841255

e-mail: info@crowncountry-inn.co.uk **Website:** www.crowncountry-inn.co.uk

   AE

Hobson's Golden Glow, Black Country, Three Tuns, Clerics Cure, Bridgnorth Best Bitter

Quite how old the Crown really is, no-one really knows, but it was already long-established when it served as a "hundred house" for travelling magistrates. Warm and characterful, it certainly has all the hallmarks of a charming old rural inn, with stout beams propping up its cosy taproom, a well-stoked fire and trains of hops dangling from the woodwork. Its cuisine is not bound by tradition, though: light but still substantial modern dishes are served in the bar at lunch, while the evening menu is planned and prepared with a dash of imagination. Local vegetables, rare-breed meats, a fine English cheeseboard and even local spring water demonstrate a taste for regional produce. The large garden and terrace are popular with walkers from nearby Wenlock Edge.

Food serving times

Tuesday-Saturday:
12pm-1.45pm,
6.45pm-8.45pm

Sunday: 12pm-1.45pm

Closed 25 December

Prices

Meals: a la carte £ 22/30

3 rooms: £ 50/75

Typical Dishes

Smoked salmon mousseline

Roast rump of lamb

Vanilla pannacotta

On B4378 between Much Wenlock and Craven Arms. Parking.

20 The Fox

Pave Lane,
Chetwynd Aston, Newport TF10 9LQ
Tel.: (01952)815940 – Fax: (01952)815941
e-mail: fox@brunningandprice.co.uk **Website:** www.fox-newport.co.uk

Thwaites Original, Woods Shropshire Lad, Deuchars IPA, Weetwood Cheshire Cat

Bright and uncluttered, the Fox has a welcoming feel to it. The old pattern of nooks, parlours and lounges has been opened up and the well-chosen furnishings, though mostly restored or reclaimed, fit this more modern layout very well. A collection of framed fashion-plates and cigarette cards, rural scenes and period caricatures run the length of the walls and into the more intimate rooms off to the sides. It's nearly always possible to find a quieter corner somewhere, but the Fox really excels at the big get-together. Long dining tables are perfect for eating out in eights and tens: family brunches on a Sunday or an evening catching up with friends. A sizeable menu of modern classics is delivered with friendly efficiency. Big rear terrace and garden.

Food serving times

Monday-Saturday: 12pm-10pm

Sunday: 12pm-9.30pm

Closed 25 December for food, 26 December

Prices

Meals: a la carte £ 18/31

Typical Dishes

Pan fried scallops
Roast duck breast
Bread & butter pudding

1.5 mi South of Newport by A41 (Wolverhampton rd). Parking.

21 Hundred House

Bridgnorth Rd,
Norton TF11 9EE

Tel.: (01952)730353 – Fax: (01952)730355
e-mail: reservations@hundredhouse.co.uk **Website:** www.hundredhouse.co.uk

 **Black Country Real Ales, Highgate & Walsall Mild, Bridgnorth Brewery Bitter and guest ales**

Run for over twenty years by two generations of the Phillips family, this inn has a quirky style all of its own. History seems deeply ingrained into its web of rooms, with their tiled floors, open fires and oak panelling, and the dried herbs and hops hanging from ceilings add to the rustic flavour. Hearty food on the menus includes classics such as steak and kidney pie, venison casserole and sausage and mash, as well as dishes which take their influences from further afield, such as tapas, Thai green curry and Greek salad. Ingredients are sourced from local suppliers – and none more so than the inn's own beautiful herb and flower garden. The country style bedrooms offer comfort as well as character with features such as half testers and four posters; and if you enjoy swinging then you've come to the right place - thanks to the velvet covered seats artfully suspended from the beams in some of the rooms.

Food serving times

Monday-Sunday:
12pm-2.30pm, 6pm-10pm

Accommodation closed
25-26 December

Prices

Meals: £ 18/19
and a la carte £ 20/35

10 rooms: £ 30/125

Typical Dishes

Asparagus & mushroom risotto
Roast skate wing
Rhubarb cheesecake

7 mi. South of Telford on A 442. Parking.

22 The Armoury

Victoria Quay,
Welsh Bridge, Shrewsbury SY1 1HH
Tel.: (01743)340525
e-mail: armoury@brunningandprice.co.uk **Website:** www.brunningandprice.co.uk

   AE

 **Wadworth 6X, Roosters APA, Shropshire Gold, Shropshire Lad, Three Tuns XXX, Weetwood Cheshire Cat**

This 18C former warehouse has a fascinating history: built for military use, it's done service as a bakery and a World War II convalescent home, and even been moved brick by brick to this spot in sight of the old bridge, where it cries out for a bankside terrace to enjoy the summer sunshine. Inside, gilt-framed mirrors, engravings and Edwardiana cover the brick walls, yard upon yard of old books are rivalled only by row upon rows of malts and liqueurs behind the bar, and a huge ceiling and tall arched windows make the open-plan room feel light and spacious. Lots of big tables, with a hotch-potch of second-hand chairs, make it ideal for a big get-together: its great popularity means there's usually a buzzy atmosphere, and the daily changing menu of modern favourites offers something for everyone.

Food serving times
Monday-Sunday:
12pm-9.30pm
Closed 25-26 December

Prices
Meals: a la carte £ 15/30

Typical Dishes
Pan-fried scallops
Braised shoulder of lamb
Ginger pannacotta

By the Welsh Bridge. Frankwell car park over Welsh Bridge.

23 The Hand and Trumpet

Main Road,
Wrinehill CW3 9BJ
Tel.: (01270)820048 – Fax: (01270)821911
Website: www.hand-and-trumpet-wrinehill.co.uk

 **Timothy Taylor Landlord, Deuchars IPA, Thwaites Original, Titanic Anchor, Woodlands Oak Beauty**

The ancient village of Wrinehill (mentioned in the Domesday Book) has made a smooth transition into the 21C with this handsomely refurbished and sizable country pub. You're immediately struck by the delightful decked terrace, overlooking duck pond and gardens. On a warm day, you might just fancy plonking yourself down here and admiring the view, but then you'd be doing the stylish interior a disservice. The well-stocked bar has a shiny tiled floor with kilims lending a rather exotic touch, and the classy feel continues into the main dining area, where book shelves and rustic prints create just the right mood of relaxation to enjoy a leisurely lunch or dinner.
Menus cover a tried-and-tested country route, with traditional dishes very much to the fore. There's a wide range of wines by the glass and draught real ales to wash it all down with. Incidentally, don't miss the pub's website, complete with a superb history of the area.

Food serving times

Monday-Saturday:
12pm-10pm

Sunday: 12pm-9.30pm

Closed 25 December

Prices

Meals: a la carte £ 22/30

Typical Dishes

Soused rainbow trout
Braised feather beef steak
Rhubarb & vanilla cake

6mi West of Newcastle-under-Lyme by A525 and A531. Parking.

24 The Baraset Barn

1 Pimlico Lane,
Alveston CV37 7RJ
Tel.: (01789)295510 – Fax: (01789)292961
e-mail: barasetbarn@lovelypubs.co.uk **Website:** www.lovelypubs.co.uk

 **Purity UBU**

A traditional-looking pub concealing a stylish, modern interior, the shimmering silvers and brushed velvet of its atmospheric lounge and intimate mezzanine blending well with its 200 year old flagstones, brick walls and wooden beams. The private dining room is a real feature and overlooks the main dining area, while the glass-fronted kitchen means that the chefs are on view hard at work. Perhaps a seat in the airy conservatory beckons or you fancy going al fresco on the contemporary continental-style terrace; this is an easy-going place with all day opening, and lingering lunches seem positively encouraged. Add a chirpy young team to the mix and you can see why they're popular – and all this before any mention of the food itself: cooking is assured and flavoursome and the modern menu offers something for everyone, from a simple Caesar salad, seared scallops or a sociable sharing plate to the more substantial steak or spit roast chicken.

Food serving times

Monday-Saturday:
12pm-2.30pm,
6.30pm-9.30pm

Sunday: 12pm-2.30pm

Closed 25 December

Prices

Meals: £ 20 (3 course lunch)/20 and a la carte £ 25/40

Typical Dishes

Sweet potato & crab samosa

Belly of pork

Coffee & pecan pudding

2mi East of Stratford-upon-Avon on B4086. Parking.

25 The Golden Cross

Wixford Road,
Ardens Grafton B50 4LG

Tel.: (01789)772420 – Fax: (01798)491358
e-mail: info@thegoldencross.net **Website:** www.thegoldencross.net

 **Purity : Ubu, Gold; Bombardier, Old Hooky, Courage Best, Youngs Winter Warmer, Revd James**

This remote, 18C pub began life as three cottages and its uneven flag floors, wooden beams and local photos give a nod to its past. With its affable atmosphere, and contented mix of drinkers and diners of all ages, you get a real sense that this pub is close to the heart of the local community - and little touches like the glossy magazines on the tables and the fact that you can buy champagne by the glass demonstrate that this is a place which really looks after its customers. The busy, confident kitchen cooks traditional British classics like fisherman's pie, toad in hole and steak and kidney pudding, whilst the oft-changing fish specials might well tempt you to opt for something from the blackboard instead. Eat well – in the bar, the more formal restaurant or out on the patio or in the garden - happy in the knowledge that everything that can be is homemade, including the chips and some particularly mouth-watering desserts.

Food serving times

Monday-Friday:
12pm-2.30pm,
5.30pm-9.30pm

Saturday: 12pm-9.30pm

Sunday: 12pm-8pm

Prices

Meals: £ 15 and a la carte £ 20/27

Typical Dishes

Goats cheese tartlet
Pork tenderloin
Rhubarb & custard brûlée

5mi Southwest of Stratford-upon-Avon by A46. Parking.

26 The Fox & Goose Inn

Front St,
Armscote CV37 8DD
Tel.: (01608)682293 – Fax: (01608)682293
e-mail: mail@foxandgoose.co.uk **Website:** www.foxandgoose.co.uk

Butcome Ale, Black Sheep, Hooky

Happily situated just north of Shipston on Stour, in the peaceful hamlet of Armscote, this creeper-clad, red brick inn has a more modern, slightly quirkier interior than its traditional outer appearance might suggest. A bright, open plan bar and dining room boast a log burner at their centre, candles sit in wrought iron holders on each table and cushions are scattered around, as are papers and magazines. A stuffed fox chases a goose along the mantelpiece, stencil drawings of animals from encyclopaedias decorate the walls, and the bright and buzzy service from T-shirted staff fits the atmosphere perfectly. Modern cooking has a delicate touch, with refined flavours and a clever combination of well-priced dishes. Four compact and fun bedrooms are decorated on a Cluedo theme, with bold colour schemes of scarlet, mustard, plum and blue, while claw foot baths with candles bring a touch of luxury to proceedings.

Food serving times
Monday-Sunday:
12pm-3pm, 6pm-9.30pm

Prices
Meals: £ 12 (lunch)
and a la carte £ 24/40

4 rooms: £ 45/115

Typical Dishes
Scallops & bacon skewers
Pan-fried sea trout
Chocolate fudge cake

2.5 mi North of Shipston-on-Stour by A3400. Parking.

27 The King's Head

21 Bearley Rd,
Aston Cantlow B95 6HY

Tel.: (01789)488242 – Fax: (01789)488137
e-mail: info@thekh.co.uk **Website:** www.thekh.co.uk

 **Brew XI, Abbot, Purity Gold**

People purportedly travel to this pretty pub from quite a distance to enjoy the now revived duck suppers for which the pub was formerly famous. They are not its only claim to fame, however, since in 1557, Shakespeare's parents reputedly held their wedding reception here. Would the wedding banquet have involved the wild venison casserole, the pheasant or the saddle of rabbit? We can only speculate; although it's probably safe to say that they would not have feasted on the pork Yuk Sung or tomato risotto now also on offer. The abstract art hanging on the walls brings a contemporary touch to the restaurant, while the tables and cushion-clad chairs would not look out of place in a French farmhouse. With its low, heavily beamed ceiling, flag stoned floors and large stone fireplaces, the main lounge bar is equally as charming, while if it's privacy you're after, there are also several smaller nooks in which to make yourself cosy.

Food serving times

Monday-Saturday:
12pm-2.30pm,
6.30pm-9.30pm

Sunday: 12.30pm-3pm

Closed 25 December

Prices

Meals: £ 15
(3 course lunch/dinner)
and a la carte £ 20/30

Typical Dishes

Black pudding salad
Duck breast
Rhubarb & apple crumble

3mi south of Henley-in-Arden off B4089. Parking.

28 The Fox & Hounds Inn

Great Wolford CV36 5NQ
Tel.: (01608)674220
e-mail: enquiries@thefoxandhoundsinn.com
Website: www.thefoxandhoundsinn.com

Hook Norton, Purity Ubu, Wye Valley, Bass

A warm and welcoming family-run pub, where dried hops hang from the ceiling, a log burner nestles in the inglenook, flickering candles create a cosy atmosphere…and a stuffed fox watches your every move. Ivy-clad and set back from the road, its quintessential English character makes this the perfect Cotswolds stop-off when the fuel gauge in your bread basket reaches empty. Jamie, the chef, is passionate about growing his own vegetables, herbs and salad and sources as many of his ingredients as possible locally, so Dexter beef comes from the nearby village of Chastleton, venison hails from Todenham and seasonal game is gleaned from local shoots. The concise blackboard menu allows him to retain the freshness of the dishes whilst demonstrating his sound culinary understanding and his bold, wholesome cooking benefits from a pure style, entertaining no extraneous ingredients or flavours. Bedrooms are simple and neat, with a spacious feel.

4mi north-east of Moreton-in-Marsh by A44. Parking.

Food serving times

Tuesday-Saturday:
12pm-2pm, 6.30pm-9pm

Sunday:12pm-2pm

Prices

Meals: a la carte £ 20/40

3 rooms: £ 55/90

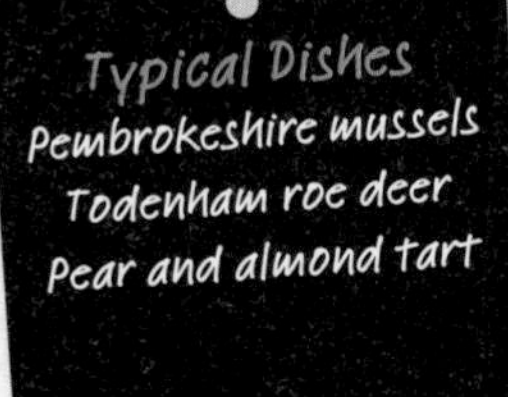

Typical Dishes

Pembrokeshire mussels
Todenham roe deer
Pear and almond tart

29 The Howard Arms

Lower Green,
Ilmington CV36 4LT
Tel.: (01608)682226 – Fax: (01608)682226
e-mail: info@howardarms.com **Website:** www.howardarms.com

Inspectors' favourites

   VISA MC AE

 **Old Hooky, Purity UBU, Fox's Hat Tiger Bitter**

This warm gold stone inn, situated on the green of a peaceful village, is the very essence of the English country pub. Outside there's a pleasant terrace and garden, while inside there are gleaming flag floors, an inglenook fireplace and old portraits of the owners' family on the walls. Based on seasonal produce, the menu changes weekly and with a whole host of local suppliers, you can expect to find strictly regional produce on your plate; beef is from Hereford, lamb from Warwickshire and game from the local Estates. Dishes are wide-ranging and might include goat's cheese rarebit or smoked duck and orange salad, followed by seared sea trout, mixed grill of Old Spot pork or warm salad of scallops. Desserts could include chocolate Bakewell tart, poached William pear shortbread or vanilla pannacotta with elderflower and raspberry jelly. Bedrooms are cosy, featuring antique furniture and designer fabrics, and one even has wooden beams.

4 mi Northwest of Shipston-on-Stour. Located in the centre of the village. Parking.

Food serving times

Monday-Sunday:
12pm-3pm, 6pm-10pm

Closed 25 December

Prices

Meals: a la carte £ 15/25

8 rooms: £ 88/150

Typical Dishes

Mackerel salad

Pan-fried scallops

Shortbread & rhubarb sauce

30 The Boot Inn

Old Warwick Rd,
Lapworth B94 6JU
Tel.: (01564)782464 – Fax: (01564)784989
e-mail: bootinn@hotmail.com **Website:** www.thebootatlapworth.co.uk

Tetley, Old Speckled Hen, Hobgoblin

Make sure you book ahead if you want to eat at the Boot; it gets deservedly busy despite – or even perhaps because of - its village location, close to the junction of the Grand Union and Stratford-upon-Avon canals. The front pub area, with its central bar and surrounding warren of little nooks and crannies, has a cosy, rustic feel to it, whilst the large main dining room, with its wooden floor and stylish décor, is on a different level, both literally and metaphorically. On sunny days, the favoured seats are those in the garden, but wherever you sit, the welcome is a warm one, and the service from t-shirted staff is friendly and attentive. The modern menus contain a mix of classics that take you on a gastronomical tour around Europe and beyond, so you'll find plates of a Baltic or Iberian flavour to share, and dishes such as pie of the day or steak alongside pot au feu or crispy oriental duck salad.

Food serving times
Monday-Sunday:
12.30pm-2.30pm,
6.30pm-10pm

Closed 25 December

Booking essential

Prices
Meals: a la carte £ 22/30

Typical Dishes
Smoked haddock risotto
Braised blade of beef
Pear tarte Tatin

2mi south-east of Hockley Heath on B4439; on the left hand side just before the village. Parking.

31 The Red Lion

Long Compton CV36 5JS
Tel.: (01608)684221 – Fax: (01608)684968
e-mail: info@redlion-longcompton.co.uk
Website: www.redlion-longcompton.co.uk

VISA MC AE

Hooky Bitter, North Cotswold Brewery, Old Speckled Hen, Old Peculier, Golden Host, Adnams Broadside

Fine oak tables, log fires, lantern style lamps and flag flooring help to create a richness and charm at the 18C, Grade II listed Red Lion, where original art decorates the walls and the tastefully made-over rooms feel cosy and intimate. Live acoustic music every fortnight attracts a local crowd, and the games room and rear terrace and garden provide extra space should the bar become too crowded. The seasonal menu offers mostly British favourites from the tried-and-tested school of cooking, so you'll find mains such as homemade steak and Hook Norton pie, savoury herb pancakes or rack of lamb, plus classic desserts such as apple crumble or chocolate mousse. Service is spot-on and smiley, creating a friendly atmosphere, and Cocoa the chocolate Labrador also makes sure you feel at home when plonks his nose in your lap and looks up at you with doleful eyes. Comfortable bedrooms are stylishly furnished in cool linen shades.

Food serving times

Monday-Thursday:
12pm-2.30pm, 6pm-9pm

Friday-Sunday:
12pm-9.30pm

Prices

Meals: a la carte £ 20/30

5 rooms: £ 55/90

Typical Dishes

Potted smoked trout
Spring chicken casserole
Warm chocolate nut brownie

5m North of Chipping Norton by A3400. Parking.

32 The Crabmill

Claverdon, Preston Bagot B95 5EE
Tel.: (01926)843342 – Fax: (01926)843989
e-mail: thecrabmill@lovelypubs.co.uk
Website: www.lovelypubs.co.uk

 **Tetleys, Abbot Ale, UBU Bitter**

This pub's beautifully timbered exterior hints at its rural character and the various rooms are a charming mix of old and new; ancient beams blending seamlessly with contemporary chocolate and pink décor. By day, the summer room sofas make a great spot for a casual lunch; by night no meals are served here, but it remains a relaxing lounge space, with plenty of papers and magazines to keep you occupied, should conversation idle. Table 6 is one of the most popular, table 1 will suit a group, while on summer days, only a seat on the summer terrace or in the garden will suffice. The modern Mediterranean menu offers generous portions of dishes such as lamb kofta, pork saltimbocca or braised shoulder of beef; specials often involve fish, and lunchtime means more than just sandwiches; with falafels, hummus and tzatziki with pitta bread, or slow cooked bolognaise alongside ploughman's and paninis. Service is bright and on the button.

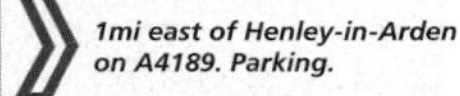
1mi east of Henley-in-Arden on A4189. Parking.

Food serving times

Monday-Saturday:
12pm-2.30pm,
6.30pm-9.30pm

Sunday: 12.30pm-3.30pm

Closed 25 December

Booking essential

Prices

Meals: a la carte £ 20/30

Typical Dishes

Bubble and squeak

Roast cod

Sticky toffee pudding

33 The Bell Inn

The Green,
Tanworth-in-Arden B94 5AL
Tel.: (01564)742212
e-mail: thebell@realcoolbars.com **Website:** www.thebellattanworthinarden.co.uk

Timothy Taylor Landlord and one guest ale

With its squashy sofas and leather bar stools, The Bell's much modernised, stylish interior has a cool and relaxed feel to it. Its open log fire and rich wood furniture and panelling help it to retain an essence of homeliness, however, and the Morris dancers occasionally seen shaking their hankies and sticks on the village green opposite add to the authentic villagey feel of the place. The food on offer here is not your typical pub grub, but its diversity, bold flavours and generous portions should please both traditionalist and the more adventurous customer. The chef's Middle Eastern experience is evident in the regularly-changing menus and dishes range from coq au vin to Algerian lamb tagine, with daily fish specials on offer too. Overnight stays here are popular with those visiting the NEC. Opt for a front-facing, newer bedroom; all are individually decorated, with sleek, minimal styling and modern furniture.

Food serving times

Monday-Saturday:
12pm-2pm, 6pm-9pm

Sunday: 12pm-3pm

Prices

Meals: a la carte £ 18/28

9 rooms: £ 60/115

Typical Dishes

Sauté king prawns
Pan-roasted lamb fillet
Crème brûlée

4.5mi Northwest from Henley-in-Arden by A3400 and Tanworth Road. Close to church. Parking.

34 The Bell Inn

Binton Rd,
Welford-on-Avon CV37 8EB
Tel.: (01789)750353 – Fax: (01789)750893
e-mail: info@thebellwelford.co.uk **Website:** www.thebellwelford.co.uk

Purity Gold, Purity UBU, Flowers OB, Hooky, Hobsons

Visitors fanning out from Stratford strike lucky when they come across this part 17C redbrick inn. If it's the summer months, they can flop down at The Bell's enticingly attractive wood-furnished outside terrace with its array of hanging baskets. Or step inside, any time of year, and admire the flagged and beamed bar, glowing fire and rustic knick-knacks. Various other rooms mean there's space to breathe in here, with a range of tables, chairs and pews to stretch out at: the recently refurbished glass roofed dining room is maybe the most stylish place to eat. Local produce is very much to the fore, with local suppliers' names printed on the back of the menus. These offer a good balance of modern British and classic cuisine. They change a couple of times a year, and are supplemented by an extensive range of daily specials.

Food serving times

Monday-Thursday:
11.30am-2.30pm,
6pm-9.30pm

Friday:
11.30am-2.30pm, 6pm-10pm

Saturday:
11am-3pm, 6pm-10pm

Sunday: 12pm-9.30pm

Prices

Meals: a la carte £ 20/29

Typical Dishes

Black pudding

Cumin roasted duck breast

Sticky toffee pudding

4mi West of Stratford-upon-Avon by B439 and a lefthand turn South. Parking.

35 The White Horse

Kenilworth Road,
Balsall Common CV7 7DT

Tel.: (01676)533207 – Fax: (01676)532827

e-mail: info@thewhitehorseatbc.co.uk **Website:** www.thewhitehorseatbc.co.uk

IPA Directors, Jennings, Otter Ale, St Austell Tribute

Modernity strikes the Midlands in the form of this monumental pub – part of the Metro Group – which, having undergone refurbishment, now boasts a spacious bar lounge with low-backed leather tub chairs, art-adorned walls and a distinctive feel. The L-shaped dining area is as good as divided in three; the conservatory part being the best in which to sit, unless the British weather is uncharacteristically fine, in which case head for either the decked front terrace or the rear paved one. The menu has a universal appeal, as attested to by the pub's popularity, and dishes are freshly prepared, with care and understanding. Meat comes from the Midland's finest; Aubrey Allen, with spit roast chickens from the pub's rotisserie particularly worth a go. Old favourites like fish pie and toad in the hole are here, as is the odd European flavour, with dishes such as lamb koftas or spaghetti. Portions are generous so two courses should suffice.

Food serving times

Monday-Sunday:
12pm-10pm

Closed 1 January

Prices

Meals: a la carte £ 18/28

Typical Dishes

Garlic mushrooms

Steak & mushroom pudding

Belgian waffles

5mi Northwest of Kenilworth by A452. Parking.

36 The Malt Shovel

Barston Lane,
Barston B92 0JP
Tel.: (01675)443223 – Fax: (01675)443223
Website: www.themaltshovelatbarston.com

 **St Austell Tribute, Bombardier, JHB, Spitfire**

The Malt Shovel is not that far from either Solihull or the M42 but, as you dine al fresco at one of the picnic tables in its lawned garden, surrounded by shrubs and hanging baskets, you certainly get the feeling that you are right out in the middle of the countryside. Not that sitting outside is the only attractive option. This cream-painted dining pub boasts a bright, modern interior with music to match; tiled floors, open fireplaces and wooden tables, chairs and banquettes all set out around a central bar, with the kitchen partly on show at one end. For more formal dining, there's also a separate restaurant in the stylish barn annex. The modern, seasonally-led menus boast a real range of dishes to suit all tastes, from toasted crumpet or cod and chips to Moroccan spiced pork, or sweet potato and red onion Korma. Food arrives well-presented and puts many local ingredients to good use.

Food serving times

Monday-Saturday:
12pm-2.30pm (bar snacks only), 6pm-9.30pm

Sunday:
12pm-4pm (bar snacks only)

Closed 25 December

Lunch bookings not accepted

Prices

Meals: £ 26 (dinner)
and a la carte £ 21/34

Typical Dishes

Seared scallops
Baked cod
Marmalade brioche & butter pudding

Off the A452 just south of Hampton-in-Arden; follow signs for Barston village. Parking.

37 The Orange Tree

Warwick Road,
Chadwick End B93 0BN
Tel.: (01564)785364 – Fax: (01564)782988
Website: www.lovelypubs.co.uk

 **IPA, Old Hooky, Tetleys**

Enjoy the relaxed and informal atmosphere at this contemporarily stylish, cream-washed dining pub, where the young staff serve up a friendly welcome to go with their efficient service. Open plan and airy, with beams and wooden floors, the interior runs over different levels and there's plenty of comfy seating to choose from. You can eat anywhere, so get friend to grab a sofa while you order the drinks from the central bar - or if the weather takes a turn for the better, head for the large gardens instead. The simple menu won't win any prizes for innovation, but this is the place to come if you're after hearty modern food, cooked with neatness and precision, and at prices that won't clean out your piggy bank. The menu has an Italian base, and reads along the lines of pizza, pasta, and grilled meats and fish, but also contains a smattering of far flung flavours in the form of dishes such as Thai crab cakes and crispy duck salad.

Food serving times

Monday-Sunday:
12pm-2.30pm,
6.30pm-9.30pm

Closed 25 December and Sunday dinner

Booking essential

Prices

Meals: £ 15 (lunch) and a la carte £ 15/22

Typical Dishes

Onion tart
Spit roast chicken
Chocolate fondant

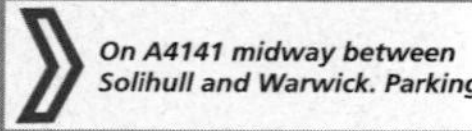

On A4141 midway between Solihull and Warwick. Parking.

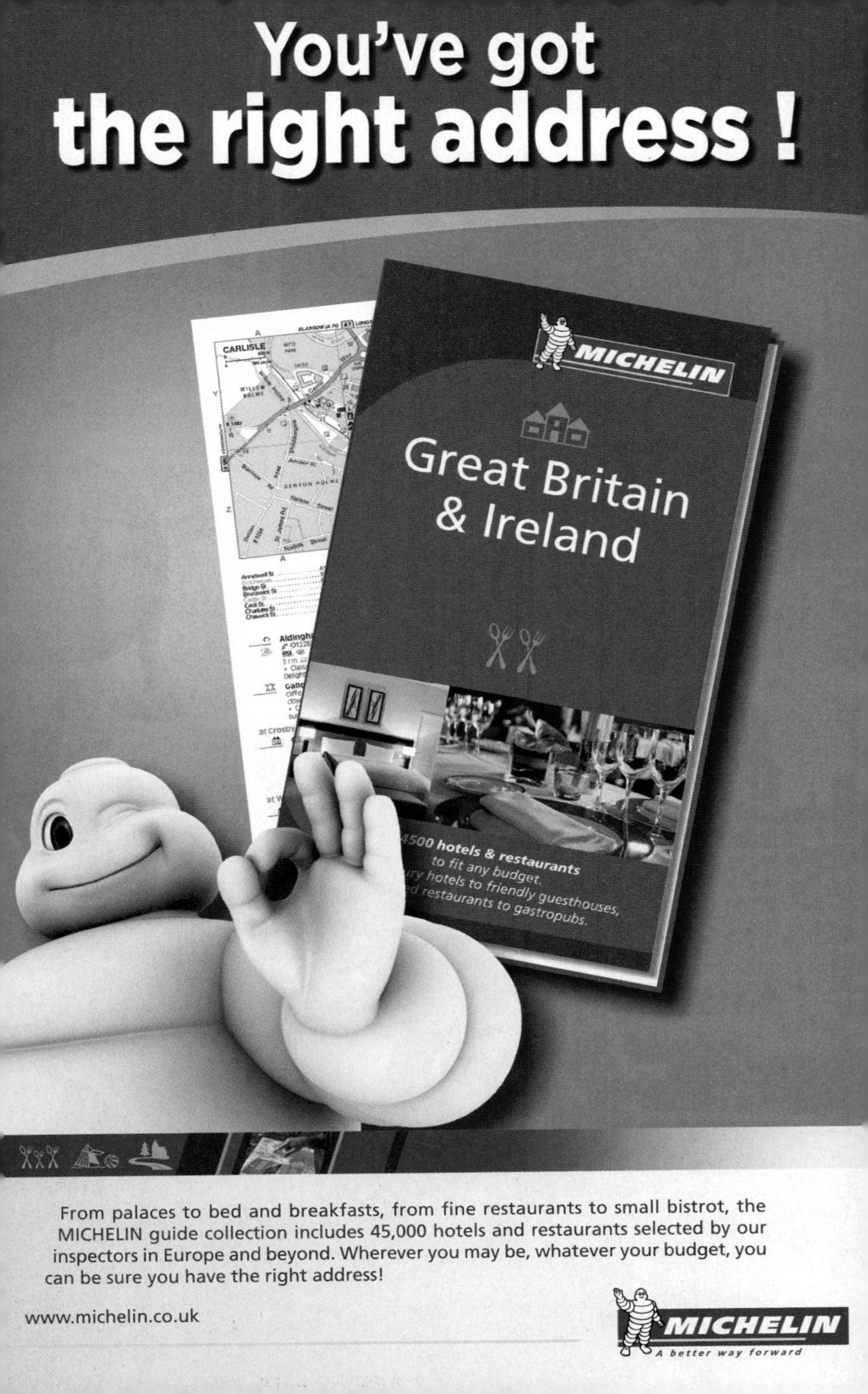
You've got
the right address !
MICHELIN
Great Britain
& Ireland
4500 hotels & restaurants
to fit any budget.
CARLISLE
From palaces to bed and breakfasts, from fine restaurants to small bistrot, the MICHELIN guide collection includes 45,000 hotels and restaurants selected by our inspectors in Europe and beyond. Wherever you may be, whatever your budget, you can be sure you have the right address!
www.michelin.co.uk
MICHELIN
A better way forward

England's biggest county has a lot of room for the spectacular; it encapsulates the idea of desolate beauty. The bracing winds of the Dales whistle through glorious meadows and deep, winding valleys, while the vast moors are fringed with picturesque country towns like Thirsk, Helmsley and Pickering. Further south the charming Wolds roll towards the sea, enhanced by such Georgian gems as Beverley and Howden. Popular history sits easily here: York continues to enchant with its ancient walls and Gothic Minster, but, owing to its Brontë links, visitors descend on the cobbled street village of Haworth with as much enthusiasm. Steam railways criss-cross the region's bluff contours, while drivers get a more streamlined thrill on the Humber Bridge. Yorkshire's food and drink emporiums range from quaintly traditional landmarks like the country tearoom and fish and chip shops proudly proclaiming to be the best in England, to warm and characterful pubs serving heart-warming local specialities.

North East
DURHAM
Middleton-in-Teesdale
Bishop Auckland
Newton Aycliffe
Sedgefield
Stockton-on-Tees
Appleby
Ullswater
Patterdale
Shap
Brough
Barnard Castle
Bowes
Darlington
Teesside
Eaglescliffe
Orton
Kirkby Stephen
Ambleside
Tebay
Windermere
Scotch Corner
Reeth
Richmond
Swale
Kendal
Sedbergh
Hawes
Leyburn
Northallerton
Bedale
Whernside
Yorkshire Dales National Park
Kirkby Lonsdale
Thirsk
Ure
NORTH YORKSHIRE
PENNINES
Ingleton
Clapham
Wharfe
Lune
Ripon
Pateley Bridge
Lancaster
Settle
Threshfield
Fountains Abbey
Boroughbridge
North West
Long Preston
Knaresborough
Harrogate
YORKSHIRE
LANCASHIRE
Gisburn
Ribble
Skipton
Ilkley
Otley
Harewood
Wetherby
Tadcaster
Clitheroe
Colne
Keighley
Blackburn
Padiham
Nelson
Bingley
Burnley
BRADFORD
LEEDS
Accrington
Halifax
Garforth
Castleford
Leyland
Darwen
Todmorden
Rawtenstall
Brighouse
Chorley
Rochdale
Dewsbury
Pontefract
Bury
Wakefield
Bolton
Huddersfield
Oldham
Holmfirth
Barnsley
Wigan
MANCHESTER
Leigh
St Helens
Ashton-under-Lyne
Glossop
Stocksbridge
Conisbrough
Altrincham
Hyde
Peak District
Rotherham
Widnes
Stockport
High Peak
SHEFFIELD
Knutsford
Wilmslow
Whaley Bridge
Castleton
Chapel-en-le-Frith
Northwich
Dronfield
CHESHIRE
National Park
Macclesfield
Buxton
Staveley
Winsford
Baslow
Middlewich
Congleton
Chatsworth House
Chesterfield
Tarporley
Bakewell
Sandbach
Crewe
Little Moreton Hall
Clay Cross
Hardwick

Hartlepool
Middlesbrough
Redcar
Marske-by-the-Sea
Saltburn-by-the-Sea
Brotton
Guisborough
Loftus
Whitby
North York Moors National Park
Cleveland Hills
Helmsley
Pickering
Scalby
Scarborough
Filey
Malton
Norton
Easingwold
Flamborough Head
Bridlington
E. RIDING
& THE HUMBER
YORKSHIRE
Wetwang
Gt. Driffield
Beeford
Market Weighton
Leven
Hornsea
Beverley
KINGSTON-UPON-HULL
Selby
Barlby
Howden
Snaith
Goole
Humber Bridge
River Humber
R. Ouse
Hedon
Withernsea
Patrington
Barton-upon-Humber
N. LINCS
Thorne
Crowle
Scunthorpe
Immingham Dock
Immingham
Kilnsea
N.E. LINCS
Grimsby
Spurn Head
Cleethorpes
Bentley
Doncaster
Epworth
Brigg
Humberside
Caistor
Rotterdam
Zeebrugge
Bawtry
Gainsborough
R. Trent
Market Rasen
Louth
East Retford
East Midlands
Mablethorpe
Wragby
Sutton-on
NOTTS.
Tuxford
Lincoln
Alford
Ollerton
Horncastle
Partney

1 The Pipe and Glass Inn

West End,
South Dalton HU17 7PN
Tel.: (01430)810246 – Fax: (01430)810246
e-mail: email@pipeandglass.co.uk **Website:** www.pipeandglass.co.uk

Inspectors' favourites

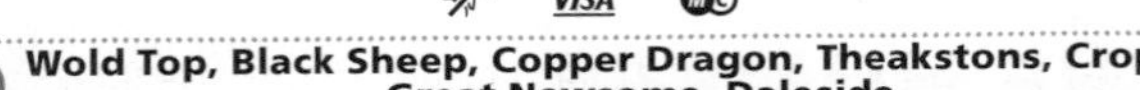
Wold Top, Black Sheep, Copper Dragon, Theakstons, Cropton, Great Newsome, Daleside

Boasting a friendly, bustling atmosphere, this well run, cream washed pub is as popular with locals as it is with visitors; all attracted by its reputation for good food, as illustrated by the framed menus, awards, press cuttings and photos which line the walls. Robust, hearty cooking makes good use of Yorkshire produce and the well priced menu covers a wide range of British dishes, with choices like prawn cocktail, omelette or a lunchtime ploughman's; terrine of hare, ham hock and foie gras; home smoked deer or line caught sea bass. The comfortable lounge area, with its leather Chesterfields and wood burning stove, is a relaxing spot for a pre-dinner drink, while the bar, with its polished wood tables, is a popular place to eat - but tables go fast, so get here early to nab one. Polite, friendly service enhances the Pipe and Glass experience still further - and they are planning to add bedrooms for 2009.

Food serving times

Tuesday-Saturday:
12pm-2pm, 6.30pm-9.30pm

Sunday: 12pm-4pm

Closed 25 December,
2 weeks January

Prices

Meals: a la carte £ 22/32

Typical Dishes

Potted Hornsea crab
Burdass Barnsley chop
Lemon verbena posset

5mi Northwest of Beverley by A164, B1248 and side road West. Parking.

2 The Falling Stone

Main St,
Thwing YO25 3DS
Tel.: (01262)470403

  MC

 **John Smith Cask, Theakston XB, Woldtop Falling Stone and 1 guest ale**

Named after a meteorite which dropped from the skies here many years ago, this brick built pub was taken over by new owners in 2007 - Peter is to be found behind the bar, while Ros takes care of front of house - and they have made it very much a part of village life, with regular quiz and theme nights. Go through the door on your right and you enter a small bar with an open fire and hunting themed pictures on the walls; take the left door for the comfortable, traditionally furnished lounge area – great for pre-dinner drinks - and a smart linen-clad restaurant. The same blackboard menu of classic pub dishes is served throughout and choices might include gammon and egg or pie and chips as well steaks and altogether more wholesome soups. This is a pub that takes its beer seriously and there's a fine selection of local ales from the Wold Brewery, including some very good bitter. Service is polite and friendly and the ambience relaxed.

Food serving times

Monday-Saturday:
11.30am-2.30pm,
6.30pm-8.45pm

Sunday: 11.30am-2.30pm

Prices

Meals: £ 7/18 and a la carte £ 15/28

Typical Dishes

Leek & potato soup
Gammon & eggs
Bread & butter pudding

9mi West of Bridlington by B1253 and minor road North. Parking.

3 Crab and Lobster

Dishforth Rd,
Asenby YO7 3QL

Tel.: (01845)577286 – Fax: (01845)577109
Website: www.crabandlobster.co.uk

 **Golden Pippin, John Smith's Cask**

The Crab and Lobster's thatched exterior may fool you into assuming it's just like any other long-established pub, but venture inside and you'll realise that this inn is one of a kind, thanks to the eclectic mix of memorabilia, ornaments, knick-knacks and pictures which clutter the rooms. There are three distinctive dining areas; a low-ceilinged bar with matted flooring, a more formal restaurant, just the place for a candlelit meal, and an airy conservatory-style extension, known as the pavilion. Outside, a cobbled terrace boasts wrought iron furniture. The Crab hasn't got a marine moniker for nothing – the emphasis here is on fresh seafood landed as locally as possible. Feast on fishcakes, fish pie, fillet of wild sea bass or Tandooried monkfish; the same extensive menu is served throughout, supplemented by daily specials chalked on blackboards, and service is polite, friendly and efficient.

Food serving times
Monday-Sunday:
12pm-2.30pm, 7pm-10pm

- Seafood -

Prices
Meals: £ 15 (lunch)
and a la carte £ 29/45

14 rooms: £ 100/230

Typical Dishes
Oak roast salmon
Fillet of wild seabass
Warm Belgian chocolate tart

 *5.25 mi Southwest of Thirsk by A168. Parking.* 

4 George and Dragon Inn

Aysgarth DL8 3AD
Tel.: (01969)663358 – Fax: (01969)663773
e-mail: info@georgeanddragonaysgarth.co.uk
Website: www.georgeanddragonaysgarth.co.uk

 **Black Sheep, Theakston, John Smith Cask, Dales Brewery**

With its proximity to the impressive Aysgarth Falls and the Dales Countryside Museum at Hawes, as well as its setting in the heart of Wensleydale, this traditional family pub packs an instant punch. There's a pleasant terrace with thatched umbrellas, and, inside, a snug little bar highlighted by a crackling fire and fine array of Yorkshire ales. The feel for local produce extends to lunchtime sandwiches with, typically, Nidderdale salmon and Swalesdale cheddar. More substantial old favourites like Wensleydale park sausages and mash or fish and chips make a reassuring appearance alongside more ambitious fare: tuck into this lot in either the airy Victorian styled dining room, or the open dining area with its display of wine knickknacks on the walls. There are seven comfy bedrooms; remember to book in advance – with its lovely scenery and superb walks, this is a popular spring and summer destination.

Food serving times
Monday-Sunday:
12pm-2pm, 5.30pm-9pm
Closed 2 weeks January

Prices
Meals: £ 13 /16
and a la carte £ 20/30
7 rooms: £ 40/85

Typical Dishes
Chicken liver paté
Seabass fillets
Lemon & treacle sponge

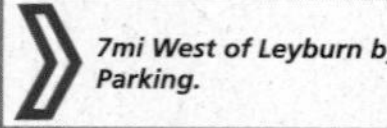
7mi West of Leyburn by A684.
Parking.

5 The Three Hares Country Inn

Main St,
Bilbrough YO23 3PH
Tel.: (01937)832128 – Fax: (01937)836186
e-mail: info@thethreehares.co.uk **Website:** www.thethreehares.co.uk

VISA AE

Timothy Taylor, Black Sheep and Farmer's Blonde

If you're spending the day at the races it's definitely worth getting up a little earlier to sample the delights of the special race day brunch at this charming whitewashed pub in the sleepy village of Bilbrough. With frequent changes of staff – including the chef – this pub has had a rocky history but this has not stopped the villagers from coming here and their patience has been rewarded with the return of the team who originally made it a hit. There's the choice of a pleasant terrace, a snug bar area or three equally characterful rooms with busy walls and a rather eclectic mix of décor. The frequently-changing menu displays a classical Yorkshire base and has a strong emphasis on local, seasonal produce. Dishes are hearty and tasty and might include pan-fried duck breast or open lasagne of wild mushrooms, with apple and pear tarte Tatin or chocolate brownie to follow. If they're available the steak burgers in particular are terrific.

Food serving times

Tuesday-Sunday and Bank Holiday Monday:
12pm-2pm, 7pm-9pm

Closed Monday except Bank Holidays

Prices

Meals: a la carte £ 23/30

Typical Dishes

Smoked salmon
Five spice roast duck
Warm chocolate pudding

5mi south-west of York on A64.
Parking.

6 The Bull

Broughton,
Skipton BD23 3AE
Tel.: (01756)792065 – Fax: (01756)792065
e-mail: janeneil@thebullatbroughton.co.uk **Website:** www.thebullatbroughton.co.uk

Bull Bitter, Copper Dragon Best, Copper Dragon 1816

Set within the grounds of the Broughton Hall Country Park Estate, just down the road from the bustling market town of Skipton, this spacious stone pub is rustic in character with its warren of little rooms and snugs, open fire, stone floors and timbered beams. The menu involves robust, classic British dishes such as shepherd's pie, fish of the day or duck breast, and the odd French touch too in the form of dishes such as cassoulet. If you're after something lighter, try fishcakes or a chicken breast ciabatta, or for a more economical option, go for the "Early bird" set price 2 course menu. There's plenty of choice, it's all homemade, and local produce is well-used. The large terrace for outside dining, and the friendly welcome served up with the food add two more good reasons why this pub is a great stop off point on your way to or from the Yorkshire Dales, or indeed a destination in its own right.

Food serving times

Monday-Saturday:
12pm-2pm, 6pm-9pm

Sunday and bank holiday Monday:
12pm-7pm

Closed Sunday dinner

Prices

Meals: £ 13 (weekdays 2 course lunch & dinner (6-7pm)) and a la carte £ 19/31

Typical Dishes

Chicken liver parfait
Home-made sausages
Sticky toffee pudding

3mi west of Skipton on A69.
In the grounds of Broughton Hall Country Park Estate. Parking.

England • Yorkshire and The Humber • North Yorkshire

7 The Red Lion

Burnsall BD23 6BU

Tel.: (01756)720204 – Fax: (01756)720292

e-mail: redlion@daelnet.co.uk **Website:** www.redlion.co.uk

 **Theakston, Timothy Taylor, John Smith**

At the heart of the small rural community of Burnsall, on the banks of the River Wharfe, lies this stone built, ivy-clad inn; a historical haven for diners, fresh from fishing, walking, hunting, touring or business. With reputedly haunted cellars dating from the 12C, and a panelled bar – formerly a Ferryman's inn dating from the 16C - there's certainly plenty of character imprinted in this inn's creaking beams. Two comfortable lounge areas are perfect for relaxing or for a spot of lunch, while the traditionally furnished restaurant is perfect for dinner. Lunchtimes might see sandwiches, meatballs and chickpea fritters on offer while an evening menu might include locally shot game casserole or free range calves liver. Bedrooms come in various shapes and sizes but the original rooms have the most character, with beams, sloping floors, uneven walls and antique furniture. The newer rooms, though less individual, also have good facilities.

Food serving times

Monday-Sunday:
12pm-2.30pm (bar snacks),
7pm-9.30pm

Prices

Meals: £ 31 (dinner)
and a la carte £ 20/30

25 rooms: £ 60/150

Typical Dishes

Provençal fish soup
Pheasant au vin
Crème brûlée

3mi Southeast of Grassington by B6265 West and B6160 South. Parking.

8 The Abbey Inn

Byland Abbey YO61 4BD
Tel.: (01347)868204 – Fax: (01347)868678
e-mail: abbeyinn@english-heritage.org.uk **Website:** www.bylandabbeyinn.com

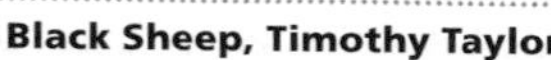

With stones borrowed from the beautiful 12C Cistercian Abbey and evidence of a medieval hostelry underfoot, this delightful period inn is steeped in history. Set in a breathtaking location, it displays heritage colours, stone walls, flag flooring and historic documents aplenty, with intimate front rooms looking out to the Abbey, and a larger Victorian-Gothic themed room boasting a large glass roof. Cooking is seasonal and local, employing simple techniques to allow natural flavours to show through; it ranges from light bites and a set menu at lunch to a more substantial à la carte supplemented by specials in the evening. This may include tian of crab with pink grapefruit or tea-smoked venison with pickled rhubarb, followed by rack of Swaledale lamb or East Coast Whiting, with sweet Yorkshire or vanilla milk pudding for dessert. Charming bedrooms, two with Abbey views, boast spacious, luxurious bathrooms and Mousey Thompson furnishings.

Food serving times

Wednesday-Saturday: 12pm-2.30pm, 6pm-9pm

Sunday: 12pm-2.30pm

Closed 24 December dinner, 25-26 December, 31 December dinner, 1 January

Prices

Meals: £ 17 (lunch) and a la carte £ 17/28

3 rooms: £ 95/199

Typical Dishes
Savoury Fat Rascal
Roast cod
Lemon & orange tart

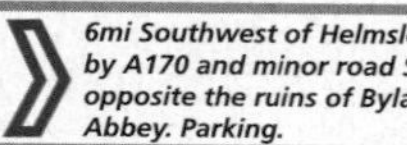

6mi Southwest of Helmsley by A170 and minor road South; opposite the ruins of Byland Abbey. Parking.

Carlton Husthwaite

9 Carlton Bore

Carlton Husthwaite THIRSK YO7 2BU
Tel.: (01845)501265
e-mail: chefhessel@aol.com **Website:** www.carltonbore.co.uk

 **John Smith, Old Bore Bitter, Black Sheep, Hambleton Ales**

Sister to the Old Bore in West Yorkshire, this spacious 17C inn is situated at the heart of a delightful stone and brick built village, with pleasant countryside views. The owner's experience shines through here, especially in the kitchen, where they have a passion for local ingredients and try hard to source only Yorkshire based produce. Suppliers are recognised in a list on the menu or next to the dishes which they have contributed to, and some are even depicted in caricatures on the pub walls. The diverse menu is immensely appealing, featuring dishes such as parsnip bhajis, wood pigeon pie and Yorkshire Brack and butter pudding. Of particular note are the Wood Deli Platters – where you create your own dish from a selection of salad, fish and meats – and The Whole Nine Yards, a board of nine Yorkshire dairies' cheeses. With three boar's heads watching over you and food like this, there's no shortage of reasons for you to pig out.

Food serving times

Tuesday-Saturday:
12pm-2.15pm, 6pm-9.30pm

Sunday: 12pm-8pm

Prices

Meals: a la carte £ 17/25

Typical Dishes
Goats cheese tart
Lamb shoulder
Poached rhubarb

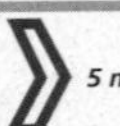

5 mi southeast of Thirsk off A19

10 Foresters Arms

Carlton-in-Coverdale DL8 4BB
Tel.: (01969)640272 – Fax: (01969)640272
e-mail: chambersmic@hotmail.co.uk **Website:** www.forestersarms-carlton.co.uk

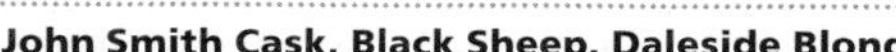

John Smith Cask, Black Sheep, Daleside Blonde

Whether you've built up an appetite walking, grouse shooting or having fun fighting folly at the Forbidden Corner, the Foresters Arms will provide welcome sustenance and an open fire by which to warm yourself. Situated at the entrance of the rural village of Carlton, this small, stone-built pub has two characterful, picture-filled, flag-floored rooms in which to eat, plus a formal beamed dining room which is open in the evenings, and seats outside for sunny afternoons. The welcome and the service are friendly, and the keen owners have put the emphasis here firmly onto the food, with traditional home-cooked dishes, made wherever possible with locally sourced ingredients. Specials are chalked up on the blackboard by the bar and you can choose between dishes such as Roe deer steak, pheasant breast or seafood parcel. Three rooms offer a comfortable bed for the night; décor ranges from cottage-style to modern.

Food serving times

Tuesday: 6.30pm-8.30pm

Wednesday-Saturday: 12pm-1.45pm, 6.30pm-8.30pm

Sunday: 12pm-2.30pm

Closed 24 December dinner, Bank Holiday dinner

Prices

Meals: £ 15 and a la carte £ 20/26

3 rooms: £ 65/79

4.5 mi Southwest of Middleham by Coverdale rd. Parking next to pub in village car park.

11 Fox and Hounds

Carthorpe DL8 2LG
Tel.: (01845)567433 – Fax: (01845)567155
e-mail: helenjt36@btinternet.com **Website:** www.foxandhoundscarthorpe.co.uk

Worthingtons, Black Sheep

This pub has been in the same family for more than 25 years and its walls and shelves are stacked with ornaments, plates, photos and old farm equipment attesting to its recent past. Its sense of history goes back further than this, however, and the forge and water pump in the restaurant bear witness to its time as the village smithy. Situated close to the A1 in a small rural village, this pretty, ivy-clad pub serves up locally-sourced produce in a selection of classic, homemade pub dishes, with specials chalked up on the blackboard menu. You can eat in the bar or at an old wooden table in the beamed dining room and service is friendly and polite. Can't decide on a dessert? Then try tasting them all in the "Fox and Hounds Special." There's also a cabinet containing homemade meringues, jams, chutneys and the like to take away, so you can thrill your taste buds further in the privacy of your own home.

Food serving times

Tuesday-Sunday:
12pm-2pm, 7pm-9.30pm

Closed 25 December,
26 December dinner,
first week in January

Prices

Meals: £ 16 (weekdays)
and a la carte £ 18/28

Typical Dishes

Ham hock terrine
Fillet steak
Sticky ginger pudding

9mi North of Ripon by minor road via Wath and Kirklington. Parking.

12 Ye Old Sun Inn

Main Street,
Colton LS24 8EP
Tel.: (01904)744261
e-mail: kelly.mccarthy@btconnect.com **Website:** www.yeoldsuninn.co.uk

 **Timothy Taylor Landlord, Black Sheep Bitter, Cropton Brewery "2 pints" and weekly changing guest beers**

It's a family affair at Ye Old Sun Inn; he's in the kitchen, while she serves out front, and they also run a small deli selling homemade goodies including cheese, oils, jams, chutneys and freshly baked bread. The four small dining areas have a homely, rustic feel, with open coal fires and period prints and photos, and while the sun theme adds further charm inside, the spacious gardens and decked terrace provide somewhere to sit when it comes out for real. Cooking is classically based, with an international flavour, so menus might include Dales lamb or stuffed vine leaves, steak and ale pie or Thai BBQ chicken. Menus change on a monthly basis, and the food is tasty, seasonal and local – with some of the ingredients grown in the inn's own poly tunnel and herb garden. The selection of freshly churned ice creams will have you licking your lips in anticipation, while the chef's dinky dessert platter wins the prize for the best named pud.

Food serving times

Tuesday-Saturday:
12pm-2pm, 6pm-9.30pm

Sunday: 12pm-4pm

Closed 26 December,
1-21 January

Prices

Meals: £ 17 (lunch)
and a la carte £ 18/25

Typical Dishes
Smoked salmon
Trio of local pork
Jam roly poly

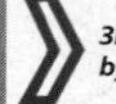
3mi Northeast of Tadcaster by A659 and A64. Parking.

13 The Tiger Inn

Coneythorpe HG5 0RY
Tel.: (01423)330439 – Fax: (01423)331095
e-mail: ifgill@btinternet.com **Website:** www.tiger-inn.co.uk

 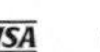 

Tetley's Cask Bitter, Fuller's London Pride, Hambleton's Best Bitter

A cuddly toy tiger surveys proceedings from his elevated position at one end of the bar, but despite an interesting theory about a travelling circus, no one seems sure of the origins of this red brick pub's unusual name. Atypical in name, yet traditional in nature, its style comes from the classic school of pub furnishing, with green wood panels, pew seating and countryside prints on the walls. Its front rooms, whose windows overlook the green, are where the locals gather for a drink; there's a beamed room ideal for larger groups, plus more formal dining rooms at the rear. Cooking is robust and hearty; with a modern take on a classic British menu, and fairly-priced dishes might include fish pie, boiled salt beef, Yorkshire hotpot or roast saddle of rabbit. The sweetly-named "Soup made this morning" tells you all you need to know about the food's freshness; there are sandwiches and nibbles, plus a blackboard menu of mostly fish specials.

Food serving times

Tuesday-Friday:
12pm-2.30pm, 5.45pm-9pm

Saturday:
12pm-2.30pm,
5.45pm-9.30pm

Sunday: 12pm-2.30pm

Closed 25 December

Prices

Meals: £ 15 and a la carte £ 20/25

Typical Dishes

Devilled whitebait
Rib-eye steak
Lemon posset

3.5mi north-east of Knaresborough by A59. Parking.

14 Wyvill Arms

Constable Burton DL8 5LH
Tel.: (01677)450581

VISA MC

John Smith, Theakston, Black Sheep, Guinness, Kronenburg, Fosters

Lest you forget you're in the middle of the countryside, all areas of this ivy-clad stone pub contain a liberal sprinkling of rustically-themed decorative pictures, fabrics and ornaments. There's a choice of eating areas: a small bar with an open fire, a dining area with stone floors, banquette seating and linen laid tables, plus a more formal dining area, with high-backed leather chairs. Cooking is hearty and robust and menus make use of local ingredients such as black pudding and Wensleydale cheese, with moments of individuality among the more classic pub fare. If the weather's playing ball, the neat gardens, with resident wishing well, have a terrace for outside dining. Bedrooms here are simple but neat. Make use of your location to go walking, riding or cycling on the Dales and to view the gardens at Constable Burton Hall, or travel slightly further afield to Jervaulx Abbey, where Wensleydale cheese was reputedly created.

3.5mi East of Leyburn on A684. Parking.

Food serving times
Tuesday-Sunday:
12pm-2pm, 6pm-9.30pm

Prices
Meals: a la carte £ 24/36

2 rooms: £ 55/75

Typical Dishes
Seared scallops
Loin of lamb
Three way brûlée

15 The Durham Ox

Westway,
Crayke YO61 4TE

Tel.: (01347)821506 – Fax: (01347)823326
e-mail: enquiries@thedurhamox.com **Website:** www.thedurhamox.com

 **Timothy Taylor Landlord, Theakston**

Complete with curled up cat, the cosy, characterful interior of this 300 year old inn has a distinctly rustic feel with carved wood panels, flagstone floor and open fires. Homemade hampers are for sale in the deli shop and you can eat in either bar or in the boldly decorated, beamed dining room. Country style bedrooms are situated in the adjacent block of converted farm cottages and the rear courtyard with its fixed marquee has great views over the surrounding countryside. The famous Durham Ox, exhibited around the country in the early 19C, reportedly reached a maximum weight of 270 stone. If you consider yourself to have the constitution of an ox, then select a dish from the à la carte menu. You'll find hearty British cooking, with a wide-ranging choice including local meat and game. Available at both lunch and dinner, a snack from the "bar bites" menu might be a better option for those of a more delicate disposition.

Food serving times

Monday-Saturday:
12pm-2.30pm, 6pm-9pm

Sunday:
12pm-3pm, 6pm-8.30pm

Closed 25 December

Prices

Meals: a la carte £ 16/26

4 rooms: £ 60/120

Typical Dishes

Baked Queen scallops
Braised lamb shank
Treacle tart

2 mi East of Easingwold on Helmsley rd. Parking.

16 The Travellers Rest

Dalton DL11 7HU
Tel.: (01833)621225
e-mail: annebabsa@aol.com

 **Black Sheep Best Bitter**

This stone-built pub sits in a small rural hamlet, reached down the narrow country roads which branch off from the A66. Although its ivy-clad exterior suggests a traditional Yorkshire inn, inside it's actually quite plainly decorated, but the friendly welcome from staff and locals alike more than makes up for any neutrality of décor. Order your drinks at the copper-topped bar and soak in the atmosphere; with its beamed ceilings, open fire and pictures of local life hanging on the walls, you'll soon find this inn has retained plenty of old fashioned charm. Most people eat in the dining room, but you can also dine in the bar rooms. Casually-dressed staff are polite and keen, and serve classically based dishes from the constantly evolving blackboard menus, made with whatever's fresh in that day. After an hour or two, you should certainly feel well rested – and ready to explore the moors and Dales.

Food serving times

Tuesday-Saturday:
6pm-9.30pm

Sunday: 12pm-2.30pm

Closed 25-26 December, 1 January

Prices

Meals: a la carte £ 17/30

Typical Dishes

Goats cheese tart
Herb crusted halibut
Meringue & passion fruit cream

7.5mi north-west of Scotch Corner by A66. Parking.

17 The Blue Lion

East Witton DL8 4SN
Tel.: (01969)624273 – Fax: (01969)624189
e-mail: bluelion@breathe.net **Website:** www.thebluelion.co.uk

Theakstons Best Bitter, Black Sheep Riggwelter, Black Sheep Best Bitter

We all know a Red Lion but a Blue Lion? Well it's a little different and that's exactly what this pub is: a refreshing change from the status quo. The pleasant village of East Witton provides the perfect setting, but if you picked it up and moved it this pub would still exude charm and character aplenty. Solid stone floors, walls filled with countryside memorabilia, open fires and gentle candlelight provide a warm, friendly glow, while the delightful bar is stocked with real ales and a good selection of wines. With seasonality and traceability at their core, the tasty mix of classic and modern dishes changes daily, and the locally bagged game in particular is always a welcome sight. In a similar style to the bar, the bedrooms – split between the pub and the outbuildings – are warm, cosy and feature lots of wood. If you're after a true and honest pub then look no further, The Lion and its experienced owner definitely win the blue ribbon.

Food serving times
Monday-Sunday:
12pm-2.15pm, 7pm-9.15pm
Booking essential

Prices
Meals: a la carte £ 21/35
15 rooms: £ 68/135

Typical Dishes
Goats cheese
Roast fillet of cod
Dark chocolate terrine

3mi Southeast of Leyburn on A6108. Parking.

18 The Plough Inn

Main Street,
Fadmoor YO62 7HY
Tel.: (01751)431515 – Fax: (01751)432492
e-mail: enquiries@theploughfadmoor.co.uk

   VISA 

Black Sheep Best Bitter, Tetleys Cask

Set in a small village, overlooking the green, this is the sort of country pub people are happy to travel some distance to eat at, but it also goes down well with the hungry hikers who happen upon it. A friendly welcome greets you, service is informal yet organised, and the exposed beams, quarry tiled floors and open fires provide a characterful and relaxing environment in which to dine. There are various little rooms and snugs to choose from, with walls covered in framed maps and pictures, and a decked terrace and small garden for use when the sun has got his hat on. On the extensive table and blackboard menus you'll find the sort of classic pub food that would fill a hungry ploughman, like homemade steak and ale pie, a choice of warming soups, or rice pudding, and flavours range from the local, with dishes such as creamy Wensleydale mushrooms, to the more international with Thai fishcakes or seafood paella.

Food serving times
Monday-Saturday:
12pm-1.45pm,
6.30pm-8.45pm

Sunday:
12pm-1.45pm, 7pm-8.45pm

Closed 25-26 December and 1 January

Booking essential

Prices
Meals: a la carte £ 18/31

Typical Dishes
Duck & mango spring rolls
Roast chicken breast
Coffee & Tia Maria tiramisu

2.25mi north-west of Kirbymoorside. Parking.

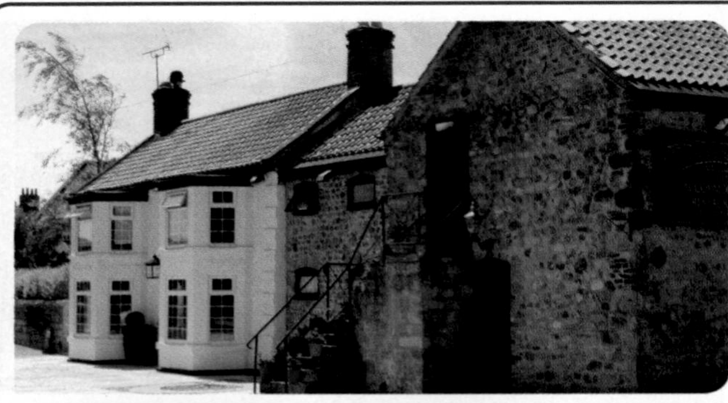

19 The General Tarleton Inn

Boroughbridge Rd,
Ferrensby HG5 0PZ
Tel.: (01423)340284 – Fax: (01423)340288
e-mail: gti@generaltarleton.co.uk **Website:** www.generaltarleton.co.uk

 **Black Sheep Bitter, Timothy Taylor Landlord**

With four spacious rooms, a bright glass-roofed courtyard and al fresco dining either in the garden or on the lovely decking, you're spoilt for choice at this 18C coaching inn. One of the forerunners of today's gastropubs, it still leads the way, the menu featuring a strong seasonal, local base, with traceability and supplier relationships at its core. There's no longer a distinction between the brasserie and restaurant, so the same menu of tasty, warming dishes is served throughout. Several old favourites can always be found, maybe fish and chips or steak and ale pie, while other dishes could include crispy belly pork or seafood in a pastry bag (their speciality), followed by char-grilled haunch of venison or corn-fed Goosnargh duckling in gingerbread sauce; and for dessert, perhaps Yorkshire custard tart with Armagnac soaked prunes or pannacotta with green apple sorbet. Bedrooms are individually styled, luxurious and very comfortable.

From A1 at Boroughbridge, take A6055 road towards Knaresborough; the inn is on the right hand side. Parking.

Food serving times

Monday-Saturday:
6pm-9.15pm

Sunday: 12pm-2pm

Bar meals lunch Monday-Saturday and dinner Sunday

Prices

Meals: £ 16 (lunch)
and a la carte £ 25/35

14 rooms: £ 107/129

Typical Dishes

Seafood moneybags
Braised shoulder of lamb
Trio of rhubarb

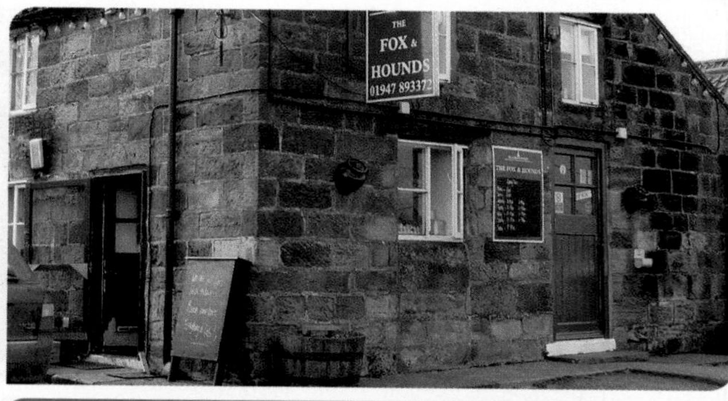

20 Fox & Hounds

Goldsborough YO21 3RX
Tel.: (01947)893372

 **Leffe Blonde**

Part of the Mulgrave Estate, this friendly pub is situated in a delightful coastal hamlet close to the historic port of Whitby, just a stone's throw from the North Sea. Starting life as a farm building, it now looks more like somebody's home than a pub; outside there's a small garden with bench seating, while inside there are two cosy, very traditional rooms with open fires. To say the food here is seasonal is an understatement; the concise blackboard menu is constantly evolving – changing as much as twice as a day – and produce is strictly local, with the odd organic touch. Fresh fish is a speciality so you're likely to find dishes such as local sea bass or seared haddock; followed maybe, by poached Yorkshire rhubarb. Cooking is straightforward, unfussy and devoid of any unnecessary showiness, and, best of all, prices won't break the bank. Unfortunately, a fire in mid-2008 has led to closure but it's hoped that it will re-open soon.

Food serving times

Wednesday-Saturday:
12pm-1pm, 6.30pm-8pm

Sunday: 12pm-1pm

Closed Christmas, New Year and Bank Holidays

Prices

Meals: a la carte £ 21/34

Typical Dishes

Chicken liver crostini
Seared halibut fillet
Bluestones goats cheese

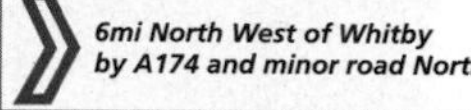

6mi North West of Whitby by A174 and minor road North

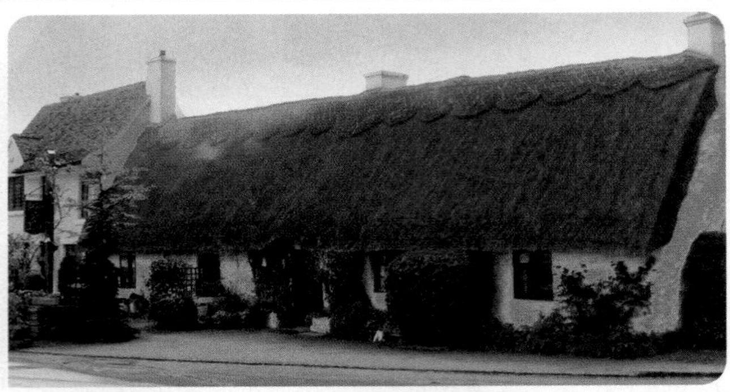

21 The Star Inn

High St,
Harome YO62 5JE

Tel.: (01439)770397 – Fax: (01439)771833
e-mail: jpern@thestaratharome.co.uk **Website:** www.thestaratharome.co.uk

Inspectors' favourites

  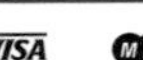 

Leeds Brewery, Hambleton Ales

Twinkling brightly in the firmament, this aptly named star's reputation precedes it, so you will need to book well ahead for one of its eight restaurant tables; or alternatively, arrive early to dine in the deliciously snug beamed bar. Cooking is a celebration of the pub's Yorkshire roots and dishes combine traditional Northern flavours with more up-to-date nuances, using ingredients sourced from local estates and farms. How unusual, yet how welcome it is to see words such as woof, hare, lovage and parkin on a menu. Dining in the restaurant allows access to the cosy, romantic coffee loft where you can enjoy complementary cheese and crackers with your after dinner drink; there's a seriously compiled wine list and staff provide professional service. Luxuriously-appointed rooms have a stylish country feel and the gastronomic empire spawned by this beautiful 700 year old inn's success now includes a herb garden, a butcher's shop and a deli.

Food serving times

Monday-Saturday:
11.30am-2pm,
6.15pm-9.30pm

Sunday: 12pm-6pm

Closed 25 December

Booking essential

Prices

Meals: a la carte £ 25/40

15 rooms: £ 120/230

Typical Dishes

Black pudding & foie gras

Fillet of John Dory

Yorkshire curd tartlet

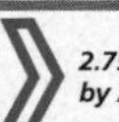

2.75 mi Southeast of Helmsley by A170. Parking.

22 **The Angel Inn**

Hetton BD23 6LT

Tel.: (01756)730263 – Fax: (01756)730363
e-mail: info@angelhetton.co.uk
Website: www.angelhetton.co.uk

 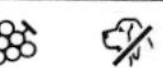  VISA  AE

Black Sheep Bitter, Black Sheep Ale, Timothy Taylor Landlord

The awards hanging among the cartoons and pictures on the walls of this beamed 18C inn are a clue to the quality of the dining experience to be had here; just as the clusters of wine bottles on every flat surface, and the adjoining "wine cave" where tastings are held, point to the exceptional calibre of the wine list. Such a pub does tend to get very busy, so make sure you book ahead – and avoid a table by the bar where drinkers waiting for a table in the dining room tend to stand. The kitchen makes good use of local produce to inform both the rustic bar menu and the à la carte, with choices including Swinton Park venison, Bolton Abbey mutton and Yorkshire lamb, beef and pheasant, and smartly dressed staff in waistcoats and ties provide polite, friendly service. Bedrooms are set in a converted stone built farm building. All are very individual and spacious with high quality furniture and fabrics and plenty of extra little touches.

5.75mi North of Skipton by B6265. Parking.

Food serving times

Monday-Friday:
12pm-2.15pm, 6pm-9pm

Saturday:
12pm-2.15pm, 6pm-9.30pm

Sunday: 12pm-2pm

Closed 25 December,
1st week January

Booking essential

Prices

Meals: £ 23/35 and a la carte £ 25/35

5 rooms: £ 130/155

Typical Dishes

Black pudding croquettes
Slow-roast duckling
Sticky toffee pudding

23 The Charles Bathurst Inn

Langthwaite DL11 6EN
Tel.: (01748)884567 – Fax: (01748)884599
e-mail: info@cbinn.co.uk **Website:** www.cbinn.co.uk

 **Black Sheep Best Bitter, Riggwelter, Theakston Best Bitter, John Smith Best Bitter**

Set high on the hills of Arkengarthdale, with views out over the surrounding countryside, the CB inn, as it is known locally, enjoys a strong reputation in the area. Dating from the 18C, although sympathetically extended, the spacious bar has various timbered rooms and snugs to sit in. Photos and paintings of the region decorate the walls and the local servers are well-organised and chatty. Curiously and more curiously, the daily-changing menus are written on the mirrors above the fire - but thankfully there are no slithy toves on offer here. There is something to suit every taste though; modern British cooking blends with the classics and there's the odd sunny European influence too- from the tarts to the terrines, all making good use of local produce. For those staying overnight, bedrooms are large and individually styled with period furniture and two comfortable lounges are also available.

Food serving times
Monday-Sunday:
12pm-2pm, 6.30pm-9pm
Closed 25 December

Prices
Meals: a la carte £ 20/35
19 rooms: £ 93/120

Typical Dishes
Duck liver & pork terrine
Lamb shank
Lemon & lime cheesecake

3.25mi Northwest of Reeth on Langthwaite rd. Parking.

24 The Sandpiper Inn

Market Pl,
Leyburn DL8 5AT

Tel.: (01969)622206 – Fax: (01969)625367
e-mail: hsandpiper99@aol.com **Website:** www.sandpiperinn.co.uk

 **Black Sheep, Copper Dragon**

A friendly Yorkshire welcome is extended to the Dale walkers who come to refuel at this stone built part 16C pub, situated just off the main square in the market town of Leyburn.Visitors can rest their blistered feet by the fire in the traditionally furnished, split-level, beamed bar, or plump for a seat in the neatly laid-out dining room with its polished wood furniture. A small enclosed terrace out the back provides a third alternative for when it's sunny, but you'll have to come inside to read the blackboard menus, found hanging on the walls amidst the general clutter of decorative pictures, books and ornaments. Influences from across Europe are found in the good sized daily-changing menus, so the chicken is Moroccan, the tomatoes are sunblushed and local lamb comes with a garlic sauce. Two pleasant bedrooms are upstairs on the first floor, with a third over the road in a converted cottage.

Food serving times

Monday-Sunday:
12pm-2.30pm, 6.30pm-9pm

Closed 25 December and 1 January

Sometimes closed Tuesdays in winter

Prices

Meals: a la carte £ 24/33

2 rooms: £ 65

Typical Dishes

Seasonal soup
Crispy duck leg
Trio of chocolate

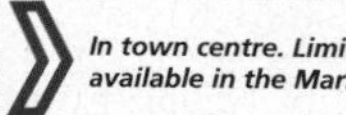

In town centre. Limited parking available in the Market Place.

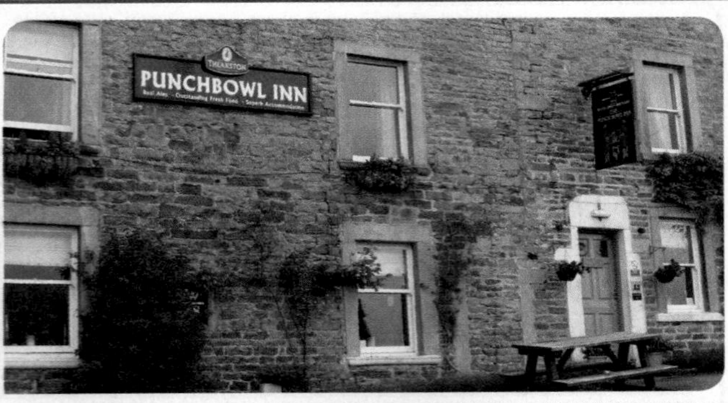

25 The Punch Bowl Inn

Low Row DLL 6PF
Tel.: (01748)886233
e-mail: info@pbinn.co.uk **Website:** www.pbinn.co.uk

 **Black Sheep Best Bitter, Rigwelter, John Smith Smooth, Theakston Best Bitter**

In the heart of Swaledale, with splendid views over the countryside, the 17C stone built Punch Bowl Inn has always been a popular stopping off point for walkers - and never more so than now. Having been thoroughly modernised, it reopened at the end of 2006 under the capable ownership of the proprietors of the nearby CB Inn, who, in their appreciation for abbreviation, now refer to it the PB Inn. Modernised it may have been, but with open fires, solid wood floors and a bar crafted by Robert "Mousey" Thompson, it's retained a wealth of rustic charm, and the atmosphere is one of relaxed informality, with customers seemingly blissed out on endorphins from all that fresh Yorkshire air and exercise. As at the CB, menus are writ large on mirrors above the fire, and have a strong sense of the seasons, so expect tasty stew and sticky toffee pudding in the winter and salads in the summer. Bedrooms are stylish, spacious and supremely comfortable.

Food serving times
Monday-Sunday:
12pm-2pm, 6.30pm-9pm
Closed 25 December

Prices
Meals: a la carte £ 18/32
11 rooms: £ 60/115

Typical Dishes
Duck liver salad
Salmon fillet
Yorkshire parkin

 *In the middle of hamlet* 

26 The Appletree

Marton YO62 6RD
Tel.: (01751)431457 – Fax: (01751)430190
e-mail: appletreeinn@supanet.com **Website:** www.appletreeinn.co.uk

  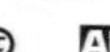

John Smith Cask, Moorhouse TJ's Tipple, Woldtop Falling Stone, Great Newsome Prickly Back Otchan, Suddaby's Windfall

"A [trip to the] apple a day keeps the doctor away". In the sleepy village of Marton you'll find this spacious, welcoming stone-built pub, with the very tree after which it was named still going strong in the garden. To help you with your five-a-day there is a one acre kitchen plot and an orchard close by: so, supplemented by regular donations of home-grown produce from the locals, it's not hard for the chef to keep an eye on his ingredients. Seasonality is important here, with careful preparation and cooking techniques ensuring that the best natural flavours are obtained. The menu changes weekly and may include Yorkshire blue cheese soufflé, followed by roast fillet of hare or braised Marton beef; and puddings such as Yorkshire treacle tart, lavender meringue, or as many tasty mini desserts as you like. Best of all, if you can't decide what to have just take some home with you, as there is a counter full of homemade produce for sale.

Food serving times

Wednesday-Sunday:
12pm-2pm, 6pm-9.30pm

Closed 25 December and 2 weeks January

Prices

Meals: a la carte £ 14/28

Typical Dishes

Whitby crab cheesecake
Confit belly of pork
Black "n" Blue
Marton mess

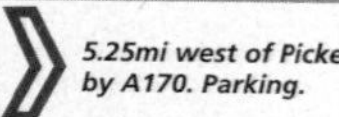

5.25mi west of Pickering by A170. Parking.

27 The Dawnay Arms

Newton-on-Ouse YO32 2BR
Tel.: (01347)848345
e-mail: dine@thedawnayarms.co.uk
Website: www.thedawnayatnewton.co.uk

 **Tetleys Cask, Timothy Taylor, Golden Best, Copper Dragon**

Having been the subject of a hefty conversion in 2007, this capacious 18C inn – named after the last owners of nearby Beningbrough Hall - boasts a handsome rustic style, thoroughly in tune with its rural surroundings. It's got the low beamed ceilings and the roaring fires. It's got the walls filled with countryside art and the solid stone floors. It's got the locally-crafted chunky wood tables. All that, and a stuffed armadillo too. A native Yorkshireman cooks up tasty, good value dishes in the kitchen, with everything fresh, homemade and seasonal; the lunch menu offers sandwiches and pub classics like shepherd's pie alongside fish stew or slow roast rump of lamb, while the dinner menu might tempt you with confit pork belly or ballotine of chicken. If you don't fancy eating in the bar, try the more formal rear dining room; it looks out over the terrace and gardens and down to the River Ouse, where the occasional guest arrives by boat.

Food serving times

Monday-Sunday:
12pm-2.30pm, 6pm-9.30pm

Closed 2 weeks in January

Prices

Meals: a la carte £ 20/35

Typical Dishes

Potted Whitby crab
Local roe deer
Champagne jelly

8mi North West of York by A19 and minor road West

28 The Black Swan

Oldstead YO61 4BL
Tel.: (01347)868387
e-mail: enquiries@blackswanoldstead.co.uk
Website: www.blackswanoldstead.co.uk

 **Black Sheep, Copper Dragon**

All too often nowadays, village pubs – traditionally at the hub of village life – are taken over by out-of-towners. Not so The Black Swan; owned and run by a family who have lived and farmed in Oldstead for generations. Originally a 16C house, it's been lovingly converted and features a cosy downstairs bar with open fire and oak fittings by the famous "Mousey" Thompson. Food is served mainly in the spacious upstairs dining room and in a smaller, slightly more formal room. Everything, including the black pudding, is homemade and the seasonal produce is locally sourced whenever possible. Dishes might include slow-roasted belly pork, pan-fried red mullet or braised shin of beef and Black Sheep ale pie; there are simpler dishes for children and a decent selection of real ales and local beers. With all this – and laudably low prices – it's no wonder the locals are flocking in. Bedrooms are currently being refurbished; due to open early 2009.

Food serving times
Tuesday-Sunday:
12pm-2pm, 6pm-9pm

Prices
Meals: a la carte £ 20/28

Typical Dishes
Smoked kipper tartlet
Roast belly pork
Baked egg custard tart

6mi South West of Helmsley by A170 and minor road via Byland Abbey

29 The Golden Lion

6 West End,
Osmotherley DL6 3AA
Tel.: (01609)883526
Website: www.goldenlionosmotherley.co.uk

 **North York Dales Brewing Co, Timothy Taylor, Daleside, Salamander**

Walkers stopping off at this old, stone built inn for a simple, satisfying Yorkshire meal will not be disappointed. There's plenty of choice for everyone on the well-priced, seasonal menus; and while traditional British dishes such as fish and steaks are just the right type of food to fill you up, ready once more to face the moors, there are also salads, pasta dishes and vegetarian options if you're after something lighter. Ingredients are locally sourced - and even the burgers and the ice cream are homemade. Set in the centre of a picturesque rural market village, the beamed candlelit interior of the pub is rustic through and through. There's a first floor dining area decorated with potted plants, but the fire lit ground floor bar is the best place to sit. The pub is well-run, and keen, friendly service from staff in T-shirts and aprons suggests that they are used to being busy. Three delightful bedrooms have a spacious, modern feel.

Food serving times

Monday-Tuesday: 6pm-9pm

Wednesday-Sunday: 12pm-2.30pm, 6pm-9pm

Closed 25 December

French Mediterranean

Prices

Meals: a la carte £ 17/24

3 rooms: £ 60

Typical Dishes

Smoked haddock risotto

Pan-fried pork & Parma ham

Poached pear & chocolate sauce

6 mi Northeast of Northallerton by A684. Parking in the village.

30 The Yorke Arms

Ramsgill-in-Nidderdale HG3 5RL
Tel.: (01423)755243 – Fax: (01423)755330
e-mail: enquiries@yorke-arms.co.uk
Website: www.yorke-arms.co.uk

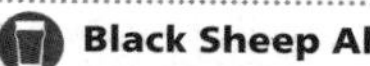

Black Sheep Ale

Set in unspoilt countryside near Gouthwaite reservoir, this part 17C, delightfully ivy clad former shooting lodge is quite simply one of England's most charming inns. Handsomely styled with carved wooden furniture, antiques, oriental rugs and bright, gilt-framed oils, two welcoming dining rooms feel closer in atmosphere to a country house than a village pub, and the formal, structured service is that of a restaurant rather than an inn, but as a dining experience it's calm, refined and, at its best, quite delightful. Precise and consistent seasonal cooking balances classical style with a subtle regional identity. Good value lunch Monday to Saturday and you can make the most of a lovely riverside terrace and gardens, or flop onto the squashy sofas in the lounge. Superlative, stylish and contemporary bedrooms have been recently refurbished.

Food serving times

Monday-Sunday:
12pm-2pm, 7pm-9pm

Closed Sunday dinner to non residents

Accommodation rates include dinner

Prices

Meals: £ 25 (lunch) and a la carte £ 45/55

12 rooms: £ 100/340

Typical Dishes

Whitby crab
Loin of rabbit
Grand Marnier & chocolate soufflé

5 mi Northwest of Pateley Bridge by Low Wath rd. Parking.

31 The Crown Inn

Roecliffe YO5 9LY

Tel.: (01423)322300 – Fax: (01423)322035

e-mail: info@crowninnroecliffe.com **Website:** www.crowninnroecliffe.com

VISA MC

Sharps Doombar, Theakstons Best, Old Speckled Hen, Pride of Pendle, Black Sheep, Fireside Ale, Bombardier, John Smith Cask

Recently refurbished, this 16C coaching inn's cosy inner boasts a solid stone floor, wooden beams and open fires; the bar is lined with local pictures and foodie photos and a butcher's block is piled high with countryside magazines through which to flick. Sourcing is given its rightful significance by the Crown's kitchen and the food served here has a broad Yorkshire burr; the result being distinctive, reliable, no nonsense bar meals such as winter vegetable broth, homemade game pie, braised pork neck and locally handmade pork sausages. For a more formal experience, head for a linen-laid table in the elegant dining room where you can sample classical, carefully-crafted cooking in the form of confit of beef shin and roasted marrowbone, wild venison or Scarborough lemon sole. Menus are supplemented by daily-changing blackboard specials - the fish are particularly tasty. Bedrooms are currently being refurbished; due to open in early 2009.

Food serving times

Monday-Saturday:
12pm-2.30pm, 6pm-9.30pm

Sunday:
12pm-2.30pm, 6pm-7pm

Prices

Meals: a la carte £ 20/40

Typical Dishes

Sweet Thai belly pork
Wild Cornish seabass
Trio of Wakefield rhubarb

1mi West of Boroughbridge by minor road

32 The Anvil Inn

Main St,
Sawdon YO13 9DY
Tel.: (01723)859896
e-mail: theanvilinnsawdon@btinternet.com **Website:** www.theanvilinnsawdon.co.uk

Black Sheep Best, Copper Dragon, Daleside, Hambleton Ales, Bradfield Brewery, Wold Top

Twenty years ago, you would have found blacksmiths working in this solid stone building. Now the atmosphere is more sedate, though much evidence of former days lives on: an old furnace, bellows, tools and the original anvil are all in situ. Close by, in the village of Sawdon, stunning views over Dalby Dale prevail, and the rustic charm of the inn – all candle-lit tables, country style paraphernalia and log-burning stove - loses nothing by comparison. Yorkshire ales are pulled in the locals' bar and the intimate dining room is like a home-from-home. Mark, one of the owners and also the chef here, trained at local college and his roots are in evidence with seriously considered, good value dishes using dishes primarily sourced from the nearby moors and dales. And the portions are good, too!

Food serving times

Tuesday-Saturday:
12pm-2pm, 6.30pm-9pm

Sunday: 12pm-3pm

Closed 26 December, 1 January and 2 weeks in January

Prices

Meals: a la carte £ 18/28

Typical Dishes

Mushroom rarebit
Fillets of wild seabass
Fresh mint pannacotta

12mi Southwest of Scarborough by A170 to Brompton and minor road north. Parking.

33 The Hare Inn

Scawton YO7 2HG
Tel.: (01845)597769
e-mail: geoff@brucearms.com **Website:** www.thehareinn.co.uk

 **Timothy Taylor Landlord, Black Sheep Best Bitter**

One and a half miles from the beautiful Rievaulx Abbey and gardens, in the very rural location of Scawton, sits The Hare, with its smart yellow exterior. There is a spacious main dining room, whose walls are filled with photos, prints and hanging hop bines, and an adjacent room with linen-laid tables; although the best place to sit is probably in the main bar by the open-fired stove, where you can become acquainted with the friendly resident Labrador, Teal. Cooking is satisfying, seasonal and freshly prepared, with vibrant use of local ingredients. The menu has a classical base, but there's something here to suit every taste, with meat, seafood and vegetarian offerings as well as daily specials chalked up on the blackboard. Any visitor here will recognise the truth Samuel Johnson expressed so well when he said, "There is nothing which has yet been contrived by man, by which so much happiness is produced as by a good tavern or inn".

Food serving times
Tuesday-Saturday:
12pm-2pm, 6.30pm-9.30pm
Sunday: 12pm-2pm
Closed Sunday dinner and Monday

Prices
Meals: a la carte £ 20/30

Typical Dishes
Ham hock terrine
Confit of duck
Pannacotta & soft fruit

 *Between Thirsk and Helmsley off north side of A170. Parking.* 

Fox and Hounds

Main St,
Sinnington YO62 6SQ
Tel.: (01751)431577 – Fax: (01751)432791
e-mail: foxhoundsinn@easynet.co.uk **Website:** www.thefoxandhoundsinn.co.uk

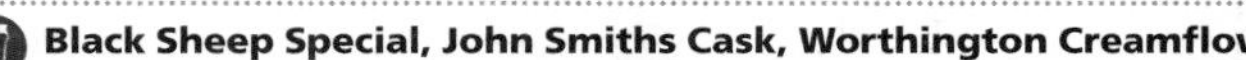

Black Sheep Special, John Smiths Cask, Worthington Creamflow

This extended 18C coaching inn is found on the river Seven, in the sleepy village of Sinnington, at the base of the North York moors. Its handsome stone exterior has long been a welcoming sight to tourists and locals alike, and inside there's a beamed bar and traditionally styled residents lounge, as well as a more modern, formal restaurant, set in the rear extension. Hungry as a hunter? Lunchtime menus offer classic dishes, such as steak or fish and chips, as well as lighter dishes, whilst the evening menu has a more international flavour to it, with dishes such as skewers of tiger prawns and king scallops or spiced monkfish. Uniformed staff provide polite, attentive service and the atmosphere is relaxed and friendly, with several open fires and a large garden. Weary as a woodlouse after all that walking? Retire to one of the compact bedrooms - quite cottagey in style, with flowery drapes and décor.

Food serving times

Monday-Saturday:
12pm-2pm, 6.30pm-9pm

Sunday:
12pm-2pm, 6.30pm-8.30pm

Closed 25-26 December

Prices

Meals: a la carte £ 19/32

10 rooms: £ 49/130

Typical Dishes

Grilled fillet of seabass
Daube of Galloway beef
Glazed lemon tart

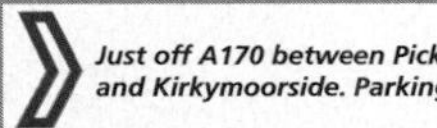

Just off A170 between Pickering and Kirkymoorside. Parking.

35 Coachman Inn

Pickering Road West,
Snainton YO13 9PL

Tel.: (01723)859231 – Fax: (01723)850008

e-mail: james@coachmaninn.co.uk **Website:** www.coachmaninn.co.uk

Woldtop

This stone-built, Grade II listed building has stood on the same site just outside Snainton since 1776, providing sustenance for travellers on the York to Scarborough road. These days, travellers and locals alike receive a warm Irish welcome, whilst also being well provided for on the food front: cooking is fresh, seasonal and homemade; produce is traceable to local farms and dishes are traditional, yet in keeping with modern influences. Lunchtime means a choice of sandwiches and classics such as sausage and mash or smoked salmon, while the evening menu offers more substantial dishes like lamb Wellington, venison steak or pan-fried pork medallions. The contemporary dining room has a view over the lawn – if you're planning on a formal meal, this is probably better, not to mention more spacious, but the traditional flagstoned bar takes some beating for warmth and character. Individually styled, spacious bedrooms offer good home comforts.

Food serving times

Tuesday: 7pm-9pm

Wednesday-Sunday: 12pm-2pm, 7pm-9pm

Closed Monday and lunch Tuesday

Prices

Meals: a la carte £ 20/30

5 rooms: £ 50/70

Typical Dishes

Warm crispy duck salad
Roast chicken
Grilled fresh pineapple

0.5 mi West by A170 on B1258.
Parking.

The Blackwell Ox Inn

36 The Blackwell Ox Inn

Huby Rd,
Sutton-on-the-Forest YO61 1DT
Tel.: (01347)810328 – Fax: (01347)812738
e-mail: enquiries@blackwelloxinn.co.uk **Website:** www.blackwelloxinn.co.uk

Timothy Talor Landlord, Black Sheep Bitter, Theakstons Best Bitter

Unlike its namesake – a six foot Teeswater ox – this early 19C brick-built pub is warm and welcoming, featuring cosy sofas beside a snug open fire and inviting linen-laid tables in the restaurant. There is a concise set menu and more extensive à la carte, which feature a twice-daily selection of hearty, straightforward dishes. Seasonality, traceability and good supplier relationships are important here and the chef acknowledges this by listing the food's origins on the menu. There are many old favourites to be found, such as cod, steak or sausages, alongside some more adventurous choices which might include roast crown of partridge with confit bacon, wild halibut with osso bucco or salmon fillet with spiced lentils and chorizo. Since also becoming Manager, the chef has gained more control over the pub and this is definitely for the better. Bedrooms are finished to a high standard; some featuring four-posters or Victorian roll-top baths.

Food serving times
Monday-Sunday:
12pm-2.30pm, 6pm-9.30pm

Prices
Meals: £ 14 and a la carte £ 19/28

7 rooms: £ 95/110

8mi North of York by B1363.
Parking.

Typical Dishes
Smoked haddock rarebit
Braised brisket of beef
Warm chocolate pudding

Sutton-on-the-Forest

37 Rose & Crown

Main St,
Sutton-on-the-Forest YO61 1DP
Tel.: (01347)811333 – Fax: (01347)811333
e-mail: ben@rosecrown.co.uk **Website:** www.rosecrown.co.uk

 **Black Sheep Best, Timothy Taylor Landlord**

This is a relatively plain-looking pub from the outside, with a relatively plain-sounding name, but venture inside and you'll find that the food is anything but. The confident kitchen knows how to handle ingredients; dishes are refreshingly free from over-elaboration and prices are good when you consider the quality of the produce. The menu has a modern British/European base and the popular fish dishes are prepared with particular with care and precision; you might find lamb or venison alongside sea bass, sea trout or lemon sole. The traditionally-styled, wood-floored bar has kept its original feature fireplaces and beams, while the dining room and conservatory have a stylishly informal feel to them, and the outside eating area and garden are delightful in the summer months. The Rose and Crown is situated in Sutton-on-the-Forest, a pretty village not far from York, where Laurence Sterne penned Tristram Shandy.

Food serving times

Tuesday-Saturday:
12pm-2pm, 6pm-9pm

Sunday: 12pm-3pm

Closed first 2 weeks January, Sunday dinner and Monday

Prices

Meals: a la carte £ 20/30

Typical Dishes

Black pudding & Parma ham
Fillet of pollock
Vanilla crème brûlée

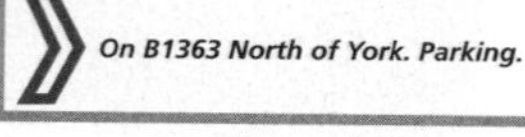

On B1363 North of York. Parking.

38 The Stone House Inn

Thruscross HG3 4AH

Tel.: (01943)880325

Website: www.stonehouseinn.co.uk

VISA MC AE

Timothy Taylor, Theakstons, Deuchars

Unless you're a seasoned walker you are unlikely to stumble across this 300 year old coaching inn, as it's set high up in the remote Yorkshire dales and is very exposed. Surrounded by countryside vistas, it retains many of its original features, including wooden beams, exposed stone walls and flagged floors; with a pair of welcoming fires making even the bleakest day seem brighter. It's ideal for the family, with the friendly staff accommodating your needs, from help with highchairs to handing out activity packs. A family man himself, the owner cleverly recruited his two young children, Rosie and Ashley, to help compile the kids menu, and what could be better than a menu for children, designed by children? For older guests, the wide-ranging main menu features everything from salads and curries to British pub classics – all made from local, seasonal produce – whilst the specials display dishes of a more ambitious nature.

Food serving times

Monday-Sunday:
12pm-9pm

Prices

Meals: a la carte £ 16/23

Typical Dishes

Brie & onion tartlet
Cod loin
Classic lemon tart

10mi West of Harrogate by A59 and minor road North

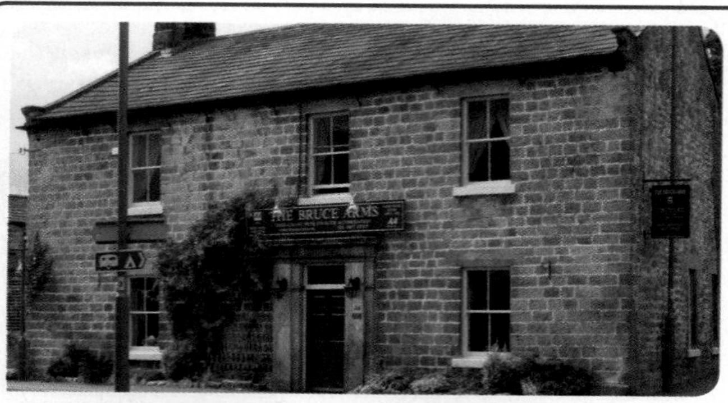

39 The Bruce Arms

Main St,
West Tanfield HG4 5JJ
Tel.: (01677)470325 – Fax: (01677)470925
e-mail: info@bruce-arms.co.uk **Website:** www.bruce-arms.co.uk

VISA MC AE

Black Sheep Bitter, Timothy Taylor Landlord

Situated on a roundabout between Masham and Ripon, its young owners are bringing their experience to bear at this 200 year old stone pub. Its characterful bar boasts flagstone floors and a wood burner while four vast port barrels above the bar make you question how on earth they got them up there in the first place. The bar area opens out into a traditional carpeted area with a mix of old pub chairs and a few leather armchairs, and you can either eat here or in the more formal, linen-laid burgundy-walled dining room. Blackboards display lunch dishes, some sandwiches and the day's specials, while the concise printed dinner menu offers starters such as scallops or terrine of ham hock and mains such as roast duck breast or salmon. The choice may be limited, but the food is well prepared, neatly presented and won't break the bank. There is a small decked terrace area at the front and two en suite bedrooms are available upstairs.

Food serving times

Tuesday-Sunday:
12pm-3pm, 6pm-9.30pm

Closed Monday

Prices

Meals: £ 24 and a la carte £ 12/27

2 rooms: £ 85

Typical Dishes

Seared loin of venison
Fillet of turbot
Chocolate & praline mousse

Between Masham and Ripon on A6108. Parking.

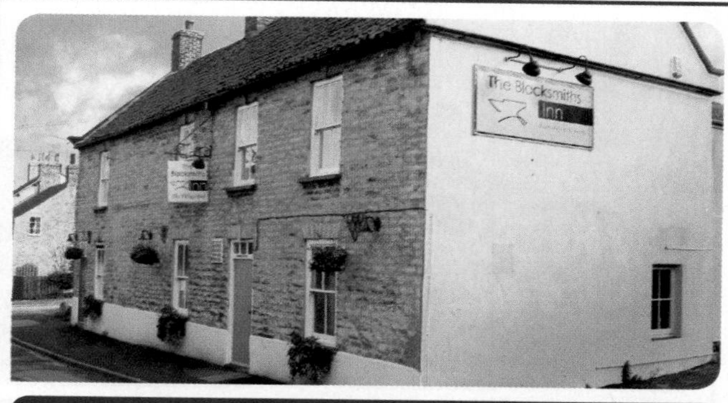

40 The Blacksmiths Inn

Main St,
Westow YO60 7NE

Tel.: (01653)618365 – Fax: (01653)618394
e-mail: info@blacksmithsinn.co.uk **Website:** www.blacksmithsinn.co.uk

VISA MC

Jennings Bitter, Jennings Cumberland

With a name like this there could only be two options: either this pub was the old haunt of a group of blacksmiths or this building was formerly used as a blacksmith's workshop. Inside lies the answer, where an axe and a huge brick forge are in situ, alongside other evidence of its former smithy trade. For a light snack you can stay in the bar area, where the old forge now houses a roaring open fire; for a more substantial meal you must head to one of the two dining rooms next door, where large matching tables rest on solid wood floors. Changing every four weeks to accommodate seasonal produce and availability, the à la carte menu features a classical Yorkshire base. Starters might include steamed mussels, pan-fried duck breast or goat's cheese tartlets, whilst main dishes might offer herb encrusted rack of lamb, red mullet with cauliflower purée or pan-fried venison with caramelised parsnips.

Food serving times

Tuesday: 5.30pm-9pm

Wednesday-Saturday and Bank Holiday Monday: 12pm-2pm, 5.30pm-9pm

Sunday: 12pm-4pm

Closed Monday and lunch Tuesday

Prices

Meals: a la carte £ 15/30

6 rooms: £ 40/70

Typical Dishes

Pan-seared scallops
Pan-fried loin of venison
Dark chocolate fondant

6.5 mi Southwest of Moulton off the A64 past Kirkham Priory. Parking.

41 The Stone Trough Inn

Kirkham Abbey,
Whitwell-on-the-Hill YO60 7JS
Tel.: (01653)618713 – Fax: (01653)618819
e-mail: info@stonetroughinn.co.uk **Website:** www.stonetroughinn.co.uk

Tetley Cask Ale, Timothy Taylor Landlord, Copper Dragon Golden Pippin, Black Sheep Best Bitter, Theakston Old Peculier

On the Eastern end of the Howardian Hills, just off the A64, and near the ruins of Kirkham Abbey, sits the erroneously-named Stone Trough Inn. A large stone-built building, it has various little beamed rooms and charming snugs and the rustic feel is further enhanced by the pictures, ornaments, antiques and farm machinery which decorate the panelled walls. A games room with pool table offers welcome diversion should the conversation falter and the outside terrace is a great spot for fine weather dining. The extensive bar and restaurant menus offer traditional British favourites made with local produce, so you know that nothing has travelled too far to reach your plate; crab is from Whitby, beef is from Kilburn, lamb from Flaxton, and some fruit and herbs are even grown in the pub's own garden. More modern dishes also feature, with European flavours to the fore, and daily specials compete for your attention too.

Food serving times

Tuesday-Saturday and Bank Holiday Monday: 12pm-2.15pm, 6.45pm-9.30pm

Sunday: 12pm-2.15pm

Closed 25 December

Bar meals at lunchtime

Prices

Meals: a la carte £ 20/34

Typical Dishes

Duck & pistachio terrine

Braised lamb shank

Armagnac parfait

5mi Southwest of Malton off A64 following signs for Kirkham Priory. Parking.

42 The Cricket Inn

Penny Lane,
Totley S17 3AZ
Tel.: (0114)2365256
e-mail: simon@cricketinn.co.uk

 **Thornbridge Brewery - Jaipur, Kipling, Lord Harples, Cricketers**

Pleasant bird song and the satisfying thwack of leather on willow are among the only sounds to be heard from the garden of this characterful stone pub. Set in a valley, about six miles outside of Sheffield, this bustling inn is a million miles from hectic city life. Cooking is hearty, robust and very satisfying, and dishes can arrive on anything from slates to wooden boards. The extensive menu covers everything from bar snacks, platters and pies through to grills and roasts, with a variety of cheeses, pudding, cakes and pastries to follow. With much of the produce being source locally it has a strong Yorkshire base, and speciality dishes such as "Stump" – a regional and aptly named side dish of mashed root vegetables – can often be found. The menu also suggests an ideal beer to accompany each starter and main course, most of which are supplied by the local Thornbridge brewery. Make sure you arrive early, as bookings aren't accepted.

Food serving times
Monday-Sunday:
12pm-2.30pm, 5pm-9.30pm

Prices
Meals: £ 18 and a la carte
£ 20/35

Typical Dishes
Sheffield style fishcake
Steak & kidney pie
Steamed syrup sponge pudding

6mi South West of Sheffield by A61 and A621

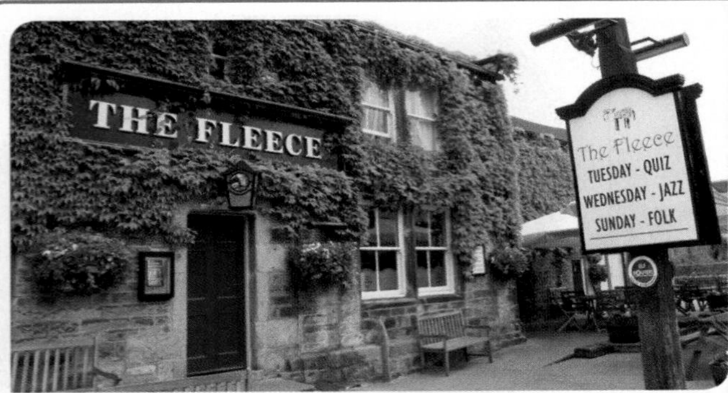

43 The Fleece

152-154 Main St,
Addingham LS29 0LY
Tel.: (01943)830491
e-mail: thefleece@mac.com **Website:** www.fleeceaddingham.com

VISA MC AE

Tetleys Cask, Black Sheep Bitter, Copper Dragon, Timothy Taylor Landlord, Golden Pippin

Set on the main street of the village of Addingham, this large, ivy-clad inn is a popular meeting place for locals who congregate to drink and discuss the day's events in its small public bar. Often equally as busy is the larger lounge and dining area; decorated with countryside pictures and knick-knacks, and whose beamed ceilings and stone floors and walls bear testament to the building's 18C genesis. The large blackboard menus displayed on the walls change frequently according to what's fresh and what's in season. Homely dishes with Yorkshire roots, such as locally sourced steak and meat pies offer lots of comfort appeal but the wide-ranging menus also include more contemporary dishes too. Service from friendly local staff remains efficient and polite, even when there's a rush on, and the hugely generous portions that they place in front of you present an enjoyable challenge you find you just have to conquer.

Food serving times

Monday-Saturday:
12pm-2.15pm, 6pm-9.15pm

Sunday: 12pm-8pm

Prices

Meals: a la carte £ 21/30

Typical Dishes

Calves liver
Seafood grill
Chocolate box

On the busy through road in the centre of Addingham. Parking.

44 Shibden Mill Inn

Shibden Mill Fold,
Halifax HX3 7UL
Tel.: (01422)365840 – Fax: (01422)362971
e-mail: simonheaton@shibdenmillinn.com **Website:** www.shibdenmillinn.com

   AE

Shibden Mill Bitter, John Smith Cask, Theakstons XB and three weekly changing guest bitters

What was the mill pond many years ago is now the car park, and the mill has long since stopped grinding corn, but a sense of historic charm still inhabits this inn, with its cosy, cluttered rooms and snugs. The menus offer a little bit of everything, and while there are a few Mediterranean influences, traditional dishes such as fish pie, lamb casserole and roast Yorkshire beef dominate; there is even a platter of "British bites" on offer, including chicken pie, smoked salmon, and mini fish cakes. Regular "Guinea pig nights" involve the sampling of new dishes; thus named to refer to the fact that you are being "experimented on," rather than because you might actually find yourself feasting on one of the furry creatures, as popular as they may be fricasseed in some parts of the world. Refurbished bedrooms have good facilities; the five newest - in what was previously a derelict barn - are the largest and most modern.

Food serving times

Monday-Saturday:
12pm-2pm, 5.30pm-9.30pm

Sunday: 12pm-7.30pm

Closed 25 and 31 December dinner

Prices

Meals: £ 18 (lunch)
and a la carte £ 22/32

11 rooms: £ 68/136

Typical Dishes
Chicken liver parfait
Shibden burger and chips
Chocolate cheesecake

2.25 mi Northeast by A58 and Kell Lane (turning left at Stump Cross Pub), on Blake Hill Rd. Parking.

45 Olive Branch

Manchester Rd,
Marsden HD7 6LU
Tel.: (01484)844487
e-mail: mail@olivebranch.uk.com **Website:** www.olivebranch.uk.com

  VISA 

 **Dob Cross Bitter, Golden Warrior**

Set on a busy main road this stone-built drovers inn houses many small and characterful rooms, each adorned with food-themed pictures, sepia photos, old menus and more. Most tables are set for dining and there's a chatty, bustling atmosphere, while for the warmer weather, a decked terrace and secluded garden are hidden round the back. The large menu displays an even split between meat and seafood, ranging from pigeon and venison, to sea bass and monkfish; with daily specials displayed on large yellow post-it notes around the bar. Taking on a traditional style, cooking is robust, hearty and straightforward, and uses local produce wherever possible. Service is friendly, if sometimes lacking a little in direction. Bedrooms are modern, comfortable and unique; Serengeti displays wooden statues and printed fabrics, while Duck features ornamental fowl and a bath time friend. Be prepared to have your breakfast order ready when you check in.

Food serving times
Wednesday-Friday:
12pm-1.45pm,
6.30pm-9.30pm
Saturday: 6.30pm-9.30pm
Sunday: 1pm-8.30pm
Closed 26 December and first 2 weeks in January

Prices
Meals: £ 11 (3 course lunch/dinner)/19
and a la carte £ 27/38
3 rooms: £ 55/70

Typical Dishes
Baked Whitby crab
Beef Bourguignon
Bread & butter pudding

 *1 mi Northeast on A62. Parking.* 

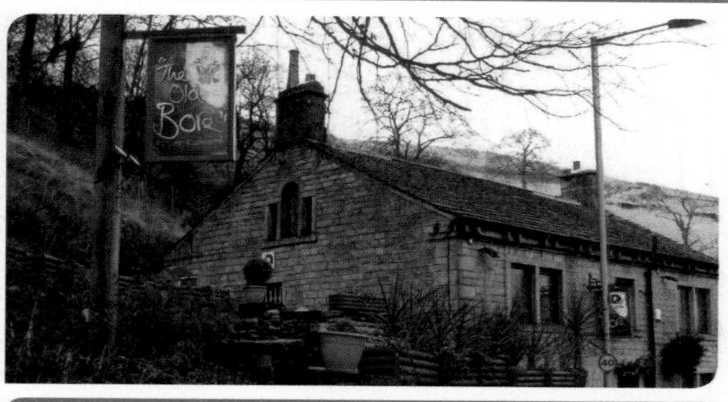

46 The Old Bore

Oldham Rd,
Rishworth HX6 4QU
Tel.: (01422)822291
e-mail: chefhessel@aol.com **Website:** www.oldbore.co.uk

  VISA  AE

 **Bore Bitter, Timothy Taylor Landlord, Black Sheep Best**

A surprisingly short distance from the M62, this personally run pub is wonderfully inviting, not least because of its delightful side terrace, popular in hot weather. In the colder months, a comfy red leather seat by the open fire in the bar is best, surrounded by hunting print walls full of knick knacks and pewter tankards hanging from the beams. Two main dining rooms are very smartly dressed and food here takes a similarly luxurious approach, with truffles, foie gras and other high quality local ingredients carefully employed to create classical British dishes. The main à la carte changes on a monthly basis; choices might include home smoked sea trout, English snails and black pudding, cod tikka, rabbit saddle or roast partridge, while for those concerned about the coffers, the daily set menu offers a less pricey alternative. Regular events such as cookery demonstrations and jazz evenings pull in the crowds. The Old Bore? Far from it.

Food serving times

Wednesday-Sunday:
12pm-2.15pm, 6pm-9.30pm

Closed first 2 weeks in January

Prices

Meals: £ 10 (3 course lunch & dinner) and a la carte £ 25/35

Typical Dishes

Crispy belly pork
Pan-fried venison steak
Chocolate brownie

6mi Southwest of Halifax by A58 and A672. Parking.

47 The Millbank

Mill Bank,
Sowerby Bridge HX6 3DY
Tel.: (01422)825588
e-mail: eat@themillbank.com **Website:** www.themillbank.com

 **Tetley, Timothy Taylor Landlord**

The Millbank was in the vanguard of the modernised-pub-with-good-food movement and continues to pull in the punters, who create quite a buzz. It's split between a small bar and a dining room but it's the food that's the draw here. The conservatory extension to the dining room is the place to sit if you want to admire the views which stretch over the Ryburn Valley. Local artists' work adds to the contemporary feel of the place and uniformed staff provide courteous, if at times slightly impersonal, service. The menu is quite an extensive document but prices are good when one considers the quality of the ingredients and the skill and understanding with which they are used. The cooking can be considered either restaurant style food with a rustic edge or sophisticated pub grub. What you can expect is plenty of choice and something that all pubs should have – a section marked "British Classics".

Food serving times
Tuesday-Thursday:
12pm-2.30pm, 6pm-9.30pm
Friday-Saturday:
12pm-2.30pm, 6pm-10pm
Sunday:
12.30pm-4.30pm, 6pm-8pm
Closed first week in January, first 2 weeks in October
Booking essential

Prices
Meals: a la carte £ 18/31

Typical Dishes
Cold poached sea trout
Yorkshire venison steak
Chocolate fondant cake

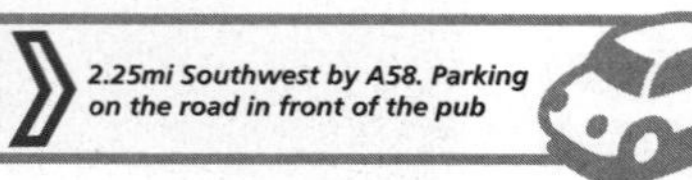

48 Woodman Inn

Thunderbridge HD8 0PX
Tel.: (01484)605778 – Fax: (01484)604110
e-mail: thewoodman@connectfree.co.uk **Website:** www.woodman-inn.co.uk

 **Timothy Taylor Best, Timothy Taylor Landlord, Black Sheep**

If you're following one of the many footpaths that pass close to the Southern Pennines, make sure you stop off at this small hamlet, in the quiet wooded valley. Built from local Yorkshire stone, this traditional 19C inn boasts a wood-faced bar – complete with convivial locals – a leather furnished lounge and more formal linen-laid restaurant. The latter is only open in the evenings and is great for special occasions but stay in the bar for a more atmospheric day-to-day affair; service is polite and efficient, wherever you sit. The extensive menus change in line with the seasons and have a distinctive British bias. Lunch sees hearty classics served in generous portions, while the evening dishes take on a more complex, ambitious approach; you might find rack of lamb, pan-fried sea bream or twice cooked pork belly, with specials displayed on a blackboard. Located in a row of nearby weaver's cottages, bedrooms are simple and well-kept.

Food serving times

Monday-Thursday:
12pm-9.30pm (bar snacks), 7pm-9.30pm

Friday-Saturday:
12pm-9.30pm

Sunday: 12pm-3pm,
till 8pm for bar snacks

Closed 25 December dinner

Prices

Meals: a la carte £ 14/27

12 rooms: £ 45/78

Typical Dishes

Bang bang king prawn skewers

Pan-fried sea bream

Tasting selection

5.75mi Southeast of Huddersfield by A629, after Kirkburton follow signs to Thunderbridge. Parking.

49 The Fox and Hounds

Hall Park Road,
Walton LS23 7DQ
Tel.: (01937)842192

   AE

John Smiths Smooth, Black Sheep, Timothy Taylor Landlord, Spitfire

Tucked away in the centre of a sleepy little West Yorkshire village east of Wetherby, this characterful stone pub has two rooms set for dining, plus a cosy snug – home to Basil, the stuffed fox, in his basket – which also has tables set aside for local drinkers. Pleasant country décor takes in low beamed ceilings and framed countryside prints; the table mats are adorned with hunting cartoons and a fish tank on the bar provides a relaxing diversion as you sup your pint. The chef may be Mexican, but the menu tends towards classic British dishes, with more adventurous offerings available on the specials board. Cooking is hearty and robust and makes good use of local produce; the wide choice further extended by an early evening menu of pub favourites. The atmosphere is friendly and service is chatty and knowledgeable; look out for owner Alan who doubles as local Conservative councillor, and local girl Maggie who's been here for 25 years.

Food serving times

Monday-Sunday:
12pm-2pm, 5.30pm-9pm

Booking essential

Prices

Meals: a la carte £ 16/25

3mi East of Wetherby by minor road; between A659 and B1224. Parking.

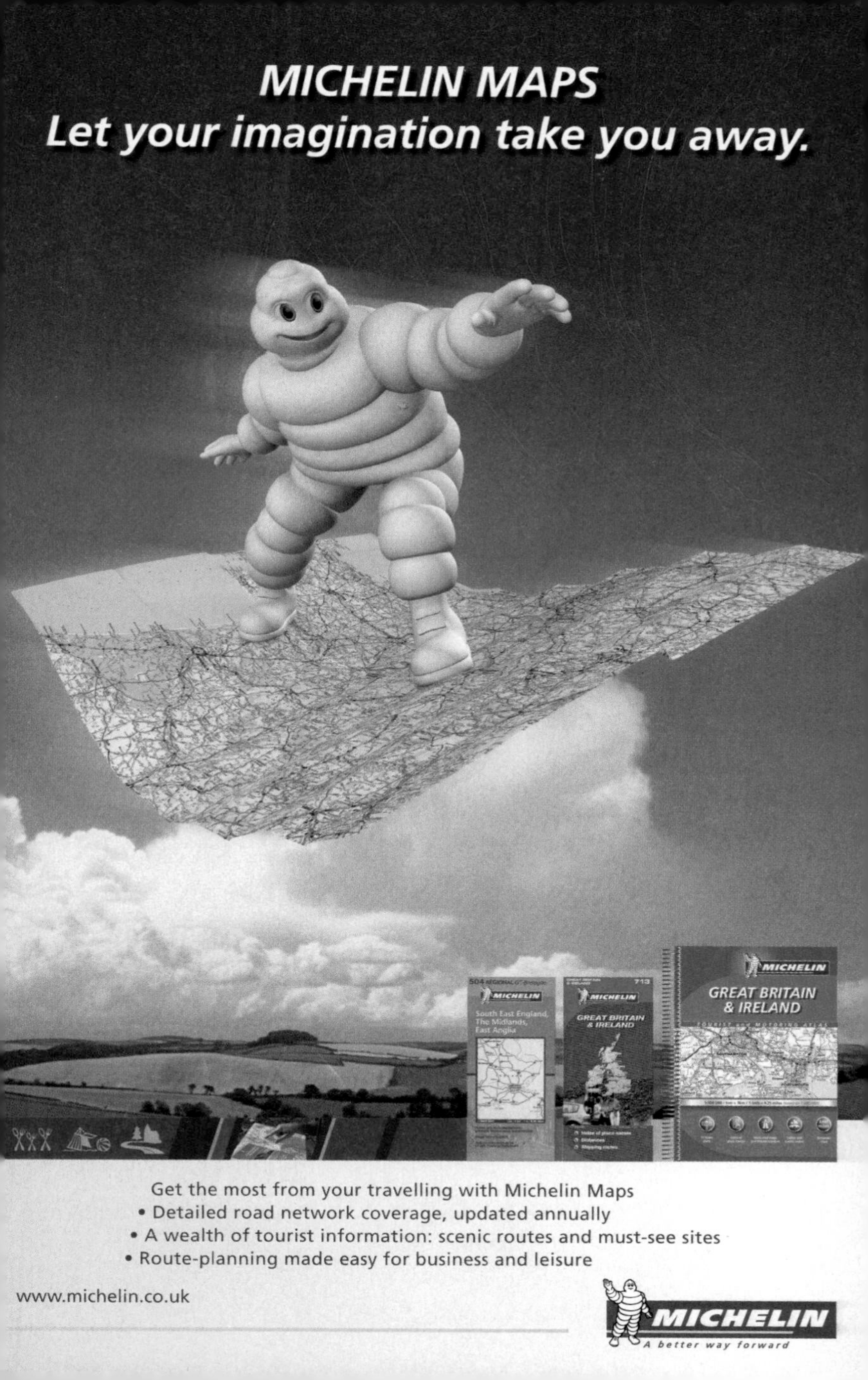
MICHELIN MAPS
Let your imagination take you away.
MICHELIN
South East England, The Midlands, East Anglia
MICHELIN
GREAT BRITAIN & IRELAND
MICHELIN
GREAT BRITAIN & IRELAND
Get the most from your travelling with Michelin Maps
• Detailed road network coverage, updated annually
• A wealth of tourist information: scenic routes and must-see sites
• Route-planning made easy for business and leisure
www.michelin.co.uk
MICHELIN
A better way forward

Scotland may be small, but its variety is immense. The vivacity of Glasgow can seem a thousand miles from the vast peatland wilderness of Caithness and Sutherland's Flow Country; the arty vibe of Georgian Edinburgh a world away from the remote and tranquil Ardnamurchan peninsula. And how many people link Scotland to its beaches? But wide golden sands trim the Atlantic at South Harris, and the coastline of the Highlands boasts empty islands and turquoise waters. Meantime, Fife's coast draws golf fans to St Andrews and the more secretive delights of the East Neuk, an area of fishing villages and stone harbours. Wherever you travel, the scent of a dramatic history prevails in the shape of castles, cathedrals and rugged lochside monuments to the heroes of old. Food and drink embraces the traditional, too, typified by Aberdeen's famous Malt Whisky Trail. And what better than Highland game, fresh fish from the Tweed or haggis, neeps and tatties to complement a grand Scottish hike…

SCOTLAND
Northern Ireland
Ireland
North West
EDINBURGH
GLASGOW
BELFAST
Lewis
Stornoway
St. Kilda
Tarbert
North Uist
Lochmaddy
South Uist
Lochboisdale
Barra
Castlebay
Skye
Uig
Dunvegan
Portree
Kyle of Lochalsh
Rhum
Mallaig
Coll
Tiree
Tobermory
Mull
Craignure
Fionnphort
Oban
Colonsay
Firth of Lorn
Islay
Port Askaig
Jura
Port Ellen
Kintyre
Campbeltown
Lochgilphead
Dunoon
Rothesay
Greenock
Dumbarton
Brodick
Arran
Ardrossan
Firth of Clyde
Kilmarnock
Ayr
Cairnryan
Stranraer
Kirkcudbright
Dumfries
Moffat
Hawick
Peebles
Lanark
Hamilton
Falkirk
Stirling
Kinross
Crieff
Perth
Crianlarich
Fort William
Ben Nevis
1344
Loch Linnhe
Loch Ness
Inverness
Nairn
Elgin
Grantown
Aviemore
Newtonmore
Cairngorm Mountains
1309
Braemar
Dingwall
Ullapool
Lochinver
Tongue
Lairg
Brora
Dornoch
Dunnet
HIGHLANDS
Sea of the Hebrides
Little Minch
The Minch
HEBRIDES
Grampian
R. Tay
R. Spey
Malin Head
Giant's Causeway
Buncrana
Lough Foyle
Portrush
Coleraine
Ballycastle
Antrim Glens
Letterkenny
Londonderry / Derry
Donegal
Strabane
Omagh
Ballymena
Larne
Bundoran
Sligo
Enniskillen
Armagh
Lisburn
Bangor
Boyle
Monaghan
Newry
Newcastle
Dundalk
Longford
North Channel
Man
Peel
Ramsey
Douglas
Carlisle
Workington
Whitehaven
Keswick
Windermere
Solway Firth
Lake District
Hadrian
1
2
3
4
5
6
8
9
10
11
12
13
14
15
16
17
18
19
20
21
22
23
24

Yell
Unst
Shetland
Hillswick
Sandness
Mainland
Lerwick
Sumburgh
Bergen
Aberdeen
Stromness

Orkney
Westray
Lerwick
Rousay
Sanday
Mainland
Stronsay
Stromness
Kirkwall
Hoy
Pentland Firth
Aberdeen
Wick

NORTH SEA

MER DU NORD

Banff
Fraserburgh
Keith
105
Peterhead
Spey
A96
Stromness
Lerwick
1
Aberdeen
2
Stonehaven
68
A90
Montrose
Arbroath
St. Andrews
Firth of Forth
North Berwick
A1
7
Berwick-upon-Tweed
R. Tweed
Coldstream
110
Jedburgh
North East
A696
Blyth
Bergen
Stavanger
Haugesund
Kristiansand
Tynemouth
Newcastle upon Tyne
South Shields
Sunderland
Gateshead
Durham
Hartlepool
A1
A66
Middlesbrough
Darlington
Whitby

1 Cock and Bull

Ellon Rd,
Blairton, Balmedie AB23 8XY
Tel.: (01358)743249 – Fax: (01358)742466
e-mail: info@thecockandbull.co.uk **Website:** www.thecockandbull.co.uk

VISA AE

Deuchars IPA, Caledonian

"Where ancient meets modern without so much as a jolt," it says in the Cock and Bull's promo blurb. And that's just the half of it. This former shepherds' watering hole looks over fields to the North Sea. Inside, there are three distinct areas: two of them, the lounge/bar and the restaurant, are delightfully atmospheric, cluttered with artefacts (some African themed), old record players, sewing machines, posters and fabrics (plus anything else you might care to mention). Open fires complete a feast for the eyes and the senses. A more contemporary conservatory with polished wood tables and chairs completes the picture. Extensive menus cover the full range from "popular pub fare" to "fine dining", as well as heartily ample one-course dishes with Scottish produce to the fore. Service is very friendly from staff used to being run off their feet.

Food serving times
Monday-Saturday: from 12pm (bar snacks only), 5.30pm-8.45pm
Sunday: 12pm-6.45pm
Closed 25-26 December and 1-2 January

Prices
Meals: a la carte £ 12/25

Typical Dishes
Haggis, neeps & tatties
Creel broth
Sticky toffee pudding

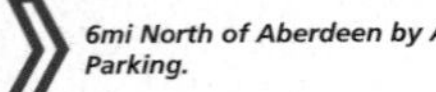

6mi North of Aberdeen by A90. Parking.

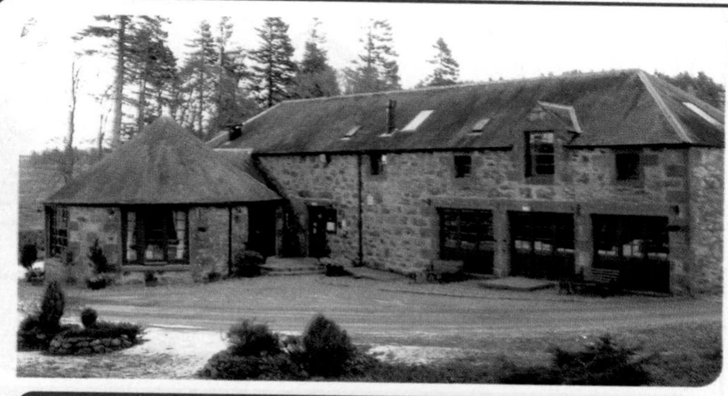

2 The Steading

(at Lochside Lodge and Roundhouse restaurant), Bridgend of Lintrathen DD8 5JJ

Tel.: (01575)560340 – Fax: (01575)560251

e-mail: enquiries@lochsidelodge.com **Website:** www.lochsidelodge.com

 **Inveralmond Ale : Ossians or other**

The more informal counterpart to the Roundhouse restaurant, the Steading's name is a reminder of its humble origins as an old farm building. The original stone walls are now decorated with all sorts of agricultural tools, rural fitments, and some country sports memorabilia, some of the mystery items look like they might fall into all three categories. Cushioned pews are pulled up to solid wood tables and a brasserie style lunch menu is served along with the same menu on offer in the Roundhouse restaurant at dinner. If you're just after a drink, there's a little bar to one side, with newspapers and magazines within easy reach of the leather seats. Four pine-fitted bedrooms, in the converted hayloft, all have a dash of tartan or floral colour and plenty in the way of thoughtful, homely touches.

Food serving times

Tuesday-Saturday:
12pm-1.30pm,
6.30pm-8.30pm

Closed 25-26 December and 1-31 January and 2 weeks October

Prices

Meals: £ 35 (dinner Sundays) and a la carte £ 18/20

6 rooms: £ 70/120

Typical Dishes

Terrine of chicken
Casserole of Angus beef
Poached pear

8mi West of Kirriemuir by B951.
Parking.

3 The Oyster Inn

Connel PA37 1PJ
Tel.: (01631)710666 – Fax: (01631)710042
e-mail: stay@oysterinn.co.uk **Website:** www.oysterinn.co.uk

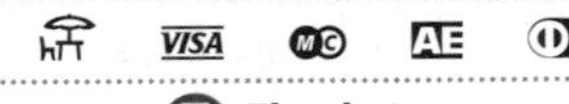

Theakstons

You get three for the price of one here: a restaurant, a neighbouring pub plus accommodation. Add to this the Falls of Lora – a naturally occurring spectacle of white water and whirlpools as the tides rise and fall - and you'll have to agree that Connel really is your oyster. The restaurant is spacious and contemporary in style, with a small terrace and a view of the loch. The adjacent pub, The Ferryman's, is much more traditional, with scrubbed wooden tables, log fires, real ales, a large range of malts and a pool table. Built in the 18C to serve the erstwhile ferry's passengers, it is known locally as The Glue Pot – be sure to touch the pot for luck. The same menu is served in both establishments – simple, seasonal homemade classics, daily specials with the emphasis on fresh seafood, plus a choice of homemade cakes and scones. Bedrooms are comfortable and modern, and bunk style budget rooms are also available for groups.

Food serving times
Monday-Sunday:
12pm-2.3pm, 6pm-9pm
Bar meals at lunch time

Prices
Meals: a la carte £ 18/28
11 rooms: £ 52/114

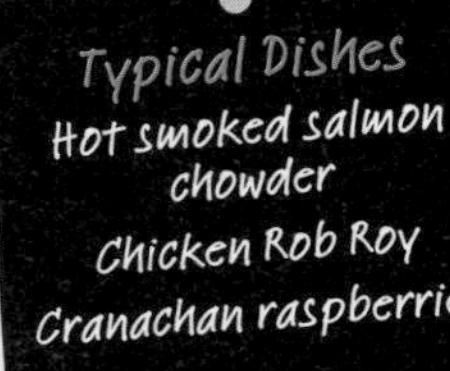

5mi North of Oban by A85.
Parking.

4 The Kilberry Inn

Kintyre - Kilberry PA29 6YD
Tel.: (01880)770223
e-mail: relax@kilberryinn.com
Website: www.kilberryinn.com

No real ales offered

Remotely set and reached along a scenic single track road, the team at the whitewashed, red-roofed Kilberry Inn extend a traditionally warm, Scottish welcome to any travellers who pass their way. A charming place, with high ceilings and log fires, its exposed stone walls are hung with artwork by local artists and there are two simply furnished main areas in which to dine, with banquette seating, wooden tables – some with tablecloths - and decorative orchids. Cooking here has a local base, with the emphasis on fresh seafood, and West Coast ingredients range from Loch Fyne langoustines and scallops to local cheeses and meats; carefully prepared, and good value for money. The comfortable bedrooms here are simple yet stylish, with all the facilities you will need. Whether you're travelling on foot, by bike or by boat, Kilberry is a great base for exploring this unspoilt area, and a trip to a whisky distillery is a must.

Food serving times

Monday-Sunday:
12.15pm-2.15pm,
6.30pm-9pm

Closed January to mid-March

Prices

Meals: a la carte £ 20/31

4 rooms: £ 45/90

Typical Dishes

Kilberry potted crab
Seared monkfish
Rhubarb & vanilla ice cream

15mi West of Tarbet by B8024. Parking.

5 Tayvallich Inn

Tayvallich PA31 8PL
Tel.: (01546)870282
e-mail: rfhanderson@aol.com **Website:** www.tayvallichinn.co.uk

 **Loch Fyne Maverick, Loch Fyne Avalanche**

Driving up the single track road along the banks of Loch Sween, towards the quaintly isolated village of Tayvallich, population circa 100, you know that when you reach it, the view from this inn is going to be just as impressive. And you are not disappointed; sitting outside on the decked terrace there's not even a sheet of glass to separate you from the glorious tranquillity of the harbour. Running a business in such a location means that the owner gets the best local seafood delivered fresh to him. Not surprisingly, the very seasonal menu has a distinctly fishy flavour and simple dishes focused on prawns, lobster, scallops and the like dominate, with the odd steak or burger, made with meat sourced from a local farm, also thrown in. Now, when you survey the rustic, open bar and simply decorated dining room, it's hard to believe that this building was a bus garage until the 1970s. Young staff provide efficient service.

Food serving times

Monday-Sunday:
12pm-2pm, 6pm-9pm

Closed 25-26 December

Closed November to March, Monday-Tuesday

Prices

Meals: a la carte £ 16/32

Typical Dishes

Moules marinières
Pan-fried seabass
Amaretto crème brûlée

12mi West of Lochgilphead by A816,B841 and B8025:on west shore of Loch Sween. Parking.

6 Black Bull

13-15 Market Place,
Lauder TD2 6SR
Tel.: (01578)722208 – Fax: (01578)722419
e-mail: enquiries@blackbull-lauder.com **Website:** www.blackbull-lauder.com

Broughton Ales, High House Brewery

Can there be anything more satisfying than catching your own dinner? The owners of this former coaching inn, not too far from river, loch and coast will be more than happy to cook it for you - but beware fishy tales from the neighbouring table about the one that got away. Located on the busy main road between Newcastle and Edinburgh, this inn was built in the 1750s, with a former church hall added in the 19th century. Traditionally decorated, the bar area is comfortable and cosy whereas the dining room is slightly more formal. Friendly local staff serve home-cooked dishes throughout, from a menu that changes with the season, and if you're wanting a place to lay your head at the end of a hard day's fishing, there is a choice of comfortable bedrooms available, with good facilities. With its pretty window boxes and hanging baskets, this village inn will soon have you falling for its charms; hook, line and sinker.

Food serving times
Monday-Sunday:
12pm-2.30pm, 5pm-9pm

Prices
Meals: a la carte £ 18/30
8 rooms: £ 68/90

Typical Dishes
Fish cake
Venison Bourguignon
Praline Armagnac mousse

25mi South of Edinburgh by A7 and B6362. Parking.

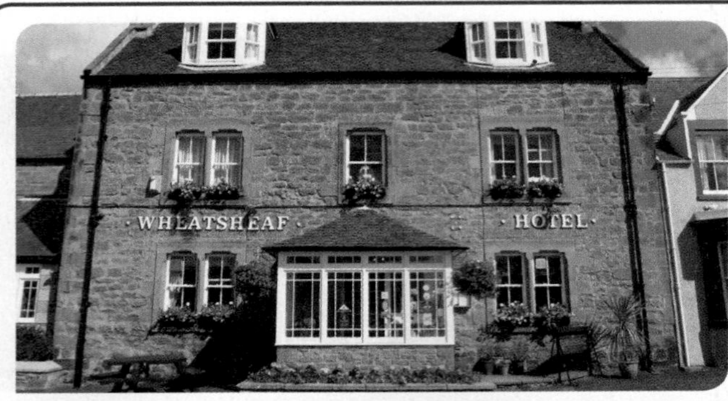

7 The Wheatsheaf

Main Street, Swinton TD11 3JJ
Tel.: (01890)860257 – Fax: (01890)860688
e-mail: reception@wheatsheaf-swinton.co.uk
Website: www.wheatsheaf-swinton.co.uk

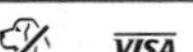

 **Caledonian IPA**

If fishing on the Tweed was good but your catching was bad, a meal at The Wheatsheaf is sure to assuage you. Well-run by a keen husband and wife team, this stone built inn is set on the main street in this Borders village, overlooking the green. Inside, there are numerous cosy little lounges in which to relax, with soft seating, suites and sofas and the obligatory log fire, although the fishing theme on the walls might well remind you of the one that got away. Classic, unfussy dishes with a modern twist bring out the flavour of local produce, with fish sourced from Eyemouth harbour, as well as Borders beef, and lamb and organic pork from traditional butchers. If you hope to try your luck again on the morrow, you'll rest well in modern, comfortable, individually furnished bedrooms, with good facilities and extra touches. And don't have nightmares, just remember; there are plenty more fish in the Tweed.

Food serving times

Monday-Sunday:
12pm-2pm, 6pm-9pm

Closed 25-26 December and 2 January

Prices

Meals: a la carte £ 19/39

10 rooms: £ 75/102

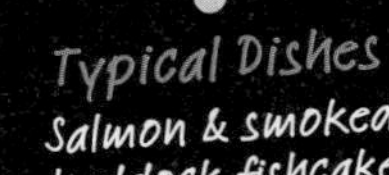

Typical Dishes

Salmon & smoked haddock fishcake

Loin of Highland venison

Ginger & pear pudding

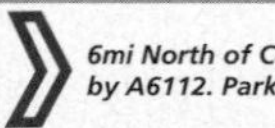

6mi North of Coldstream by A6112. Parking.

8 The Sorn Inn

35 Main St,
Sorn KA5 6HU
Tel.: (01290)551305 – Fax: (01290)553470
e-mail: craig@sorninn.com **Website:** www.sorninn.com

 **No real ales offered**

The Sorn Inn throws up an interesting choice to the diner: do you mingle with the locals whilst eating in the "Chop House" next to the bar, or would you rather dine in the more formal restaurant with its clothed tables, candles and flowers? Both have a pleasant – if very different - feel to them, and, although they offer separate menus, the same kitchen cooks for both, using the freshest and best of local produce – and at prices that won't put you into the red. Expect to eat grilled beef steaks, homemade burgers, pasta and fresh fish in the Chop House, or rabbit, pigeon and braised pork belly in the restaurant. This whitewashed village inn is family-run and the staff are friendly, welcoming and professional. Solve the dining conundrum by staying for the weekend; four good-sized bedrooms furnished in a modern style offer a very good value night's sleep - and breakfast is a tasty treat too.

Food serving times

Tuesday-Friday:
12pm-2pm, 6pm-9pm

Saturday: 12pm-9pm

Sunday: 12.30pm-7.30pm

Closed 2 weeks in January and Monday

Prices

Meals: £ 15 (lunch)
and a la carte £ 19/28

4 rooms: £ 40/75

Typical Dishes

Roast wood pigeon
Cassoulet of red mullet
Calvados rice pudding

2mi East of Catrine by B713.
Parking.

9 Iglu

2B Jamaica Street,
Edinburgh EH3 6HH
Tel.: (0131)4765333
e-mail: mail@theiglu.com **Website:** www.theiglu.com

 **Belhaven Best, Wild Cat**

It's hidden away in the old part of town, but once you're in the vicinity, there's no missing Iglu's vivid blue exterior. Inside, it's just as modern, with plasma screens, low tub chairs and funky music playing on the ground floor, and framed photos for sale, fish tanks and potted plants upstairs. Ethical eating is the ethos, and the motto is "wild, organic and local," so you can eat with a clear conscience, safe in the knowledge that your food has had a happy life and hasn't had to travel too far to your plate. And it's not just the food either; there are juices and smoothies, organic wines and fair trade coffee on offer too. Using the freshest and best seasonal ingredients available means that the menu changes frequently; dishes might include game pie, organic cod, wild boar burger stack and vegetarian haggis. Thus named because it's a snug place of tranquillity, Iglu can actually become pretty busy, so it's sensible to book ahead.

Food serving times

Monday-Sunday:
12pm-3pm, 6pm-10pm

Closed 25 December dinner, 26 December, 1-2 January

Prices

Meals: £ 12 (lunch) and a la carte £ 22/32

Typical Dishes

Fishcakes
Lamb shank
Baked chocolate fondant

In the New Town, off the west side of Howe Street.

10 The Kings Wark

36 The Shore,
Leith EH6 6QU
Tel.: (0131)5549260

 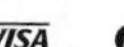

 **Deuchar IPA, Caley 80/-, Harvestons Bitter & Twisted and Schiehallion**

At the mouth of the harbour in gentrified Leith stands The King's Wark, with its distinctive blue front. Originally built in 1434 as a royal armoury and store to hold wines and other provisions for King James I, the building has also been used as a naval yard and a royal palace, was later destroyed by fire and then rebuilt. Its history is reflected in its characterful interior, all exposed stone and beams; the welcome is effusive and a fireside seat nice and warm. Due to its popularity, it can get quite busy - misanthropes might call it cramped, while philanthropists would probably prefer cosy. Especially strong on fish and seafood, the handwritten, weekly-changing menu offers proper, unpretentious Scottish food to fill your belly, and what it might lack in presentation, it more than makes up for in flavour. Well-known for its special all-day weekend breakfasts, you'll have to book well in advance if you want join the fun.

Food serving times

Monday-Saturday:
12pm-3pm, 6pm-10pm

Sunday:
11am-3pm, 6pm-10pm

Closed 25-26 December, 1 January

Prices

Meals: a la carte £ 13/29

Typical Dishes

Rabbit, trotter & leek rillette

Stuffed pork loin

Mixed Scottish berries

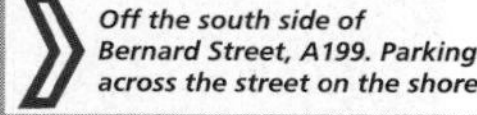

Off the south side of Bernard Street, A199. Parking across the street on the shore.

11 Babbity Bowster

16-18 Blackfriars St,
Glasgow G1 1PE
Tel.: (0141)5525055 – Fax: (0141)5527774

Deuchars IPA, Kelburn Misty Law and regularly changing guest beers

"Wha learned you to dance, / Babbity Bowster, Babbity Bowster? / Wha learned you to dance, / Babbity Bowster, brawly?" It was the regular custom in Scotland to wind up every dancing-ball with a dance called the Babbity Bowster, and the framed musical score to it hangs here on the wall of the bar, although the only dancing likely to occur these days might be a jig along to the live music on Saturday afternoons. Something of a city institution, this double-fronted Georgian-style building stands in the Merchant City area, which is currently being regenerated. Food on the short bar menu is simple yet wholesome, with local dishes including cullen skink, neeps and tatties, but if you'd prefer something a little more adventurous, you might instead choose to dine upstairs in the small restaurant with its open plan kitchen, and away from the drinkers (although it's best to phone ahead and check it's open before booking).

Food serving times

Monday-Sunday:
12pm-6.30pm (bar snacks only), 6.30pm-10.30pm

Closed 25 December

Prices

Meals: a la carte £ 16/26

Typical Dishes

Cullen skink
Seared scallops
Apple frangipane tart

In city centre North of the Central railway station. Parking for hotel guests only.

12 Summer Isles (Bar)

Achiltibuie IV26 2YG
Tel.: (01854)622282 – Fax: (01854)622251
e-mail: info@summerisleshotel.co.uk **Website:** www.summerisleshotel.co.uk

 **Isle of Skye Hebridean Gold, Young Pretender and Red Cullin, Deuchars IPA,**

An idyllically named establishment for an idyllic setting – this super bar and hotel faces the eponymous isles, far away from the madding crowd at the end of a 20 mile single track road. The bar is the "village pub", attached to the hotel but separate from it. Its simple, rustic ambience is perfect for the setting: sit in wooden booths and take in the wild, untouched landscape. You'll dine on seafood platters and rustic dishes such as casseroles and lamb shank; in the summer, don't miss the chance to eat al fresco. If you plump for the hotel, you'll be sampling precisely judged cuisine which has earned a Michelin Star for its excellence. There's every chance you'll stay the night: look forward to bedrooms ranging from simple and restrained to smart and sophisticated.

Food serving times

Monday-Sunday:
12pm-3pm, 5pm-8.30pm

Closed November to Easter

- Seafood - Bookings not accepted

Prices

Meals: a la carte £ 25/45

13 rooms: £ 85/200

Typical Dishes
Scallops baked in the shell
Saddle of venison
Summer fruit flan

15mi Northwest of Ullapool by A835 and minor road west from Drumrunie. Parking.

13 Applecross Inn

Shore St,
Applecross IV54 8LR
Tel.: (01520)744262 – Fax: (01520)744400
e-mail: applecrossinn@globalnet.co.uk **Website:** www.applecross.uk.com

 **Skye Brewing Co**

Run by the aptly named Judith Fish, the remote Applecross Inn attracts people from far and wide wanting to sample the bountiful seafood and local meats, from local prawns and crab to venison, featured on their extensive blackboard menus. That this inn gets so busy seems even more miraculous when you take into account the journey involved in getting here, for the tiny hamlet of Applecross is reached either via a twenty-four mile single track costal road or via a hair-raising mountain pass with such steep gradients and sharp bends that learner drivers are advised not to attempt it. Anyone brave enough is rewarded with all the charm you would expect from a cosy Highland inn, plus stunning views across the water to the Island of Raasay and the distant hills of Skye. As befits an inn which used to be a row of fishermen's cottages, bedrooms are small, but all offer sea views and, after recent modernisation, are smart and comfortable.

Food serving times
Monday-Sunday:
12pm-9pm
Closed 25 December,
1 January

Prices
Meals: a la carte £ 15/30
7 rooms: £ 70/100

Typical Dishes
Applecross Bay prawns
King scallops
Raspberry cranachan

From Kishorn via the Bealach nam Bo (Alpine pass) or round by Shieldaig and along the coast. Parking.

14 Badachro Inn

Badachro IV21 2AA
Tel.: (01445)741255 – Fax: (01445)741319
e-mail: lesley@badachroinn.com **Website:** www.badachroinn.com

An Teallach Ales, Caledonian 80/-

Nestled on the South shore of Loch Gairloch, this pub inhabits a superbly sheltered spot in a little secluded inlet, a stone's throw away from the jetty. Two moorings are available if you are arriving by boat and a smart decked area provides great views over the Loch. If the weather is being typically Scottish, you can still sit outside, as there's a canopy of sail cloth to protect you from the drizzle, but if the wind picks up or the temperatures drop too low, the conservatory is your next best bet. Inside, the atmosphere is cosily rustic, with a beamed bar, open fire and local maritime charts on the walls. Menus make good use of the local catch – lobsters, prawns and crabs are especially abundant in this area - and sandwiches and simple salads are available at lunchtimes. There are plenty of pre or post-prandial walks to be enjoyed, or you could take a boat trip and sail off into the scenery.

Food serving times

Monday-Sunday:
12pm-3pm, 6pm-9pm

Closed 25 December

Prices

Meals: a la carte approx.
£ 20

Typical Dishes
Crab salad
Gairloch langoustines
Chocolate & coffee truffle pot

6mi South of Gairloch by A832 and B8056. Parking and 2 moorings for boats.

15 Cawdor Tavern

The Lane,
Cawdor IV12 5XP

Tel.: (01667)404777 – Fax: (01667)404777

e-mail: enquiries@cawdortavern.info **Website:** www.cawdortavern.info

 VISA MC AE

Orkney Dark Island, Red McGregor, Atlas Latitude, Atlas Nimbus

"All hail, Macbeth, hail to thee, thane of Cawdor!" Although in real life, Macbeth actually died a few centuries before it was built, the nearby tourist attraction of Cawdor Castle is famous for its role in Shakespeare's tragedy, and this pub was originally its joiners' workshop. Nowadays, with its exposed beams and wood panelling, it has the feel of a traditional country pub about it and, as the same menu is served throughout, there's a choice between the bar with a pool table, the characterful lounge bar or the restaurant. This is a smoothly run establishment and therefore tends to get busy, especially at weekends, so guarantee yourself a seat by booking ahead. A large menu provides lots of choice, with plenty of Scottish favourites and a selection of specials. Cooking is fresh and robust and a lighter menu is also available at lunch. "Now, good digestion wait on appetite, / And health on both!"

Food serving times

Monday-Saturday:
12pm-2pm, 5.30pm-9pm

Sunday:
12pm-3pm, 5.30pm-9pm

Closed 25 December,
1 January

Booking essential

Prices

Meals: a la carte £ 13/26

Typical Dishes

Chicken liver parfait
Pork cutlet
Drambuie pannacotta

5mi South of Nairn by B9090.
Parking.

16 Kylesku Hotel

Kylesku IV27 4HW
Tel.: (01971)502231 – Fax: (01971)502313
e-mail: info@kyleskuhotel.co.uk **Website:** www.kyleskuhotel.co.uk

 **Bottles: Skye : Red Cuillin, Black Cuillin; Black Isle : Red Kite, Yellowhammer; Cairngorm Wildcat, Hebridean Gold**

This former coaching inn is situated in a peaceful village on the shores of two sea-lochs, in the heart of Scotland's first "Global Geopark", an area of great geological value. Whether you choose to sit in the bar or outside, there are fabulous panoramic views over Loch Glendhu to the mountains beyond, with similarly impressive outlooks from most of the homely bedrooms. In the bar, two blackboards display the day's menu: one, a seasonal à la carte, the other, a list of daily specials. As you would hope, specialities come in the form of local meat and game – lamb, beef and wild venison from the Highlands – and fresh seafood, which is landed daily on the slipway beside the Hotel; this may include haddock, scallops, crab, lobster or langoustines. With both hot and cold smoking taking place on site, salmon also features highly. After you've eaten lunch, head down to the waters edge, where you can catch a boat trip to the nearby seal colony.

32mi North of Ullapool by A835, A837 and A894. Public car park in the village 50m walk.

Food serving times

Monday-Sunday:
12pm-2.30pm, 7pm-8.30pm

Closed mid-October to end February

Bar snacks at lunchtime

Prices

Meals: £ 29 (dinner) and a la carte £ 18/27

8 rooms: £ 60/88

Typical Dishes

Venison terrine
Grilled langoustines
Bread & butter pudding

17 Plockton

41 Harbour St,
Plockton IV52 8TN

Tel.: (01599)544274 – Fax: (01599)544475
e-mail: info@plocktonhotel.co.uk **Website:** www.plocktonhotel.co.uk

   VISA MC AE

Hebredian Gold, Young Pretender, Plockton Brewery Crags Ale, Caledonian Brewery Deuchars IPA

Fine views of Loch Carron are a more than adequate reason to visit this attractive little National Trust village near the Kyle of Lochalsh. The eponymous inn – a delightful pair of wee cottages on the lochside – is the place to indulge the views while supping a pint with the locals, who flock here. The bar's the centre of activity, but if you're after a quieter environment, then you can retreat to the small rear terrace or the recently installed restaurant, where it's quite possible you'll be able to order a corn on the cob, alongside an impressive list of local seafood. Plockton isn't renowned for its road network, so for those making the wise move of staying overnight, there are plenty of recently refurbished, well-kept, comfy bedrooms to tempt you.

Food serving times

Monday-Saturday:
12pm-2.15pm, 6pm-9pm

Sunday:
12.30pm-2.15pm, 6pm-9pm

Closed 25 December and 1 January

Prices

Meals: a la carte £ 14/40

15 rooms: £ 45/100

Typical Dishes

Homemade country pate
Baked monkfish
Achmore Dairy cheeses

5mi North of Kyle of Lochalsh. Parking 50 yards away in Village car park.

18 Plockton Inn

Innes Street,
Plockton IV52 8TW
Tel.: (01599)544222 – Fax: (01599)544487
e-mail: info@plocktoninn.co.uk **Website:** www.plocktoninn.co.uk

VISA

Frequently changing - Abbot Ale, Fuller's London Pride, Plockton Ale Crags

If on arrival in the picturesque village of Plockton, you find that it looks familiar, it could be because this North West Highland village was the setting for the television series, "Hamish Macbeth" in the 1990s, and is perennially popular with filmmakers, photographers and artists. The eponymous inn is situated at the seaward end of Loch Carron where the cottages hug the harbour, so it's no surprise to find out that the menu here is heavily slanted towards seafood, with freshly caught fish and shellfish caught locally. The inn has been run by the same family for over ten years and the relaxed atmosphere and warm hospitality attract locals and visitors alike. Twice-weekly live music evenings in the tourist season are particularly popular. The lounge bar is the centre of proceedings, but there's also a dining room, a rear garden and a little front terrace too. Bedrooms are well-kept and modern and some come with a sea view.

Food serving times
Monday-Sunday:
12pm-2.15pm, 6pm-9pm

Seafood

Prices
Meals: a la carte £ 15/26
14 rooms: £ 40/90

Typical Dishes
Seafood platter
King scallops
Local cheese platter

5mi North of Kyle of Lochalsh.
Parking.

19 Stein Inn

MacLeod Terr,
Stein, Isle of Skye, Waternish IV55 8GA
Tel.: (01470)592362
e-mail: angus.teresa@steininn.co.uk **Website:** www.stein-inn.co.uk

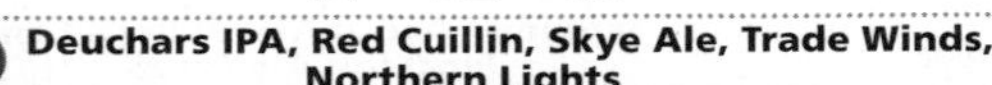

Deuchars IPA, Red Cuillin, Skye Ale, Trade Winds, Northern Lights

In a breathtakingly beautiful spot on Loch Bay, the oldest inn on Skye is run with great warmth and dedication by a chatty husband and wife team. At the heart of the place is a tiny pine-clad locals bar and a lounge with rough stone walls, tall settles and an open fire; it's good for lunchtime soup, sandwiches and a local ale, but it would be a shame not to try something more substantial in the evening in the little dining room – well-prepared seafood dishes, like Skye scallops and Scottish salmon, are the pick of a tasty menu which also includes Highland venison. But for pure relaxation and peace of mind, take one of their 90 malts down to the grassy bank or the benches looking west over the bay and watch the sun set beyond the headland. Guests staying in the cosy, well-kept bedrooms – a snip at the price – can compare the view in the morning.

Food serving times

Monday-Sunday:
12pm-4pm, 6pm-9pm

In winter:
12pm-2.30pm, 5.30pm-8pm

Closed 25 December,
1 January

- Seafood specialities -

Prices

Meals: a la carte £ 16/25

5 rooms: £ 40/50

Typical Dishes
Seared scallops
Venison steak
Highland cheeses

22mi West of Portree by A87, A850 and B886; on the shore of Loch Bay. Parking.

20 An Lochan Country Inn

Glendevon FK14 7JY

Tel.: (01259)781252 – Fax: (01259)781526

e-mail: tormaukin@anlochan.co.uk **Website:** www.anlochan.co.uk

Bitter and Twisted, Thrappledouser, Houston Brewery Ales

Its owners have given the outside a lick of paint and improved the décor within, but with its stone floored, beamed bar and open fires, this 18C roadside drovers' inn has retained its rustic roots. Sit in the spacious main dining room, its whitewashed walls offset with vivid art, and enjoy food from the fiercely Scottish sourced à la carte or set menus, where the mix of traditional and more modern dishes might include gravadlax, langoustines and local beef. There is a good range of Scottish cheeses and a nice selection of real ales and wines by the glass; the welcome is extremely warm and the service by keen, local staff is impressive. Comfortable bedrooms provide a good night's rest, so you can sleep deeply, dreaming of the whopper you're going to catch, the pheasant you're going to shoot or the hole in one you are going to hit next morning on your travels around the unspoilt Perthshire countryside.

Food serving times

Monday-Sunday:
12pm-3pm, 5.30pm-9pm

Closed 24-25 December

Prices

Meals: £ 13/25
and a la carte £ 20/60

12 rooms: £ 85/120

Typical Dishes

Stornaway black pudding

Highland beef

Treacle tart

22mi Southwest of Perth by M90 to Junction 7, A91 and A823. Parking.

Scotland • Perthshire and Kinross

21 The Anglers Inn

Main Road,
Guildtown PH2 6BS
Tel.: (01821)640329
e-mail: info@theanglersinn.co.uk **Website:** www.theanglersinn.co.uk

Inspectors' favourites

   AE

 **Independence, Lia Fail, Thrappledowser and Ossian**

Situated in a tiny hamlet in the heart of Perthshire, not far from Scone Palace where the Scottish Kings were crowned, this whitewashed pub is surrounded by soft fruit farms and distant views of the Cairngorm and Trossach Mountains. Whilst it doesn't look much from the outside (it could be any of a hundred Scottish country roadside inns), this pub is different, in fact, it's hardly a pub at all; the plain décor, laminate flooring and high-backed chairs are for diners only and you must head to the public bar next door if you are after a relaxing drink. The good value restaurant-style menu is ambitious, displaying a fairly classical French base and some good combinations. Traditional fish and chips is a bestseller but with well-prepared fresh ingredients and careful cooking, you can't go wrong with any dish. Rooms are clean and simple; for hunters and fishermen freezers are available to keep any game or fish fresh.

Food serving times

Monday-Sunday:
12pm-2pm, 6pm-9pm

Closed 25-26 December and first 2 weeks January

Prices

Meals: £ 18 (lunch) and a la carte £ 19/29

5 rooms: £ 40/100

Typical Dishes
Trio of salmon
Rack of lamb
Lemon pannacotta

7mi North of Perth by A93

22 Moulin Inn

11-13 Kirkmichael Rd,
Pitlochry PH16 5EH
Tel.: (01796)472196 – Fax: (01796)474098
e-mail: enquiries@moulinhotel.co.uk **Website:** www.pitlochryhotels.co.uk

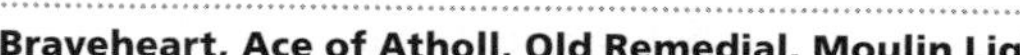

Braveheart, Ace of Atholl, Old Remedial, Moulin Light

Scottish hospitality has been dispensed on the site of this inn for more than three hundred years, during which time the hotel has grown up around it. Set in the centre of a conservation village, it's popular with tourists, walkers and locals, but if you were expecting to find a mill next door, you'll be disappointed – it is thus named simply as a derivation of the word "Maohlinn." The terrace is popular in clement weather, but it is equally, if not more relaxing to sit at one of the large tables in the cosy semi-booths and be warmed by the open fire. The neighbouring Moulin micro brewery supplies the real cask ales sold in the bar and, being Scotland, there's a fine selection of whiskies too. The chef may be French, but the food is Scottish through and through. Made with local Perthshire produce, the hearty steaks and casseroles, smoked meat platters and haggis are tasty and filling enough to mean that one course is sufficient.

Food serving times

Monday-Sunday:
12pm-9.30pm (bar food),
6pm-9pm (restaurant)

Restaurant closed
25 December

Prices

Meals: £ 24 (dinner)
and a la carte £ 16/26

15 rooms: £ 45/90

Typical Dishes

Duo of smoked meats
Rabbit casserole
Highland whisky sponge

28 mi North of Perth by A9.
Parking.

23 The Inn at Kippen

Fore Rd,
Kippen FK8 3DT

Tel.: (01786)871010 – Fax: (01786)871011
e-mail: info@theinnatkippen.co.uk **Website:** www.theinnatkippen.co.uk

 **Ossian, Thrappledowser**

Remotely set in a sleepy hamlet, surrounded by Stirlingshire countryside, the imaginatively named "Inn" is one of those places which offer both a modern sense of stylishness and a feeling of rustic cosiness. Their walls filled with old sepia photos of village life over the years, the three main dining areas boast a homely feel; the seats are pleasantly comfy and the bar reassuringly busy, while the small rear courtyard provides decked seating and a pizza oven for the warmer months. There's no messing about with the food here: hearty portions provide plenty of comfort appeal, with favourites such as sausage and mash or steak pie served alongside more elaborate seafood, steak and game dishes from the seasonal à la carte, and at weekends they have built up quite a reputation for their fresh daily fish dishes. If you wish to prolong the Kippen experience, there are several well kept, homely bedrooms, named after local parishes.

Food serving times

Monday-Sunday:
12pm-2.30pm, 6pm-9.30pm

Closed 25 December and 1-3 January

Prices

Meals: £ 13 (3 course lunch/dinner) and a la carte £ 20/35

3 rooms: £ 40/80

Typical Dishes

Arbroath smokie paté
Loin of venison
Passion fruit mousee

9mi West of Stirling by A811 and B822. Parking.

24 The Chop and Ale House

Champany,
Linlithgow EH49 7LU
Tel.: (01506)834532 – Fax: (01506)834302
e-mail: reception@champany.com **Website:** www.champany.com

 **Belhaven Best**

Housed in a simple annex to the Champany inn, in what used to be its public bar, The Chop and Ale house provides a lighter alternative to dinner at the main restaurant, without losing any of its quality. Not the ideal place for teetotal vegetarians – the clue is in the name - the exposed stone walls are filled with shotguns, fishing rods and mounted animal heads. Meat is all important here, with Aberdeen Angus steaks, Scottish lamb chops, superior homemade sausages and spit-roasted chicken on offer; and of particular note are the homemade burgers. If you're the kind of person who would never normally eat a burger, make a point of trying one here. Homemade, from the same beef that provides the restaurant with its steaks, they come with a choice of toppings and taste just great. A fire burns in the grate, the tables are closely set and the atmosphere is one of relaxed conviviality.

Food serving times

Monday-Thursday: 12pm-2pm

Friday-Sunday: all day

Closed 25-26 December, 1 January

Prices

Meals: a la carte £ 23/35

Typical Dishes

Dressed salmon

Aberdeen Angus rib eye beef

Champany's cheesecake

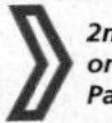

2mi noth-east of town centre on A803. At The Champany Inn. Parking.

It's nearly six hundred years since Owen Glyndawr escaped the clutches of the English to become a national hero, and in all that time the Welsh passion for unity has bound the country together like a scarlet-shirted scrum. It may be only 170 miles from north to south, but Wales contains great swathes of beauty, such as the dark and craggy heights of Snowdonia's ninety mountain peaks, the rolling sandstone bluffs of the Brecon Beacons, and Pembrokeshire's tantalising golden beaches. Bottle-nosed dolphins love it here too, arriving each summer at New Quay in Cardigan Bay. Highlights abound: formidable Harlech Castle dominates its coast, and Bala Lake has a railway that steams along its gentle shores. Hay-on-Wye's four pubs and eighteen bookshops turn perceptions on their head, and Welsh cuisine is causing a surprise or two as well: the country teems with great raw ingredients now employed to their utmost potential, from the humblest cockle to the slenderest slice of succulent lamb.

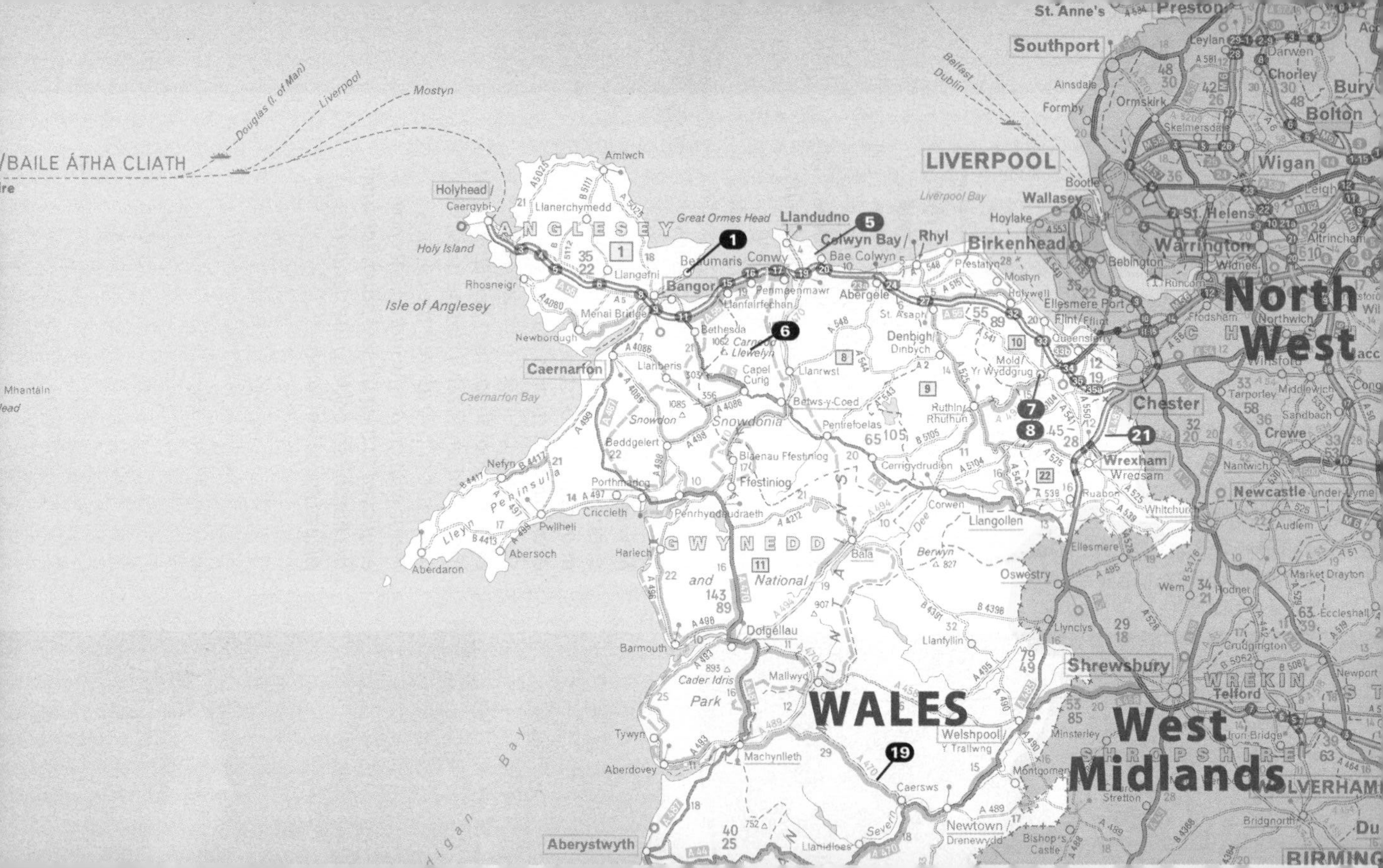

North West
West Midlands
WALES
LIVERPOOL
Liverpool Bay
Southport
St. Anne's
Preston
Wigan
Bolton
Bury
Chorley
Leyland
Ormskirk
Skelmersdale
St. Helens
Warrington
Widnes
Runcorn
Altrincham
Leigh
Northwich
Middlewich
Sandbach
Crewe
Nantwich
Newcastle under Lyme
Market Drayton
Newport
Telford
WREKIN
Shrewsbury
Oswestry
Ellesmere
Whitchurch
Chester
Wrexham
Wrecsam
Ruabon
Llangollen
Corwen
Bala
Mold / Yr Wyddgrug
Ruthin / Rhuthun
Denbigh / Dinbych
St. Asaph
Abergele
Flint / Fflint
Holywell
Prestatyn
Rhyl
Colwyn Bay / Bae Colwyn
Llandudno
Great Ormes Head
Conwy
Penmaenmawr
Llanfairfechan
Beaumaris
Bangor
Bethesda
Capel Curig
Betws-y-Coed
Llanrwst
Blaenau Ffestiniog
Ffestiniog
Snowdon
Snowdonia
Llanberis
Caernarfon
Caernarfon Bay
Beddgelert
Porthmadog
Criccieth
Pwllheli
Abersoch
Aberdaron
Nefyn
Harlech
Barmouth
Dolgellau
Cader Idris
Machynlleth
Tywyn
Aberdovey
Aberystwyth
Llanidloes
Newtown
Drenewydd
Welshpool
Y Trallwng
Montgomery
Caersws
Bishop's Castle
Stretton
Bridgnorth
GWYNEDD
Snowdonia and National Park
Isle of Anglesey
ANGLESEY
Holyhead / Caergybi
Holy Island
Llangefni
Amlwch
Menai Bridge
Rhosneigr
Newborough
Llanerchymedd
Birkenhead
Wallasey
Hoylake
Bootle
Formby
Belfast
Dublin
Douglas (I. of Man)
Liverpool
Mostyn
/BAILE ÁTHA CLIATH

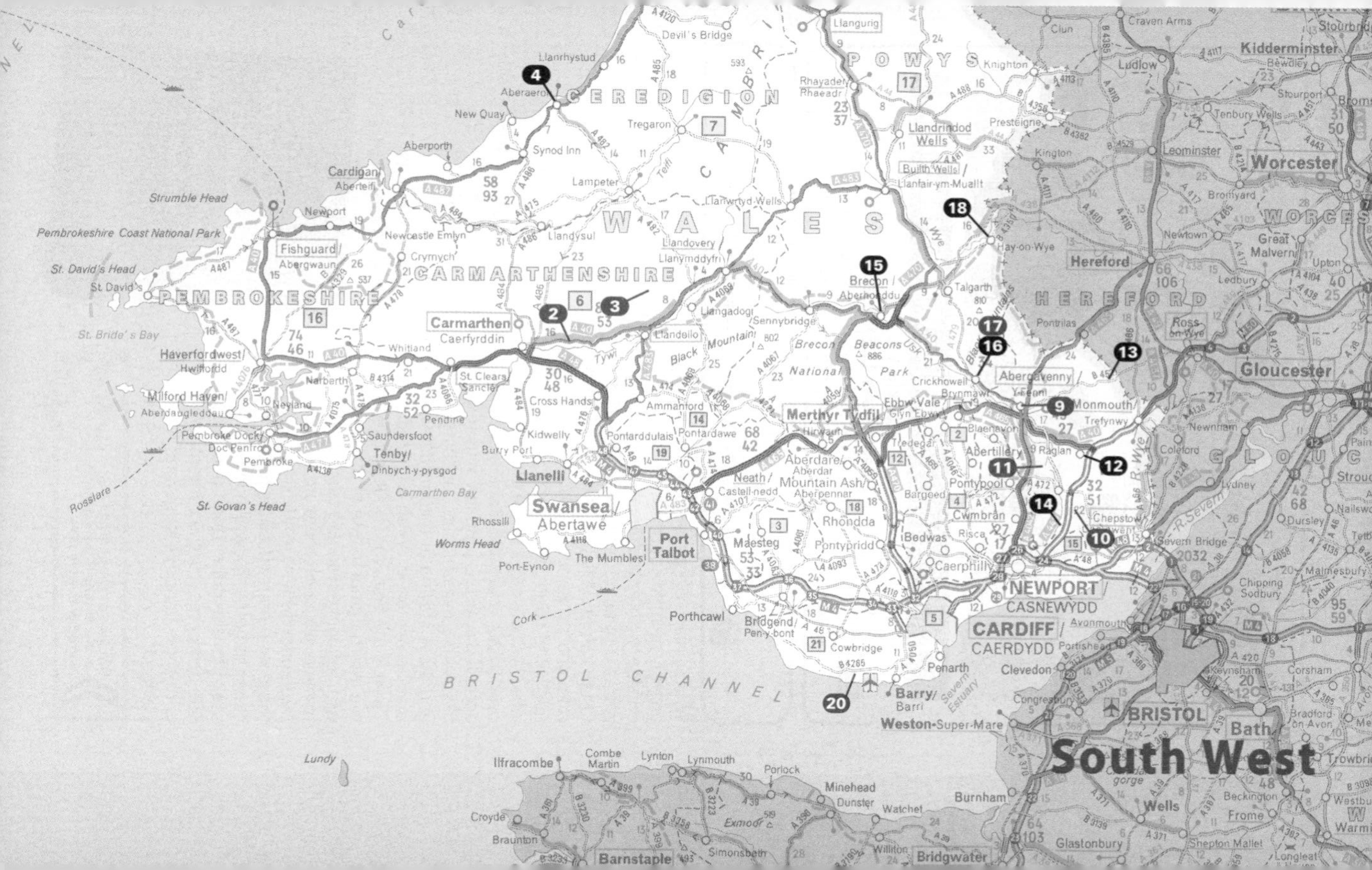

WALES
POWYS
CEREDIGION
CAMBRIA
CARMARTHENSHIRE
PEMBROKESHIRE
HEREFORD
South West
BRISTOL CHANNEL
Carmarthen Bay
St. Bride's Bay
Severn Estuary
Pembrokeshire Coast National Park
Brecon Beacons National Park
Black Mountain
Strumble Head
St. David's Head
St. Govan's Head
Worms Head
Rosslare
Cork
Lundy
Llangurig
Devil's Bridge
Llanrhystud
Aberaeron
New Quay
Aberporth
Synod Inn
Tregaron
Rhayader/ Rhaeadr
Knighton
Llandrindod Wells
Presteigne
Kington
Builth Wells/ Llanfair-ym-Muallt
Lampeter
Llanwrtyd Wells
Llandovery/ Llanymddyfri
Llandysul
Newcastle Emlyn
Cardigan/ Aberteifi
Newport
Fishguard/ Abergwaun
Crymych
St. David's
Haverfordwest/ Hwlffordd
Milford Haven/ Aberdaugleddau
Neyland
Pembroke Dock/ Doc Penfro
Pembroke
Narberth
Whitland
St. Clears/ Sanclêr
Carmarthen Caerfyrddin
Saundersfoot
Tenby/ Dinbych-y-pysgod
Pendine
Kidwelly
Cross Hands
Burry Port
Llanelli
Swansea/ Abertawe
Rhossili
Port-Eynon
The Mumbles
Port Talbot
Llandeilo
Llangadog
Sennybridge
Ammanford
Pontarddulais
Pontardawe
Neath/ Castell-nedd
Maesteg
Porthcawl
Bridgend/ Pen-y-bont
Cowbridge
Barry/ Barri
Penarth
Aberdare/ Aberdâr
Mountain Ash/ Aberpennar
Rhondda
Pontypridd
Hirwaun
Merthyr Tydfil
Brecon/ Aberhonddu
Talgarth
Hay-on-Wye
Crickhowell
Brynmawr
Ebbw Vale/ Glyn Ebwy
Tredegar
Bargoed
Bedwas
Caerphilly
Blaenavon
Abertillery
Pontypool
Cwmbran
Risca
Abergavenny/ Y Fenni
Monmouth/ Trefynwy
Raglan
Chepstow
NEWPORT/ CASNEWYDD
CARDIFF/ CAERDYDD
Pontrilas
Ross-on-Wye
Hereford
Leominster
Ludlow
Clun
Craven Arms
Kidderminster
Bewdley
Stourport
Stourbridge
Tenbury Wells
Bromyard
Worcester
Great Malvern
Newtown
Upton
Ledbury
Gloucester
Newnham
Coleford
Lydney
Severn Bridge
Dursley
Nailsworth
Stroud
Tetbury
Malmesbury
Chipping Sodbury
Avonmouth
Portishead
Clevedon
Congresbury
Weston-Super-Mare
BRISTOL
Keynsham
Bath
Corsham
Bradford on Avon
Trowbridge
Beckington
Frome
Westbury
Warminster
Shepton Mallet
Longleat
Wells
Glastonbury
Burnham
Bridgwater
Watchet
Williton
Minehead
Dunster
Porlock
Exmoor
Lynmouth
Lynton
Combe Martin
Ilfracombe
Croyde
Braunton
Barnstaple
Simonsbath

1 Ye Olde Bull's Head Inn

Castle St,
Beaumaris LL58 8AP

Tel.: (01248)810329 – Fax: (01248)811294
e-mail: info@bullsheadinn.co.uk **Website:** www.bullsheadinn.co.uk

VISA MC AE

Draught Bass, Draught Hancocks and 1 guest beer

What a place of contrasts! A welcoming, brightly painted coaching inn from the outside, with a traditional old bar complete with the ubiquitous horse brasses and tartan carpet while, on the other side, a calm and contemporary lounge. And at the rear is the bright and breezy Brasserie, in what was once the stable block and which overlooks a courtyard. Bookings are still not accepted which is probably why it quickly fills, with a mix of locals, lunching ladies and those staying at the inn. The menu may be written in Welsh and English but Tapas is the first word on it and highlights the international nature of the cooking, with influences ranging from Italy to India, although there are more traditional dishes like Welsh rib-eye for those who prefer flavours to be kept closer to home. It's worth leaving some space for the rather good puddings. The bedrooms mix the contemporary with some period features and more are planned.

Food serving times

Monday-Saturday:
12pm-2pm (brasserie),
7pm-9.30pm

Sunday:
12pm-2pm, 6pm-9pm
(brasserie)

Closed 25 December,
26 December for food,
1 January for food

Prices

Meals: a la carte £ 16/22

13 rooms: £ 80/110

Typical Dishes

Asparagus & quail eggs
Mackerel fillets
Rhubarb & raspberry crumble

On the east side of the town centre. Parking in town centre and other free car parks.

2 Y Polyn

Nantgaredig SA32 7LH
Tel.: (01267)290000
e-mail: ypolyn@hotmail.com **Website:** www.ypolynrestaurant.co.uk

  VISA MC

Ffos-y-Ffin Ales, Three Arches, Deuchars IPA

With a wealth of experience shared between the owners, you can be sure that they know what they're doing here. Set in a great corner location on a rural road, next to a stream and with views across the surrounding fields, this pub attracts diners from far and wide. The whole place feels like a modern, rustic style dining room and despite the casual attire of the servers, most guests dress to the nines. Cooking is classical but with a modern element and, as you would expect, is hearty, tasty and uses local produce wherever possible. The simpler lunch selection is priced accordingly, while in the evening the choice expands under a set menu, each dish arriving with a complimentary side of veg; some main courses do attract a supplement. There's a sensibly priced wine list and the host enjoys making recommendations. In the hallway, co-owner and restaurant consultant Simon Wright's articles are on display and copies of his book are for sale.

Food serving times

Tuesday-Saturday:
12pm-2pm, 7pm-9pm

Sunday: 12pm-2pm

Closed 2 weeks October

Prices

Meals: 28 and a la carte
£ 18/25

Typical Dishes

Pear & Roquefort salad
Roast rump of lamb
Yoghurt pannacotta

5mi East of Carmarthen on A40. From Nantgaredig South 1mi by B4310 on B4300. Parking.

3 The Angel Inn

Salem SA19 7LY
Tel.: (01558)823394
e-mail: eat@angelsalem.co.uk **Website:** www.angelsalem.co.uk

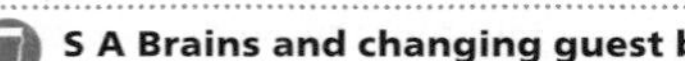
S A Brains and changing guest beer

You drive up a narrow, twisty road to reach this cream-coloured pub, which, fittingly, given its name, is located next to the village chapel. Inside, it's traditionally ornate, and well-kept by its keen young owners, if a little impervious to the modern world. The inviting bar lounge contains an assortment of comfy chairs and sofas in which to sink and the spacious Edwardian style dining room contains large, well-spaced tables. The chef -a former Welsh chef of the year- produces elaborate cooking which combines classic, modern and local influences. Welsh specialities offered might include lamb, salmon and cheeses, but, if you're on a time limit, beware- the wide choice available on the blackboard lunch menu might have you dawdling for far too long. The friendly atmosphere here attracts many locals as well as visitors, and you'll find the welcome extended here is as wide as the village of Salem is small.

Food serving times

Tuesday: 7pm-9pm

Wednesday-Saturday and Bank Holiday Monday: 12pm-2pm, 7pm-9pm

Sunday: 12pm-2pm

Closed Sunday dinner, Monday (except Bank Holiday Monday), Tuesday lunch

Prices

Meals: a la carte £ 20/32

Typical Dishes

Smoked salmon sushi nori roll

Tenderloin of pork

Six mini desserts

3mi North of Llandeilo by A40 off Pen y bane road. Parking.

4 Harbourmaster

Quay Parade,
Aberaeron SA46 0BA
Tel.: (01545)570755
e-mail: info@harbour-master.com **Website:** www.harbour-master.com

Inspectors' favourites

 **Tomos Watkin, Evan Evans BB**

Having bought and expanded into the old Sea Aquarium next door, The Harbourmaster reopened in Easter 2008 after a major refit and refurbishment. Its brand new bedrooms all have bright colours to reflect being by the sea and are named after boats built in the harbour. The room where the bar counter once stood has now been restyled as the new restaurant, complete with nautical pictures, and offers an appealing menu where Welsh Black beef and lamb, and assorted local seafood are permanent fixtures. Those wanting more relaxed surroundings should try the new bar, with its large U shaped counter and views into the kitchen. Here the offerings are more pub-like in design. The choice between fishcakes, Caesar salad, oatcakes with Welsh cheeses or venison sausages with parsnip mash and gravy will probably be made easier by the day's weather. Brunch is also available for those spending the day at a more leisurely pace.

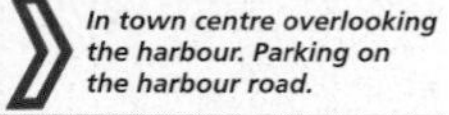

In town centre overlooking the harbour. Parking on the harbour road.

Food serving times

Monday: 6.30pm-9pm

Tuesday-Sunday:
12pm-2.30pm, 6.30pm-9pm

Closed 25 December

Prices

Meals: a la carte £ 20/35

13 rooms: £ 55/250

Typical Dishes

Crab risotto
Ystwyth Valley sirloin
Chocolate fondant

5 Pen-y-Bryn

Pen-y-Bryn Rd,
Upper Colwyn Bay, Colwyn Bay LL29 6DD
Tel.: (01492)533360 – Fax: (01492)536127
Website: www.penybryn-colwynbay.co.uk

 **Thwaites Original, Wessex Spring, Conwy Castle Bitter, Ormes Best, Wadworth 6X, Derby Dashingly Dark, Timothy Taylor Landlord**

Just a little further down the road from the zoo, inside this unremarkable-looking building, you can actually observe urban man feeding in his natural habitat. This spacious, open-plan pub with wood floors, a central bar and low ceilings provides shelter for this animal, open fires provide warmth, and the framed pictures, posters and articles on the walls make him feel at home in his environment. The large rear gardens and terrace provide space for man to move about outside, and he enjoys nothing better than sunning himself out here on hot afternoons. A varied diet is on offer on the daily-changing blackboard menus, with dishes ranging from hearty Welsh lamb hotpot or fish pie to Thai green curry, and the not-so-naked ape likes to sit at the wooden tables provided in order to feast on the large portions. Being a sociable creature, man tends to gather in groups, and he is well looked after by the polite, organised staff.

Food serving times

Monday-Saturday:
12pm-9.30pm

Sunday: 12pm-9pm

Closed dinner
25-26 December and
1 January

Prices

Meals: a la carte £ 18/28

Typical Dishes

Sautéed lambs kidneys
Hearty fish stew
Meringue & fruit compote

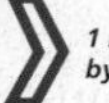

1 mi Southwest of Colwyn Bay by B5113. Parking.

6 The Groes Inn

Tyn-y-Groes LL32 8TN
Tel.: (01492)650545 – Fax: (01492)650855
e-mail: reception@groesinn.com **Website:** www.groesinn.com

 **Great Orme Brewery, Burton Cask Ale**

This foliage-clad roadside inn is reputed to be the oldest in Wales, and it certainly has all the character you'd expect from a five-hundred year old. Old beams hang overhead, and the atmospheric bar and various little rooms and snugs are filled with bric-à-brac, ornaments, and pictures. The dining room is more formally laid out with smartly dressed tables, and the cooking offers a comprehensive mix of classic and traditional pub fare, supplemented by the blackboard menu. No reinvention of the wheel happens here – food is robust, satisfying and recognisable. The inn may be old, but the bedroom extensions are right up-to-date. Large, comfortable and individually decorated with warm fabrics, stylish furniture and good facilities, some also have terraces or balconies overlooking the surrounding countryside. With the foothills of Snowdonia on one side, and the Conwy river on the other, whichever way you're facing, the view will be good.

2mi from Conwy Castle by B5106 towards Trefriw; the inn is on the right. Parking.

Food serving times

Monday-Sunday:
12pm-2.15pm, 6.30pm-9pm

Closed 25 December

Prices

Meals: £ 30 (dinner)
and a la carte £ 23/30

14 rooms: £ 85/189

Typical Dishes

Groes smokie

Crispy lamb & feta salad

Eton mess

7 Glas Fryn

Raikes Lane,
Sychdyn, Mold CH7 6LR
Tel.: (01352)750500 – Fax: (01352)751923
e-mail: glasfryn@brunningandprice.co.uk **Website:** www.glasfryn-mold.co.uk

Timothy Taylor Landlord, Thwaites Original, Wadworth 6X, Deuchars IPA, Black Sheep

Another well-run pub from the Brunning and Price stable, bought in a dilapidated state, renovated, and now an imposing red-brick structure complete with extension. Inside it's all open plan spaciousness, wooden floors and furniture, neutral colour schemes and walls covered in neatly exhibited photos, pictures, books and the like, as well as the huge blackboard menus. You know that the food on offer will include wholesomely classic dishes, that the choice will be extensive and that the service will remain efficient even during busy periods, which is a good job seeing how many people come here. Situated a little way out of the town centre, right by the entrance to the Theatr Clwyd, residents of Mold and beyond mingle happily with customers ranging from theatregoers to farmers to ensure the atmosphere is buzzing, particularly at weekends. A seat on the terrace or in the large garden is recommended when the weather acquiesces.

Food serving times

Monday-Saturday:
12pm-9.30pm

Sunday: 12pm-9pm

Closed 25-26 December

Prices

Meals: a la carte £ 18/28

Typical Dishes

Pancetta salad
Chicken breast
Hot waffle & honeycomb ice cream

1 mi North by A5119 on Civic Centre rd. Parking.

8 The Stables

Mold CH7 6AB

Tel.: (01352)840577 – Fax: (01352)840872

e-mail: info@soughtonhall.co.uk **Website:** www.soughtonhall.co.uk

   MC AE

Plassey, Stables and guest ales such as Honey Pot, Dick Turpin, Inn-Keepers

Set in the grounds of a large 18C Italianate mansion, you can probably deduce from its name what part this attractive red brick building used to play in proceedings, but in case you missed the connection, the stalls are still here, the tables are named after racehorses and the menus divided into punters' starters and mains, owners' and trainers' starters and mains, and the final furlong (desserts). The characterful interior boasts rustic décor with beamed ceilings, heavy wood tables, open fires and cobbled and stone flooring. Upstairs is the restaurant and a large wine shop, and the terrace out the back is a great spot for al fresco summer dining. Modern British menus offer everything from lunchtime light bites to sandwiches, steaks, seafood and steamed pudding, while more elaborate dishes might include venison Wellington or pan-seared king scallops. Local staff provide friendly, informal service, but make sure you book ahead.

Food serving times

Monday-Saturday:
12pm-9.30pm

Sunday: 1pm-9pm

Booking essential

Prices

Meals: a la carte £ 24/31

Typical Dishes

Baked banana & Parma ham

Lamb shank

Strawberry cheesecake

2.5mi North by A 5119 on Altami Rd. Parking.

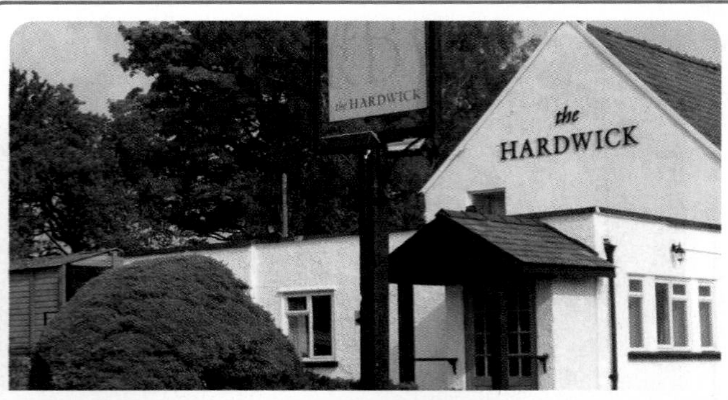

9 The Hardwick

Old Raglan Rd,
Abergavenny NP7 9AA
Tel.: (01873)854220 – Fax: (01873)854623
e-mail: stephen@thehardwick.co.uk **Website:** www.thehardwick.co.uk

Inspectors' favourites

 **Rhymney Brewery, Otley Brewery, Breconshire Brewery**

To pass by this simple, whitewashed pub would be a culinary crime, but with its unassuming exterior, could be all too easily done. Having appeared on the BBC's "Great British Menu", chef Stephen Terry has become somewhat of a local celebrity, but he takes it in his stride and can often be found chatting away to the locals. With wooden tables arranged on slate floors the pub is simply furnished but this helps to frame the fabulous mountain views that can be seen from the tables by the windows. The philosophy here is simplicity and the use of local produce is paramount, so much so that Stephen can often be found not on the phone, but on the farm when placing his orders. Menus are lengthy and feature both British and Mediterranean influences, ranging from eggs Benedict and duck hash to rare breed middle white pork and roast skate wings. Some dishes come with a choice of portion size and there's a good value set menu at lunch

Food serving times

Tuesday-Saturday:
12pm-3pm, 6.30pm-10pm

Sunday: 12pm-3pm

Closed 25-26 December and 2-3 January

Prices

Meals: £ 21 (lunch)
and a la carte £ 25/36

Typical Dishes

Eggs royale
Shoulder of pork
Amalfi lemon fool

2mi Southeast by A40 and B4598.
Parking.

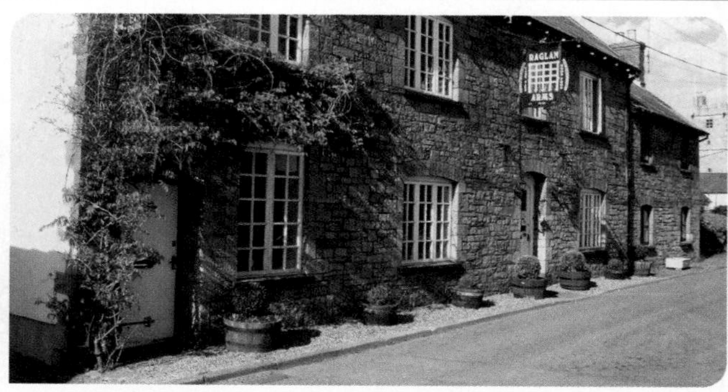

10 Raglan Arms

Llandenny NP15 1DL

Tel.: (01291)690800 – Fax: (01291)690155

e-mail: raglanarms@aol.com **Website:** www.raglanarms.com

   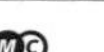 AE

 **Wye Valley Butty Bach, Breconshire Welsh Pale Ale**

An Englishman, a Frenchman and a Swedish woman walked into The Raglan Arms, and the landlord said, "Is this some sort of joke?" No, of course he didn't, but the three of them took over the pub; out went the pool table, carpet and fruit machines, and in came a bit of charm in the form of mismatched pine furniture, an old settle, a dresser and a butcher's chopping block. Old wood beams and a stone tiled floor add to the rustic ambience, and there's enough room in the tardis-like interior to have several tables exclusively for drinkers, plus a lounge with comfy leather sofas and an open fireplace. Cooking is British with Mediterranean influences, and, sourced from nearby farms, ingredients are reassuringly local. Lunchtime sees traditional pub classics such as steak or sausage and mash, while dinner is more substantial and might include braised beef or rack of lamb. Relying on the latest catch, seafood also features highly.

Food serving times

Tuesday-Saturday:
12pm-3pm, 6.30pm-9.30pm

Sunday: 12pm-3pm

Closed 26-27 December

Prices

Meals: a la carte £ 20/24

Typical Dishes

Black pudding salad

Grilled halibut fillet

Glazed lemon tart

4.25mi Northeast of Usk by A472 off B4235. Parking.

11 The Foxhunter

Nant-y-Derry NP7 9DD
Tel.: (01873)881101
e-mail: info@thefoxhunter.com **Website:** www.thefoxhunter.com

Old Speckled Hen, S A Gold, Bath Ales, Wye Valley Ales (in bottles)

Having learned his skills in the big smoke, Matt Tebbutt made his way back to this unspoilt village in Wales in order to demonstrate them, and having acquired The Foxhunter has proceeded to do just that. The stone pub started life as the stationmaster's house but is now decked out in true gastropub style; all cheery and bright with foodie prints on the walls, dark wood floors, and solid wood tables, and Matt's wife Lisa ensures an informal, friendly atmosphere front of house. You'll find both bold British cooking and European dishes on the menus, but whether you're eating cottage pie or salmorejo, à la carte or table d'hôte, you can rest assured that the ingredients are fresh, seasonal and locally sourced. In fact, so passionate are they here about using local produce that you can even go out with a professional forager in order to search out some of the ingredients for your dinner – and it doesn't get more immediate than that.

Food serving times

Tuesday-Saturday:
12pm-2pm, 7pm-9.30pm

Sunday: 12pm-2pm

Closed 25-26 December

Prices

Meals: £ 22 (lunch)
and a la carte £ 20/35

Typical Dishes

Braised octopus
Old Spot pork
Raspberry syllabub

6.5 mi South of Abergavenny by A4042 and minor rd. Parking.

12 The Clytha Arms

Raglan NP7 9BW
Tel.: (01873)840206 – Fax: (01873)840209
e-mail: clythaarms@tiscali.co.uk

 **Rhymney Bitter, Evans & Evans BB, Felinfoel Double Dragon and 300 guest beers during a year**

Distinctive is a word that applies equally well to the appearance, the character and the cooking at the Clytha Arms. The walls of the pub are painted pink, the atmosphere is one of chaotic charm and the menu uncommonly eclectic. You'll receive a warm welcome and the interior is full of character, with open fires, wooden floors, bench seating and an old games board calling you to try your luck at traditional bar games such as dominoes and skittles. Food is of a high quality and the à la carte and set menus offer a choice of dishes, ranging from the Welsh to the international, with bar snacks and tapas also served in the bar. When the Welsh weather is fine, a seat in the extensive lawned grounds is imperative. Comfortable, individually-styled bedrooms are available if you are making a weekend of it; one has a four-poster bed, and in all, little extras such as magazines and toiletries are provided.

Food serving times

Monday: 7pm-9.30pmTuesday-Saturday and Bank Holiday Monday: 12.30pm-2.30pm, 7pm-9.30pm

Sunday: 12.30pm-2.30pm

Closed 25 December

Prices

Meals: £ 25 and a la carte £ 28/38

4 rooms: £ 60/100

Typical Dishes

Leek & laverbread rissoles

Mixed grill

Welsh cheese board

3mi West on the Clytha road (Old Abergavenny Road). Parking.

13 The Bell at Skenfrith

Skenfrith NP7 8UH
Tel.: (01600)750235 – Fax: (01600)750525
e-mail: enquiries@skenfrith.co.uk
Website: www.skenfrith.co.uk

 **Timothy Taylor Landlord, St Austell Tribute, Golden Valley**

Rather than the devil, here it's the angel that's in the detail. Nothing is too much trouble for the owners of our 2007 pub of the year. Bedrooms are the height of luxury, with home made biscuits, touchpad TVs, CD and DVD players, and local information guides are provided for your perusal. Dining tables resplendent with garden-picked flowers have been polished till they gleam, service is unhurriedly attentive and the extensive wine list is a delight for oenophiles. The daily-changing menu offers classic French cuisine, with a twist of innovation, you'll find the names of the local suppliers proudly posted on blackboards in the bar, and the kitchen garden produces its own organic vegetables and herbs. In the beamed interior, country meets contemporary, with flagstone floors and comfy sofas. All this plus the rolling Monmouthshire countryside dotted with sheep, a river, a bridge and a castle all begging to be explored.

Food serving times

Monday-Saturday:
12pm-2.30pm, 7pm-9.30pm

Sunday:
12pm-2.30pm, 7pm-9pm

Closed 2 weeks late January to early February, Mondays November to Easter

Prices

Meals: £ 19 (lunch) and a la carte £ 26/32

11 rooms: £ 75/220

Typical Dishes

Carpaccio of beef fillet

Fillet of wild seabass

Passion fruit mousse

11mi West of Ross-on-Wye by A49 on B4521. Parking.

14 The Newbridge

Tredunnock NP15 1LY
Tel.: (01633)451000 – Fax: (01633)451001
e-mail: newbridge@evanspubs.co.uk **Website:** www.evanspubs.co.uk

    AE

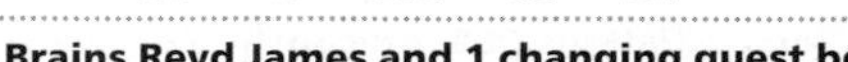

Brains Revd James and 1 changing guest beer

Radio 2 DJ Chris Evans appears to be steadily building up a portfolio of country pubs. Having bought The Newbridge, he invited the former restaurant manager and chef of nearby Celtic Manor Hotel to run the place for him. They have a hard act to follow as the previous owner had established quite a following and knew his wines, although this new management team are keen to maintain an interesting list. The main room splits into two and is linked by a spiral staircase. Not only can you dine at one of the tables overlooking the River Usk but the pub has fishing rights for one side of it and can arrange permits and rods. The kitchen's experience at the smarter end of the hospitality business is clearly evident on the menu, although there are lighter offerings available at lunch. It has an innate understanding of what goes with what and dishes come neatly presented. The bedrooms are comfortably furnished.

Food serving times
Monday-Sunday:
7.30am-10.30am,
12pm-3pm, 7pm-10pm

Closed 26-31 December

Booking advisable

Prices

Meals: a la carte £ 18/25

6 rooms: £ 90/135

Typical Dishes

White onion risotto

Rump of Usk Valley lamb

Warm chocolate fondant

Five minutes drive from the centre of Caerleon, on the banks of the River Usk. Parking.

15 The Felin Fach Griffin

Felin Fach,
Brecon LD3 0UB
Tel.: (01874)620111 – Fax: (01874)620120
e-mail: enquiries@eatdrinksleep.ltd.uk **Website:** www.felinfachgriffin.co.uk

Inspectors' favourites

 **Tomos Watkins OSB, Breconshire Brewery Red Dragon, Cwrw Braf Smooth**

As you enter this terracotta-coloured converted farmhouse, you get the feeling you've arrived somewhere special. Friendly, cool and with a style so laid back it's almost horizontal, this place will soon oblige you to join in its relaxed vibe and you'll find yourself curling up next to the fire in one of the large leather sofas. The chef has a notable C.V. and produces modern, seasonal food worth trekking over the Brecon Beacons to taste. Dishes are made using local produce and lunch menus offer quality food at decent prices. The owners' company is called EatDrinkSleep, and once they've ensured that you've had your fill of the first two, you'll be more than ready for the latter. Simply decorated, stylish rooms, several with four-posters and all containing books rather than televisions, will ensure that you do so like the proverbial baby. Breakfast next morning like a country lady or gent, soothed by the warmth of the Aga.

Food serving times

Monday: 6.30pm-9.30pm

Tuesday-Sunday and Bank Holiday Monday: 12.30pm-2.30pm, 6.30pm-9.30pm

Closed 24-25 December and 4 days in January

Prices

Meals: £ 19/27 and a la carte £ 21/35

7 rooms: £ 60/110

Typical Dishes

Tartare of smoked salmon

Welsh saddle of lamb

Bara-brith bread & butter pudding

4.75mi Northeast of Brecon by B4602 off A470. Parking.

16 The Bear

High St,
Crickhowell NP8 1BW

Tel.: (01873)810408 – Fax: (01873)811696
e-mail: bearhotel@aol.com **Website:** www.bearhotel.co.uk

  AE

 **Revd James, Bass, Ruddles Best, Skirrid**

Nestled between the Black Mountains and the Brecon Beacons, the pretty town of Crickhowell is home to the landmark that is the Bear. This former coaching inn's long-established owners know what the locals like and provide it for them in spades: good food, a warm welcome and a friendly atmosphere. Dating back to 1432, with its open fires and antiques, its busy beamed bar is an undeniably characterful place in which to eat, and there are also two separate dining rooms, each with a charm of their own. In summer, hanging baskets provide a blaze of colour and the garden comes alive. The popular bar menu offers a range of hearty dishes, plus lighter meals and sandwiches; the restaurant menu combines the traditional with the more modern, and a daily-changing specials menu also adds to the choice. Traditionally styled bedrooms are gradually being upgraded and given a more contemporary edge, whilst retaining their character and comfort.

Food serving times

Monday:
12pm-2pm, (3pm-10pm bar snacks only)

Tuesday-Saturday:
12pm-2pm, 7pm-9.30pm

Sunday:
12pm-2pm, (bar snacks only until 9.30pm)

Closed 25 December dinner

Prices

Meals: a la carte £ 18/29

34 rooms: £ 70/150

Typical Dishes

Welsh rarebit
Salmon & herb fishcakes
Bread & butter pudding

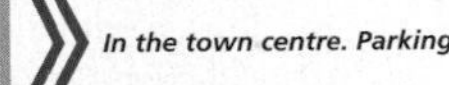
In the town centre. Parking.

17 Nantyffin Cider Mill Inn

Brecon Rd,
Crickhowell NP8 1SG

Tel.: (01873)810775 – Fax: (01873)810986

e-mail: info@cidermill.co.uk **Website:** www.cidermill.co.uk

 **Brains Reverend James, Rhymney B**

One of the first Welsh pubs to get the "gastro" treatment, this converted 16C cider mill is passionately run and serves fresh, modern food at decent prices. With its salmon-pink tinge, it's certainly hard to miss, and inside you'll find two charming bars which have an inviting feel to them. Eat in either of these or in the more formal cloth-clad dining room - it used to be the old apple store and is still home to the original cider press. Cooking is wholesome and full of flavour without being overpowering, and is made with seasonal ingredients, some of which come from the owners' farm. The produce may be local, but the menu is global, with British classics mixing with dishes from Europe and beyond. The blackboard menu changes according to what produce is available and the set lunch menu is particularly good value. Wines and ales are given serious regard here, too - and draft cider is also unsurprisingly a feature.

Food serving times

Monday (April-September):
12pm-2.30pm,
6.30pm-9.30pm

Tuesday-Sunday:
12pm-2.30pm,
6.30pm-9.30pm

Closed Monday from October to March

Prices

Meals: a la carte £ 22/30

Typical Dishes

Greek mezze

Rib eye of Welsh Black beef

Affogato

1.5mi West of Crickhowell on A40. Parking.

18 Old Black Lion

26 Lion St,
Hay-on-Wye HR3 5AD

Tel.: (01497)820841 – Fax: (01497)822960
e-mail: info@oldblacklion.co.uk **Website:** www.oldblacklion.co.uk

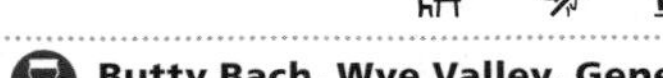
Butty Bach, Wye Valley, General Picton, Rhymney Brewery

"Some books are to be tasted, others to be swallowed, and some few to be chewed and digested," said Francis Bacon. Bibliophiles may get their fill of books in the myriad second hand bookshops to be found in literary Hay-on Wye, but staying at Old Black Lion will ensure food for the body as well as for the soul. Long renowned for its competence in all things culinary, this pub serves traditional dishes as well as meals with a more international flavour, and lighter options are available on the bar menu. A part-13C inn which can reputedly count Oliver Cromwell among previous guests, its style is fittingly rustic with exposed timber beams and scrubbed pine tables, and the well-maintained bedrooms, part-furnished with antiques, maintain the historical feel. Whether you're here with the crowds for the town's annual festival or during a quieter spell, a pleasant service is provided by local staff and a warm welcome extended.

Food serving times

Monday-Sunday:
12pm-2.30pm, 6.30pm-9.30pm

Closed 25 December

Prices

Meals: a la carte £ 21/31

10 rooms: £ 48/95

Typical Dishes

Gorgonzola & poached pear

Beef Wellington

Bailey's bread & butter pudding

In the town centre. Parking.

Pontdolgoch

19 The Talkhouse

Pontdolgoch SY17 5JE
Tel.: (01686)688919
e-mail: info@talkhouse.co.uk
Website: www.talkhouse.co.uk

 **No real ales offered**

The Talkhouse might be the talk of the town because of the quality of its food, but when you step inside this unassuming 17C former coaching inn, it's the surprising stylishness of its interior which is sure to become a talking point. Tastefully fitted out with the floral fabric and furnishings of Wales' famous daughter, Laura Ashley, on one side there is a comfortable lounge with sofas, and on the other, a cosy rustic beamed bar. This leads to dining areas which in turn overlook an immaculate garden, great for dining al fresco in the summer months. The charm doesn't stop there but also extends to the elegantly characterful bedrooms, each with very individual fittings and decoration, and the smooth service by the friendly young owners. Regularly changing blackboard menus offer bold, wholesome cooking, made from locally sourced, seasonal ingredients, and portions are generous, bordering on philanthropic.

Food serving times

Monday-Saturday: 6.30pm-8.45pm

Sunday: 12pm-1.30pm

Closed 25-26 December, first 2 weeks January

Prices

Meals: a la carte £ 22/32

3 rooms: £ 70/95

Typical Dishes

Poached pear & Brie
Welsh fillet of beef
Lemon tart

1.5mi Northwest of Caersws on A470. Parking.

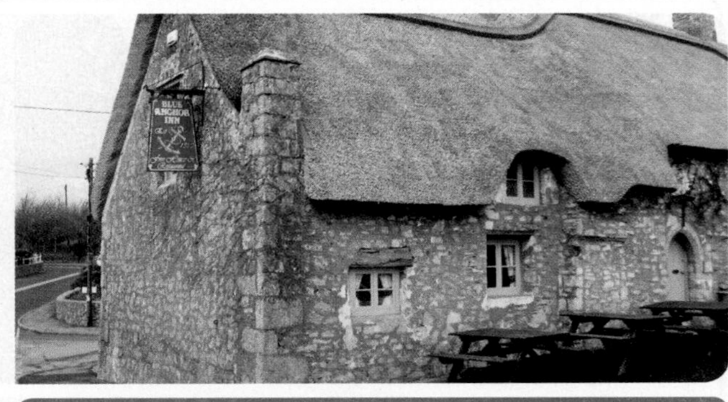

20 The Blue Anchor Inn

East Aberthaw CF62 3DD
Tel.: (01446)750329
Website: www.blueanchoraberthaw.com

Hereford Pale Ale, Theakston Old Peculier, Wadworth 6X, Brains Bitter and one guest ale

Apart from a ten-month hiatus following a fire in 2004, when its loyal local following mourned its loss, this popular inn has purportedly been trading since 1380. The long-established family owners haven't been at the helm for quite this long, but they were never going to let a little fire see them off, and having re-thatched the inn, were soon back behind the bar, much to the relief of many. The extremely characterful interior, with its open fires, flagstone floors, hidden corners and soft lighting provides a charming backdrop for a meal, and local ladies provide amiable, chatty service. The bar menu offers baguettes, salads and jacket potatoes, plus a selection of traditional meals, while the menu for the formal upstairs restaurant features more substantial dishes, such as slow cooked pork belly, roast local venison or rump of Welsh lamb. Dishes are cooked using locally grown or reared produce and desserts are proudly homemade.

Food serving times

Monday-Saturday:
12pm-2pm, 7pm-9.30pm

Sunday: 12.30pm-2.30pm

Prices

Meals: a la carte £ 15/25

Typical Dishes

Tempura of tiger prawns

Loin of venison

Carrot & orange cake

Turn at the cement factory and follow the road for approximately 1 mile.Car Parking opposite the pub.

21 Pant-yr-Ochain

Old Wrexham Rd, Gresford LL12 8TY
Tel.: (01978)853525 – Fax: (01978)853505
e-mail: pant.yr.ochain@brunningandprice.co.uk
Website: www.brunningandprice.co.uk

Flowers Original, Timothy Taylor Landlord, Weetwood Cheshire Cat, Purple Moose Glas Lyn

As old as it is large, you can still see the previous owners' coat of arms on the outside of the cream washed building, and the Tudor wattle and daub walls in the alcove behind its 16C inglenook fireplace. As large as it is popular, this spacious, open plan inn has plenty of different rooms for drinking and dining, and a buzzy, bustling atmosphere. Inside, there's a conservatory, a book-lined library, a dining room, and a large central bar, all stylishly furnished, with many nooks and crannies in which to nestle. This grand country house is also set in delightful gardens and the picnic tables overlooking the lake are in demand when the weather is fine. The extensive menu doesn't try to reinvent the wheel, sticking to classics like burgers and Ploughman's but the kitchen also does its thing with belly pork and seabass. The staff are masters of polite, friendly service which doesn't lose its edge when the pressure's on.

Food serving times

Monday-Saturday: 12pm-9.30pm

Sunday: 12pm-9pm

Closed 25-26 December

Booking essential

Prices

Meals: a la carte £ 19/28

Typical Dishes

King prawns

Steak & kidney pudding

Rhubarb fool

3.5mi Northeast of Wrexham by A483 on B5445: then 1 mi South from Gresford . Parking.

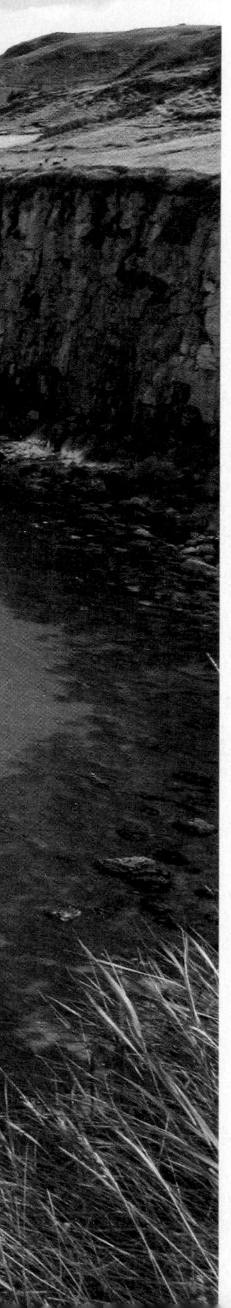

The presiding image of Northern Ireland for outsiders is buzzing Belfast, lying defiantly between mountain and coast. Its City Hall and Queen's University retain the power to impress, and it was within its mighty shipyards that the Titanic first saw the light of day. But the rest of the Six Counties demands attention, too. The forty thousand stone columns of the Giant's Causeway step out into the Irish Sea, part of a grand coastline, though Antrim can also boast nine scenic inland glens. County Down's rolling hills culminate in the alluring slopes of Slieve Donard in the magical Mourne Mountains, while Armagh's Orchard County is a riot of pink in springtime. Fermanagh's glassy, silent lakelands are a tranquil attraction, rivalled for their serenity by the heather-clad Sperrin Mountains, towering over Tyrone and Derry. On top of all this is the cultural lure of boisterous oyster festivals and authentic horse fairs, while farmers' markets are now prominent all across the province.

Scotland
NORTHERN IRELAND
Ireland
Wales
DUBLIN
BELFAST
Giant's Causeway
Antrim Glens
Coll
Tiree
Mull
Tobermory
Craignure
Fionnphort
Oban
Fort William
Loch Linnhe
Colonsay
Lochgilphead
Loch Fyne
Islay
Port Askaig
Jura
Port Ellen
Rothesay
Kintyre
Brodick
Arran
Campbeltown
Firth of Clyde
Malin Head
Buncrana
Lough Foyle
Portrush
Coleraine
Ballycastle
Letterkenny
Londonderry / Derry
Donegal
Omagh
Bundoran
Sligo
Enniskillen
Loughs
Erne
Armagh
Lough Neagh
Lisburn
Larne
Bangor
Cairnryan
Stranraer
North Channel
Monaghan
Boyle
Cavan
Newry
Newcastle
Dundalk
Longford
Roscommon
Lough Ree
Ardee
Drogheda
Navan
Athlone
Mullingar
Kinnegad
R. Boyne
Ballinasloe
IRL
Tullamore
Naas
Dún Laoghaire
Bray
Birr
Portlaoise
Roscrea
Glendalough
Wicklow
Carlow
Kilkenny
Cashel
Clonmel
Caher
Arklow
R. Barrow
R. Suir
New Ross
Enniscorthy
IRISH S
Man
Peel
Anglesey
Holyhead
Caernarfon
Snowdon

1 The Distillers Arms

140 Main St,
Bushmills BT57 8QE
Tel.: (028)20731044 – Fax: (028)20732843
e-mail: simon@distillersarms.com **Website:** www.distillersarms.com

 **No real ales offered**

Situated at the top of the town, the traditional white-painted exterior of The Distillers Arms belies its spacious, modern interior. There's a comfortable lounge and airy bar where a tapas-style menu – from oysters to cold sausage and mustard - is served, and a horseshoe shaped restaurant where colourful, contemporary oil paintings hang on the stone walls. The dining area is large enough to accommodate groups of tourists fresh from the Giant's Causeway and the old whiskey distillery, and while they're here, they can take advantage of the new wine shop attached, to purchase beers, spirits and speciality wines. The bold, straightforward lunch menu offers robust cooking served in hearty, fulfilling portions with dishes such as steak and Guinness or seafood chowder, while dinner is a more elaborate affair with choices such as roasted seabass or fruits de mer. The owner takes a hands-on approach and service is enthusiastic and effective.

Food serving times

Monday-Sunday:
12pm-3pm, 5.30pm-9pm

Closed 25-26 December and Monday and Tuesday in winter

Prices

Meals: a la carte £ 20/25

Typical Dishes

Whiskey cured salmon
Venison stew
Walnut & honey tart

Close to the Bushmills whiskey distillery. Parking.

2 The Pheasant

410 Upper Ballynahinch Rd,
Annahilt BT26 6NR

Tel.: (028)92638056 – Fax: (028)92638026

e-mail: pheasantinn@aol.com **Website:** www.barretro.com/pheasant

 **No real ales offered**

The Pheasant is a homily to the Irish generosity of spirit; a generously-sized establishment serving generously-sized portions. There's a larger than life stag painted on the wall, and even the car park is generously proportioned – but then it would need to be to fit in all its customers' cars. The bar manages to feel spacious yet cosy at the same time, with its flag and tiled flooring, colourful seating and soft lighting, and the well-established team dressed in black know the drill. The menus contain a little bit of everything, so there should be a dish or two to suit everybody's taste. Plump for a fajita or a wrap, perhaps a seafood dish, some pheasant or duck, or a steak from the grill. Get your thinking caps on if you're visiting on a Thursday, as it's quiz night and there are prizes to be won. Stick around till the Friday and you'll need your dancing shoes instead, when a variety of groups provide the live music.

Food serving times

Monday-Saturday:
12pm-2.15pm, 5pm-9pm

Sunday:
12pm-8pm (bar snacks only)

Closed 25-26 December
and 12-13 July

Prices

Meals: £ 15
(lunch) and a la carte
£ 15/30

Typical Dishes

Tea smoked duck

Norwegian poached salmon

Honeycomb meringue roulade

1mi North of Annahilt on Lisburn rd. Parking.

3 Coyle's

44 High St,
Bangor BT20 5AZ
Tel.: (028)91270362 – Fax: (028)91270362
Website: www.coylesbistro.co.uk

 **No real ales offered**

Northern Ireland's most popular coastal resort deserves a great venue to eat and drink, and at Coyle's it's hit paydirt. There's no mistaking the pubby appearance: a black exterior, advertising real music and hard liquor! The ground floor bar keeps that image intact. It's intimate and friendly with a welcoming ambience, and, apart from the liquor, there's an up-to-date menu where classics meet dishes with an international accent. A board directs you upstairs for the restaurant proper. This comes as a bit of a surprise: there's a touch of the art deco/nouveau about it, with stained glass and old framed posters such as a '40s ad for Craven A cigarettes. Although the rather basic tables and chairs don't really do justice to their surroundings, the cooking ticks all the right boxes. It's a harmonious blend of safe, traditional styles with more ambitious, but well executed, dishes.

Food serving times

Tuesday-Saturday:
12pm-3pm, 5pm-9pm

Sunday:
12pm-3pm, 5pm-8pm

Closed 25 December

Bar meals at lunch time.
Restaurant closed dinner Monday.

Prices

Meals: a la carte £ 15/28

Typical Dishes

Soup of the day
Braised beef & champ
Baked mocha fondant

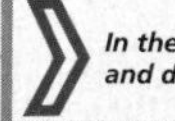

In the town centre. Pay and display parking 2min walk.

4 Grace Neill's

33 High St,
Donaghadee BT21 0AH
Tel.: (028)91884595 – Fax: (028)91889631
e-mail: info@graceneills.com **Website:** www.graceneills.com

  VISA  

 **No real ales offered**

You'd expect a pub reputed to be the oldest in Ireland to have more character and atmosphere than most and Grace Neill's doesn't disappoint. In fact, if you listen very carefully, you might just be able to hear the faint echoes of the past over the creaking of the floorboards - tales of seafaring and smugglers, famous former customers and the figure of a ghost. The charmingly traditional beamed front snug leads through to a high-ceilinged library bar, which in turn leads through to the more modern dining space with its small open kitchen. Eclectic menus cover all bases, from the classics like beef and Guinness pie to the more contemporary dishes, such as king prawn tempura - but whatever dish you choose the food is wholesome and flavourful. Fancy making sweet music? Then borrow the guitar and tin whistles kept behind the bar. More discord than harmony? Perhaps it's best left to the professionals.

Food serving times

Monday-Thursday:
12pm-3pm, 5.30pm-9pm

Friday-Saturday:
12pm-3pm, 5.30pm-9.30pm

Sunday: 12pm-8pm

Closed 25 December

Prices

Meals: a la carte £ 14/26

Typical Dishes

Strangford mussels
Fillets of seabass
Chocolate cheesecake

 *In town centre. Parking.* 

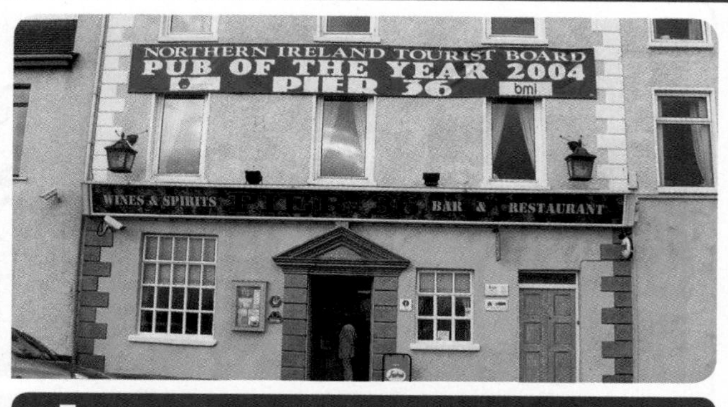

5 Pier 36

36 The Parade,
Donaghadee BT21 0HE
Tel.: (028)91884466 – Fax: (028)91884636
e-mail: info@pier36.co.uk **Website:** www.pier36.co.uk

 **No real ales offered**

What will stay with you long after your trip to Pier 36 will be the hospitality offered by the hands-on family proprietors, and the personal service by their pleasant team of staff. That and the location – it's not every pub that can boast a harbourside position within spitting distance of an impressive lighthouse. Inside, it's all on one level, but spacious; there's a traditional front bar with open fire and stone floors, where meals are served all day, and a more modern area to the rear. Menus, including a list of specials, are longer than they need to be, but involve a real range of dishes, from the traditional – burgers, steak and the like - to dishes such as Moroccan chicken or fillet of Barbary duckling; and freshly caught seafood reels the regulars in time and time again. Add comfortable bedrooms with good facilities plus the pull of live jazz on Wednesday nights and you can see why this place is often full to the rafters.

Food serving times

Monday-Sunday:
12pm-9.30pm

- Seafood specialities -

Prices

Meals: a la carte £ 20/35

5 rooms: £ 50/90

Typical Dishes

Portavogie prawn cocktail

Locally smoked cod fillet

Traditional rice brûlée

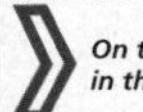

On the harbour front. Parking in the street at the rear.

6 Buck's Head Inn

77-79 Main St,
Dundrum BT33 0LU
Tel.: (028)43751868 – Fax: (028)44811033
e-mail: buckshead1@aol.com **Website:** www.thebucksheaddundrum.co.uk

 **No real ales offered**

Situated in the historic village of Dundrum, best known for its ruined Norman castle, this mustard-coloured inn looks every inch the traditional pub from the front, with its window boxes and big gold signage. In contrast, the restaurant area overlooking the walled garden to the rear – open in the evening only - has a much more contemporary appearance. Lunch is served in the bar, as is high tea; a popular early evening choice with walkers fresh from Dundrum Bay or the Mourne Mountains, happy to warm themselves by the open fire and admire the oil paintings for sale on the walls. Seafood is the speciality on the modern, internationally-influenced menus, where Dundrum Bay mussels might come au naturel and oysters might come Thai style, while chicken might come as simple chicken supreme or spicy, with a noodle salad. The long-established owners take the wine list seriously and it's well worth investigating.

Food serving times

Monday (May-September):
12pm-2.30pm, 5pm-9.30pm

Tuesday-Sunday:
12pm-2.30pm, 5pm-9.30pm

Closed 24-25 December and Monday October-April

- Seafood specialities -

Prices

Meals: a la carte £ 20/29

Typical Dishes
Pork belly
Monkfish
Buttermilk pannacotta

 *In the village. Parking in the street.* 

7 Mourne Seafood Bar

10 Main St,
Dundrum BT33 0LU
Tel.: (028)43751377 – Fax: (028)43751161
e-mail: bob@mourneseafood.com **Website:** www.mourneseafood.com

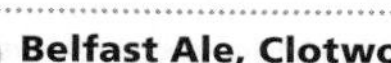 **Belfast Ale, Clotworthy Ale**

Standing over the road from the popular Buck's Head Inn, this rather untypical seafood bar was previously the current owner's home, and the name plaque "Downshire Manor" can still be found on the front. He also runs an oyster and mussel farm in Carlingford Lough, source of many dishes here, while other produce is brought in from the local boats. Bob (the owner) is keen for people to try "bi-catch" species rather than fish under pressure such as cod, and this simple, casual bar is a great place to give it a go: prices are reasonable and fair. There's a core menu: meanwhile, waiters take time to explain the six or seven daily blackboard specials. Wet fish is available to buy and chef is happy to suggest the best way to cook if asked. It's not just seafood on the menu here: locally reared chicken and steaks also make an appearance. An excellent local reputation is building, so, if it's summertime, do make sure you book first.

Food serving times

Monday-Sunday:
12pm-9pm

Closed Thursday to Sunday in winter

- Seafood - Booking essential in summer
in summer

Seafood

Prices

Meals: a la carte £ 19/30

Typical Dishes

Mourne oysters
Grilled lobster
Homemade apple pie

In the village. Parking across the street and in the village.

Hillsborough

8 The Plough Inn

3 The Square,
Hillsborough BT26 6AG
Tel.: (028)92682985 – Fax: (028)92682472
e-mail: pattersonderek@hotmail.co.uk **Website:** www.barretro.com

 **Belfast Blonde, Hilden Pale Ale**

A well-established, family-run inn, the vastly extended Plough Inn has a well-deserved local following. You get three for the price of one here; a pub, a bistro and a café, all serving slightly different menus, and appealing to slightly different people. The traditional dark wood bar area with its horse brass is still popular with older diners, younger ones head for the trendy bistro upstairs, whilst families tend to congregate in the café, where children are welcome. The bar serves traditional dishes such as sausage and mash as well as more modern dishes like Thai Green Curry or smoked goose and chorizo Caesar salad - and the older folks flock in for the good value specials to be had here. Upstairs, the bistro menu is similar, if a little more trendy, whilst the café serves food like burgers, wraps and paninis. Wherever you choose to eat, all dishes come in generous helpings and staff are only too happy to help.

Food serving times
Monday-Sunday:
12pm-2.30pm, 5pm-9.30pm

Prices
Meals: a la carte £ 18/30

Typical Dishes
Seafood tempura
Spring lamb
Rich chocolate nemesis

At the top of the hill in the square. Parking.

It's reckoned that Ireland offers forty luminous shades of green, and of course an even more famous shade of black liquid refreshment. But it's not all wondrous hills and down-home pubs. The country does other visitor-friendly phenomena just as idyllically: witness the limestone-layered Burren, cut-through by meandering streams, lakes and labyrinthine caves; or the fabulous Cliffs of Moher, unchanged for millennia, looming for mile after mile over the wild Atlantic waves. The cities burst with life: Dublin is now one of Europe's coolest capitals, and free-spirited Cork enjoys a rich cultural heritage. Kilkenny mixes a renowned medieval flavour with a taste for excellent pubs; Galway, one of Ireland's prettiest cities, is enhanced by an easy, boho vibe. Best of all, perhaps, is to sit along the quayside of a fishing village in the esteemed company of a bowl of steaming fresh mussels or gleaming oysters and the taste of a distinctive micro-brewery beer (well, makes a change from stout…).

Northern Ireland
REP. OF IRELAND
IRL
DUBLIN
Malin Head
Giant's Causeway
Buncrana
Lough Foyle
Portrush
Letterkenny
Londonderry / Derry
Coleraine
Strabane
Donegal
Bundoran
Omagh
Enniskillen
Armagh
Lisburn
Monaghan
Newry
Newcastle
Dundalk
Ardee
Drogheda
Navan
Belmullet
Ballina
Achill
Castlebar
Westport
Sligo
Boyle
Knock
Cavan
Longford
Clifden
Connemara
Lough Mask
Lough Corrib
Roscommon
Lough Ree
Athlone
Mullingar
Galway
Ballinasloe
Kinnegad
R. Boyne
Aran
Cliffs of Moher
Ennistimon
Loughrea
Tullamore
Naas
Dún Laoghaire
Bray
Birr
Lough Derg
Glendalough
Limerick
Listowel
Wicklow
Carlow
Kilkenny
Tipperary
Cashel
Dingle
Tralee
Arklow
Lakes of Killarney
Killarney
Clonmel
Caher
New Ross
Enniscorthy
Cahersiveen
Macgillycuddy's Reeks
R. Blackwater
Mallow
Fermoy
Carrick-on-Suir
Ring of Kerry
Kenmare
Waterford
Wexford
Rosslare
Glengarriff
Cork
Dungarvan
Youghal
Bantry
Cobh
Carnsore Point
Skibbereen
Swansea
St. George's Channel
St. David's
Milford Haven
Islay
Port Ellen
Tiree
1
2
3
4
5
6
7
8
9
10
11
12
13
14
15
16
17

1 Vaughan's Anchor Inn

Main Street,
Liscannor
Tel.: (065)7081548 – Fax: (065)7068977
Website: www.vaughans.ie

There aren't many pubs where you can sit and sip a pint of the black stuff, have a natter over a seafood platter and then pick up your groceries. One such place is to be found in the picturesque fishing village of Liscannor, along the rugged road to the much-visited Cliffs of Moher. This is a proper pub; lively and full of traditional character, from its bay window full of nautical bric à brac to its long bar spanning almost three rooms and its collection of football banners and scarves. Family-run, it has built up a fine reputation over the last three decades, and chef Denis' seafood-based menus are a big part of the reason why. Eat at simple wooden tables in the cosy, old-style bar or in the newer but equally informal restaurant; typical pub favourites are on offer at lunch, with more adventurous, elaborate meals - from oysters and lobster to duck and foie gras - served in the evening. Bedrooms are too modest for us to recommend.

Food serving times
Monday-Sunday:
12pm-9.30pm
Closed 25 December
- Seafood -

Prices
Meals: a la carte € 24/39

Typical Dishes
Sea scallops
Roast native lobster
Sherry trifle

On coast road 1.5mi from Lahinch on main route to Cliffs of Moher. Parking.

2 Poacher's Inn

Clonakilty Rd,
Bandon
Tel.: (023)41159

 **No real ales offered**

You've a passion for cooking but you work in recruitment, so what do you do? If you're Barry McLoughlin, you take the bull by the horns and persuade the owner of a nearby restaurant to let you work in the kitchens on a Saturday. You enjoy it so much that you resign from the day job and enrol on a cookery course…fast forward five years and you're successfully running your own pub in your home town of Bandon; the strong local following attracted by a winning combination of smart, comfortable surroundings and wholesome, homecooked food. Sandwiches, fish pies, steaks and the like make up the simple menu available in the cosy bar, supplemented by a daily changing blackboard menu of ten or more - mostly fish – specials. Fresh, local seafood is also very much the order of the day in the intimate upstairs restaurant, where cheery, attentive service keeps things ticking along nicely, and the good value Sunday lunch is particularly popular.

Food serving times

Monday-Wednesday:
12pm-7pm (bar snacks)

Thursday-Saturday:
12pm-7pm (bar snacks),
7pm-10pm

Sunday & Bank Holidays:
12pm-7pm (bar snacks),
7pm-10pm

Prices

Meals: a la carte € 30/40

Typical Dishes

Crab & prawn cake
Seafood crumble
Strawberries & cream

 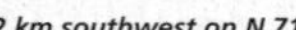
2 km southwest on N 71

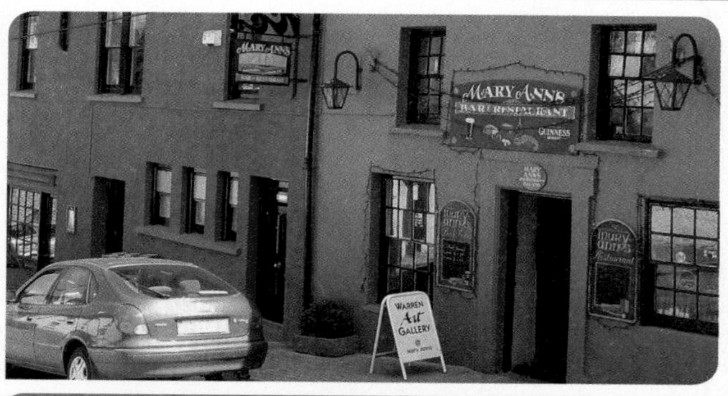

3 Mary Ann's

Castletownshend
Tel.: (028)36146 – Fax: (028)36920
e-mail: maryanns@eircom.net **Website:** www.westcorkweek.com/maryanns

 **No real ales offered**

Don't go searching round this pub for someone called Mary Ann – it's actually named after a previous owner – the current ones have been here since 1988 and go by the names of Fergus and Patricia. Eat at simple wooden tables in the bar or head upstairs to dine on tablecloths; in the summer, it's the huge outside terrace which accommodates the crowds, when the pub gets busy with sailors stopping for the night in the harbour. Not too many pubs can boast their own art gallery, but this one can, and it attracts visitors up this steep, narrow street from far and wide. Called The Warren Gallery, it houses the owner's collection of modern Irish art, mostly bought at auction on his travels around the country. The food served here may not quite qualify as a work of art, but it's extremely tasty and there's plenty of it; portions are huge, with masses of vegetables, and the emphasis is firmly on fresh fish and seafood.

Food serving times

Monday (April-October): 12pm-2.30pm, 6pm-9pm

Tuesday: 12pm-2.30pm (April-October), 6pm-9pm

Wednesday-Sunday: 12pm-2.30pm, 6pm-9pm

Closed 24-26 December, last 3 weeks in January

Bookings not accepted

Prices

Meals: a la carte € 20/45

Typical Dishes

Seafood selection

Rack of lamb

Chocolate & raspberry cheesecake

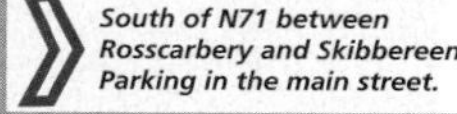

South of N71 between Rosscarbery and Skibbereen. Parking in the main street.

4 An Súgán

41 Wolfe Tone St,
Clonakilty

Tel.: (023)33498 – Fax: (023)33825

e-mail: ansugan4@eircom.net **Website:** www.ansugan.com

  **No real ales offered**

Located in the middle of a busy town, this colourful pub is popular with locals and visitors alike. It's spotless inside, and full of character: water jugs and old meat plates hang from the ceiling, and you can see hundreds of business cards which have been wedged into the old wood beams by visitors over the years. There are always plenty of locals enjoying the bar side banter, while the wood-panelled dining room upstairs, decorated with antique theatre programmes, tends to get busy in the evenings. Simple, home cooked food is served daily: the lunch menu is chalked up on a board, offering dishes such as seafood pie, smoked salmon and the famous Clonakilty black pudding, while the evening à la carte offers more choice, with fresh local seafood featuring heavily – including lobster when available - and daily-changing specials written on blackboards. Smartly dressed staff provide friendly service.

Food serving times

Monday-Sunday:
from 12.30pm

Closed 25-26 December and Good Friday

Prices

Meals: a la carte € 28/40

Typical Dishes

Black & white pudding terrine

Fresh hake

Apple pie

East of town centre. Parking in the street.

5 **Dalton's**

3 Market St,
Kinsale
Tel.: (021)4778025
e-mail: fedalton@eircom.net **Website:** www.kinsalecookingschool.com

 **No real ales offered**

The eponymous owners, Francis and Colm; a friendly husband and wife team, run this jolly town-centre pub with consummate ease. He cooks; she serves, and the pub's loyal local following attests to the merits of both. A distinctive red-painted building, adorned with pretty window boxes, inside it fosters a cosy, traditional air with a small fire, tiled floor, attractive pine panelling and brown leather banquettes. The menu offers mostly seafood and is limited to ten or so dishes, although a daily meat and a fish special are also chalked up on the blackboard. Wholesome and hearty dishes include the perennial favourites of fish chowder and crab fishcakes with salsa, and there's a smattering of home cooked desserts to finish your meal off with a flourish. Food here is a daytime event only and at night Dalton's reverts to its status as a bar; so expect plenty of singing, chatting and drinking, but not necessarily in that order.

Food serving times
Monday-Saturday:
12pm-5pm
Closed 2 weeks Christmas

Prices
Meals: a la carte € 15/25

Typical Dishes
Mussels & seafood chowder
Beef & Guinness stew
Blackberry & apple crumble

In the town centre. Parking 2 minutes away in St. Multose car park at the top of the road.

6 The Cellar Bar

Upper Merrion St,
Dublin

Tel.: (01)6030600 – Fax: (01)6030700
e-mail: info@merrionhotel.com **Website:** www.merrionhotel.com

 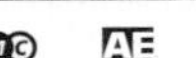

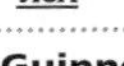 **Guinness, Smithwicks**

One of Dublin's favourite places for lunch is hidden away behind the elegant façade of an old Georgian town house, now the Merrion Hotel. The superbly restored wine vaults are now a smart destination bar by night, a bar-brasserie by day, and a city institution all round, so beat the lunchtime rush and find an alcove table under the brick and granite arches or pull up a spare stool at the long bar. Even on the busiest days, smiling, super-efficient bar staff keep things moving, serving up everything from hot roast beef sandwiches and Caesar salad to bacon and cabbage or Irish stew; plum frangipane tart with deliciously smooth ice cream is an occasional special and deserves to be tried.

Food serving times

Monday-Saturday:
12pm-2.30pm, 6pm-9pm

Closed 25 December

Prices

Meals: a la carte € 29/43

Typical Dishes

Smoked salmon & trout paté

Honey-glazed loin of bacon

Iced Bailey parfait

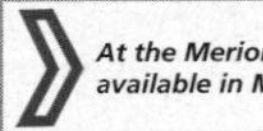

At the Merion Hotel. Parking available in Merrion Square.

7 John J Burke

Mount Gable House, Clonbur

Tel.: (094)9546175

e-mail: tibhurca@eircom.net **Website:** www.burkes-clonbur.com

  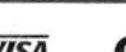

 **No real ales offered**

Four generations of the Burke family have presided over this popular pub, each keeping it true to tradition, much like the unspoilt village of Clonbur in which it resides. The big open bar has a cavernous feel, with high ceilings and walls filled with knick-knacks; keep an eye out for the miniature football figures painted in the different counties' colours, lined up their current standings above the bar. If the weather's inclement, you might choose to sit by the open fire in the rear restaurant; on a sunny day it's best to be out on the terrace, with its view over the garden and of the distant Mount Gable. Light meals are available at lunchtimes, with an à la carte of more hearty meat or fish dishes in the evenings. There's a pool room for those handy with a cue, but if armchair sports are more your thing then head for the snug – once an old shop – to catch the all important scores on the flat screen. Upstairs simple bedrooms await.

Food serving times

Monday-Friday: from 10am (bar snacks), 6.30pm-9pm (April-September only)

Saturday-Sunday: from 10am (bar snacks), 6.30pm-9pm

Closed 25 December

Live music Sunday

Prices

Meals: a la carte € 25/47

4 rooms: € 40/80

Typical Dishes

Bacon & feta salad

Battered cod

Apple tart

West of Cong. On street parking.

8 Moran's Oyster Cottage

The Weir,
Kilcolgan
Tel.: (091)796113
e-mail: moranstheweir@eircom.net

 **No real ales offered**

Situated in a tiny hamlet, and accessed via country lanes, unless you'd heard of this inn, you'd never know it was there. Chances are, though, if you're in this part of the world, you most definitely will have heard of it, as its reputation for all things edible and from the sea tends to precede it - and the pictures on the walls show in whose famous footsteps you follow. In the summer, the place gets packed out; and don't be too surprised if you see the odd coach driving up here, for the place is now virtually a tourist attraction. What's the big deal? Well, it makes for a very pleasant spot on a sunny day, watching the swans glide by, and with its 18C origins, thatched roof and cosy front bar, it certainly has plenty of character. It's well-run and the service is friendly, but primarily people come here for the oysters. The seafood is fresh and simply prepared, and includes smoked salmon, crabs, prawns - and oysters. Always oysters.

Food serving times

Monday-Sunday:
12pm-10pm

Closed 24-26 December and Good Friday

- Seafood -

Prices

Meals: a la carte € 26/40

Typical Dishes

Native oysters
Seafood special
Baileys cheesecake

5 minutes from the village of Clarinbridge. Parking in road.

9 Keogh's Bar

Main St,
Kinvara

Tel.: (091)637145 – Fax: (091)637028
e-mail: keoghsbar@eircom.net **Website:** www.kinvara.com/keoghs

 **No real ales offered**

Dying for a drink or a bite to eat? In your rush to park the car and cross the threshold of this red-hued pub, be careful which door you take, for picking the wrong one could mean that you end up communing with a different sort of spirit entirely in next door's funeral parlour. Assuming you've chosen the correct entrance, you'll find yourself in a traditional Irish bar: there's a small front lounge decorated with old memorabilia and photos of local Gaelic football teams, a separate bar busy with locals, and a dining area furnished with simple wooden tables, where most folks sit to eat. Gateway to the Burren, Kinvara is a pretty fishing village on the Galway coast, so as is to be expected, there's plenty of seafood on the menu, but they also offer traditional hearty dishes such as roast beef and lamb or lasagne, as well as paninis for those with smaller appetites, and a range of classic desserts such as bread and butter pudding.

Food serving times
Monday-Sunday:
9.30am-6pm, 6pm-10pm
Closed 25 December

Prices
Meals: a la carte € 17/30

Typical Dishes
Black pudding
Fresh haddock
Bread & butter pudding

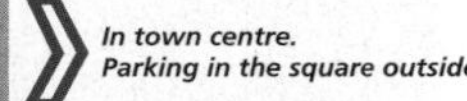
In town centre.
Parking in the square outside.

10 O'Neill's (The Point) Seafood Bar

Renard Point,
Cahersiveen
Tel.: (066)9472165 – Fax: (087)2595345
e-mail: oneillsthepoint@eircom.net

 **No real ales offered**

Located down on the western edge of the Iveragh Peninsula, where the car ferry leaves for Valencia Island, The Point is one of those places people return to time and time again. One of the reasons behind this enthusiasm would have to be the friendly nature of the pub's owners. Their welcome is so warm, it's positively toasty, and having been at the reins for two decades now, they've certainly learnt more than just the basics when it comes to pleasing their customers. The concise seafood menu serves up whatever is freshest and wettest that day; perhaps some lobster, monkfish, squid or shrimp - and of course salmon, as one would expect opposite a smoked salmon factory. The lunchtime
menu is shorter, but somewhat cheaper; they don't accept credit cards and there are no desserts – but there is a short wine list and the Irish coffee goes down a treat. Simply furnished, the bar is decorated with maritime memorabilia - and a Leeds United shield.

Food serving times

Monday-Saturday:
12.30pm-3.30pm (only June-October), 6pm-9.30pm

Sunday: 6pm-9.30pm

Closed November-December and January-March

- Seafood - Bar lunch.
Bookings not accepted

Prices

Meals: a la carte € 32/50

Typical Dishes
Deep-fried squid
Lobster
Irish coffee

West of Cahirsiveen: follow the signs for the ferry. Parking.

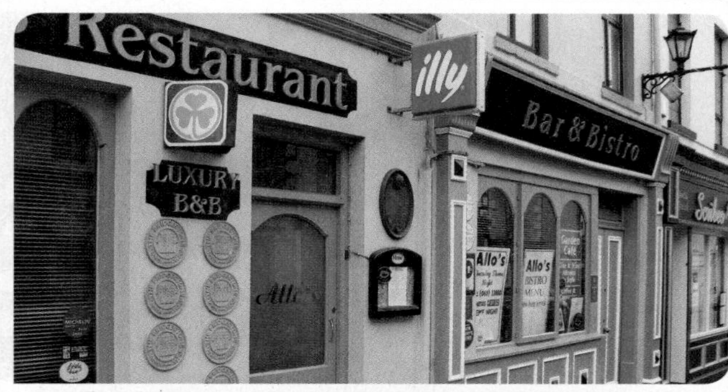

11 Allo's Bar

41 Church St,
Listowel
Tel.: (068)22880 – Fax: (068)22803
e-mail: allos@eircom.net

Large selection of Irish whiskies

Right in the heart of Listowel, famous for its annual literary and horse-racing festivals, sits this characterful pub, brightly painted in shades of yellow and orange. Step inside and it's as if you've entered a time warp; jugs hang from the ceiling, old adverts for tobacco and whiskey dot the walls, and rows of books line the shelves. There's a small snug at the front, and you can eat either in the bar, with its very long counter, or more formally next door in the restaurant, above cherry wood floorboards reputed to have come from the London Stock Exchange. Lunchtime sees a simple menu of snacks and nibbles on offer, while there's a full à la carte of traditional Irish meat and fish dishes in the evening as well as themed evenings every Thursday. Antique-furnished bedrooms are reached via a steep, narrow staircase; room 1 boasts a four poster bed and roll top bath, while 2 and 3 offer a comfortable night's slumber in a sleigh bed.

In the town centre, off North corner of the Square. On street parking.

Food serving times

Tuesday-Saturday:
12pm-7pm (bar snacks),
7pm-9.15pm

Closed Sunday-Monday

Prices

Meals: a la carte € 17/45

3 rooms: € 50/100

Typical Dishes

Smoked salmon risotto
Char-grilled monkfish
Raspberry & cinnamon torte

12 The Oarsman

Bridge St,
Carrick-on-Shannon

Tel.: (071)9621733 – Fax: (071)9621734
e-mail: info@theoarsman.com **Website:** www.theoarsman.com

 **Galway Hooker**

If you're cruising on down to Carrick-on-Shannon, the boating capital of inland Ireland, or maybe angling for a fish in one of its many surrounding lakes, make time to pay a visit to the suitably named Oarsman. Owned and run by the Maher family, who have been involved in the hospitality industry for generations, it's set on a busy street in the town centre; a friendly, characterful place with a lively local feel. Its double-fronted windows are filled with county flags and bric à brac, and the old-fashioned charm continues inside, with dark wood panelled walls filled with photos, mirrors and ornaments. Menus offer a mix of snacks, salads, soups and sandwiches as well as popular pub favourites, daily blackboard specials and more restaurant-style dishes, all made with produce gleaned from the local landscape. Swift, efficient service from polite and chatty staff is the other key ingredient in a pleasant lunch or evening out.

Food serving times

Tuesday-Saturday:
12pm-6.30pm (bar snacks only), 6.30pm-9.30pm

Closed 25 December and Good Friday

Prices

Meals: a la carte € 19/40

Typical Dishes

Bacon & shallot terrine
Pan-fried duck breast
Vanilla poached peaches

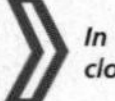 *In the town centre.Nearby parking close to river and bridge.* 

13 Crockets on the Quay

The Quay Village,
Ballina
Tel.: (096)75930 – Fax: (096)70069
e-mail: info@crocketsonthequay.ie **Website:** www.crocketsonthequay.ie

 **No real ales offered**

Despite appearances – it's housed in a bright orange building outside the town – this is a proper Irish pub, with a spacious, dimly lit and atmospheric interior; wooden floors, beams and a huge central bar. There's a more modern, relaxed area to the rear, where turned down televisions keep you up to date with the sports scores, and the adjacent, stone built former boat house is home to the more formal restaurant, where the same menu is served. Fresh, hearty cooking uses quality ingredients and there's plenty of choice on the menu, with pub favourites like fish and chips and fillet of Irish beef alongside dishes such as pan-fried hake fillet, roast breast of Barbary duck and warm Connemara smoked salmon. There's a terrace out front with a view over the river, staff are ultra-friendly and the place well run. Modest bedrooms offer simple comforts; choose six, seven or eight, as they are above the restaurant and therefore the quietest.

Food serving times

Monday-Sunday:
12.30pm-9.30pm

Closed 25 December and Good Friday

Prices

Meals: € 30 (dinner) and a la carte € 27/45

8 rooms: € 45/80

Typical Dishes

Caesar salad
Sea trout
Warm Belgian waffles

 *On the northeast edge of town besides the River Moy* 

14 JJ Gannons

Main St,
Ballinrobe

Tel.: (094)9541008 – Fax: (094)9520018
e-mail: info@jjgannons.com **Website:** www.jjgannons.com

 **Good range of bottled beer**

Situated on the busy one way system, in the very centre of town, the traditionally-fronted JJ Gannons started life in 1838 and, having been numerous things over the years, including a grain store, a garage and even a funeral parlour, is now a modern pub, owned and run by a third generation of Gannons. Given a new lease of life back in 2004, it boasts a stylish, seductively-lit front bar with wood floors, exposed stone and white and chocolate bucket chairs and banquettes. There's a dimly-lit chill out area called the bunker, a small terrace and a smart, spacious rear restaurant which lets in plenty of natural light. A fantastic selection of wines by the glass complements an interesting menu of modern classics available in both the bar and the restaurant, and the informal service matches the laid back ambience. Bedrooms are comfortable and modern, with bright colour schemes, flat screen TVs, dark wood furniture and sleek bathrooms.

Right in the centre of town on the one-way system

Food serving times

Monday-Sunday:
8am-5pm (bar snacks),
5pm-9.30pm

Closed 25 December and Good Friday

Prices

Meals: a la carte € 23/45

10 rooms: € 65/150

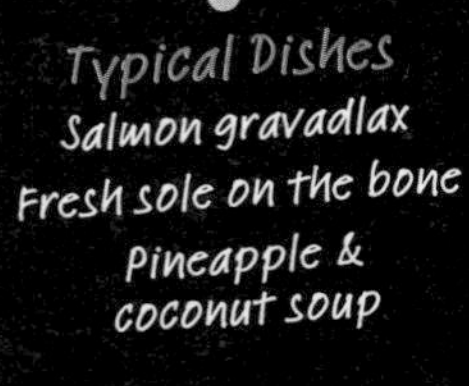

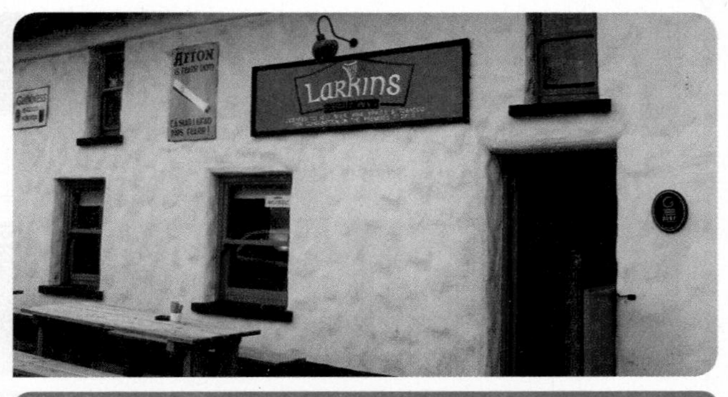

15 **Larkins**

Garrykennedy
Tel.: (067)23232 – Fax: (067)23933
e-mail: info@larkinspub.com **Website:** www.larkinspub.com

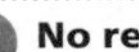 **No real ales offered**

This thatched, whitewashed inn at the end of the lane looks barely big enough to swing the proverbial pussycat, leave alone house a whole troop of Irish dancers, but Larkins is actually a lot larger on the inside than it appears from the out, and plenty big enough to accommodate the local live music groups who entertain from Wednesday to Sunday. Whitewashed walls covered with old pictures and classic adverts spark off nostalgia, as do the cabinets behind the bar full of old food packets and tins. There is a simple lunch menu and a longer evening version, both of which offer wholesome, hearty cooking served in portions which will satisfy the healthiest of appetites. Homemade soda bread is served at the start of your meal, and you can choose from dishes ranging from steak burger and stew to sea bass and salmon, via seafood chowder and spicy chicken salad. The rear garden and dining room overlook the shores of Lough Derg.

Food serving times
May-October:
Monday-Sunday: all day
November-April:
Monday-Thursday:
from 5pm
Friday-Sunday all day
Closed 25 December, Good Friday

Prices
Meals: a la carte € 20/35

Typical Dishes
Steamed Atlantic mussels
Honeyroast duckling
Banoffie pie

9km west of Nenagh by R494 and minor road north. Free public car park opposite.

16 Sheebeen

Rosbeg,
Westport

Tel.: (098)26528 – Fax: (098)24396
e-mail: info@croninssheebeen.com **Website:** www.croninssheebeen.com

 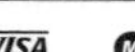 VISA MC

 **Guinness, Smithwicks, Budweiser, Carlsberg, Heineken, Bulmers**

This attractive whitewashed, thatched pub is situated to the west of town, looking out over Clew Bay and in the shadow of famed mountain, Croagh Patrick. According to legend, this was where St. Patrick fasted for 40 days and 40 nights before banishing all the snakes from Ireland, and thousands of Catholics make a pilgrimage up the mountain every year on the last Sunday in July; some barefoot, and some on their knees as a penance. Fasting not your thing? Cooking here is fresh and simple – everything is homemade, including the bread - with the more interesting dishes to be found among the large selection of daily specials. Try the local fish and seafood, which is accurately prepared and full of flavour – perhaps cod terrine, smoked salmon mousse, lobster, sea trout or John Dory. Live music nights take place every Friday and Saturday; but during the week, don't be surprised to hear Peggy Lee blasting out of the system instead.

Food serving times
Monday-Sunday:
12pm (4pm November-March)-9.30pm (bar snacks), 6pm-9.30pm

Prices
Meals: a la carte € 25/38

Typical Dishes
Braised pig's cheek salad
Roast monkfish
Raspberry délice

To the west of town beyond Westport Quay

17 The Lobster Pot

Carne

Tel.: (053)9131110 – Fax: (053)9131401

 **Smithwicks (Irish Ale)**

A long-standing family owned pub, the Lobster Pot is a veritable Wexford institution. Its success is in part due to the fact that it has a vision and clearly sticks to it; a vision so fantastically full of all things fishy that you can't help but feel that the Carne should change its name to Pesce just to fit in. We're talking platefuls of Wexford cockles and mussels, smoked salmon or mackerel, crab, prawns, or simply the finest, freshest oysters available. This is cuisine that's been washed in with the tide; cooked precisely, served without pretence – and delicious washed down with a pint of Guinness. You can bet you won't be the only one to have heard about the place, though, so to guarantee your appetite is sated, aim to arrive early - preferably when they open. Grab a seat out front or in one of four semi-divided snugs; the nautical knick-knacks which clutter the walls will keep you occupied until someone arrives to take your order.

Food serving times

Wednesday-Saturday:
12pm-11.30pm,
6pm-12.30am

Closed 25-26 December, January, 1st week in February and Monday except Bank Holidays when closed Tuesday

- Seafood -

Prices

Meals: a la carte € 25/50

Typical Dishes

Seafood chowder
Prime sirloin steak
Pear & almond pie

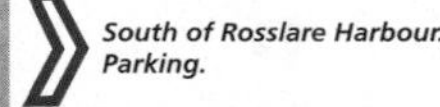

South of Rosslare Harbour.
Parking.

Republic of Ireland • Wexford

A

B

C

D

Y

Z

A

B

C

D

E

F

L

M

N

O

P

Q

R

S

T

V

W

Y

I. Pompe / Hemis.fr